Ford Fiesta
Service and Repair Manual

John S Mead

(1595-336-1AA4)

Models covered

Ford Fiesta models with petrol engines; Hatchback, Van & Courier,
including XR2i, RS Turbo, RS 1800, CTX automatic transmission models & special/limited editions
999 cc, 1118 cc, 1297 cc, 1392 cc, 1596 cc, 1597 cc & 1796 cc

Does not cover Diesel engine models

© Haynes Publishing 1997

A book in the **Haynes Service and Repair Manual Series**

ABCDE
FGHIJ
K

2

Printed by **J H Haynes & Co. Ltd, Sparkford, Nr Yeovil,
Somerset BA22 7JJ**

Haynes Publishing
Sparkford, Nr Yeovil, Somerset BA22 7JJ, England

Haynes North America, Inc
861 Lawrence Drive, Newbury Park, California 91320, USA

Editions Haynes S.A.
147/149, rue Saint Honoré, 75001 PARIS, France

Haynes Publishing Nordiska AB
Fyrisborgsgatan 5, 754 50 Uppsala, Sverige

ISBN **1 85960 087 5**

British Library Cataloguing in Publication Data
A catalogue record for this book is available from the British Library.

Contents

LIVING WITH YOUR FORD FIESTA

Introduction	Page	**0•4**
Safety First!	Page	**0•5**

ROADSIDE REPAIRS

Introduction	Page	**0•6**
If your car won't start	Page	**0•6**
Jump starting	Page	**0•7**
Wheel changing	Page	**0•8**
Identifying leaks	Page	**0•9**
Towing	Page	**0•9**

WEEKLY CHECKS

Introduction	Page	**0•10**
Underbonnet check points	Page	**0•10**
Engine oil level	Page	**0•12**
Coolant level	Page	**0•12**
Brake fluid level	Page	**0•13**
Power steering fluid level	Page	**0•13**
Screen washer fluid level	Page	**0•14**
Battery	Page	**0•14**
Tyre condition and pressure	Page	**0•15**
Wiper blades	Page	**0•16**
Bulbs and fuses	Page	**0•16**
Lubricants and fluids	Page	**0•17**
Tyre pressures	Page	**0•18**

MAINTENANCE

Routine Maintenance and Servicing

Servicing Specifications	Page	**1•2**
Maintenance schedule	Page	**1•4**
Maintenance procedures	Page	**1•9**
Every 5000 miles (8 000 km)	Page	**1•9**
Every 10 000 miles (16 000 km)	Page	**1•11**
Every 20 000 miles (32 000 km)	Page	**1•19**
Every 30 000 miles (48 000 km)	Page	**1•21**
Every 40 000 miles	Page	**1•25**
Every 60 000 miles	Page	**1•25**
Every 3 years	Page	**1•26**

Contents

REPAIRS & OVERHAUL

Engine and Associated Systems

HCS engine in-car repair procedures	Page 2A•1
CVH and PTE engine in-car repair procedures	Page 2B•1
Zetec engine in-car repair procedures	Page 2C•1
Engine removal and overhaul procedures	Page 2D•1
Cooling, heating and ventilation systems	Page 3•1
Fuel system - carburettor engines	Page 4A•1
Fuel system - central fuel injection engines	Page 4B•1
Fuel system - electronic fuel injection engines	Page 4C•1
Fuel system - sequential electronic fuel injection engines	Page 4D•1
Exhaust and emission control systems	Page 4E•1
Starting and charging systems	Page 5A•1
Ignition system	Page 5B•1

Transmission

Clutch	Page 6•1
Manual transmission	Page 7A•1
Automatic transmission	Page 7B•1
Driveshafts	Page 8•1

Brakes and Suspension

Braking system	Page 9•1
Suspension and steering	Page 10•1

Body Equipment

Bodywork and fittings	Page 11•1
Body electrical system	Page 12•1

Wiring Diagrams

	Page 12•19

REFERENCE

Dimensions and weights	Page REF•1
Vehicle identification	Page REF•3
General Repair Procedures	Page REF•4
Jacking and vehicle support	Page REF•5
Radio/cassette anti-theft system - precaution	Page REF•5
Buying spare parts	Page REF•5
Conversion factors	Page REF•6
Tools and Working Facilities	Page REF•7
MOT test checks	Page REF•10
Fault Finding	Page REF•14
Glossary of Technical Terms	Page REF•22

Index

	Page REF•27

Introduction

Introduced early in 1989, the models covered in this manual replace the previous highly successful Fiesta range. A great deal of development has led to the Fiesta being equipped with the standard of refinement more commonly found on executive class cars.

As on the previous models, front-wheel-drive from a transverse engine/transmission arrangement is retained, whilst the front and rear suspension has been completely redesigned to give a high standard of roadholding and comfort. Key advances over the previous range include the option of an anti-lock braking system on certain models, sophisticated engine management systems, new and modified engines delivering more power and better fuel economy, and the provision of a five-door bodyshell.

The model range is extensive with three-door, five-door, Van and Courier bodystyles, four-speed, five-speed and CTX automatic transmissions, as well as an impressive array of trim specification levels and equipment options.

The power unit fitted is dependent on model. The options initially were revised versions of the engines fitted to the earlier Fiesta range, these being the 1.0 and 1.1 litre HCS overhead valve engine, and the 1.4 and 1.6 litre CVH overhead camshaft engines. A 1.3 litre version of the HCS engine became available in 1991. For the 1992 model year, the new 1.8 litre DOHC 16-valve Zetec (originally known as Zeta) engine was introduced, followed a year later by a 1.6 litre version. For the 1995 model year a revised version of the CVH engine, known as the PTE engine, was added to the range.

The fuel system fitted is also dependent on model, and will be either carburettor, CFi (central fuel injection), EFi (electronic fuel injection - with turbocharger on RS Turbo models) or SEFi (sequential electronic fuel injection). All fuel injection engines have electronic engine management control to the ignition and fuel systems to provide greater efficiency and performance, with later models featuring extensive emissions control systems to ensure compliance with the most stringent of the emissions control standards currently in force.

As with earlier variants of the Fiesta range, all models are designed with the emphasis on economical motoring, ease of maintenance and good performance.

Acknowledgements

Thanks are due to Champion Spark Plug, who supplied the illustrations showing spark plug conditions and to Duckhams Oils, who provided lubrication data. Certain other illustrations are the copyright of the Ford Motor Company, and are used with their permission. Thanks are also due to Sykes-Pickavant Limited, who provided some of the workshop tools, and to all those people at Sparkford who helped in the production of this manual.

Your Fiesta Manual

The aim of this manual is to help you get the best value from your vehicle. It can do so in several ways. It can help you decide what work must be done (even should you choose to get it done by a garage), provide information on routine maintenance and servicing, and give a logical course of action and diagnosis when random faults occur. However, it is hoped that you will use the manual by tackling the work yourself. On simpler jobs it may even be quicker than booking the car into a garage and going there twice, to leave and collect it. Perhaps most important, a lot of money can be saved by avoiding the costs a garage must charge to cover its labour and overheads.

The manual has drawings and descriptions to show the function of the various components so that their layout can be understood. Then the tasks are described and photographed in a clear step-by-step sequence.

We take great pride in the accuracy of information given in this manual, but vehicle manufacturers make alterations and design changes during the production run of a particular vehicle of which they do not inform us. No liability can be accepted by the authors or publishers for loss, damage or injury caused by any errors in, or omissions from, the information given.

Fiesta 1.1 Ghia

Fiesta Courier

Working on your car can be dangerous. This page shows just some of the potential risks and hazards, with the aim of creating a safety-conscious attitude.

General hazards

Scalding

• Don't remove the radiator or expansion tank cap while the engine is hot.
• Engine oil, automatic transmission fluid or power steering fluid may also be dangerously hot if the engine has recently been running.

Burning

• Beware of burns from the exhaust system and from any part of the engine. Brake discs and drums can also be extremely hot immediately after use.

Crushing

• When working under or near a raised vehicle, always supplement the jack with axle stands, or use drive-on ramps. *Never venture under a car which is only supported by a jack.*
• Take care if loosening or tightening high-torque nuts when the vehicle is on stands. Initial loosening and final tightening should be done with the wheels on the ground.

Fire

• Fuel is highly flammable; fuel vapour is explosive.
• Don't let fuel spill onto a hot engine.
• Do not smoke or allow naked lights (including pilot lights) anywhere near a vehicle being worked on. Also beware of creating sparks (electrically or by use of tools).
• Fuel vapour is heavier than air, so don't work on the fuel system with the vehicle over an inspection pit.
• Another cause of fire is an electrical overload or short-circuit. Take care when repairing or modifying the vehicle wiring.
• Keep a fire extinguisher handy, of a type suitable for use on fuel and electrical fires.

Electric shock

• Ignition HT voltage can be dangerous, especially to people with heart problems or a pacemaker. Don't work on or near the ignition system with the engine running or the ignition switched on.

• Mains voltage is also dangerous. Make sure that any mains-operated equipment is correctly earthed. Mains power points should be protected by a residual current device (RCD) circuit breaker.

Fume or gas intoxication

• Exhaust fumes are poisonous; they often contain carbon monoxide, which is rapidly fatal if inhaled. Never run the engine in a confined space such as a garage with the doors shut.
• Fuel vapour is also poisonous, as are the vapours from some cleaning solvents and paint thinners.

Poisonous or irritant substances

• Avoid skin contact with battery acid and with any fuel, fluid or lubricant, especially antifreeze, brake hydraulic fluid and Diesel fuel. Don't syphon them by mouth. If such a substance is swallowed or gets into the eyes, seek medical advice.
• Prolonged contact with used engine oil can cause skin cancer. Wear gloves or use a barrier cream if necessary. Change out of oil-soaked clothes and do not keep oily rags in your pocket.
• Air conditioning refrigerant forms a poisonous gas if exposed to a naked flame (including a cigarette). It can also cause skin burns on contact.

Asbestos

• Asbestos dust can cause cancer if inhaled or swallowed. Asbestos may be found in gaskets and in brake and clutch linings. When dealing with such components it is safest to assume that they contain asbestos.

Special hazards

Hydrofluoric acid

• This extremely corrosive acid is formed when certain types of synthetic rubber, found in some O-rings, oil seals, fuel hoses etc, are exposed to temperatures above 400°C. The rubber changes into a charred or sticky substance containing the acid. *Once formed, the acid remains dangerous for years. If it gets onto the skin, it may be necessary to amputate the limb concerned.*
• When dealing with a vehicle which has suffered a fire, or with components salvaged from such a vehicle, wear protective gloves and discard them after use.

The battery

• Batteries contain sulphuric acid, which attacks clothing, eyes and skin. Take care when topping-up or carrying the battery.
• The hydrogen gas given off by the battery is highly explosive. Never cause a spark or allow a naked light nearby. Be careful when connecting and disconnecting battery chargers or jump leads.

Air bags

• Air bags can cause injury if they go off accidentally. Take care when removing the steering wheel and/or facia. Special storage instructions may apply.

Diesel injection equipment

• Diesel injection pumps supply fuel at very high pressure. Take care when working on the fuel injectors and fuel pipes.

⚠ *Warning: Never expose the hands, face or any other part of the body to injector spray; the fuel can penetrate the skin with potentially fatal results.*

Remember...

DO

• Do use eye protection when using power tools, and when working under the vehicle.

• Do wear gloves or use barrier cream to protect your hands when necessary.

• Do get someone to check periodically that all is well when working alone on the vehicle.

• Do keep loose clothing and long hair well out of the way of moving mechanical parts.

• Do remove rings, wristwatch etc, before working on the vehicle – especially the electrical system.

• Do ensure that any lifting or jacking equipment has a safe working load rating adequate for the job.

DON'T

• Don't attempt to lift a heavy component which may be beyond your capability – get assistance.

• Don't rush to finish a job, or take unverified short cuts.

• Don't use ill-fitting tools which may slip and cause injury.

• Don't leave tools or parts lying around where someone can trip over them. Mop up oil and fuel spills at once.

• Don't allow children or pets to play in or near a vehicle being worked on.

The following pages are intended to help in dealing with common roadside emergencies and breakdowns. You will find more detailed fault finding information at the back of the manual, and repair information in the main chapters.

If your car won't start and the starter motor doesn't turn

☐ If it's a model with automatic transmission, make sure the selector is in 'P' or 'N'.
☐ Open the bonnet and make sure that the battery terminals are clean and tight.
☐ Switch on the headlights and try to start the engine. If the headlights go very dim when you're trying to start, the battery is probably flat. Get out of trouble by jump starting (see next page) using a friend's car.

If your car won't start even though the starter motor turns as normal

☐ Is there fuel in the tank?
☐ Is there moisture on electrical components under the bonnet? Switch off the ignition, then wipe off any obvious dampness with a dry cloth. Spray a water-repellent aerosol product (WD-40 or equivalent) on ignition and fuel system electrical connectors like those shown in the photos. Pay special attention to the ignition coil wiring connector and HT leads.

A Check that the spark plug HT leads are securely connected to the spark plugs.

B Also check that the leads are secure in the ignition module.

C Check the security and condition of the battery terminals.

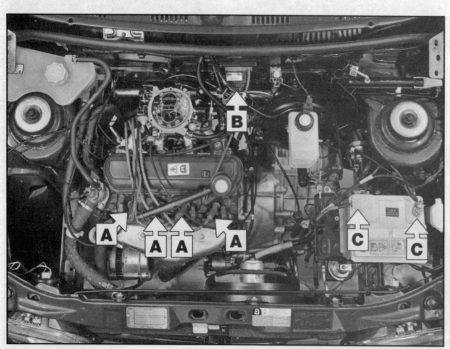

Check that all electrical connections are secure (with the ignition switched off) and spray them with a water dispersant spray like WD-40 if you suspect a problem due to damp.

Jump starting

When jump-starting a car using a booster battery, observe the following precautions:

✔ Before connecting the booster battery, make sure that the ignition is switched off.

✔ Ensure that all electrical equipment (lights, heater, wipers, etc) is switched off.

✔ Make sure that the booster battery is the same voltage as the discharged one in the vehicle.

✔ If the battery is being jump-started from the battery in another vehicle, the two vehcles MUST NOT TOUCH each other.

✔ Make sure that the transmission is in neutral (or PARK, in the case of automatic transmission).

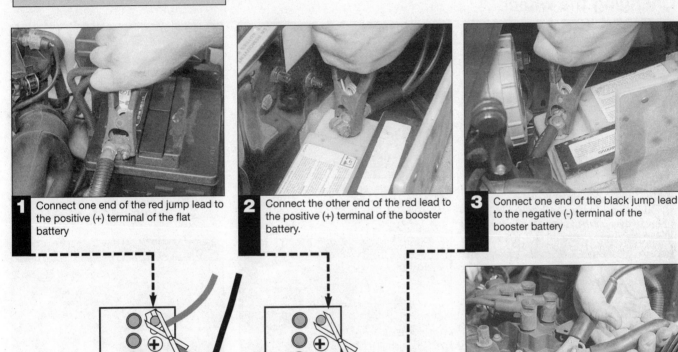

1 Connect one end of the red jump lead to the positive (+) terminal of the flat battery

2 Connect the other end of the red lead to the positive (+) terminal of the booster battery.

3 Connect one end of the black jump lead to the negative (-) terminal of the booster battery

4 Connect the other end of the black jump lead to a bolt or bracket on the engine block, well away from the battery, on the vehicle to be started.

5 Make sure that the jump leads will not come into contact with the fan, drive-belts or other moving parts of the engine.

6 Start the engine using the booster battery, then with the engine running at idle speed, disconnect the jump leads in the reverse order of connection.

Wheel changing

Some of the details shown here will vary according to model. For instance, the location of the spare wheel and jack is not the same on all cars. However, the basic principles apply to all vehicles.

 Warning: Do not change a wheel in a situation where you risk being hit by other traffic. On busy roads, try to stop in a lay-by or a gateway. Be wary of passing traffic while changing the wheel – it is easy to become distracted by the job in hand.

Preparation

☐ When a puncture occurs, stop as soon as it is safe to do so.
☐ Park on firm level ground, if possible, and well out of the way of other traffic.
☐ Use hazard warning lights if necessary.

☐ If you have one, use a warning triangle to alert other drivers of your presence.
☐ Apply the handbrake and engage first or reverse gear.
☐ Chock the wheel diagonally opposite the

one being removed – a couple of large stones will do for this.
☐ If the ground is soft, use a flat piece of wood to spread the load under the foot of the jack.

Changing the wheel

1 Remove the jack and wheel brace from the engine compartment. *On Courier models the jack is behind a plastic cover in front of the right-hand rear light cluster.*

2 Remove the spare wheel from its carrier by lowering the carrier using the wheel brace, then lifting out the wheel.

3 Remove the wheel centre trim, either by pulling it straight off, or by prising it off using the end of the wheelbrace.

4 Slacken each wheel nut by half a turn using the wheel brace.

5 Position the jack under the reinforced jacking point. Turn the handle clockwise until the wheel is clear of the ground. Unscrew the nuts and remove the wheel.

6 Fit the spare wheel, and screw in the nuts. Lightly tighten the nuts with the wheel brace then lower the vehicle to the ground.

Finally...

☐ Remove the wheel chocks. Stow the jack and tools in the appropriate locations in the car.

☐ Don't leave the spare wheel cradle empty and unsecured – it could drop onto the ground while the car is moving.

☐ Check the tyre pressure on the wheel just fitted. If it is low, or if you don't have a pressure gauge with you, drive slowly to the nearest garage and inflate the tyre to the correct pressure. Have the damaged tyre or wheel repaired, or renew it, as soon as possible.

7 Securely tighten the wheel nuts in the sequence shown, then refit the wheel trim.

8 Stow the punctured wheel in the carrier and raise the carrier fully. Note that the wheel nuts should be slackened and then retightened to the specified torque at the earliest opportunity.

Identifying leaks

Puddles on the garage floor or drive, or obvious wetness under the bonnet or underneath the car, suggest a leak that needs investigating. It can sometimes be difficult to decide where the leak is coming from, especially if the engine bay is very dirty already. Leaking oil or fluid can also be blown rearwards by the passage of air under the car, giving a false impression of where the problem lies.

 Warning: Most automotive oils and fluids are poisonous. Wash them off skin, and change out of contaminated clothing, without delay.

 The smell of a fluid leaking from the car may provide a clue to what's leaking. Some fluids are distinctively coloured. It may help to clean the car carefully and to park it over some clean paper overnight as an aid to locating the source of the leak.
Remember that some leaks may only occur while the engine is running.

Sump oil

Engine oil may leak from the drain plug...

Oil from filter

...or from the base of the oil filter.

Gearbox oil

Gearbox oil can leak from the seals at the inboard ends of the driveshafts.

Antifreeze

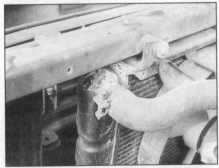

Leaking antifreeze often leaves a crystalline deposit like this.

Brake fluid

A leak occurring at a wheel is almost certainly brake fluid.

Power steering fluid

Power steering fluid may leak from the pipe connectors on the steering rack.

Towing

When all else fails, you may find yourself having to get a tow home – or of course you may be helping somebody else. Long-distance recovery should only be done by a garage or breakdown service. For shorter distances, DIY towing using another car is easy enough, but observe the following points:

☐ Use a proper tow-rope – they are not expensive. The vehicle being towed must display an 'ON TOW' sign in its rear window.

☐ Always turn the ignition key to the 'on' position when the vehicle is being towed, so that the steering lock is released, and that the direction indicator and brake lights will work.

☐ Only attach the tow-rope to the towing eyes provided.

☐ Before being towed, release the handbrake and select neutral on the transmission.

☐ Note that greater-than-usual pedal pressure will be required to operate the brakes, since the vacuum servo unit is only operational with the engine running.

☐ On models with power steering, greater-than-usual steering effort will also be required.

☐ The driver of the car being towed must keep the tow-rope taut at all times to avoid snatching.

☐ Make sure that both drivers know the route before setting off.

☐ Only drive at moderate speeds and keep the distance towed to a minimum. Drive smoothly and allow plenty of time for slowing down at junctions.

☐ On models with automatic transmission, special precautions apply. If in doubt, do not tow, or transmission damage may result.

Introduction

There are some very simple checks which need only take a few minutes to carry out, but which could save you a lot of inconvenience and expense.

These "Weekly checks" require no great skill or special tools, and the small amount of time they take to perform could prove to be very well spent, for example;

☐ Keeping an eye on tyre condition and pressures, will not only help to stop them wearing out prematurely, but could also save your life.

☐ Many breakdowns are caused by electrical problems. Battery-related faults are particularly common, and a quick check on a regular basis will often prevent the majority of these.

☐ If your car develops a brake fluid leak, the first time you might know about it is when your brakes don't work properly. Checking the level regularly will give advance warning of this kind of problem.

☐ If the oil or coolant levels run low, the cost of repairing any engine damage will be far greater than fixing the leak, for example.

Underbonnet check points

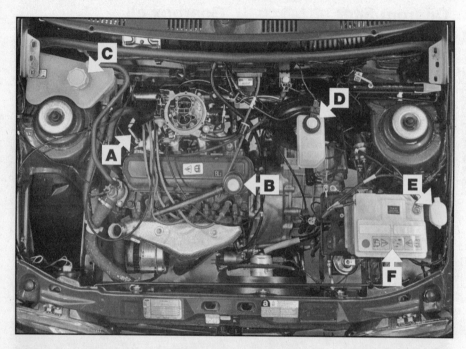

◀ 1.1 litre HCS carburettor engine

A *Engine oil level dipstick*

B *Engine oil filler cap*

C *Expansion tank pressure cap*

D *Brake fluid reservoir*

E *Screen washer reservoir filler cap*

F *Battery*

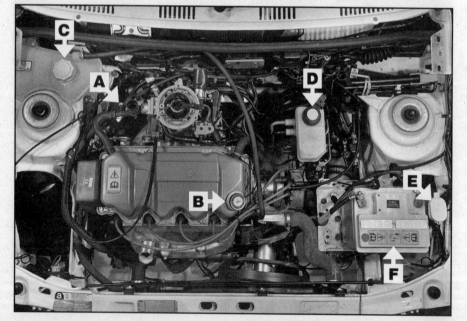

◀ 1.4 litre CVH CFi fuel injection engine

A *Engine oil level dipstick*

B *Engine oil filler cap*

C *Expansion tank pressure cap*

D *Brake fluid reservoir*

E *Screen washer reservoir filler cap*

F *Battery*

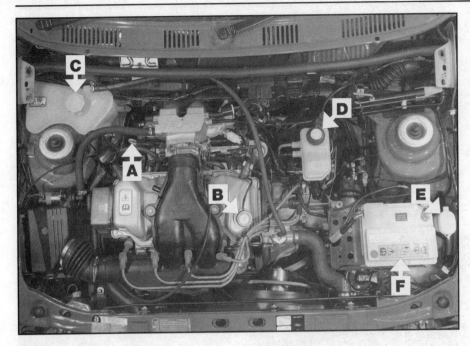

◀ 1.6 litre CVH EFi fuel injection engine

A *Engine oil level dipstick*

B *Engine oil filler cap*

C *Expansion tank pressure cap*

D *Brake fluid reservoir*

E *Screen washer reservoir filler cap*

F *Battery*

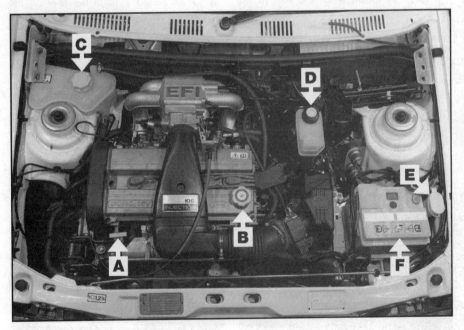

◀ 1.8 litre Zetec SEFi fuel injection engine

A *Engine oil level dipstick*

B *Engine oil filler cap*

C *Expansion tank pressure cap*

D *Brake fluid reservoir*

E *Screen washer reservoir filler cap*

F *Battery*

Engine oil level

Before you start

✔ Make sure that your car is on level ground.
✔ Check the oil level before the car is driven, or at least 5 minutes after the engine has been switched off.

HAYNES HiNT *If the oil is checked immediately after driving the vehicle, some of the oil will remain in the upper engine components, resulting in an inaccurate reading on the dipstick!*

The correct oil

Modern engines place great demands on their oil. It is very important that the correct oil for your car is used (See "Lubricants, fluids and tyre pressures").

Car Care

● If you have to add oil frequently, you should check whether you have any oil leaks. Place some clean paper under the car overnight, and check for stains in the morning. If there are no leaks, the engine may be burning oil (see "Fault Finding").

● Always maintain the level between the upper and lower dipstick marks (see photo 3). If the level is too low severe engine damage may occur. Oil seal failure may result if the engine is overfilled by adding too much oil.

1 The dipstick is brightly coloured for identification and is located at the front or rear of the engine, depending on model (see "Underbonnet check points" for exact location). Withdraw the dipstick.

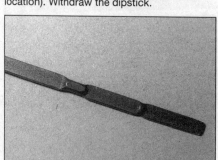
3 Note the oil level on the end of the dipstick which should be between the upper ("MAX") mark and lower ("MIN") mark. Approximately 0.5 to 1.0 litre of oil will raise the level from the lower to the upper marks.

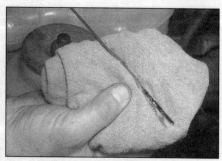
2 Using a clean rag or paper towel remove all oil from the dipstick. Insert the clean dipstick back into the engine as far as it will go, then withdraw it again.

4 Oil is added through the filler on the cylinder head cover. Unscrew or pull off the filler cap and top-up the level; a funnel may help to reduce spillage. Add the oil slowly, checking the level on the dipstick frequently. Avoid overfilling (see "Car Care").

Coolant level

⚠ **Warning: DO NOT attempt to remove the expansion tank pressure cap when the engine is hot, as there is a very great risk of scalding. Do not leave open containers of coolant about as it is poisonous.**

Car Care

● Adding coolant should not be necessary on a regular basis. If frequent topping-up is required, it is likely there is a leak. Check the radiator, all hoses and joint faces for any signs of staining or wetness, and rectify as necessary.

● It is important that antifreeze is used in the cooling system all year round, not just during the winter months. Don't top-up with water alone, as the antifreeze will become too diluted.

1 The coolant level varies with the temperature of the engine. When the engine is cold, the coolant level should be up to the "MAX" mark on the side of the tank. When the engine is hot, the level may rise to above the "MAX" mark.

2 If topping-up is necessary, **wait until the engine is cold.** Slowly unscrew the expansion tank cap, to release any pressure present in the cooling system, and remove it.

3 Add a mixture of water and antifreeze through the expansion tank filler neck until the level is up to the "MAX" mark. Refit the cap and tighten it securely.

Brake fluid level

Warning:
Brake hydraulic fluid can harm your eyes and damage painted surfaces, so use extreme caution when handling and pouring it.
Do not use fluid that has been standing open for some time, as it absorbs moisture from the air which can cause a dangerous loss of braking effectiveness.

HAYNES HiNT
• *Make sure that your car is on level ground.*
• *The fluid level in the reservoir will drop slightly as the brake pads wear down, but the fluid level must never be allowed to drop below the "MIN" mark.*

Safety First!

● If the reservoir requires repeated topping-up, this is an indication of a fluid leak somewhere in the system, which should be investigated immediately.

● If a leak is suspected, the car should not be driven until the braking system has been checked. Never take any risks where brakes are concerned.

1 The "MAX" and "MIN" marks are indicated on the side of the reservoir. The fluid level must be kept between the marks at all times.

2 If topping-up is necessary, first wipe the area around the filler cap with a clean rag before removing the cap. This will prevent dirt entering the system.

3 Unscrew the reservoir cap and carefully lift it out of position, taking care not to damage the level sender float. Inspect the reservoir, if the fluid is dirty, the hydraulic system should be drained and refilled (see Chapter 1).

4 Carefully add fluid, taking care not to spill it on surrounding components. Use only the specified hydraulic fluid; mixing different types of fluid can cause damage to the system. After topping-up to the correct level, refit the cap securely and wipe off any spilt fluid.

Power steering fluid level

Before you start:

✔ Park the vehicle on level ground.
✔ Set the steering wheel straight-ahead.
✔ The engine should be turned off.

HAYNES HiNT *For the check to be accurate, the steering must not be turned once the engine has been stopped.*

Safety First!

● The need for frequent topping-up indicates a leak, which should be investigated immediately.

1 The fluid reservoir is located either behind the battery, or at the front right-hand side of the engine compartment, according to model. When the engine is cold, the fluid level should be up to the "MIN" mark on the reservoir; when hot it should be up to the "MAX" mark. The fluid should never be allowed to fall below the "MIN" mark.

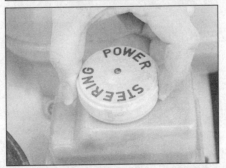

2 If topping-up is necessary, wipe clean the area around the reservoir filler neck and unscrew the filler cap from the reservoir.

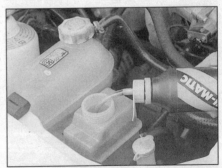

3 Use the specified type of fluid and do not overfill the reservoir. When the level is correct, securely refit the cap.

Screen washer fluid level*

Screenwash additives not only keep the windscreen clean during foul weather, they also prevent the washer system freezing in cold weather - which is when you are likely to need it most. Don't top-up using plain water as the screenwash will become too diluted, and will freeze during cold weather. On no account use coolant antifreeze in the washer system - this could discolour or damage the paintwork.

*On models so equipped, the screen washer fluid is also used to clean the tailgate rear window.

1 The washer reservoir itself is actually located under the wheelarch; release the cap and observe the level in the reservoir by looking down the filler neck.

2 When topping-up the reservoir, a screenwash additive should be added in the quantities recommended on the bottle.

Battery

Caution: *Before carrying out any work on the vehicle battery, read the precautions given in "Safety first" at the start of this manual.*

✔ Make sure that the battery tray is in good condition, and that the clamp is tight. Corrosion on the tray, retaining clamp and the battery itself can be removed with a solution of water and baking soda. Thoroughly rinse all cleaned areas with water. Any metal parts damaged by corrosion should be covered with a zinc-based primer, then painted.

✔ Periodically (approximately every three months), check the charge condition of the battery as described in Chapter 5A.

✔ If the battery is flat, and you need to jump start your vehicle, see *Roadside Repairs*.

1 The battery is located at the left-hand front of the engine compartment. The exterior of the battery should be inspected periodically for damage such as a cracked case or cover.

2 Check the tightness of the battery cable clamps to ensure good electrical connections. You should not be able to move them. Also check each cable for cracks and frayed conductors.

HAYNES HiNT

Battery corrosion can be kept to a minimum by applying a layer of petroleum jelly to the clamps and terminals after they are reconnected.

3 If corrosion (white, fluffy deposits) is evident, remove the cables from the battery terminals, clean them with a small wire brush, then refit them. Automotive stores sell a useful tool for cleaning the battery post...

4 ...as well as the cable clamps.

Tyre condition and pressure

It is very important that tyres are in good condition, and at the correct pressure - having a tyre failure at any speed is highly dangerous. Tyre wear is influenced by driving style - harsh braking and acceleration, or fast cornering, will all produce more rapid tyre wear. As a general rule, the front tyres wear out faster than the rears. Interchanging the tyres from front to rear ("rotating" the tyres) may result in more even wear. However, if this is completely effective, you may have the expense of replacing all four tyres at once! Remove any nails or stones embedded in the tread before they penetrate the tyre to cause deflation. If removal of a nail does reveal that the tyre has been punctured, refit the nail so that its point of penetration is marked. Then immediately change the wheel, and have the tyre repaired by a tyre dealer.

Regularly check the tyres for damage in the form of cuts or bulges, especially in the sidewalls. Periodically remove the wheels, and clean any dirt or mud from the inside and outside surfaces. Examine the wheel rims for signs of rusting, corrosion or other damage. Light alloy wheels are easily damaged by "kerbing" whilst parking; steel wheels may also become dented or buckled. A new wheel is very often the only way to overcome severe damage.

New tyres should be balanced when they are fitted, but it may become necessary to re-balance them as they wear, or if the balance weights fitted to the wheel rim should fall off. Unbalanced tyres will wear more quickly, as will the steering and suspension components. Wheel imbalance is normally signified by vibration, particularly at a certain speed (typically around 50 mph). If this vibration is felt only through the steering, then it is likely that just the front wheels need balancing. If, however, the vibration is felt through the whole car, the rear wheels could be out of balance. Wheel balancing should be carried out by a tyre dealer or garage.

1 Tread Depth - visual check

The original tyres have tread wear safety bands (B), which will appear when the tread depth reaches approximately 1.6 mm. The band positions are indicated by a triangular mark on the tyre sidewall (A).

2 Tread Depth - manual check

Alternatively, tread wear can be monitored with a simple, inexpensive device known as a tread depth indicator gauge.

3 Tyre Pressure Check

Check the tyre pressures regularly with the tyres cold. Do not adjust the tyre pressures immediately after the vehicle has been used, or an inaccurate setting will result.

Tyre tread wear patterns

Shoulder Wear

Underinflation (wear on both sides)
Under-inflation will cause overheating of the tyre, because the tyre will flex too much, and the tread will not sit correctly on the road surface. This will cause a loss of grip and excessive wear, not to mention the danger of sudden tyre failure due to heat build-up.
Check and adjust pressures
Incorrect wheel camber (wear on one side)
Repair or renew suspension parts
Hard cornering
Reduce speed!

Centre Wear

Overinflation
Over-inflation will cause rapid wear of the centre part of the tyre tread, coupled with reduced grip, harsher ride, and the danger of shock damage occurring in the tyre casing.
Check and adjust pressures

If you sometimes have to inflate your car's tyres to the higher pressures specified for maximum load or sustained high speed, don't forget to reduce the pressures to normal afterwards.

Uneven Wear

Front tyres may wear unevenly as a result of wheel misalignment. Most tyre dealers and garages can check and adjust the wheel alignment (or "tracking") for a modest charge.
Incorrect camber or castor
Repair or renew suspension parts
Malfunctioning suspension
Repair or renew suspension parts
Unbalanced wheel
Balance tyres
Incorrect toe setting
Adjust front wheel alignment
Note: *The feathered edge of the tread which typifies toe wear is best checked by feel.*

Wiper blades

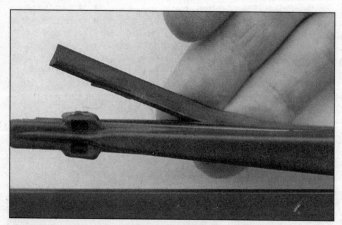

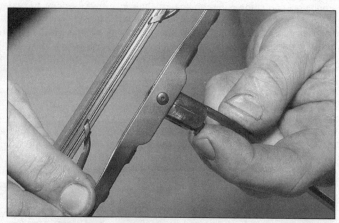

1 Check the condition of the wiper blades; if they are cracked or show any signs of deterioration, or if the glass swept area is smeared, renew them. For maximum clarity of vision, wiper blades should be renewed annually as a matter of course.

2 To remove a wiper blade, pull the arm fully away from the glass until it locks. Swivel the blade through 90º, press the locking tab with your finger and slide the blade out of the arm's hooked end.

✔ Don't forget to check the tailgate wiper blade as well. To remove the blade, depress the retaining tab and slide the blade out of the hooked end of the arm.

Bulbs and fuses

✔ Check all external lights and the horn. Refer to the appropriate Sections of Chapter 12 for details if any of the circuits are found to be inoperative.

✔ Visually check all accessible wiring connectors, harnesses and retaining clips for security, and for signs of chafing or damage.

> **HAYNES HiNT** *If you need to check your brake lights and indicators unaided, back up to a wall or garage door and operate the lights. The reflected light should show if they are working properly.*

1 If a single indicator light, stop light or headlight has failed it is likely that a bulb has blown and will need to be replaced. Refer to Chapter 12 for details. If both stop lights have failed, it is possible that the stop light switch is faulty or needs adjusting (see Chapter 12).

2 If more than one indicator light or headlight has failed it is likely that either a fuse has blown or that there is a fault in the circuit (see Chapter 12). The fuses are located in the fuse box below the facia on the driver's side. Lift off the cover to inspect the fuses.

3 To replace a blown fuse, simply pull it out from its contacts in the fuse block. Fit a new fuse of the same rating (see Chapter 12). If the fuse blows again, it is important that you find out why - a complete checking procedure is given in Chapter 12.

Lubricants and fluids

Engine (except 1.6/1.8 litre Zetec) . . . . Multigrade engine oil to specification API SG/CD or better, viscosity 5W/50 to 10W/30 (Duckhams QS, QXR, Hypergrade Plus, Hypergrade or 10W/40 Motor Oil)

Engine (1.6/1.8 litre Zetec) . . . . Multigrade engine oil to specification API SG/CD or better, viscosity 5W/50 to 10W/30 (Duckhams QS, QXR, or 10W/40 Motor Oil)

Cooling system . . . . Ethylene glycol-based antifreeze to Ford specification ESD-M97B-49-A (Duckhams Antifreeze & Summer Coolant)

Manual transmission . . . . SAE 80 high pressure gear oil to Ford specification SQM2C-9008-A (Duckhams Hypoid 80W/90)

Automatic transmission . . . . Transmission fluid to Ford specification ESP-M2C-166-H (Duckhams Uni-Matic)

Braking system . . . . Hydraulic fluid to Ford specification SAM-6C-9103A, DOT 4 or equivalent (Duckhams Universal Brake and Clutch Fluid)

Power steering . . . . Transmission fluid to Ford specification ESP-M2C-166-H (Duckhams Uni-Matic)

Wheel hub bearing grease (front and rear) . . . . Grease to Ford specification SAM-1C-9111A (Duckhams LB10)

Choosing your engine oil

Oils perform vital tasks in all engines. The higher the engine's performance, the greater the demand on lubricants to minimise wear as well as optimise power and economy. Duckhams tailors lubricants to the highest technical standards, meeting and exceeding the demands of all modern engines.

HOW ENGINE OIL WORKS

• Beating friction

Without oil, the surfaces inside your engine which rub together will heat, fuse and quickly cause engine seizure. Oil, and its special additives, forms a molecular barrier between moving parts, to stop wear and minimise heat build-up.

• Cooling hot spots

Oil cools parts that the engine's water-based coolant cannot reach, bathing the combustion chamber and pistons, where temperatures may exceed 1000°C. The oil assists in transferring the heat to the engine cooling system. Heat in the oil is also lost by air flow over the sump, and via any auxiliary oil cooler.

• Cleaning the inner engine

Oil washes away combustion by-products (mainly carbon) on pistons and cylinders, transporting them to the oil filter, and holding the smallest particles in suspension until they are flushed out by an oil change. Duckhams oils undergo extensive tests in the laboratory, and on the road.

Note: It is antisocial and illegal to dump oil down the drain. To find the location of your local oil recycling bank, call this number free.

Tyre pressures (cold)

	Front	Rear
135 R 13-S:		
Normal loading (up to three persons)	2.1 (30)	2.0 (29)
Fully laden (over three persons)	2.3 (33)	2.8 (40)
145 R 13-S:		
Normal loading (up to three persons)	1.8 (26)	1.8 (26)
Fully laden (over three persons)	2.3 (33)	2.8 (40)
145 R 13 78R (Courier models):		
Normal loading (driver plus 170 kg load)	2.3 (33)	2.5 (36)
Fully-laden (over normal load, up to maximum - see VIN plate)	2.3 (33)	2.8 (40)
155/70 R 13-S:		
Normal loading (up to three persons)	2.0 (29)	1.8 (26)
Fully laden (over three persons)	2.3 (33)	2.8 (40)
165/65 R 13-S:		
Normal loading (up to three persons)	1.8 (26)	1.8 (26)
Fully laden (over three persons)	2.3 (33)	2.8 (40)
165/65 R 13-H		
Normal loading (up to three persons)	2.0 (29)	2.0 (29)
Fully-laden (over three persons)	2.3 (33)	2.8 (40)
165/70 R 13 79T (Courier models):		
Normal loading (driver plus 170 kg load)	2.3 (33)	2.5 (36)
Fully-laden (over normal load, up to maximum - see VIN plate)	2.3 (33)	2.8 (40)
175/60 R 13, 175/60 R 13-H:		
Normal loading (up to three persons)	1.8 (26)	1.8 (26)
Fully-laden (over three persons)	2.3 (33)	2.8 (40)
185/55 R 14 79H:		
Normal loading (up to three persons)	2.0 (29)	2.0 (29)
Fully-laden (over three persons)	2.3 (33)	2.8 (40)
185/55 R 14 78V:		
Normal loading (up to three persons)	2.0 (29)	1.8 (26)
Fully-laden (over three persons)	2.1 (30)	2.3 (33)
185/60 R 13 80H:		
Normal loading (up to three persons)	2.0 (29)	1.8 (26)
Fully laden (over three persons)	2.1 (30)	2.3 (33)

Note: *For sustained high speeds above 100 mph (160 km/h), increased pressures are necessary. Consult the driver's handbook supplied with the vehicle. Pressures apply only to original-equipment tyres, and may vary if other makes or type is fitted; check with the tyre manufacturer or supplier for correct pressures if necessary.*

Chapter 1
Routine maintenance and servicing

1

Contents

Air cleaner element renewal 24
Automatic transmission fluid level check 20
Automatic transmission fluid renewal 26
Auxiliary drivebelt check and renewal 4
Bodywork, paint and exterior trim check 18
Brake check 14
Brake fluid renewal 31
Coolant renewal 23
Door, tailgate and bonnet check and lubrication 16
Driveshaft rubber gaiter and CV joint check 11
Emission control system check 25
Engine compartment wiring check 6
Engine oil and filter renewal 3
Exhaust system check 12
Front wheel alignment check 28
Fuel filter renewal 30

Handbrake adjustment 27
Idle speed and mixture check and adjustment 9
Idle speed control valve cleaning and maintenance 22
Intensive maintenance 2
Introduction 1
Manual transmission oil level check 8
Road test 19
Roadwheel nut tightness check 15
Seat belt check 17
Spark plug renewal and HT component check 21
Steering, suspension and roadwheel check 10
Timing belt renewal 29
Underbody and fuel/brake line check 13
Underbonnet check for fluid leaks and hose condition 5
Valve clearance adjustment 7

Degrees of difficulty

Easy, suitable for novice with little experience
Fairly easy, suitable for beginner with some experience
Fairly difficult, suitable for competent DIY mechanic
Difficult, suitable for experienced DIY mechanic
Very difficult, suitable for expert DIY or professional

Lubricants and fluids

Refer to end of *"Weekly Checks"*

Capacities

Engine oil

At oil and filter change:

HCS engines	3.25 litres
CVH and PTE engines	3.50 litres
Zetec engines	4.25 litres
Difference between dipstick minimum and maximum level notches ...	0.5 to 1.0 litre

Cooling system

HCS engines	7.1 litres
CVH and PTE engines	7.6 litres
Zetec engines	7.0 litres

Fuel tank	42.0 litres
Manual transmission	3.1 litres
Automatic transmission	3.5 litres

Engine

Direction of crankshaft rotation	Clockwise (seen from right-hand side of vehicle)

Oil filter:

HCS, CVH and PTE engines	Champion C104
Zetec engines	Champion C148

Cooling system

Coolant protection at standard 40% antifreeze/water mixture ratio:

Slush point	-25°C (-13°F)
Solidifying point	-30°C (-22°F)
Coolant specific gravity at standard 40% antifreeze/water mixture ratio and 15°C/59°F - with no other additives in coolant	1.061

Fuel system

Idle speed*:

1.0, 1.1 and 1.3 litre HCS (carburettor) engines	750 ± 50 rpm (cooling fan running)

1.4 and 1.6 litre CVH (carburettor) engines:

Manual transmission	800 ± 50 rpm (cooling fan running)
CTX automatic transmission	850 ± 50 rpm (cooling fan running)

1.6 litre CVH (EFi fuel injection) engines:

Idle speed	900 ± 50 rpm
Base idle speed	750 ± 50 rpm

Idle mixture CO content*:

1.0, 1.1 and 1.3 litre HCS (carburettor) engines	1.0 ± 0.5%
1.4 litre CVH (carburettor) engines	1.5 ± 0.25%
1.6 litre CVH (carburettor) engines	1.5 ± 0.5%

1.6 litre CVH (fuel injection) engines:

Non turbo models	0.8 ± 0.25%
Turbo models	1.5 ± 0.25%

*Note: *The idle speed and mixture CO content is only adjustable on the engines shown above. On all other engines, it is controlled by the engine management system, and cannot be checked or adjusted without specialised test equipment.*

Air filter element:

1.0, 1.1 and 1.3 litre HCS engines	Champion W153
1.4 litre CVH and PTE engines	Champion W226
1.6 litre CVH (carburettor) engines	Champion W226
1.6 litre CVH (fuel injection) engines	Champion U557
1.6 and 1.8 litre Zetec engines	Champion U612

Fuel filter:

HCS, CVH (fuel injection) and PTE engines:

Without quick-release fuel line fittings	Champion L204
With quick-release fuel line fittings	Champion type not available
Zetec engines	Champion L218

Ignition system

Firing order:

HCS engines	1-2-4-3 (No 1 cylinder at timing chain end of engine)
All other engines	1-3-4-2 (No 1 cylinder at timing belt end of engine)

Spark plugs*:

HCS engines	Champion RS9YCC or RS9YC
1.4 and 1.6 litre CVH (carburettor) engines	Champion RC7YCC or RC7YC
1.6 litre CVH (EFi fuel injection) and PTE engines	
Non-turbo models	Champion RC7YCC4 or RC7YC4
Turbo models	Champion C61YC
1.6 and 1.8 litre Zetec engines	Champion RE7YCC

Electrode gap*:

HCS engines	1.0 mm
1.4 litre CVH (carburettor) engines	0.8 mm
1.4 litre CVH (CFi fuel injection) and PTE engine	1.0 mm
1.6 litre CVH (carburettor) engines:	
With Champion RC7YCC	0.8 mm
With Champion RC7YC	0.7 mm
1.6 litre CVH (EFi fuel injection) engines:	
Non-turbo models	1.0 mm
Turbo models	0.7 mm
1.6 and 1.8 litre Zetec engines	1.3 mm

Spark plug (HT) leads:

HCS engines	Champion LS-28
1.4 and 1.6 litre CVH (carburettor) engines	Champion LS-14
1.4 litre CVH (CFi fuel injection) and PTE engines	Champion LS-14
1.6 litre CVH (EFi fuel injection) engines	Champion LS-26
1.6 and 1.8 litre Zetec engines	Champion type not available
Maximum resistance per lead	30 000 ohms

* Information on spark plug types and electrode gaps is as recommended by Champion Spark Plug. Where alternative types are used, refer to their manufacturer's recommendations.

Braking system

Minimum front brake pad lining thickness	1.5 mm
Minimum rear brake shoe lining thickness	1.0 mm

Tyres

Tyre pressures	See "Weekly Checks"

Wiper blades

Windscreen	Champion X-4803
Tailgate/rear window	Champion X-4103

Torque wrench settings

	Nm	lbf ft
Auxiliary drivebelt cover fasteners	8	6
Auxiliary drivebelt adjustment:		
Adjusting bolt (sliding arm)	22	16
Central (locking) bolt	22	16
Pinion (adjuster) nut	12	9
Alternator mounting bolts	24	18
Tensioner pulley centre bolt (HCS engines)	20	15
Engine oil drain plug	24	18
Manual transmission filler/level plug	20	15
Spark plugs:		
HCS engines	18	13
CVH and PTE engines	24	18
Zetec engines	15	11
Roadwheel nuts	71 to 100	52 to 74

The maintenance schedule for these vehicles, based on the manufacturer's recommendations, is as described below - note that the schedule starts from the vehicle's date of registration. These are the minimum maintenance intervals recommended by the factory for Fiestas driven daily, but subjected only to "normal" use. If you wish to keep your vehicle in peak condition at all times, you may wish to perform some of these procedures even more often. Because frequent maintenance enhances the efficiency, performance and resale value of your vehicle, we encourage you to do so. If your usage is not "normal", shorter intervals are also recommended - the most important examples of these are noted in the schedule. These shorter intervals apply particularly if you drive in dusty areas, tow a caravan or trailer, sit with the engine idling or drive at low speeds for extended periods (ie, in heavy traffic), or drive for short distances (less than four miles) in below-freezing temperatures.

When your vehicle is new, it should be serviced by a Ford dealer service department to protect the factory warranty. In many cases, the initial maintenance check is done at no cost to the owner. Note that this first free service (carried out by the selling dealer 1500 miles or 3 months after delivery), although an important check for a new vehicle, is not part of the regular maintenance schedule, and is therefore not mentioned here.

It should be noted that for the 1992 model year, for all models except RS Turbo, the service time/mileage intervals were extended by the manufacturer to the periods shown in this schedule. Although these intervals can be applied retrospectively, owners of earlier vehicles may notice a discrepancy between this schedule and the one shown in the Service Guide supplied with the vehicle.

Every 250 miles (400 km) or weekly

☐ Refer to *"Weekly Checks"*.

Every 5000 miles (8000 km) or 6 months, whichever occurs first

Note: *Frequent oil and filter changes are good for the engine. We recommend changing the oil at the mileage specified here, or at least twice a year if the mileage covered is less.*

☐ Renew the engine oil and filter (Section 3).

Every 10 000 miles (16 000 km) or 12 months, whichever occurs first

Carry out all operations listed above, plus the following:

☐ Check the auxiliary drivebelt (Section 4).
☐ Check under the bonnet for fluid leaks and hose condition (Section 5).
☐ Check the condition of all engine compartment wiring (Section 6).
☐ Check the valve clearance adjustment - HCS engines only (Section 7).
☐ Check the manual transmission oil level (Section 8).
☐ Check the engine idle speed and mixture - HCS and CVH engines only, where possible (Section 9).
☐ Check the steering, suspension and roadwheels (Section 10).
☐ Check the driveshaft rubber gaiters and CV joints (Section 11).
☐ Check the exhaust system (Section 12).
☐ Check the underbody, and all fuel/brake lines (Section 13).
☐ Check the brake system (Section 14).
☐ Check the security of all roadwheel nuts (Section 15).
☐ Check the doors, tailgate and bonnet, and lubricate their hinges and locks (Section 16).
☐ Check the seat belts (Section 17).
☐ Check the condition of the bodywork, paint and exterior trim (Section 18).
☐ Road test (Section 19).
☐ Check the automatic transmission fluid level (Section 20).

Every 20 000 miles (32 000 km) or two years, whichever occurs first

Carry out all operations listed above, plus the following:

☐ Renew the spark plugs and check the condition of the HT leads - all engines except Zetec (Section 21).
☐ Clean the idle speed control valve (Weber type) - CVH EFi engines only (Section 22).

Every 30 000 miles (48 000 km) or three years, whichever occurs first

Carry out all operations listed above, plus the following:

☐ Renew the coolant (Section 23).
☐ Renew the air cleaner filter element and check the air cleaner temperature control system - carburettor engines only (Section 24).
☐ Check the emission control systems (Section 25).
☐ Renew the spark plugs and check the condition of the HT leads - Zetec engines (Section 21).
☐ Renew the automatic transmission fluid (Section 26).
☐ Check the handbrake adjustment (Section 27).
☐ Check the front wheel alignment (Section 28).
Note: *If the vehicle is used regularly in dusty or polluted conditions, the air cleaner filter element should be renewed at more frequent intervals.*

Every 40 000 miles

☐ Renew the timing belt - CVH and PTE engines only (Section 29).

Every 60 000 miles

☐ Renew the timing belt - Zetec engines only (Section 29).
☐ Renew the fuel filter (Section 30).

Every three years (regardless of mileage)

☐ Renew the brake fluid (Section 31).

1.1 litre HCS carburettor engine (air cleaner removed for clarity)

1 Engine oil filler cap
2 Engine oil level dipstick
3 Cooling system expansion tank
4 Brake fluid reservoir
5 Windscreen/tailgate washer fluid reservoir cap
6 Battery
7 Vehicle identification plate
8 Thermostat housing
9 Radiator cooling fan thermal switch multi-plug
10 Alternator
11 Starter motor solenoid
12 CTX automatic transmission fluid level dipstick
13 Exhaust heatshield/airbox
14 Brake pressure control valves
15 Top of suspension strut mounting assembly
16 Carburettor
17 Fuel feed hose
18 Anti-dieselling (fuel-cut off) solenoid connection
19 Throttle kicker
20 Throttle kicker control solenoid
21 Ignition module
22 Heater blower motor cover
23 Windscreen wiper motor mounting bracket

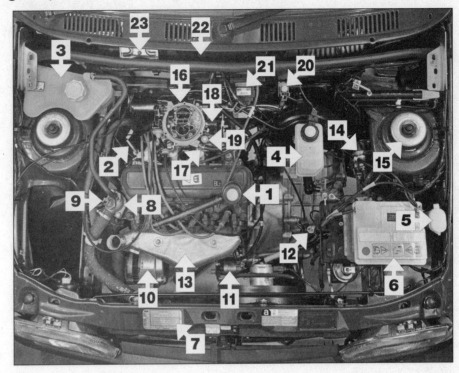

1

1.4 litre CVH CFi fuel injection engine (air cleaner removed for clarity)

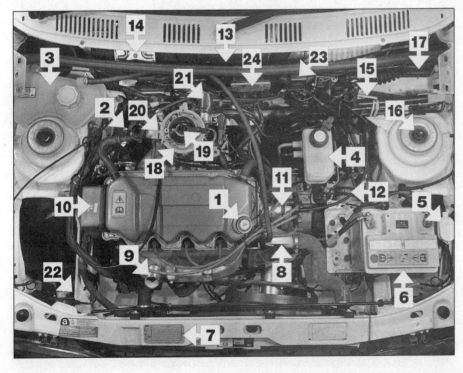

1 Engine oil filler cap
2 Engine oil level dipstick
3 Cooling system expansion tank
4 Brake fluid reservoir
5 Windscreen/tailgate washer fluid reservoir cap
6 Battery
7 Vehicle identification plate
8 Thermostat housing
9 Pre-heat tube
10 Timing belt cover
11 Distributor
12 Fuel filter
13 Heater blower motor cover
14 Windscreen wiper motor mounting bracket
15 Jack and wheelbrace retaining bolt
16 Top of suspension strut mounting assembly
17 EEC IV engine management module cover
18 CFi unit
19 Fuel injector
20 Fuel pressure regulator
21 Throttle plate control motor
22 Carbon canister
23 Manifold absolute pressure sensor
24 Ignition module

1.6 litre (XR2i) CVH EFi fuel injection engine

1 Engine oil filler cap
2 Engine oil level dipstick
3 Cooling system expansion tank
4 Brake fluid reservoir
5 Windscreen/tailgate washer fluid reservoir cap
6 Battery
7 Vehicle identification plate
8 Thermostat housing
9 Timing belt cover
10 Top of suspension strut mounting assembly
11 Windscreen wiper motor mounting bracket
12 Jack and wheelbrace retaining bolt
13 Distributorless (E-DIS) ignition coil
14 Fuel filter
15 Air cleaner
16 Air inlet duct
17 Idle speed control valve
18 Fuel pressure regulator
19 Throttle housing
20 Upper section of inlet manifold
21 Intake air temperature sensor
22 Fuel trap
23 EEC IV engine management module cover
24 Manifold absolute pressure sensor
25 Ignition module

1.8 litre (XR2i) Zetec SEFi fuel injection engine

1 Engine oil filler cap
2 Engine oil level dipstick
3 Cooling system expansion tank
4 Braking system fluid reservoir
5 Windscreen/tailgate washer fluid reservoir cap
6 Battery
7 VIN plate
8 Thermostat housing
9 Timing belt cover
10 Top of suspension strut mounting assembly
11 Windscreen wiper motor mounting bracket
12 Jack and wheelbrace retaining bolt
13 Distributorless (E-DIS) ignition coil
14 Fuel filter
15 Air cleaner
16 Air inlet duct
17 Idle speed control valve
18 Fuel pressure regulator
19 Throttle housing
20 Inlet manifold
21 Throttle position sensor
22 Fuel system pressure release/test point
23 EEC IV engine management module cover
24 Mass air flow sensor
25 Ignition module

Front underside view of the 1.4 litre CVH CFi fuel injection model

1 Engine oil sump
2 Front suspension lower arm
3 Brake caliper assembly
4 Driveshaft
5 Alternator
6 Auxiliary drivebelt cover
7 Steering rack gaiter
8 Windscreen/tailgate washer pump
9 Carbon canister
10 Oxygen sensor
11 Catalytic converter (exhaust) rubber insulator mounting
12 Catalytic converter assembly
13 Underbody heatshields
14 Gearchange mechanism shift rod
15 Gearchange mechanism stabiliser bar

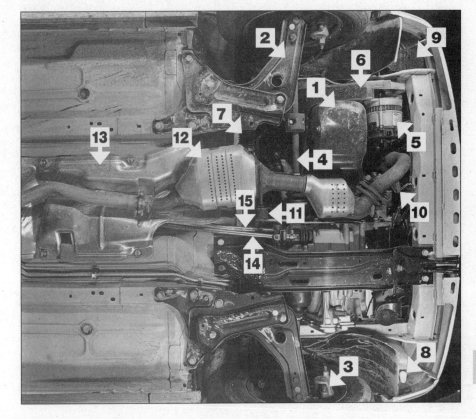

Front underside view of the 1.8 litre (XR2i) Zetec SEFi fuel injection model

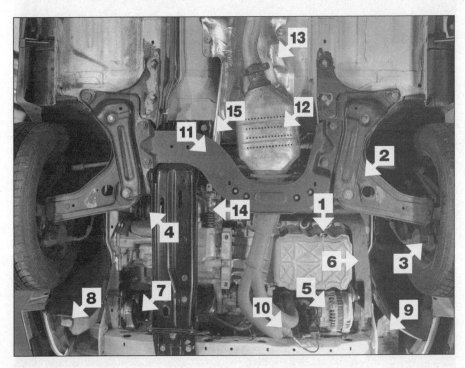

1 Engine oil drain plug
2 Front suspension lower arm
3 Brake caliper assembly
4 Driveshaft
5 Alternator
6 Auxiliary drivebelt cover
7 Horn
8 Windscreen/tailgate washer pump
9 Carbon canister
10 Oxygen sensor
11 Front suspension crossmember
12 Catalytic converter
13 Underbody heat shields
14 Gearchange mechanism shift rod
15 Gearchange mechanism stabiliser bar

1

Rear underside view of the 1.4 litre CVH CFi fuel injection model

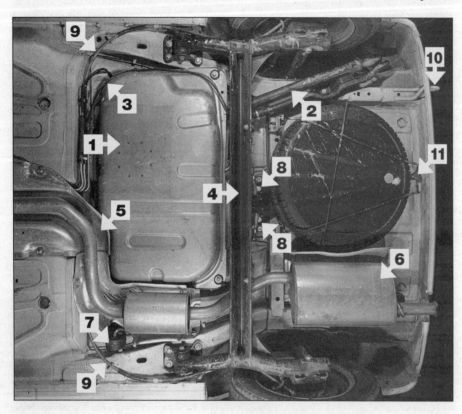

1 Fuel tank
2 Fuel filler pipe
3 Fuel tank ventilation hose
4 Twist beam rear axle assembly
5 Underbody heatshields
6 Exhaust rear silencer
7 Exhaust rubber insulator mounting
8 Load apportioning valves (on vehicles with the anti-lock braking system)
9 Handbrake cable
10 Rear towing eye
11 Spare wheel carrier hook (on the retaining bolt)

Rear underside view of the Courier van model

1 Fuel tank
2 Fuel filler pipe
3 Fuel tank ventilation hose
4 Rear axle assembly - spring torsion bars visible
5 Rear axle pivot brackets
6 Rear suspension dampers
7 Exhaust system rear silencer
8 Braking system light-laden valve
9 Handbrake cables
10 Rear towing eye
11 Spare wheel carrier

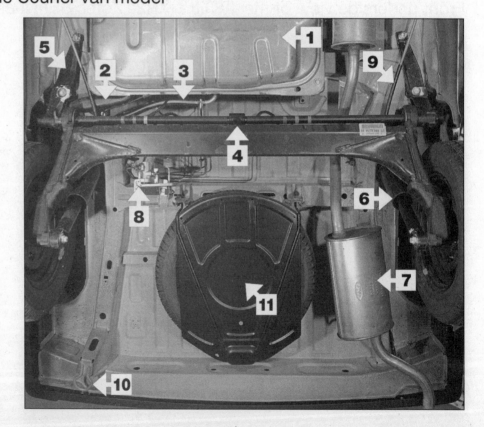

1 Introduction

This Chapter is designed to help the home mechanic maintain his/her vehicle for safety, economy, long life and peak performance.

This Chapter contains a master maintenance schedule, followed by Sections dealing specifically with each task in the schedule. Visual checks, adjustments, component renewal and other helpful items are included. Refer to the accompanying illustrations of the engine compartment and the underside of the vehicle for the locations of the various components.

Servicing your vehicle in accordance with the mileage/time maintenance schedule and the following Sections will provide a planned maintenance programme, which should result in a long and reliable service life. This is a comprehensive plan, so maintaining some items but not others at the specified service intervals will not produce the same results.

As you service your vehicle, you will discover that many of the procedures can - and should - be grouped together, because of the particular procedure being performed, or because of the close proximity of two otherwise-unrelated components to one another. For example, if the vehicle is raised for any reason, the exhaust should be inspected at the same time as the suspension and steering components.

The first step of this maintenance programme is to prepare yourself before the actual work begins. Read through all the

Sections relevant to the work to be carried out, then make a list and gather together all the parts and tools required. If a problem is encountered, seek advice from a parts specialist or a dealer service department.

2 Intensive maintenance

1 If, from the time the vehicle is new, the routine maintenance schedule is followed closely, and frequent checks are made of fluid levels and high-wear items, as suggested throughout this manual, the engine will be kept in relatively good running condition, and the need for additional work will be minimised.

2 It is possible that there will be some times when the engine is running poorly due to the lack of regular maintenance. This is even more likely if a used vehicle, which has not received regular and frequent maintenance checks, is purchased. In such cases, additional work may need to be carried out, outside of the regular maintenance intervals.

3 If engine wear is suspected, a compression test (refer to Part A, B or C of Chapter 2) will provide valuable information regarding the overall performance of the main internal components. Such a test can be used as a basis to decide on the extent of the work to be carried out. If, for example, a compression test indicates serious internal engine wear, conventional maintenance as described in this Chapter will not greatly improve the performance of the engine, and may prove a

waste of time and money, unless extensive overhaul work (Chapter 2D) is carried out first.

4 The following series of operations are those often required to improve the performance of a generally poor-running engine:

Primary operations

a) Clean, inspect and test the battery (See "Weekly Checks").

b) Check all the engine-related fluids (See "Weekly Checks").

c) Check the condition of the auxiliary drivebelt (Section 4).

d) Check and if necessary adjust the valve clearances on HCS engines (Section 7).

e) Renew the spark plugs and clean and inspect the HT leads (Section 21).

f) Check the condition of the air cleaner filter element and renew if necessary (Section 24).

g) Check and if necessary adjust the idle speed and mixture settings - where applicable (Section 9).

h) Renew the fuel filter - fuel injection models (Section 30).

i) Check the condition of all hoses, and check for fluid leaks (Section 5).

5 If the above operations do not prove fully effective, carry out the following operations:

Secondary operations

All the items listed under "Primary operations", plus the following:

a) Check the charging system (Chapter 5A).

b) Check the ignition system (Chapter 5B).

c) Check the fuel system (Chapter 4A, 4B, 4C and 4D).

e) Renew the ignition HT leads (Section 21).

Every 5000 miles (8000 km) or 6 months, whichever occurs first

3 Engine oil and filter renewal

> **HAYNES HINT**
> *Frequent oil changes are the best preventive maintenance the home mechanic can give the engine, because ageing oil becomes diluted and contaminated, which leads to premature engine wear.*

1 Make sure that you have all the necessary tools before you begin this procedure **(see illustration).** You should also have plenty of rags or newspapers handy, for mopping up any spills.

2 To avoid any possibility of scalding, and to protect yourself from possible skin irritants and other harmful contaminants in used engine oils, it is advisable to wear gloves when carrying out this work.

3 Access to the underside of the vehicle is greatly improved if the vehicle can be lifted on a hoist, driven onto ramps, or supported by axle stands (see *"Jacking and Vehicle Support"*).

> ⚠️ *Warning: Do not work under a vehicle which is supported only by an hydraulic or scissors-type jack, or by bricks, blocks of wood, etc.*

3.2 These tools are required when changing the engine oil and filter

4 If this is your first oil change, get under the vehicle and familiarise yourself with the position of the engine oil drain plug location in the sump. The engine and exhaust components will be warm during the actual work, so try to anticipate any potential problems while the engine and accessories are cool.

5 The oil should preferably be changed when the engine is still fully warmed-up to normal operating temperature, just after a run (the needle on the temperature gauge should be in the "Normal" sector of the gauge); warm oil and sludge will flow out more easily. Park the vehicle on firm, level ground, apply the handbrake firmly, then select 1st or reverse gear (manual transmission) or the "P" position (automatic transmission). Open the bonnet and remove the engine oil filler cap from the cylinder head cover, then remove the oil level dipstick from its tube (see *"Weekly Checks"*).

6 Raise the front of the vehicle, and support it securely on axle stands (see *"Jacking and Vehicle Support"*). Remove the front right-hand roadwheel to provide access to the oil

1

3.7a Engine oil drain plug location in the sump on HCS, CVH and PTE engines

3.7b Removing the engine oil drain plug on the Zetec engine

3.9 Removing the oil filter on the CVH engine using a strap wrench

filter; if the additional working clearance is required, remove also the auxiliary drivebelt cover.

7 Being careful not to touch the hot exhaust components, place the drain pan under the drain plug, and unscrew the plug **(see illustrations)**. If possible, try to keep the plug pressed into the sump while unscrewing it by hand the last couple of turns.

> **HAYNES HiNT**
> *As the drain plug releases from the threads, move it away sharply, so the stream of oil issuing from the sump runs into the pan, not up your sleeve!*

8 Allow some time for the old oil to drain, noting that it may be necessary to reposition the pan as the oil flow slows to a trickle. Check the condition of the plug's sealing washer and renew it if worn or damaged. When the oil has completely drained, wipe clean the drain plug and its threads in the sump and refit the plug, tightening it to the specified torque wrench setting.

9 Reposition the drain pan under the oil filter then, using a suitable filter removal tool,

unscrew the oil filter from the cylinder block, oil pump or oil filter adaptor, as applicable; be prepared for some oil spillage **(see illustration)**. Check the old filter to make sure that the rubber sealing ring hasn't stuck to the engine; if it has, carefully remove it. Withdraw the filter through the wheel arch, taking care to spill as little oil as possible.

10 Using a clean, lint-free rag, wipe clean the cylinder block around the filter mounting. If there are no specific instructions supplied with it, fit a new oil filter as follows. Apply a light coating of clean engine oil to the filter's sealing ring **(see illustration)**. Screw the filter into position until it seats, then tighten it through a further half- to three-quarters of a turn *only* **(see illustration)**. Tighten the filter by hand only - do not use any tools.

11 Remove the old oil and all tools from under the vehicle, refit the roadwheel, and lower the vehicle to the ground.

12 Refill the engine with oil, using the correct grade and type of oil, as given in *"Lubricants, fluids and tyre pressures"*. Pour in half the specified quantity of oil first, then wait a few minutes for the oil to run to the sump. Continue adding oil a small quantity at a time, until the level is up to the lower notch on the

dipstick. Adding approximately 0.5 to 1.0 litre (depending on model) will raise the level to the dipstick's upper notch.

13 Start the engine. The oil pressure warning light will take a few seconds to go out while the new filter fills with oil; do not race the engine while the light is on. Run the engine for a few minutes, while checking for leaks around the oil filter seal and the drain plug.

14 Switch off the engine, and wait a few minutes for the oil to settle in the sump once more. With the new oil circulated and the filter now completely full, recheck the level on the dipstick, and add more oil as necessary.

15 Dispose of the used engine oil safely, with reference to *"General repair procedures"* in the Reference Sections of this manual.

OIL CARE
FOLLOW THE CODE

OIL BANK LINE
0800 66 33 66

Note: It is antisocial and illegal to dump oil down the drain. To find the location of your local oil recycling bank, call this number free.

3.10a Lubricate the filter's sealing ring with clean engine oil before installing the filter on the engine

3.10b Fitting the new oil filter on the Zetec engine

4.3 Remove the auxiliary drivebelt lower cover from inside the wheel arch

4.4 Check the auxiliary drivebelt for signs of wear like these. Very small cracks across the drivebelt ribs are acceptable. If the cracks are deep, or if the drivebelt looks worn or damaged in any other way, renew it. This is the "polyvee" type belt, but the checks on the V-belt type are the same

CRACKS RUNNING ACROSS "V" PORTIONS OF BELT

ACCEPTABLE

1/2"

MISSING TWO OR MORE ADJACENT RIBS 1/2" OR LONGER

CRACKS RUNNING PARALLEL TO "V" PORTIONS OF BELT

UNACCEPTABLE

Every 10 000 miles (16 000 km) or 12 months, whichever comes first

4 Auxiliary drivebelt check and renewal

General

1 The number of auxiliary drivebelts fitted and their type depends on engine, and on whether the vehicle is equipped with power steering. The drivebelt(s) are located on the right-hand end of the engine and will be either of the V-belt type or the flat, multi-ribbed (or "polyvee") type. The belt drives the alternator, water pump and, on CVH and Zetec engines with power steering, the power steering pump from the engine's crankshaft pulley. On HCS engines with power steering, one belt drives the alternator and water pump and a separate belt drives the power steering pump.

2 The good condition and proper tension of the auxiliary drivebelt is critical to the operation of the engine. Because of their composition and the high stresses to which they are subjected, drivebelts stretch and deteriorate as they get older. They must, therefore, be regularly inspected.

Check

3 With the engine switched off, open and support the bonnet, then locate the auxiliary drivebelt(s) on the right-hand end of the engine (*Be very careful, and wear protective gloves to minimise the risk of burning your hands on hot components, if the engine has recently been running*). For improved access, jack up the front right-hand side of the vehicle, support it securely on an axle stand, remove the roadwheel, then (where fitted) remove the auxiliary drivebelt lower cover from inside the wheel arch (**see illustration**).

4 Using an inspection light or an electric torch, and rotating the engine when necessary with a spanner applied to the crankshaft pulley bolt, check the whole length of the drivebelt(s) for cracks, separation of the rubber, and torn or worn ribs (**see illustration**). Also check for fraying and glazing, which gives the drivebelt a shiny appearance. Both sides of the drivebelt(s) should be inspected, which means you will have to twist the drivebelt(s) to check the underside. Feel the relevant drivebelt where you can't see it. If you are in any doubt as to the condition of the drivebelt(s), renewal is necessary (go to paragraph 23).

> **HAYNES HINT**
> *Turning the engine will be much easier if the spark plugs are removed first (Section 21).*

Drivebelt tension

5 The tension must be adjusted manually on all V-belt type drivebelts, on flat "polyvee" type drivebelts fitted to early Zetec engines, and on "polyvee" type drivebelts fitted to HCS engines to drive the power steering pump. The "polyvee" type drivebelts used on later Zetec engines and PTE engines are fitted with an automatic tensioner to maintain the correct belt adjustment.

6 For models on which the tension can be adjusted manually, open the bonnet. Jack up

2 mm
2 mm

H 23318

4.7 Checking drivebelt adjustment - V-belt types

Note that the 4 mm dimension is the total belt swing and is equal to 2 mm of deflection

the front right-hand side of the vehicle, and support it securely on an axle stand. Remove the roadwheel, then (where fitted) remove the auxiliary drivebelt lower cover from inside the wheel arch.

7 Ford technicians use a special tension gauge and various other special tools for checking drivebelt adjustment, but for DIY purposes, checking the belt tension using finger pressure gives a good indication of correct adjustment. Apply firm finger pressure midway between the pulleys on the longest run of the belt, and look for a deflection of approximately 2.0 mm (i.e. a total drivebelt "swing" of approximately 4.0 mm) (**see illustration**).

8 If adjustment is necessary, proceed as follows according to belt type.

V-belt with sliding arm type adjuster

9 Loosen off the alternator mounting bolts and sliding arm adjustment bolts, pivot the alternator as required to provide the correct drivebelt tension, then retighten the bolts to secure (**see illustration**).

10 Refit the auxiliary drivebelt cover (where applicable) and roadwheel, then lower the vehicle to the ground.

11 Run the engine for about five minutes, then recheck the tension.

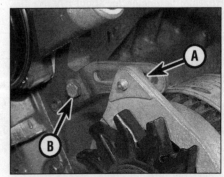

4.9 Alternator sliding arm adjustment bolt (A) and sliding arm mounting bolt (B) - V-belt with sliding arm type adjuster

1

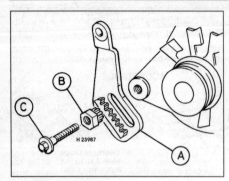

4.12a Rack-and-pinion type auxiliary drivebelt adjuster

A Adjuster arm
B Pinion (adjuster) nut
C Central (locking) bolt

V-belt and flat "polyvee" type drivebelt with rack-and-pinion type adjuster

12 Loosen off the alternator mounting bolts and the adjusting arm mounting bolt. Slacken the pinion central locking bolt, and turn the pinion nut as required to take up the tension of the drivebelt. Hold it at the required setting, and tighten the central bolt securely to lock the adjuster arm and set the tension **(see illustrations)**.

13 Tighten the alternator mounting and adjusting arm bolts securely.

14 Refit the auxiliary drivebelt cover (where applicable) and roadwheel, then lower the vehicle to the ground.

15 Run the engine for about five minutes, then recheck the tension.

Flat "polyvee" type drivebelt with tensioner pulley adjuster (HCS engine power steering pump drivebelt)

16 Slacken the tensioner pulley centre bolt then turn the adjuster bolt at the base of the tensioner pulley bracket, as required, to take up the tension of the drivebelt. When the belt deflection is correct, tighten the adjuster pulley centre retaining bolt.

17 Refit the auxiliary drivebelt cover (where applicable) and roadwheel, then lower the vehicle to the ground.

18 Run the engine for about five minutes, then recheck the tension.

Flat "polyvee" type drivebelt with automatic adjuster

19 As mentioned above, this type of drivebelt is tensioned by an automatic tensioner; regular checks are not required, and manual "adjustment" is not possible.

20 If you suspect that the drivebelt is slipping and/or running slack, or that the tensioner is otherwise faulty, it must be renewed. To do this, remove the drivebelt as described below, then unbolt and remove the tensioner. On fitting the new tensioner, ensure that it is aligned correctly on its mountings, and tightened to the specified torque wrench setting.

4.12b When the tension is correct, hold the adjuster nut, and tighten the central bolt securely to lock the adjuster arm

Renewal

21 Open the bonnet. Jack up the front right-hand side of the vehicle, and support it securely on an axle stand. Remove the roadwheel, then remove the auxiliary drivebelt lower cover (where fitted) from inside the wheel arch.

22 The routing of the drivebelt around the pulleys is dependent on the drivebelt type, and on whether power steering is fitted. Before removing the drivebelt, it's a good idea to sketch the belt run around the pulleys; this will save a lot of frustration when it comes to refitting. Note that on HCS engines with power steering, to renew the alternator/water pump drivebelt it will be necessary to remove the power steering pump drivebelt first.

23 If the existing drivebelt is to be refitted, mark it, or note the maker's markings on its flat surface, so that it can be installed the same way round.

24 To renew a drivebelt with manual adjustment, slacken the belt tension fully as described above, according to type. Slip the belt off the pulleys, then fit the new belt, ensuring that it is routed correctly. If fitting a flat "polyvee" type drivebelt, arrange it on the grooved pulleys so that it is centred in their grooves, and not overlapping their raised sides. With the belt in position, adjust the tension as previously described.

25 To renew the flat, "polyvee" type drivebelt with automatic adjuster, reach up between the body and the engine (above the crankshaft pulley), and apply a spanner to the hexagon in the centre of the automatic tensioner's pulley. Rotate the tensioner pulley clockwise to release its pressure on the drivebelt, then slip the drivebelt off the crankshaft pulley, and release the tensioner again **(see illustration)**. Note that on certain models, a self-cocking tensioner is fitted, and that this will remain in the released position. Working from the wheel arch or engine compartment as necessary, and noting its routing, slip the drivebelt off the remaining pulleys and withdraw it.

26 Check all the pulleys, ensuring that their grooves are clean, and removing all traces of

4.25 Automatic drivebelt tensioner - "polyvee" type drivebelt

Turn tensioner clockwise to release tension

oil and grease. Check that the tensioner works properly, with strong spring pressure being felt when its pulley is rotated clockwise, and a smooth return to the limit of its travel when released.

27 If the original drivebelt is being refitted, use the marks or notes made on removal, to ensure that it is installed to run in the same direction as it was previously. To fit the drivebelt, arrange it on the grooved pulleys so that it is centred in their grooves, and not overlapping their raised sides, and is routed correctly. Start at the top, and work down to finish at the crankshaft pulley; rotate the tensioner pulley clockwise, slip the drivebelt onto the crankshaft pulley, then release the tensioner again.

28 Using a spanner applied to the crankshaft pulley bolt, rotate the crankshaft through at least two full turns clockwise to settle the drivebelt on the pulleys, then check that the drivebelt is properly installed.

29 Refit the auxiliary drivebelt cover (where applicable) and roadwheel, then lower the vehicle to the ground.

5 Underbonnet check for fluid leaks and hose condition

General

1 High temperatures in the engine compartment can cause the deterioration of the rubber and plastic hoses used for engine, accessory and emissions systems operation. Periodic inspection should be made for cracks, loose clamps, material hardening and leaks.

2 Carefully check the large top and bottom radiator hoses, along with the other smaller-diameter cooling system hoses and metal pipes; do not forget the heater hoses/pipes which run from the engine to the bulkhead. Inspect each hose along its entire length, replacing any that is cracked, swollen or shows signs of deterioration. Cracks may become more apparent if the hose is

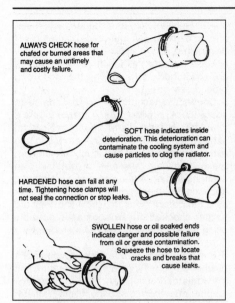

ALWAYS CHECK hose for chafed or burned areas that may cause an untimely and costly failure.

SOFT hose indicates inside deterioration. This deterioration can contaminate the cooling system and cause particles to clog the radiator.

HARDENED hose can fail at any time. Tightening hose clamps will not seal the connection or stop leaks.

SWOLLEN hose or oil soaked ends indicate danger and possible failure from oil or grease contamination. Squeeze the hose to locate cracks and breaks that cause leaks.

5.2 Hoses, like drivebelts, have a habit of failing at the worst possible time - to prevent the inconvenience of a blown radiator or heater hose, inspect them carefully as shown here

squeezed **(see illustration)**. If you are using non-Ford specification antifreeze, and so have to renew the coolant every two years or so, it's a good idea to renew the hoses at that time, regardless of their apparent condition.

3 Make sure that all hose connections are tight. A leak in the cooling system will usually show up as white- or rust-coloured deposits on the areas adjoining the leak; if the spring clamps that are used to secure the hoses in this system appear to be slackening, they should be renewed to prevent the possibility of leaks.

4 Some other hoses are secured to their fittings with clamps. Where clamps are used, check to be sure they haven't lost their tension, allowing the hose to leak. If clamps aren't used, make sure the hose has not expanded and/or hardened where it slips over the fitting, allowing it to leak.

5 Check all fluid reservoirs, filler caps, drain plugs and fittings etc, looking for any signs of leakage of oil, transmission and/or brake hydraulic fluid, coolant and power steering fluid. If the vehicle is regularly parked in the same place, close inspection of the ground underneath it will soon show any leaks. As soon as a leak is detected, its source must be traced and rectified. Where oil has been leaking for some time, it is usually necessary to use a steam cleaner, pressure washer or similar, to clean away the accumulated dirt, so that (when the engine is run again) the exact source of the leak can be identified.

Vacuum hoses

6 It's quite common for vacuum hoses, especially those in the emissions system, to be colour-coded, or to be identified by coloured

stripes moulded into them. Various systems require hoses with different wall thicknesses, collapse resistance and temperature resistance. When renewing hoses, be sure the new ones are made of the same material.

7 Often the only effective way to check a hose is to remove it completely from the vehicle. If more than one hose is removed, be sure to label the hoses and fittings to ensure correct installation.

8 When checking vacuum hoses, be sure to include any plastic T-fittings in the check. Inspect the fittings for cracks, and check the hose where it fits over the fitting for distortion, which could cause leakage.

9 A small piece of vacuum hose (quarter-inch inside diameter) can be used as a stethoscope to detect vacuum leaks. Hold one end of the hose to your ear, and probe around vacuum hoses and fittings, listening for the "hissing" sound characteristic of a vacuum leak.

 Warning: When probing with the vacuum-hose stethoscope, be very careful not to come into contact with moving engine components such as the auxiliary drivebelt, radiator electric cooling fan, etc.

Fuel hoses

Warning: There are certain precautions which must be taken when inspecting or servicing fuel system components. Work in a well-ventilated area, and do not allow open flames (cigarettes, appliance pilot lights, etc.) or bare light bulbs near the work area. Mop up any spills immediately, and do not store fuel-soaked rags where they could ignite.

10 Check all fuel hoses for deterioration and chafing. Check especially for cracks in areas where the hose bends, and also just before fittings, such as where a hose attaches to the fuel filter.

11 High-quality fuel line, usually identified by the word "Fluoroelastomer" printed on the hose, should be used for fuel line renewal. Never, under any circumstances, use unreinforced vacuum line, clear plastic tubing or water hose for fuel lines.

12 Spring-type clamps are commonly used on fuel lines. These clamps often lose their tension over a period of time, and can be "sprung" during removal. Replace all spring-type clamps with screw clamps whenever a hose is replaced.

Metal lines

13 Sections of metal piping are often used for fuel line between the fuel filter and the engine. Check carefully to be sure the piping has not been bent or crimped, and that cracks have not started in the line.

14 If a section of metal fuel line must be renewed, only seamless steel piping should be used, since copper and aluminium piping don't have the strength necessary to withstand normal engine vibration.

15 Check the metal brake lines where they enter the master cylinder and ABS hydraulic unit (if used) for cracks in the lines or loose fittings. Any sign of brake fluid leakage calls for an immediate and thorough inspection of the brake system.

6 Engine compartment wiring check

1 With the vehicle parked on level ground, apply the handbrake firmly and open the bonnet. Using an inspection light or a small electric torch, check all visible wiring within and beneath the engine compartment.

2 What you are looking for is wiring that is obviously damaged by chafing against sharp edges, or against moving suspension/ transmission components and/or the auxiliary drivebelt, by being trapped or crushed between carelessly-refitted components, or melted by being forced into contact with the hot engine castings, coolant pipes, etc. In almost all cases, damage of this sort is caused in the first instance by incorrect routing on reassembly, after previous work has been carried out.

3 Depending on the extent of the problem, damaged wiring may be repaired by rejoining the break or splicing-in a new length of wire, using solder to ensure a good connection, and remaking the insulation with adhesive insulating tape or heat-shrink tubing, as appropriate. If the damage is extensive, given the implications for the vehicle's future reliability, the best long-term answer may well be to renew that entire section of the loom, however expensive this may appear.

4 When the actual damage has been repaired, ensure that the wiring loom is re-routed correctly, so that it is clear of other components, and not stretched or kinked, and is secured out of harm's way using the plastic clips, guides and ties provided.

5 Check all electrical connectors, ensuring that they are clean, securely fastened, and that each is locked by its plastic tabs or wire clip, as appropriate. If any connector shows external signs of corrosion (accumulations of white or green deposits, or streaks of "rust"), or if any is thought to be dirty, it must be unplugged and cleaned using electrical contact cleaner. If the connector pins are severely corroded, the connector must be renewed; note that this may mean the renewal of that entire section of the loom - see your local Ford dealer for details.

6 If the cleaner completely removes the corrosion to leave the connector in a satisfactory condition, it would be wise to pack the connector with a suitable material which will exclude dirt and moisture, preventing the corrosion from occurring again; a Ford dealer may be able to recommend a suitable product.

7 Check the condition of the battery

1

connections - remake the connections or renew the leads if a fault is found. Use the same techniques to ensure that all earth points in the engine compartment provide good electrical contact through clean, metal-to-metal joints, and that all are securely fastened. (In addition to the earth connection at the engine lifting eye, and that from the transmission to the body/battery, there are others in various places, so check carefully).

8 Refer to Section 21 for details of spark plug (HT) lead checks.

7 Valve clearance adjustment

Refer to Chapter 2, Part A.

8 Manual transmission oil level check

1 The manual transmission does not have a dipstick. To check the oil level, raise the vehicle and support it securely on axle stands, making sure that the vehicle is level. On the lower front side of the transmission housing, you will see the filler/level plug. Unscrew and remove it - an Allen key or bit will probably be required (see illustration).

2 With the plug removed, check the oil level. To do this accurately, make up an oil level check dipstick from a short length of welding rod or similar material. Make a 90° bend in the rod, then mark the downward leg in 5 mm increments. The dipstick is then inserted through the filler plug orifice so that the unmarked leg rests flat on the plug orifice threads, with the marked leg dipped in the oil. Withdraw the dipstick and read off the level of oil.

3 The oil level must be maintained between 0 and 5 mm below the lower edge of the filler/level plug hole. Top up (if necessary), using fresh transmission oil of the specified type and using a syringe, or a plastic bottle and tube. Refit and tighten the filler/level plug to the specified torque on completion.

4 The need for regular topping-up can only be due to a leak, which should be found and rectified without delay.

5 Regular oil changing is not specified by the manufacturer's, but the oil can be drained, if required, by removing the selector shaft cap nut and locking assembly.

9 Idle speed and mixture check and adjustment

General

1 Many of the engines fitted to Fiesta models are equipped with fuel injection systems of one sort or another which are entirely controlled by the engine management system. On most of these vehicles, it isn't possible to make any adjustments to the idle speed or the mixture settings without specialist test equipment of a type usually only found at a Ford dealer or fuel injection specialist. However, the very nature of these highly-sophisticated systems means they don't go out of tune very often (if ever), so that it's one less maintenance operation to worry about.

2 On carburettor engines and 1.6 litre EFi fuel injection engines, certain checks and adjustments are necessary as part of the service requirements, and these are described below.

Idle speed and mixture check and adjustment - carburettor engines

Note: *Later carburettors are fitted with tamperproof mixture adjusting screws, consisting of a hexagon-shaped socket with a pin in the centre. Such screws require the use of Ford service tool 23-032 to alter their settings; if this tool (or a suitable equivalent) is not available, the CO level will have to be checked, and any necessary adjustment will have to be made, by a Ford dealer.*

3 Before carrying out the following checks and adjustments, ensure that the spark plugs are in good condition and correctly gapped (Section 21). To carry out the checks/adjustments, an accurate tachometer and an exhaust gas analyser (CO meter) will be required.

4 Make sure that all electrical components are switched off during the following procedures.

5 Connect a tachometer to the engine in accordance with its manufacturer's instructions, and insert the probe of an exhaust gas analyser (CO meter) into the exhaust tailpipe. As previously mentioned, these items are essential in obtaining an accurate setting. If they are not available, an approximate check/adjustment can be made as a temporary measure, providing they are further checked out as soon as is possible using a tachometer and a CO meter (or by a Ford dealer).

6 Run the engine at a fast idle speed until it reaches its normal operating temperature and the radiator cooling fan cuts in. Turn the engine off, then disconnect the radiator cooling fan lead at the thermostatic switch connector. Now connect a temporary wire to the fan switch multi-plug, as shown (see illustration) to enable the fan to operate continuously during the following checks and adjustments (if this is specified). Take care to keep clear of the fan during the following operations when working in the engine compartment.

7 Where fitted, disconnect the throttle kicker vacuum pipe, and plug the end. To identify the throttle kicker unit, refer to Chapter 4A.

8 Check that the vehicle lighting and other electrical loadings (apart from the radiator cooling fan) are switched off, then restart the engine. Increase the engine speed to 3000 rpm for 30 seconds, and repeat this at three-minute intervals during the check/adjustment procedures. This will ensure that any excess fuel is cleared from the inlet manifold.

9 Ensure that the throttle is fully released, allow the meters to stabilise for a period of 5 to 30 seconds is normally sufficient, then check the idle speed against that specified. If adjustment is necessary, turn the idle speed adjusting screw until the engine is idling at the specified speed (see illustrations). Any checks and adjustments must be completed within 30 seconds of the meters stabilising.

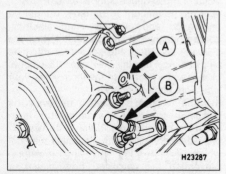

8.1 Manual transmission oil level/filler plug (A), and selector shaft cap nut (B)

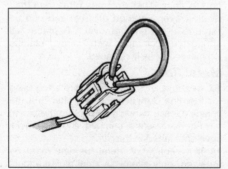

9.6 Cooling fan thermostatic switch multi-plug with temporary bridging wire connected

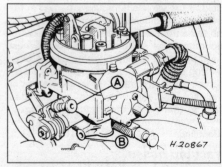

9.9a Idle speed adjusting screw (A) and mixture adjusting screw (B) (Weber TLM carburettor)

9.9b Idle speed adjusting screw (A) and mixture adjusting screw (B) (Weber TLDM carburettor)

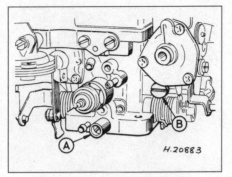

9.9c Idle speed mixture adjusting screw (A) and idle speed adjusting screw (B) (Weber DFTM carburettor)

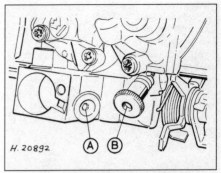

9.9d Idle speed mixture adjusting screw (A) and idle speed adjusting screw (B) (Weber TLD carburettor)

10 If adjustment to the mixture is required, the tamperproof cap will need to be removed from the carburettor to gain access to the mixture screw. To do this, first unclip the fuel trap from the side of the air cleaner unit, then remove the air cleaner unit, ensuring that the crankcase ventilation trap remains connected. Prise free the tamperproof cap (with the aid of a thin-bladed screwdriver), then with the vacuum and emissions control pipes connected to it, relocate the air cleaner unit temporarily into position.

11 Turn the mixture adjustment screw clockwise to weaken the mixture, or anti-clockwise to richen it, until the CO reading is as given in the Specifications. If a CO meter is not being used, weaken the mixture as described, then enrich the mixture

9.16 Adjusting the idle mixture CO content on the 1.6 litre EFi engine

until the maximum engine speed is obtained, consistent with even running.

12 If necessary, re-adjust the idle speed then check the CO reading again. Repeat as necessary until both the idle speed and CO reading are correct.

13 Where required by law (as in some European countries), fit a new tamperproof cap to the mixture adjustment screw.

14 Disconnect the tachometer and the CO meter, refit the air cleaner unit, and reconnect the fan switch lead to complete.

Base idle speed and mixture check and adjustment - 1.6 litre EFi engines

15 Proceed as described above in paragraphs 3 to 6 inclusive, then continue as follows.

16 Run the engine at a fast idle speed until it reaches its normal operating temperature and the cooling fan cuts in. Check the CO content of the exhaust, and compare it against the specified reading. If the CO content reading is incorrect, it can be adjusted by prising free the tamperproof cap for access to the mixture CO adjustment screw (see illustration), and turning the screw in the required direction to suit.

17 The operational idle speed is controlled by the EEC IV engine management module and is not adjustable. However, if the base idle speed is incorrect, the module will not have an accurate datum point from which to establish

the normal operational idle speed. If idle problems have been experienced, the base idle speed should be checked as follows.

18 Disconnect the multi-plug from the idle speed control valve and increase the engine speed to 2000 rpm, hold it at that speed for 30 seconds, then fully release the throttle and check if the base idle speed registered is as specified.

19 If adjustment is necessary, prise free the tamperproof plug using a suitable small screwdriver to gain access to the base idle speed adjustment screw in the throttle body. Turn the screw in the required direction to adjust the base idle speed to the specified amount. Turning the screw anti-clockwise increases the idle speed (see illustration).

20 Increase the engine speed to 2000 rpm again, hold it at that speed for 30 seconds, then fully release the throttle once more. Check and further adjust the base idle speed if required, then fit a new tamperproof plug into position.

21 Reconnect the idle speed control valve multi-plug and check that the engine speed briefly rises to about 900 rpm, then drops down to the specified normal idle speed.

22 On completion, disconnect the tachometer and the CO meter, but continue running the engine at idle speed for a period of about five minutes, to enable the engine management module to relearn its values before switching it off.

10 Steering, suspension and roadwheel check

Front suspension and steering check

1 Chock the rear wheels then jack up the front of the car and support it on axle stands (see "Jacking and Vehicle Support").

2 Visually inspect the balljoint dust covers and the steering gear gaiters for splits, chafing or deterioration (see illustrations). Any wear of these components will cause loss of

9.19 Base idle speed adjustment screw (arrowed) on the 1.6 litre EFi engine

10.2a Check the condition of the track rod end balljoint dust cover (arrowed)

1

10.2b Check the condition of the lower arm balljoint dust cover (arrowed)

10.2c Check the condition of the steering rack gaiters

11.2 Check the driveshaft gaiters by hand for cracks and/or leaking grease

lubricant, together with dirt and water entry, resulting in rapid deterioration of the balljoints or steering gear.

3 Check the power-assisted steering fluid hoses (where fitted) for chafing or deterioration, and the pipe and hose unions for fluid leaks. Also check for signs of fluid leakage under pressure from the steering gear rubber gaiters, which would indicate failed fluid seals within the steering gear.

4 Grasp the roadwheel at the 12 o'clock and 6 o'clock positions, and try to rock it. Very slight free play may be felt, but if the movement is appreciable, further investigation is necessary to determine the source. Continue rocking the wheel while an assistant depresses the footbrake. If the movement is now eliminated or significantly reduced, it is likely that the hub bearings are at fault. If the free play is still evident with the footbrake depressed, then there is wear in the suspension joints or mountings.

5 Now grasp the wheel at the 9 o'clock and 3 o'clock positions, and try to rock it as before. Any movement felt now may again be caused by wear in the hub bearings or the steering track rod balljoints. If the outer track rod end balljoint is worn, the visual movement will be obvious. If the inner joint is suspect, it can be felt by placing a hand over the rack-and-pinion rubber gaiter, and gripping the track rod. If the wheel is now rocked, movement will be felt at the inner joint if wear has taken place.

6 Using a large screwdriver or flat bar, check for wear in the suspension mounting bushes by levering between the relevant suspension component and its attachment point. Some movement is to be expected, as the mountings are made of rubber, but excessive wear should be obvious. Also check the condition of any visible rubber bushes, looking for splits, cracks or contamination of the rubber.

7 With the vehicle standing on its wheels, have an assistant turn the steering wheel back-and-forth, about an eighth of a turn each way. There should be very little, if any, lost movement between the steering wheel and roadwheels. If this is not the case, closely observe the joints and mountings previously described, but in addition, check the steering column universal joints for wear, and also check the rack-and-pinion steering gear itself.

Rear suspension check

8 Chock the front wheels then jack up the rear of the car and support it on axle stands (see *"Jacking and Vehicle Support"*). Remove the rear roadwheels.

9 Check the rear hub bearings for wear, using the method described for the front hub bearings (paragraph 4).

10 Using a large screwdriver or flat bar, check for wear in the suspension mounting bushes by levering between the relevant suspension component and its attachment point. Some movement is to be expected, as the mountings are made of rubber, but excessive wear should be obvious. Check the condition of the shock absorbers and their bushes/mountings. On Van models, check the leaves of the leaf springs for signs of cracking, distortion, or other damage.

Roadwheel check and balancing

11 Periodically remove the roadwheels, and clean any dirt or mud from the inside and outside surfaces. Examine the wheel rims for signs of rusting, corrosion or other damage. Light alloy wheels are easily damaged by "kerbing" whilst parking, and similarly, steel wheels may become dented or buckled. Renewal of the wheel is very often the only course of remedial action possible.

12 The balance of each wheel and tyre assembly should be maintained, not only to avoid excessive tyre wear, but also to avoid wear in the steering and suspension components. Wheel imbalance is normally signified by vibration through the vehicle's bodyshell, although in many cases it is particularly noticeable through the steering wheel. Conversely, it should be noted that wear or damage in suspension or steering components may cause excessive tyre wear. Out-of-round or out-of-true tyres, damaged wheels and wheel bearing wear/maladjustment also fall into this category. Balancing will not usually cure vibration caused by such wear.

13 Wheel balancing may be carried out with the wheel either on or off the vehicle. If balanced on the vehicle, ensure that the wheel-to-hub relationship is marked in some way prior to subsequent wheel removal, so that it may be refitted in its original position.

11 Driveshaft rubber gaiter and CV joint check

1 The driveshaft rubber gaiters are very important, because they prevent dirt, water and foreign material from entering and damaging the constant velocity (CV) joints. External contamination can cause the gaiter material to deteriorate prematurely, so it's a good idea to wash the gaiters with soap and water occasionally.

2 With the vehicle raised and securely supported on axle stands, turn the steering onto full-lock, then slowly rotate each front wheel in turn. Inspect the condition of the outer constant velocity (CV) joint rubber gaiters, squeezing the gaiters to open out the folds. Check for signs of cracking, splits, or deterioration of the rubber, which may allow the escape of grease, and lead to the ingress of water and grit into the joint **(see illustration)**. Also check the security and condition of the retaining clips. Repeat these checks on the inner CV joints. If any damage or deterioration is found, the gaiters should be renewed as described in Chapter 8.

3 At the same time, check the general condition of the outer CV joints themselves, by first holding the driveshaft and attempting to rotate the wheels. Any appreciable movement in the CV joint indicates wear in the joint, wear in the driveshaft splines, or a loose driveshaft retaining nut. Repeat this check on the inner joints, by holding the inner joint yoke and attempting to rotate the driveshaft.

12 Exhaust system check

1 With the engine cold (at least three hours after the vehicle has been driven), check the complete exhaust system, from its starting

point at the engine to the end of the tailpipe. Ideally, this should be done on a hoist, where unrestricted access is available; if a hoist is not available, raise and support the vehicle on axle stands.

2 Check the pipes and connections for evidence of leaks, severe corrosion, or damage. Make sure that all brackets and rubber mountings are in good condition, and tight; if any of the mountings are to be renewed, ensure that the replacements are of the correct type **(see illustration)**. Leakage at any of the joints or in other parts of the system will usually show up as a black sooty stain in the vicinity of the leak. **Note:** *Exhaust sealants should not be used on any part of the exhaust system upstream of the catalytic converter - even if the sealant does not contain additives harmful to the converter, pieces of it may break off and foul the element, causing local overheating.*

3 At the same time, inspect the underside of the body for holes, corrosion, open seams, etc, which may allow exhaust gases to enter the passenger compartment. Seal all body openings with silicone or body putty.

4 Rattles and other noises can often be traced to the exhaust system, especially the rubber mountings. Try to move the system, silencer(s) and catalytic converter. If any components can touch the body or suspension parts, secure the exhaust system with new mountings.

5 Check the running condition of the engine by inspecting inside the end of the tailpipe; the exhaust deposits here are an indication of the engine's state of tune. The inside of the tailpipe should be dry, and should vary in colour from dark grey to light grey/brown; if it is black and sooty, or coated with white deposits, the engine is in need of a thorough fuel system inspection.

13 Underbody and fuel/brake line check

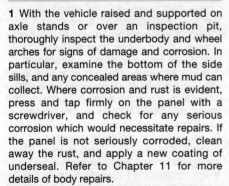

1 With the vehicle raised and supported on axle stands or over an inspection pit, thoroughly inspect the underbody and wheel arches for signs of damage and corrosion. In particular, examine the bottom of the side sills, and any concealed areas where mud can collect. Where corrosion and rust is evident, press and tap firmly on the panel with a screwdriver, and check for any serious corrosion which would necessitate repairs. If the panel is not seriously corroded, clean away the rust, and apply a new coating of underseal. Refer to Chapter 11 for more details of body repairs.

2 At the same time, inspect the PVC-coated lower body panels for stone damage and general condition.

3 Inspect all of the fuel and brake lines on the underbody for damage, rust, corrosion and leakage. Also make sure that they are

12.2 Ensure that the exhaust system rubber mountings replacements are of the correct type - their colour is a good guide. Those nearest to the catalytic converter are more heat-resistant than the others

correctly supported in their clips. Where applicable, check the PVC coating on the lines for damage.

14 Brake check

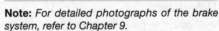

Note: *For detailed photographs of the brake system, refer to Chapter 9.*

1 The work described in this Section should be carried out at the specified intervals, or whenever a defect is suspected in the braking system. Any of the following symptoms could indicate a potential brake system defect:

a) *The vehicle pulls to one side when the brake pedal is depressed.*

b) *The brakes make scraping or dragging noises when applied.*

c) *Brake pedal travel is excessive.*

d) *The brake fluid requires repeated topping-up.*

2 A thorough inspection should be made to confirm the thickness of the linings, as follows.

Front brakes

3 Chock the rear wheels then jack up the front of the car and support it on axle stands (see *"Jacking and Vehicle Support"*).

4 For better access to the brake calipers, remove the wheels.

5 Look through the inspection window in the caliper, and check that the thickness of the friction lining material on each of the pads is not less than the recommended minimum thickness given in the Specifications. **Note:** *Bear in mind that the lining material is normally bonded to a metal backing plate.*

6 If it is difficult to determine the exact thickness of the pad linings, or if you are at all concerned about the condition of the pads, then remove them from the calipers for further inspection (refer to Chapter 9).

7 Check the remaining brake caliper in the same way.

8 If any one of the brake pads has worn down

to, or below, the specified limit, *all four* pads must be renewed as a set.

9 Measure the thickness of the discs with a micrometer, if available, to make sure that they still have service life remaining. If any disc is thinner than the specified minimum thickness, renew it (refer to Chapter 9). In any case, check the general condition of the discs. Look for excessive scoring and discolouration caused by overheating. If these conditions exist, remove the relevant disc and have it resurfaced or renewed (refer to Chapter 9).

10 Before refitting the wheels and lowering the car, check all brake lines and hoses (refer to Chapter 9). In particular, check the flexible hoses in the vicinity of the calipers, where they are subjected to most movement. Bend them between the fingers (but do not actually bend them double, or the casing may be damaged) and check that this does not reveal previously-hidden cracks, cuts or splits.

Rear brakes

11 Chock the front wheels then jack up the rear of the car and support it on axle stands (see *"Jacking and Vehicle Support"*).

12 For better access, remove the rear wheels.

13 To check the brake shoe lining thickness without removing the brake drums, prise the rubber plugs from the backplates, and use an electric torch and mirror to inspect the linings of the leading brake shoes. Check that the thickness of the lining material on the brake shoes is not less than the recommendation given in the Specifications.

14 If it is difficult to determine the exact thickness of the brake shoe linings, or if you are at all concerned about the condition of the shoes, then remove the rear drums for a more comprehensive inspection (refer to Chapter 9).

15 With the drum removed, check the shoe return and hold-down springs for correct installation, and check the wheel cylinders for leakage of brake fluid. Check the friction surface of the brake drums for scoring and discoloration. If excessive, the drum should be resurfaced or renewed.

16 Before refitting the wheels, check all brake lines and hoses (refer to Chapter 9). On completion, apply the handbrake and check that the rear wheels are locked. The handbrake also requires periodic adjustment, and if its travel seems excessive, refer to Section 27.

15 Roadwheel nut tightness check

1 Apply the handbrake.

2 Remove the wheel covers, using the flat end of the wheelbrace supplied in the tool kit (on some models it will be necessary to unscrew the retaining bolts with a special key).

1

3 Check that the roadwheel nuts are tightened to the specified torque wrench setting.
4 Refit the wheel covers.

16 Door, tailgate and bonnet check and lubrication

1 Check that the doors and tailgate/boot lid close securely. Check that the bonnet safety catch operates correctly. Check the operation of the door check straps.
2 Lubricate the hinges, door check straps, the striker plates and the bonnet catch sparingly with a little oil or grease.

17 Seat belt check

1 Check the seat belts for satisfactory operation and condition. Inspect the webbing for fraying and cuts. Check that they retract smoothly and without binding into their reels.
2 Check that the seat belt mounting bolts are tight, and if necessary tighten them to the specified torque wrench settings as given in Chapter 11.

18 Bodywork, paint and exterior trim check

1 The best time to carry out this check is after the car has been washed so that any surface blemish or scratch will be clearly evident and not hidden by a film of dirt.
2 Starting at one front corner check the paintwork all around the car, looking for minor scratches or more serious dents. Check all the trim and make sure that it is securely attached over its entire length.
3 Check the security of all door locks, door mirrors, badges, bumpers, front grille and wheel trim. Anything found loose, or in need of further attention should be done with reference to the relevant Chapters of this manual.
4 Rectify any problems noticed with the paintwork or body panels as described in Chapter 11.

19 Road test
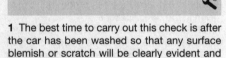

Check the operation and performance of the braking system

1 Make sure that the vehicle does not pull to one side when braking, and that the wheels do not lock prematurely when braking hard.
2 Check that there is no vibration through the steering when braking.

3 Check that the handbrake operates correctly, without excessive movement of the lever, and that it holds the vehicle stationary on a slope.
4 Test the operation of the brake servo unit as follows. With the engine switched off, depress the footbrake four or five times to exhaust the vacuum, then hold the pedal depressed. Start the engine, and there should be a noticeable "give" in the brake pedal as vacuum builds up. Allow the engine to run for at least two minutes, and then switch it off. If the brake pedal is depressed again, it should be possible to detect a hiss from the servo as the pedal is depressed. After about four or five applications, no further hissing should be heard, and the pedal should feel considerably firmer.

Steering and suspension

5 Check for any abnormalities in the steering, suspension, handling or road "feel".
6 Drive the vehicle, and check that there are no unusual vibrations or noises.
7 Check that the steering feels positive, with no excessive sloppiness or roughness, and check for any suspension noises when cornering and driving over bumps.

Drivetrain

8 Check the performance of the engine, transmission and driveshafts.
9 Check that the engine starts correctly, both when cold and when hot.
10 Listen for any unusual noises from the engine and transmission.
11 Make sure that the engine runs smoothly when idling, and that there is no hesitation when accelerating.
12 On manual transmission models, check that all gears can be engaged smoothly without noise, and that the gear lever action is not abnormally vague or "notchy".
13 On automatic transmission models, make sure that the drive seems smooth without jerks or engine speed "flare-ups". Check that all the gear positions can be selected with the vehicle at rest. If any problems are found, they should be referred to a Ford dealer.
14 Listen for a metallic clicking sound from the front of the vehicle, as the vehicle is driven slowly in a circle with the steering on full-lock. Carry out this check in both directions. If a clicking noise is heard, this indicates wear in a driveshaft joint, in which case renew the joint if necessary.

Clutch

15 Check that the clutch pedal moves smoothly and easily through its full travel, and that the clutch itself functions correctly, with no trace of slip or drag. If the movement is uneven or stiff in places, check that the cable is routed correctly, with no sharp turns.
16 Inspect both ends of the clutch inner cable, both at the transmission end and inside the car, for signs of wear and fraying.

Instruments and electrical equipment

17 Check the operation of all instruments and electrical equipment.
18 Make sure that all instruments read correctly, and switch on all electrical equipment in turn, to check that it functions properly.

20 Automatic transmission fluid level check

1 The level of the automatic transmission fluid should be carefully maintained. Low fluid level can lead to slipping or loss of drive, while overfilling can cause foaming, loss of fluid and transmission damage.
2 The transmission fluid level should only be checked when the transmission is hot (at its normal operating temperature). If the vehicle has just been driven over 10 miles (15 miles in a cold climate), and the fluid temperature is 60 to 70°C, the transmission is hot.
Caution: If the vehicle has just been driven for a long time at high speed or in city traffic in hot weather, or if it has been pulling a trailer, an accurate fluid level reading cannot be obtained. In these circumstances, allow the fluid to cool down for about 30 minutes.
3 Park the vehicle on level ground, apply the handbrake, and start the engine. While the engine is idling, depress the brake pedal and move the selector lever through all the gear positions three times, beginning and ending in "P".
4 Allow the engine to idle for one minute, then (with the engine still idling) remove the dipstick from its tube. Note the condition and colour of the fluid on the dipstick.
5 Wipe the fluid from the dipstick with a clean rag, and re-insert it into the filler tube until the cap seats.
6 Pull the dipstick out again, and note the fluid level. The level should be between the "MIN" and "MAX" marks. If the level is on the "MIN" mark, stop the engine, and add the specified automatic transmission fluid through the dipstick tube, using a clean funnel if necessary. It is important not to introduce dirt into the transmission when topping-up.
7 Add the fluid a little at a time, and keep checking the level as previously described until it is correct. The difference between the "MIN" and "MAX" marks on the dipstick is approximately 0.4 litres.
8 The need for regular topping-up of the transmission fluid indicates a leak, which should be found and rectified without delay.
9 The condition of the fluid should also be checked along with the level. If the fluid on the dipstick is black or a dark reddish-brown colour, or if it has a burned smell, the fluid should be changed. If you are in doubt about the condition of the fluid, purchase some new fluid, and compare the two for colour and smell.

Every 20 000 miles (32 000 km) or two years, whichever comes first

21 Spark plug renewal and HT component check

Note: *Spark plug renewal at this service interval is only necessary on the HCS, CVH and PTE engines. On Zetec engines, the recommended interval for spark plug renewal is every 30 000 miles or three years.*

Spark plug check and renewal

1 It is vital for the correct running, full performance and proper economy of the engine that the spark plugs perform with maximum efficiency. The most important factor in ensuring this is that the plugs fitted are appropriate for the engine. The suitable type is given in the Specifications Section at the beginning of this Chapter, on the Vehicle Emissions Control Information (VECI) label located on the underside of the bonnet (only on models sold in some areas) or in the vehicle's Owner's Handbook. If the correct type is used and the engine is in good condition, the spark plugs should not need attention between scheduled renewal intervals. Spark plug cleaning is rarely necessary, and should not be attempted unless specialised equipment is available, as damage can easily be caused to the firing ends.

2 Spark plug removal and refitting requires a spark plug socket, with an extension which can be turned by a ratchet handle or similar. This socket is lined with a rubber sleeve, to protect the porcelain insulator of the spark plug, and to hold the plug while you insert it into the spark plug hole. You will also need a set of feeler gauges, to check the spark plug electrode gap, and a torque wrench to tighten the new plugs to the specified torque **(see illustration)**.

3 To remove the spark plugs, first open the bonnet; the plugs are easily reached at the top of the engine. Note how the spark plug (HT) leads are routed and secured by clips, and on some engines, how they're positioned along the channel in the cylinder head cover. To prevent the possibility of mixing up spark plug (HT) leads, it is a good idea to try to work on one spark plug at a time.

4 If the marks on the original-equipment spark plug (HT) leads cannot be seen, mark the leads 1 to 4, to correspond to the cylinder the lead serves (No 1 cylinder is at the timing belt/chain end of the engine). Pull the leads from the plugs by gripping the rubber boot, not the lead, otherwise the lead connection may be fractured.

5 It is advisable to soak up any liquid in the spark plug recesses with a rag, and to remove any dirt from them using a clean brush, vacuum cleaner or compressed air before removing the plugs, to prevent any dirt or water from dropping into the cylinders.

Warning: Wear eye protection when using compressed air!

6 Unscrew the spark plugs, ensuring that the socket is kept in alignment with each plug - if the socket is forcibly moved to either side, the porcelain top of the plug may be broken off. If any undue difficulty is encountered when unscrewing any of the spark plugs, carefully check the cylinder head threads and tapered sealing surfaces for signs of wear, excessive corrosion or damage; if any of these conditions is found, seek the advice of a Ford dealer as to the best method of repair.

7 As each plug is removed, examine it as follows - this will give a good indication of the condition of the engine. If the insulator nose is covered with light tan to greyish-brown deposits, then the mixture is correct, and it is likely that the engine is in good condition.

8 If the tip and insulator nose are covered with hard black-looking deposits, then this is indicative that the mixture is too rich. Should the plug be black and oily, then it is likely that the engine is fairly worn, as well as the mixture being too rich.

9 If the insulator nose of the spark plug is clean and white, with no deposits, this is indicative of a weak mixture.

10 If you are renewing the spark plugs, purchase the new plugs, then check each of them first for faults such as cracked insulators or damaged threads. Note also that, whenever the spark plugs are renewed as a routine service operation, the spark plug (HT) leads should be checked as described below.

11 The spark plug electrode gap is of considerable importance as, if it is too large or too small, the size of the spark and its efficiency will be seriously impaired. The gap should be set to the value given in the Specifications Section of this Chapter. New plugs will not necessarily be set to the correct gap, so they should always be checked before fitting.

12 The spark plug gap is correct when the correct-size feeler gauge or wire gauge is a firm sliding fit between the electrodes **(see illustrations)**.

13 To adjust the electrode gap, bend open, or close up, the outer plug electrode until the correct gap is achieved **(see illustration)**. The centre electrode should never be bent, as this may crack the insulation and cause plug failure,

1

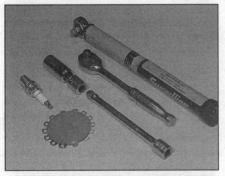

21.2 Tools required for changing spark plugs

21.12a Measuring a spark plug gap with a feeler gauge

21.12b Spark plug manufacturers recommend using a wire-type gauge when checking the gap - if the wire or feeler gauge does not slide between the electrodes with a slight drag, adjustment is required

21.13 To change the gap, bend the outer electrode only, and be very careful not to crack or chip the porcelain insulator surrounding the centre electrode

if nothing worse. If the outer electrode is not exactly over the centre electrode, bend it gently to align them. Special spark plug gap adjusting tools are available from motor accessory shops, or from certain spark plug manufacturers.

14 Before fitting the spark plugs, check that the threaded connector sleeves at the top of the plugs are tight, and that the plug exterior surfaces and threads are clean. Brown staining on the porcelain, immediately above the metal body, is quite normal, and does not necessarily indicate a "leak" between the body and insulator.

15 Apply a smear of copper-based grease or anti-seize compound to the threads of each plug, and screw them in by hand where possible. Take extra care to enter the plug threads correctly, as the cylinder head is of aluminium alloy.

It's often difficult to insert spark plugs into their holes without cross-threading them. To avoid this possibility, fit a short piece of rubber hose over the end of the spark plug. The flexible hose acts as a universal joint, to help align the plug with the plug hole. Should the plug begin to cross-thread, the hose will slip on the spark plug, preventing thread damage.

16 When each spark plug is started correctly on its threads, screw it down until it just seats lightly, then tighten it to the specified torque wrench setting. If a torque wrench is not available - and this is one case where the use of a torque wrench is strongly recommended - tighten each spark plug through *no more than* 1/4 of a turn (CVH and PTE engines) or 1/16 of a turn (HCS and Zetec engines) after it seats. HCS and Zetec engines are fitted with taper-seat spark plugs, identifiable by not having a sealing washer, and these in particular should *NEVER* be overtightened - their tapered seats mean they are almost impossible to remove if abused.

17 Reconnect the spark plug (HT) leads in their correct order, using a twisting motion on the boot until it is firmly seated on the end of the spark plug and on the cylinder head cover.

Spark plug (HT) lead, distributor cap and rotor arm check

18 The spark plug (HT) leads should be checked whenever the plugs themselves are renewed. Start by making a visual check of the leads while the engine is running. In a darkened garage (make sure there is ventilation) start the engine and observe each lead. Be careful not to come into contact with any moving engine parts. If there is a break in the lead, you will see arcing or a small spark at the damaged area.

19 The spark plug (HT) leads should be inspected one at a time, to prevent mixing up the firing order, which is essential for proper engine operation. Each original lead should be numbered to identify its cylinder. If the number is illegible, a piece of tape can be marked with the correct number, and wrapped around the lead (the leads should be numbered 1 to 4, with No 1 lead nearest the timing belt end of the engine). The lead can then be disconnected.

20 Check inside the boot for corrosion, which will look like a white crusty powder. Clean this off as much as possible; if it is excessive, or if cleaning leaves the metal connector too badly eroded to be fit for further use, the lead must be renewed. Push the lead and boot back onto the end of the spark plug. The boot should fit tightly onto the end of the plug - if it doesn't, remove the lead and use pliers carefully to crimp the metal connector inside the boot until the fit is snug.

21 Using a clean rag, wipe the entire length of the lead to remove built-up dirt and grease. Once the lead is clean, check for burns, cracks and other damage. Do not bend the lead sharply, because the conductor might break.

22 Disconnect the lead from the ignition coil by pressing together the plastic retaining catches (where fitted) and pulling the end fitting off the coil terminal. Check for corrosion and for a tight fit. If a meter with the correct measuring range is available, measure the resistance of the disconnected lead from its coil connector to its spark plug connector. If the resistance recorded for any of the leads exceeds the value specified, all the leads should be renewed as a set. Refit the lead to the coil, noting that each coil terminal is marked with its respective cylinder number, so that there is no risk of mixing up the leads and upsetting the firing order.

23 Inspect the remaining spark plug (HT) leads, ensuring that each is securely fastened at the distributor cap or ignition coil and spark plug when the check is complete. If any sign of arcing, severe connector corrosion, burns, cracks or other damage is noticed, obtain new spark plug (HT) leads, renewing them as a set. If new spark plug leads are to be fitted, remove and refit them one at a time, to avoid mix-ups in the firing order.

If new spark plug leads are to be fitted, remove the leads one at a time and fit each new lead in exactly the same position as the old one.

24 On models with distributor ignition systems, refer to Chapter 5B and remove the distributor cap then thoroughly clean it inside and out with a dry lint-free rag.

25 Examine the HT lead segments inside the cap. If they appear badly burned or pitted renew the cap. Also check the carbon brush in the centre of the cap, ensuring that it is free to move and stands proud of its holder. Make sure that there are no sign of cracks or black "tracking" lines running down the inside of the cap, which will also mean renewal if evident.

26 Inspect the rotor arm checking it for security and also for signs of deterioration as described above.

27 Refit the cap as described in Chapter 5B on completion.

22 Idle speed control valve cleaning and maintenance

Note: *The idle speed control valve may be mounted on the air cleaner, on the engine compartment bulkhead, or on the side of the inlet manifold according to valve make and year of manufacture. Valves manufactured by Weber are mounted on the air cleaner and only these valves require the periodic maintenance described below. Bulkhead and inlet manifold mounted valves are manufactured by Hitachi and are maintenance free. Refer to the warning note in Section 1 of Chapter 4C before proceeding.*

1 Remove the valve as described in Chapter 4C, Section 14.

2 Immerse the valve head in a suitable container filled with clean petrol, and allow it to soak for approximately three minutes.

3 Clean the valve bore, slots and piston with petrol, using a suitable lint-free cloth, then gently move the piston up and down in its bore using a small screwdriver **(see illustration)**. Ensure that no cloth particles enter the bore, and do not use the slots to move the piston.

4 Rinse the valve again with clean petrol, then dry it using an air line (or other source of compressed air).

⚠️ *Warning: Wear eye protection when using compressed air!*

5 Clean the mating faces of the valve and the air filter housing then refit as described in Chapter 4C, Section 14.

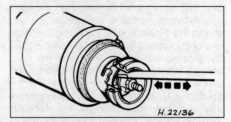

22.3 Gently move the idle speed control valve piston up and down in its bore using a small screwdriver (1.6 litre EFi engine)

Every 30 000 miles (48 000 km) or three years, whichever comes first

23 Coolant renewal

Note: *If the antifreeze used is Ford's own, the coolant need not be renewed for the life of the vehicle. If the vehicle's history is unknown, if antifreeze of lesser quality is known to be in the system, or simply if you prefer to follow conventional servicing intervals, the coolant should be changed periodically (typically, every 3 years) as described here. Refer also to "Antifreeze - notes on renewal" in this Section.*

 Warning: Do not allow antifreeze to come in contact with your skin or painted surfaces of the vehicle. Flush contaminated areas immediately with plenty of water. Don't store new coolant, or leave old coolant lying around, where it's accessible to children or pets - they're attracted by its sweet smell. Ingestion of even a small amount of coolant can be fatal! Wipe up garage-floor and drip-pan spills immediately. Keep antifreeze containers covered, and repair cooling system leaks as soon as they're noticed. Warning: Never remove the expansion tank filler cap when the engine is running, or has just been switched off, as the cooling system will be hot, and the consequent escaping steam and scalding coolant could cause serious injury.

Coolant draining

 Warning: Wait until the engine is cold before starting this procedure.

1 To drain the system, first remove the expansion tank filler cap (see *"Weekly Checks"*).

2 If additional working clearance is required, raise the front of the vehicle and support it

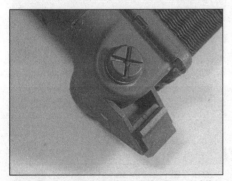

23.3 Drain plug location at the base of the radiator - use a coin to unscrew the plug

securely on axle stands (see *"Jacking and Vehicle Support"*).

3 Place a large drain tray beneath the radiator, and unscrew the radiator drain plug - you can use a small coin to do this, as the plug's slotted for this purpose **(see illustration)**. Direct as much of the escaping coolant as possible into the tray.

System flushing

4 With time, the cooling system may gradually lose its efficiency, as the radiator core becomes choked with rust, scale deposits from the water, and other sediment (refer also to *"Antifreeze - notes on renewal"* later in this Section). To minimise this, as well as using only good-quality antifreeze and clean soft water, the system should be flushed as follows whenever any part of it is disturbed, and/or when the coolant is renewed.

5 With the coolant drained, refit the drain plug, and refill the system with fresh water. Refit the expansion tank filler cap, start the engine and warm it up to normal operating temperature, then stop it and (after allowing it to cool down completely) drain the system again. Repeat as necessary until only clean water can be seen to emerge, then refill finally with the specified coolant mixture as described below.

6 If only clean, soft water and good-quality antifreeze (even if not to Ford's specification) has been used, and the coolant has been renewed at the suggested intervals, the above procedure will be sufficient to keep the system clean for a considerable length of time. If, however, the system has been neglected, a more thorough operation will be required, as follows.

7 First drain the coolant, then disconnect the radiator top and bottom hoses. Insert a garden hose into the top hose, and allow water to circulate through the radiator until it runs clean from the bottom outlet.

8 To flush the engine, insert the garden hose into the thermostat water outlet, and allow water to circulate until it runs clear from the bottom hose. If, after a reasonable period, the water still does not run clear, the radiator should be flushed with a good proprietary cleaning agent.

9 In severe cases of contamination, reverse-flushing of the radiator may be necessary. To do this, remove the radiator (Chapter 3), invert it, and insert the garden hose into the bottom outlet. Continue flushing until clear water runs from the top hose outlet. A similar procedure can be used to flush the heater matrix.

10 The use of chemical cleaners should be necessary only as a last resort. Normally, regular renewal of the coolant will prevent excessive contamination of the system.

Coolant filling

11 With the cooling system drained and flushed, ensure that all disturbed hose unions are correctly secured, and that the radiator drain plug is securely tightened. If it was raised, lower the vehicle to the ground.

12 Prepare a sufficient quantity of the specified coolant mixture (see below); allow for a surplus, so as to have a reserve supply for topping-up.

13 Slowly fill the system through the expansion tank; since the tank is the highest point in the system, all the air in the system should be displaced into the tank by the rising liquid. Slow pouring reduces the possibility of air being trapped and forming airlocks.

14 Continue filling until the coolant level reaches the expansion tank "MAX" level line, then cover the filler opening to prevent coolant splashing out.

15 Start the engine and run it at idle speed, until it has warmed-up to normal operating temperature and the radiator cooling fan has cut in; watch the temperature gauge to check for signs of overheating. If the level in the expansion tank drops significantly, top-up to the "MAX" level line, to minimise the amount of air circulating in the system.

16 Stop the engine, allow it to cool down *completely* (overnight, if possible), then uncover the expansion tank filler opening and top-up the tank to the "MAX" level line. Refit the filler cap, tightening it securely, and wash off any spilt coolant from the engine compartment and bodywork.

17 After refilling, always check carefully all components of the system (but especially any unions disturbed during draining and flushing) for signs of coolant leaks. Fresh antifreeze has a searching action, which will rapidly expose any weak points in the system.

18 If, after draining and refilling the system, symptoms of overheating are found which did not occur previously, then the fault is almost certainly due to trapped air at some point in the system, causing an airlock and restricting the flow of coolant; usually, the air is trapped because the system was refilled too quickly. In some cases, airlocks can be released by tapping or squeezing the various hoses. If the problem persists, stop the engine and allow it to cool down completely, before unscrewing the expansion tank filler cap or disconnecting hoses to bleed out the trapped air.

Antifreeze mixture

19 If the antifreeze used is not to Ford's specification, it should always be renewed at the suggested intervals (typically, every 2 or 3 years). This is necessary not only to maintain the antifreeze properties, but also to prevent

1

the corrosion which would otherwise occur as the corrosion inhibitors become progressively less effective. Always use an ethylene glycol-based antifreeze which is suitable for use in mixed-metal cooling systems.

20 If the antifreeze used is to Ford's specification, the levels of protection it affords are indicated in the Specifications Section of this Chapter. To give the recommended *standard* mixture ratio for this antifreeze, 40% (by volume) of antifreeze must be mixed with 60% of clean, soft water; if you are using any other type of antifreeze, follow its manufacturer's instructions to achieve the correct ratio. It is best to make up slightly more than the system's specified capacity, so that a supply is available for subsequent topping-up.

21 Before adding antifreeze, the cooling system should be completely drained, preferably flushed, and all hoses checked for condition and security. As noted earlier, fresh antifreeze will rapidly find any weaknesses in the system.

22 After filling with antifreeze, a label should be attached to the expansion tank, stating the type and concentration of antifreeze used, and the date installed. Any subsequent topping-up should be made with the same type and concentration of antifreeze. If topping-up using antifreeze to Ford's specification, note that a 50/50 mixture is permissible, purely for convenience.

23 Do not use engine antifreeze in the windscreen/tailgate washer system, as it will damage the vehicle's paintwork. A screenwash additive should be added to the washer system in its maker's recommended quantities.

Antifreeze - notes on renewal

24 Ford state that, where antifreeze to Ford specification ESD-M97B-49-A is used, it will last the lifetime of the vehicle. This is subject to it being used in the recommended concentration, unmixed with any other type of antifreeze or additive, and topped-up when necessary using only that antifreeze mixed

50/50 with clean water. If any other type of antifreeze is added, the lifetime guarantee no longer applies; to restore the lifetime protection, the system must be drained and thoroughly reverse-flushed before fresh coolant mixture is poured in.

25 If the vehicle's history (and therefore the quality of the antifreeze in it) is unknown, owners who wish to follow Ford's recommendations are advised to drain and thoroughly reverse-flush the system before refilling with fresh coolant mixture. If the appropriate quality of antifreeze is used, the coolant can then be left for the life of the vehicle.

26 If any antifreeze other than Ford's is to be used, the coolant must be renewed at regular intervals to provide an equivalent degree of protection; the conventional recommendation is to renew the coolant every two or three years.

27 The above assumes the use of a mixture (in exactly the specified concentration) of clean, soft water and of antifreeze to Ford's specification or equivalent. It is also assumed that the cooling system is maintained in a scrupulously-clean condition, by ensuring that only clean coolant is added on topping-up, and by thorough reverse-flushing whenever the coolant is drained.

General cooling system checks

28 The engine should be cold for the cooling system checks, so perform the following procedure before driving the vehicle, or after it has been shut off for at least three hours.

29 Remove the expansion tank filler cap, and clean it thoroughly inside and out with a rag. Also clean the filler neck on the expansion tank. The presence of rust or corrosion in the filler neck indicates that the coolant should be changed. The coolant inside the expansion tank should be relatively clean and transparent. If it is rust-coloured, drain and flush the system, and refill with a fresh coolant mixture.

30 Carefully check the radiator hoses and

heater hoses along their entire length; renew any hose which is cracked, swollen or deteriorated (see Section 5).

31 Inspect all other cooling system components (joint faces, etc.) for leaks. A leak in the cooling system will usually show up as white- or rust-coloured deposits on the area adjoining the leak. Where any problems of this nature are found on system components, renew the component or gasket with reference to Chapter 3.

32 Clean the front of the radiator with a soft brush to remove all insects, leaves, etc, embedded in the radiator fins. Be careful not to damage the radiator fins, or cut your fingers on them.

24 Air cleaner element renewal

1 The air cleaner filter element is located in the air cleaner assembly mounted either on top of the carburettor or CFi unit, or on the left-hand or right-hand side of the engine compartment at the front. Remove the air cleaner lid as follows according to type.

Carburettor and CFi fuel injection models

2 Undo the two or three retaining screws on the top of the air cleaner lid (see illustration).
3 Release the clips, and lift off the air cleaner cover (see illustration).

EFi fuel injection models

4 If the idle speed control valve is mounted on the air cleaner, disconnect the multi-plug and the air bypass hose from the valve.
5 Disconnect the flexible hose between the air cleaner lid and the air inlet duct or turbocharger air intake.
6 Release the retaining clips and lift off the air cleaner lid (see illustration).

24.2 On carburettor and CFi fuel injection engines, undo the air cleaner lid retaining screws . . .

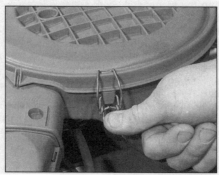
24.3 . . . then spring back the clips and lift of the lid

24.6 On EFi fuel injection engines, release the retaining clips and lift off the air cleaner lid

24.7 On SEFi fuel injection engines, disconnect the mass air flow sensor wiring multi-plug . . .

24.8 . . . slacken the hose clip and disconnect the intake hose from the air intake duct . . .

24.9 . . . then undo the retaining screws or release the clips and lift off the air cleaner lid complete with mass air flow sensor

SEFi fuel injection models

7 Disconnect the mass air flow sensor wiring multi-plug (see illustration).

8 Slacken the hose clip and disconnect the flexible rubber intake hose from the black plastic air intake duct (see illustration).

9 Undo the retaining screws or release the clips and lift off the air cleaner lid complete with mass air flow sensor (see illustration).

All models

10 Lift out the element, and wipe out the housing (see illustrations). Check that no foreign matter is visible, either in the air inlet or in the air mass meter, as applicable.

11 If carrying out a routine service, the element must be renewed regardless of its apparent condition. Note that on models so equipped, the small foam PCV filter in the rear right-hand corner of the air cleaner housing must be cleaned whenever the air filter element is renewed (see Section 25).

12 If you are checking the element for any other reason, inspect its lower surface; if it is oily or very dirty, renew the element. If it is only moderately dusty, it can be re-used after blowing it clean from the upper to the lower surface with compressed air.

 Warning: Wear eye protection when using compressed air! Because it is a pleated-paper type filter, it cannot be washed or re-oiled. If it cannot be

cleaned satisfactorily with compressed air, discard and renew it.
Caution: Never drive the vehicle with the air cleaner filter element removed. Excessive engine wear could result, and backfiring could even cause a fire under the bonnet.

13 Refitting is the reverse of the removal procedure. Ensure that the element and cover are securely seated, so that unfiltered air cannot enter the engine.

Air cleaner temperature control system check (carburettor models)

14 In order for the engine to operate efficiently, the temperature of the air entering the inlet system must be controlled within certain limits.

15 The air cleaner has two sources of air, one direct from the outside of the engine compartment, and the other from a shroud on the exhaust manifold. On HCS engines, a wax-controlled thermostatic valve controls a flap inside the air cleaner inlet. When the ambient air temperature is below a predetermined level, the flap admits air heated from the exhaust manifold shroud; as the ambient temperature rises, the flap opens to admit more cool air from the engine compartment until eventually it is fully open. A similar system is used on CVH engines, except that a vacuum actuator modifies any

opening or closing action of the temperature sensor on the flap valve, according to the level of the inlet manifold vacuum under running conditions.

HCS engines

16 This check must be made when the engine is cold. Detach and remove the air cleaner inlet trunking. Examine the position of the check valve within the duct. When the underbonnet air temperature is below 28°C, the valve must be open to allow hot air to enter the filter (see illustration).

17 Refit the inlet trunking. Start the engine and run it until it reaches its normal operating temperature, then stop the engine, remove the inlet trunking and check that the valve has closed off the air passage from the exhaust and opened the main (cool) air inlet.

18 If the flap does not operate correctly, check that it is not seized. Apart from this there is no adjustment possible, and the unit should be renewed if faulty. Refit the air inlet trunking on completion.

CVH engines

19 This check must be made when the engine is cold. Disconnect the main air inlet duct, and visibly check that the flap to the hot-air inlet is closed (i.e. open to the passage of cold air).

20 Start the engine, and check that with the

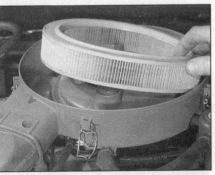

24.10a Removing the air filter element on carburettor engine models . . .

24.10b . . . and on EFi and SEFi fuel injection engine models

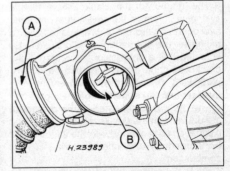

24.16 Air cleaner inlet and flap valve on the HCS engine

A Main air cleaner inlet (cool air)
B Warm air duct (flap open)

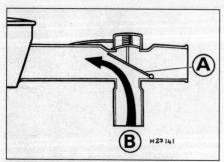

24.20 Air cleaner inlet and flap valve on the CVH engine

A Flap open (cool air inlet closed)
B Warm air inlet

25.5 Crankcase ventilation system filter on CVH engines

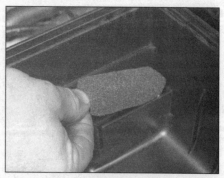

25.13 The crankcase ventilation system foam filter is located in the air cleaner housing on Zetec engines

engine idling, the hot-air inlet is open to allow warm air from the exhaust manifold area to enter the air cleaner. If the flap operates as described, it is functioning correctly **(see illustration)**.

21 If the flap fails to operate as described, check the condition of the vacuum pipe and its connections, and check that the flap valve has not seized. If these are in order, either the temperature sensor or vacuum actuator is faulty, and a new air cleaner assembly must be obtained. Refit the main air duct on completion.

25 Emission control system check

General

1 Of the emission control systems that may be fitted, only the crankcase ventilation system and the evaporative emission control systems require regular checking, and even then, the components of these systems require minimal attention.
2 Should it be felt that the other systems are not functioning correctly, the advice of a dealer should be sought.

Crankcase ventilation system

3 The function of the crankcase ventilation system is to reduce the emission of unburned hydrocarbons from the crankcase, and to minimise the formation of oil sludge. By ensuring that a depression is created in the crankcase under most operating conditions, particularly at idle, and by positively inducing fresh air into the system, the oil vapours and "blow-by" gases collected in the crankcase are drawn from the crankcase, through the air cleaner or oil separator, into the inlet tract, to be burned by the engine during normal combustion.
4 On HCS engines, the system consists of a vented oil filler cap (with an integral mesh filter) and a hose connecting it to the oil separator/engine breather valve connector on the underside of the air cleaner housing. A

further hose leads from the adapter/filter to the inlet manifold.
5 On CVH engines, a closed-circuit type crankcase ventilation system is used, the function of which is basically the same as that described for the HCS engine types, but the breather hose connects directly to the rocker cover. A separate filter is fitted in the hose to the rocker cover in certain applications **(see illustration)**.
6 The system fitted to the PTE engines is similar to that used on the earlier (CVH) engines on which these engines are based, but with revisions to the hose arrangement to suit the remotely sited air cleaner and fuel injection system layout.
7 On Zetec engines, the crankcase ventilation system main components are the oil separator mounted on the front (radiator) side of the cylinder block/crankcase, and the Positive Crankcase Ventilation (PCV) valve set in a rubber grommet in the separator's left-hand upper end. The associated pipework consists of a crankcase breather pipe and two flexible hoses connecting the PCV valve to a union on the left-hand end of the inlet manifold, and a crankcase breather hose connecting the cylinder head cover to the air cleaner assembly. A small foam filter in the air cleaner prevents dirt from being drawn directly into the engine.
8 Check that all components of the system are securely fastened, correctly routed (with no kinks or sharp bends to restrict flow) and in sound condition; renew any worn or damaged components.
9 On HCS engines, remove and inspect the oil filler cap to ensure that it is in good condition, and not blocked up with sludge.
10 Disconnect the hoses at the cap, and clean the cap if necessary by brushing the inner mesh filter with petrol, and blowing through with light pressure from an air line. Renew the cap if it is badly congested.
11 If oil leakage is noted, disconnect the various hoses and pipes, and check that all are clear and unblocked. Remove the air cleaner lid, and check that the hose from the cylinder head cover to the air cleaner housing is clear and undamaged.

12 Where fitted, the PCV valve is designed to allow gases to flow out of the crankcase only, so that a depression is created in the crankcase under most operating conditions, particularly at idle. Therefore, if either the oil separator or the PCV valve are thought to be blocked, they must be renewed (see Chapter 4E). In such a case, however, there is nothing to be lost by attempting to flush out the blockage using a suitable solvent. The PCV valve should rattle when shaken.
13 While the air filter element is removed (see Section 24), wipe out the housing, and on Zetec engines, withdraw the small foam filter from its location in the rear right-hand corner of the housing **(see illustration)**. If the foam is badly clogged with dirt or oil, it must be cleaned by soaking it in a suitable solvent, and allowed to dry before being refitted.

Evaporative emission control systems

14 Refer to the checks contained in Chapter 4E.

26 Automatic transmission fluid renewal

1 The automatic transmission fluid should only be changed when the transmission is cold.
2 Position the vehicle over an inspection pit, on vehicle ramps, or jack it up and securely support it on axle stands, but make sure that it is level.
3 Place a suitable container beneath the drain plug on the transmission sump pan. Remove the transmission fluid dipstick to speed up the draining operation.
4 Thoroughly clean the area around the drain plug in the transmission sump pan, then unscrew the plug and allow the fluid to drain into the container.
5 When all the fluid has drained (this may take quite some time) clean the drain plug, then refit it together with a new seal and tighten it securely.
6 Place a funnel with a fine mesh screen in the dipstick tube, and fill the transmission with

the specified type of fluid. It is essential that no dirt is introduced into the transmission during this operation.

7 Depending on the extent to which the fluid was allowed to drain, it is possible that the amount of fluid required when filling the transmission may be more than the specified amount (see *"Lubricants, fluids and tyre pressures"*). However, due to fluid remaining in the system, it is more likely that less than the specified amount will be required. Add about half the specified amount, then run the engine up to its normal operating temperature and check the level on the dipstick. When the level approaches the maximum mark, proceed as detailed in Section 20 to check the level and complete the final topping-up as described.

27 Handbrake adjustment

1 Chock the front wheels then jack up the rear of the car and support it on axle stands (see *"Jacking and Vehicle Support"*). Fully release the handbrake.
2 Check that the handbrake cables are correctly routed and secured by the retaining clips at the appropriate points under the vehicle.
3 The handbrake is checked for adjustment by measuring the amount of movement possible in the handbrake adjuster plungers. These are located on the inside face of each rear brake backplate **(see illustration)**. The

27.3 Handbrake adjustment plunger located on the inside face of each rear brake backplate

total movement of the two plungers combined should be between 0.5 and 2.0 mm. If the movement measured is outside of this tolerance, the handbrake is in need of adjustment. Adjustment is made altering the position of the in-line cable adjuster sleeve.
4 When adjustment to the handbrake is necessary, a new adjustment sleeve locking pin will be required, and this must therefore be obtained before making the adjustment.
5 To adjust the handbrake, first ensure that it is fully released, then firmly apply the footbrake a few times to ensure that the rear brake adjustment is taken up by the automatic adjusters. Extract the locking pin from the adjuster sleeve **(see illustration)**, then turn the sleeve to set the combined move-ment of the plungers within the tolerance

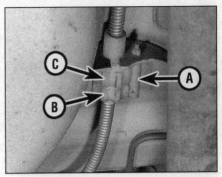

27.5 Handbrake cable adjuster locking pin (A), locknut (B) and adjuster sleeve (C)

range specified (0.5 to 2.0 mm). Turn the locking nut by hand as tight as is possible (two clicks) against the adjustment sleeve. Now grip the locknut with a suitable wrench, and turn it a further two clicks (maximum).
6 Secure the adjustment by inserting the new lock pin.
7 Check that the operation of the handbrake is satisfactory, then lower the vehicle to the ground, apply the handbrake and remove the chocks from the front wheels.

28 Front wheel alignment check

Refer to Chapter 10, Section 29.

1

Every 40 000 miles

29 Timing belt renewal

Refer to Chapter 2, Part B or C as applicable.

Every 60 000 miles

30 Fuel filter renewal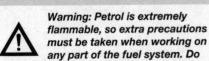

⚠️ *Warning: Petrol is extremely flammable, so extra precautions must be taken when working on any part of the fuel system. Do not smoke, or allow open flames or bare light bulbs, near the work area. Also, do not work in a garage if a natural gas-type appliance with a pilot light is present. While performing any work on the fuel*

system, wear safety glasses, and have a suitable (Class B) fire extinguisher on hand. If you spill any fuel on your skin, rinse it off immediately with soap and water.

1 On fuel injection engines, an in-line fuel filter is provided in the fuel pump outlet line. The filter is located in the engine compartment either below and behind the battery, or on the left-hand side of the engine compartment bulkhead. The renewal procedure is the same for both locations. The filter performs a vital role in keeping dirt and other foreign matter out of the fuel system, and so must be

renewed at regular intervals, or whenever you have reason to suspect that it may be clogged. It is always unpleasant working under a vehicle - pressure-washing or hosing clean the underbody in the filter's vicinity will make working conditions more tolerable, and will reduce the risk of getting dirt into the fuel system.
2 Depressurise the fuel system as described in the relevant Part of Chapter 4.
3 Disconnect the battery negative (earth) lead (refer to Chapter 5A, Section 1), then position a suitable container beneath the fuel filter to catch escaping fuel. Have a rag handy to soak

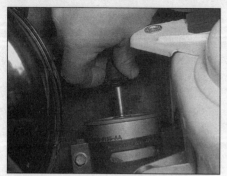

30.5 Releasing the fuel pipe unions from the filter on models with quick-release couplings

30.6a Fuel filter location below battery showing clamp bolt (arrowed). Note fuel flow direction arrows on filter body

30.6b Removing the bulkhead mounted fuel filter. Clamp bolt (arrowed)

up the fuel when the feed and outlet pipe unions are disconnected.

4 On models without quick-release couplings on the fuel lines, slowly slacken the fuel feed pipe union allowing the pressure in the fuel pipe to reduce. When the pressure is fully released, disconnect the fuel feed and outlet pipe unions.

5 On models with quick-release couplings on the fuel lines, release the fuel feed and outlet pipe unions from the filter, by squeezing together the protruding locking lugs on each union, and carefully pulling the union off the filter stub **(see illustration)**. Where the unions

are colour-coded, the feed and outlet pipes cannot be confused; where both unions are the same colour, note carefully which pipe is connected to which filter stub, and ensure that they are correctly reconnected on refitting.

6 Noting the arrows and/or other markings on the filter showing the direction of fuel flow (towards the engine), slacken the filter clamp bolt and withdraw the filter from the car **(see illustrations)**. Note that the filter will still contain fuel; care should be taken, to avoid spillage and to minimise the risk of fire.

7 On installation, slide the filter into its clamp so that the arrow marked on it faces the

correct way, then reconnect and tighten the pipe unions or slide each pipe union on to its (correct) respective filter stub, and press it down until the locking lugs click into their groove. Tighten the clamp bolt carefully, until the filter is just prevented from moving; do not overtighten, or the filter casing may be crushed.

8 Refit the fuel pump fuse and reconnect the battery earth terminal, then switch the ignition on and off five times, to pressurise the system. Check for any sign of fuel leakage around the filter unions before lowering the vehicle to the ground and starting the engine.

Every 3 years

31 Brake fluid renewal

The procedure is similar to that for the bleeding of the hydraulic system as described in Chapter 9, except that the brake fluid reservoir should be emptied by syphoning, and allowance should be made for the old fluid to be removed from the circuit when bleeding a section of the circuit.

Chapter 2 Part A:
HCS engine in-car repair procedures

Contents

Auxiliary drivebelt check and renewal . . . . .See Chapter 1
Compression test - description and interpretation 2
Crankshaft oil seals - renewal 14
Crankshaft pulley - removal and refitting 8
Cylinder head - removal and refitting 7
Cylinder head rocker cover - removal and refitting 4
Cylinder head rocker gear - removal, inspection and refitting . . . 6
Engine oil and filter renewal .See Chapter 1
Engine oil level check . . . . .See "Weekly Checks"
Engine/transmission mountings - inspection and renewal 15
Flywheel - removal, inspection and refitting 16
General information 1
Oil pump - dismantling, inspection and reassembly 13
Oil pump - removal and refitting 12
Sump - removal and refitting 11
Timing chain cover - removal and refitting 9
Timing chain, sprockets and tensioner - removal, inspection
   and refitting 10
Top Dead Centre (TDC) for No 1 piston - locating 3
Valve clearances - checking and adjustment 5

Degrees of difficulty

Easy, suitable for novice with little experience	Fairly easy, suitable for beginner with some experience	Fairly difficult, suitable for competent DIY mechanic	 Difficult, suitable for experienced DIY mechanic	Very difficult, suitable for expert DIY or professional

2A

Specifications

General

Engine type	Four-cylinder, in-line overhead valve
Engine code:	
1.0 litre carburettor models	TLB
1.1 litre carburettor models	GUE or GUD
1.1 litre CFi fuel injection models	G6A
1.3 litre carburettor models	JBC
1.3 litre CFi fuel injection models	J6B
Capacity:	
1.0 litre models	999 cc
1.1 litre models	1118 cc
1.3 litre models	1297 cc
Bore:	
1.0 and 1.1 litre models	68.68 mm
1.3 litre models	73.96 mm
Stroke:	
1.0 litre models	67.40 mm
1.1 and 1.3 litre models	75.48 mm
Compression ratio:	
Carburettor models	9.5:1
CFi fuel injection models	8.8:1
Firing order	1-2-4-3 (No 1 cylinder at timing chain end)
Direction of crankshaft rotation	Clockwise (seen from right-hand side of vehicle)

Valves

Valve clearance (cold):	
Inlet	0.20 mm
Exhaust	0.30 mm

Lubrication

Engine oil type/specification .... See "Lubricants, fluids and tyre pressures"
Engine oil capacity .... See "Lubricants, fluids and tyre pressures"
Oil pressure:
    At idle speed .... 0.60 bars
    At 2000 rpm .... 1.50 bars
Oil pump clearances:
    Outer rotor-to-body .... 0.14 to 0.26 mm
    Inner rotor-to-outer rotor .... 0.051 to 0.127 mm
    Rotor endfloat .... 0.025 to 0.06 mm

Torque wrench settings

	Nm	lbf ft
Camshaft thrust plate bolts	5	4
Camshaft sprocket bolt	18	13
Crankshaft pulley bolt	115	85
Rocker shaft pedestal bolts	43	32
Flywheel bolts	67	49
Sump:		
Stage 1	7	5
Stage 2	9	7
Stage 3 (with engine warm)	9	7
Oil pressure switch	14	10
Cylinder head bolts (may be re-used once only):		
Stage 1	30	22
Stage 2	Angle-tighten a further 90°	
Stage 3	Angle-tighten a further 90°	
Timing chain tensioner	8	6
Timing chain cover	9	7
Crankshaft rear oil seal housing	18	13
Rocker cover bolts	5	4
Oil pump	18	13
Oil pump cover	9	7
Engine mountings:		
Engine mounting (right-hand):		
Bolt to body (in wheel arch)	41 to 58	30 to 43
Nut to body (by suspension strut)	41 to 58	30 to 43
Bracket to cylinder block	54 to 72	40 to 53
Rubber insulator to bracket	71 to 95	52 to 70
Transmission mounting fasteners	Refer to Chapter 7A or 7B	

Note: Refer to Part D of this Chapter for remaining torque wrench settings.

1 General information

How to use this Chapter

This Part of Chapter 2 is devoted to repair procedures possible while the engine is still installed in the vehicle, and includes only the Specifications relevant to those procedures. Similar information concerning the 1.4 and 1.6 litre CVH and PTE engines, and the 1.6 and 1.8 litre Zetec engines, will be found in Parts B and C of this Chapter respectively. Since these procedures are based on the assumption that the engine is installed in the vehicle, if the engine has been removed from the vehicle and mounted on a stand, some of the preliminary dismantling steps outlined will not apply.

Information concerning engine/transmission removal and refitting, and engine overhaul, can be found in Part D of this Chapter, which also includes the Specifications relevant to those procedures.

Engine description

The engine is an overhead valve, water-cooled, four cylinder in-line design, designated HCS (High Compression Swirl). The engine is mounted transversely at the front of the vehicle together with the transmission to form a combined power unit.

The crankshaft is supported in three or five shell-type main bearings. The connecting rod big-end bearings are also split shell-type, and are attached to the pistons by interference-fit gudgeon pins. Each piston is fitted with two compression rings and one oil control ring.

The camshaft, which runs on bearings within the cylinder block, is chain-driven from the crankshaft, and operates the valves via pushrods and rocker arms. The valves are each closed by a single valve spring, and operate in guides integral in the cylinder head.

The oil pump is mounted externally on the crankcase, incorporates a full-flow oil filter, and is driven by a skew gear on the camshaft. On carburettor versions, the fuel pump is also driven from the camshaft, via an eccentric lobe.

Repair operations possible with the engine in the car

The following work can be carried out with the engine in the car:
a) Compression pressure - testing.
b) Cylinder head rocker cover - removal and refitting.
c) Valve clearances - adjustment.
d) Rocker shaft assembly - removal, inspection and refitting.
e) Cylinder head - removal and refitting.
f) Cylinder head and pistons - decarbonising.
g) Crankshaft pulley - removal and refitting.
h) Crankshaft oil seals - renewal.
i) Timing chain, sprockets and tensioner - removal, inspection and refitting.
j) Oil filter renewal.
k) Oil pump - removal and refitting.
l) Sump - removal and refitting.
m) Flywheel - removal, inspection and refitting.
n) Engine/transmission mountings - inspection and renewal.

Note: It is possible to remove the pistons and

connecting rods (after removing the cylinder head and sump) without removing the engine. However, this is not recommended. Work of this nature is more easily and thoroughly completed with the engine on the bench, as described in Chapter 2D.

2 Compression test - description and interpretation

1 When engine performance is down, or if misfiring occurs which cannot be attributed to the ignition or fuel systems, a compression test can provide diagnostic clues as to the engine's condition. If the test is performed regularly, it can give warning of trouble before any other symptoms become apparent.

2 The engine must be fully warmed-up to normal operating temperature, the oil level must be correct and the battery must be fully charged. The aid of an assistant will also be required.

3 On fuel injection engines, refer to Chapter 12 and remove the fuel pump fuse from the fusebox. Now start the engine and allow it to run until it stalls.

4 Disable the ignition system by disconnecting the multi-plug from the DIS or E-DIS ignition coil. Remove all the spark plugs with reference to Chapter 1 if necessary.

5 Fit a compression tester to the No 1 cylinder spark plug hole - the type of tester which screws into the plug thread is to be preferred.

6 Arrange for an assistant to hold the accelerator pedal fully depressed to the floor, while at the same time cranking the engine over for several seconds on the starter motor. Observe the compression gauge reading. The compression will build up fairly quickly in a healthy engine. Low compression on the first stroke, followed by gradually-increasing pressure on successive strokes, indicates worn piston rings. A low compression on the first stroke which does not rise on successive strokes, indicates leaking valves or a blown head gasket (a cracked cylinder head could also be the cause). Deposits on the underside of the valve heads can also cause low compression. Record the highest gauge reading obtained, then repeat the procedure for the remaining cylinders.

7 Due to the variety of testers available, and the fluctuation in starter motor speed when cranking the engine, different readings are often obtained when carrying out the compression test. For this reason, actual compression pressure figures are not quoted by Ford. However, the most important factor is that the compression pressures are uniform in all cylinders, and that is what this test is mainly concerned with.

8 Add some engine oil (about three squirts from a plunger type oil can) to each cylinder through the spark plug holes, and then repeat the test.

9 If the compression increases after the oil is added, it is indicative that the piston rings are definitely worn. If the compression does not increase significantly, the leakage is occurring at the valves or the head gasket. Leakage past the valves may be caused by burned valve seats and/or faces, or warped, cracked or bent valves.

10 If two adjacent cylinders have equally low compressions, it is most likely that the head gasket has blown between them. The appearance of coolant in the combustion chambers or on the engine oil dipstick would verify this condition.

11 If one cylinder is about 20 percent lower than the other, and the engine has a slightly rough idle, a worn lobe on the camshaft could be the cause.

12 On completion of the checks, refit the spark plugs and reconnect the HT leads and the ignition coil plug. Refit the fuel pump fuse to the fusebox.

3 Top Dead Centre (TDC) for No 1 piston - locating

1 Top dead centre (TDC) is the highest point of the cylinder that each piston reaches as the crankshaft turns. Each piston reaches its TDC position at the end of its compression stroke, and then again at the end of its exhaust stroke. For the purpose of engine timing, TDC at the end of the compression stroke for No 1 piston is used. On the HCS engine, No 1 cylinder is at the crankshaft pulley/timing chain end of the engine. Proceed as follows.

2 Ensure that the ignition is switched off. Disconnect the HT leads from the spark plugs, then unscrew and remove the plugs as described in Chapter 1.

3 Turn the engine over by hand (using a spanner on the crankshaft pulley) to the point where the timing mark on the crankshaft pulley aligns with the TDC (0) mark or TDC reference pointer on the timing cover **(see illustration)**. As the pulley mark nears the timing mark, the No 1 piston is simultaneously approaching the top of its cylinder. To ensure that it is on its compression stroke, place a finger over the No 1 cylinder plug hole, and

feel to ensure that air pressure exits from the cylinder as the piston reaches the top of its stroke.

4 A further check to ensure that the piston is on its compression stroke can be made by first removing the air cleaner (refer to the relevant Part of Chapter 4), then unbolting and removing the rocker cover, so that the movement of the valves and rockers can be observed.

5 With the TDC timing marks on the crankshaft pulley and timing cover in alignment, rock the crankshaft back and forth a few degrees each side of this position, and observe the action of the valves and rockers for No 1 cylinder. When No 1 piston is at the TDC firing position, the inlet and exhaust valve of No 1 cylinder will be fully closed, but the corresponding valves of No 4 cylinder will be seen to rock open and closed.

6 If the inlet and exhaust valves of No 1 cylinder are seen to rock whilst those of No 4 cylinder are shut, the crankshaft will need to be turned one full rotation to bring No 1 piston up to the top of its cylinder on the compression stroke.

7 Once No 1 cylinder has been positioned at TDC on the compression stroke, TDC for any of the other cylinders can then be located by rotating the crankshaft clockwise (in its normal direction of rotation), 180° at a time, and following the firing order (see Specifications).

2A

4 Cylinder head rocker cover - removal and refitting

Removal

1 Where necessary for access, remove the air cleaner as described in the relevant Part of Chapter 4.

2 Detach the HT leads from the spark plugs. Pull on the connector of each lead (not the lead itself), and note the order of fitting.

3 Remove the engine oil filler cap and breather hose (where fitted).

4 Unscrew the four retaining bolts, and lift the rocker cover clear of the cylinder head. Remove the gasket.

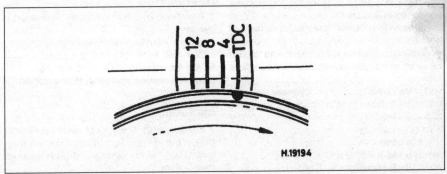

3.3 Timing mark on the crankshaft pulley aligned with the TDC (0) mark on the timing cover

4.6a Engage tags of rocker cover gasket into the cut-outs in the cover

4.6b Refitting the rocker cover

5.6 Adjusting the valve clearances

Refitting

5 Thoroughly clean the rocker cover, and scrape away any traces of old gasket remaining on the cover and cylinder head mating surfaces.

6 Fit a new gasket to the rocker cover, then refit the rocker cover (see illustrations). Tighten the cover retaining bolts to the specified torque wrench setting, in a diagonal sequence.

7 Reconnect the HT leads, and refit the air cleaner as described in Chapter 4.

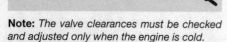

5 Valve clearances - checking and adjustment

Note: *The valve clearances must be checked and adjusted only when the engine is cold.*

1 The importance of having the valve clearances correctly adjusted cannot be overstressed, as they vitally affect the performance of the engine. If the clearances are too big, the engine will be noisy (characteristic rattling or tapping noises) and engine efficiency will be reduced, as the valves open too late and close too early. A more serious problem arises if the clearances are too small, however. If this is the case, the valves may not close fully when the engine is hot, resulting in serious damage to the engine (eg. burnt valve seats and/or cylinder head warping/cracking). The clearances are checked and adjusted as follows.

2 Set the engine to TDC for No 1 piston, as described in Section 3.

3 Remove the rocker cover as described in Section 4.

4 Starting from the thermostat end of the cylinder head, the valves are numbered as follows:

Valve No	Cylinder No
1 - Exhaust	1
2 - Inlet	1
3 - Exhaust	2
4 - Inlet	2
5 - Inlet	3
6 - Exhaust	3
7 - Inlet	4
8 - Exhaust	4

5 Adjust the valve clearances following the sequence given in the following table. Turn the crankshaft pulley 180° (half a turn) after adjusting each pair of valve clearances.

 HAYNES HiNT *Turning the engine will be easier if the spark plugs are removed first - see Chapter 1.*

Valves "rocking"	Valves to adjust
7 and 8	1 (exhaust), 2 (inlet)
5 and 6	3 (exhaust), 4 (inlet)
1 and 2	8 (exhaust), 7 (inlet)
3 and 4	6 (exhaust), 5 (inlet)

6 The clearances for the inlet and exhaust valves differ (refer to the Specifications). Use a feeler gauge of the appropriate thickness to check each clearance between the end of the valve stem and the rocker arm (see illustration). The gauge should be a firm sliding fit between the valve and rocker arm. Where adjustment is necessary, turn the adjuster bolt as required with a ring spanner to set the clearance to that specified. The adjuster bolts are of stiff-thread type, and require no locking nut.

7 On completion, refit the rocker cover as described in Section 4.

6 Cylinder head rocker gear - removal, inspection and refitting

Removal

1 Remove the rocker cover as described in Section 4.

2 Unscrew the four retaining bolts, and lift the rocker gear assembly from the cylinder head. As the assembly is withdrawn, ensure that the pushrods remain seated in their positions in the engine.

Inspection

3 To dismantle the rocker shaft assembly, extract the split pin from one end of the shaft, then withdraw the spring and plain washers from the shaft.

4 Slide off the rocker arms, the support pedestals and coil springs from the shaft, but

If the pushrods are to be removed, keep them in the correct order of fitting by labelling them 1 to 8, starting from the thermostat end of the cylinder head, or locate them in a card.

take care to keep them in their original order of fitting (see illustration).

5 Clean the respective components, and inspect them for signs of excessive wear or damage. Check that the oil lubrication holes in the shaft are clear.

6 Check the rocker shaft and arm pads which bear on the valve stem end faces for wear and scoring, and check each rocker arm on the shaft for excessive wear. Renew any components as necessary.

Refitting

7 Apply clean engine oil to the rocker shaft prior to reassembling.

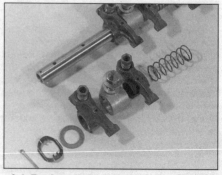

6.4 Rocker shaft partially dismantled for inspection

6.8 Flat on the rocker shaft (arrowed) to same side as rocker arm adjusting screws

8 Reassemble in the reverse order of dismantling. Make sure that the "flat" on the rear end of the rocker shaft is to the same side as the rocker arm adjusting screws (closest to the thermostat end of the cylinder head when fitted) **(see illustration)**. This is essential for the correct lubrication of the cylinder head components.

9 Refit the rocker shaft assembly. As it is fitted, ensure that the rocker adjuster screws engage with their corresponding pushrods.

10 Refit the rocker shaft retaining bolts, hand-tighten them and then tighten them to the specified torque wrench setting. As they are tightened, some of the rocker arms will apply pressure to the ends of the valve stems, and some of the rocker pedestals will not initially be in contact with the cylinder head - these should pull down as the bolts are tightened to their specified torque. If for any reason they do not, avoid the temptation to overtighten in order to pull them into position; loosen off the bolts, and check the cause of the problem. It may be that the rocker adjuster screws require loosening off in order to allow the assembly to be tightened down as required.

11 Adjust the valve clearances as described in Section 5.

7 Cylinder head -
removal and refitting

Removal

Note: *The following procedure describes removal and refitting of the cylinder head complete with inlet and exhaust manifolds. If wished, the manifolds may be removed first, as described in the relevant Part of Chapter 4, and the cylinder head then removed on its own.*

1 On fuel injection engines, depressurise the fuel system as described in Chapter 4, Part B.
2 Disconnect the battery negative (earth) lead (refer to Chapter 5A, Section 1).
3 Refer to Chapter 4A or 4B as applicable and remove the air cleaner.
4 Refer to Section 4 and remove the rocker cover.

5 Refer to Chapter 1 and drain the cooling system.
6 Disconnect the hoses from the thermostat housing.
7 Disconnect the heater (coolant) hoses from the inlet manifold and CFi unit, where applicable.

 Whenever you disconnect any vacuum lines, coolant or emissions hoses, wiring connectors and fuel lines, always label them clearly, so that they can be correctly reassembled. Masking tape and/or a touch-up paint applicator work well for marking items. Take instant photos, or sketch the locations of components and brackets.

8 Disconnect the accelerator and choke cables as applicable (see Chapter 4A or 4B).
9 Disconnect the vacuum and breather hoses from the carburettor/CFi unit, and inlet manifold as applicable.
10 Disconnect the fuel feed and return lines at the carburettor, or at the quick-release couplings, then unclip the fuel hoses from the inlet manifold; use rag to soak up any spilt fuel.
11 Disconnect the HT leads from the spark plugs and the support bracket. Unscrew and remove the spark plugs.
12 Disconnect the electrical leads from the temperature gauge sender, radiator cooling fan, the engine coolant temperature sender, and the anti-run-on (anti-dieselling) valve at the carburettor.
13 Disconnect the remaining wiring multi-plugs from the engine sensors at the inlet manifold and from the oxygen sensor (where fitted) in the exhaust manifold or downpipe.
14 On vehicles equipped with a pulse-air system, remove the pulse-air piping and filter assembly as described in Chapter 4E.
15 Chock the rear wheels then jack up the front of the car and support it on axle stands (see *"Jacking and Vehicle Support"*).
16 Undo the retaining nuts and bolts, and disconnect the exhaust downpipe from the manifold. Remove the flange gasket. (Note that both the gasket and the joint self-locking nuts must be renewed.) To prevent the exhaust system from being strained, tie the downpipe up using strong wire or a length of cord to support it. Lower the vehicle.
17 Undo the four retaining bolts and lift clear the rocker gear assembly from the cylinder head.
18 Lift out the pushrods. Keep them in order of fitting by labelling them 1 to 8, starting from the thermostat end of the cylinder head. Alternatively, push them through a piece of card in their fitted sequence.
19 Progressively unscrew and loosen off the cylinder head retaining bolts in the reverse sequence to that shown for tightening **(see illustration 7.27a)**. When they are all

loosened off, remove the bolts, then lift the cylinder head clear and remove the gasket. If it is stuck, tap it upwards using a hammer and block of wood. Do not try to turn it, as it is located by dowels; make no attempt whatsoever to prise it free using a screwdriver inserted between the block and head faces. The gasket must always be renewed; it should be noted that the cylinder head retaining bolts may be re-used, but only once. They should be marked accordingly with a punch or paint mark. If there is any doubt as to how many times the bolts have been used, they must be renewed.

20 To dismantle/overhaul the cylinder head, refer to Part D of this Chapter. It is normal for the cylinder head to be decarbonised and the valves to be reground whenever the head is removed.

Preparation for refitting

21 The mating faces of the cylinder head and cylinder block must be perfectly clean before refitting the head. Use a hard plastic or wood scraper to remove all traces of gasket and carbon; also clean the piston crowns. Take particular care during the cleaning operations, as aluminium alloy is easily damaged. Also, make sure that the carbon is not allowed to enter the oil and water passages - this is particularly important for the lubrication system, as carbon could block the oil supply to the engine's components. Using adhesive tape and paper, seal the water, oil and bolt holes in the cylinder block.

 To prevent carbon entering the gap between the pistons and bores, smear a little grease in the gap. After cleaning each piston, use a small brush to remove all traces of grease and carbon from the gap, then wipe away the remainder with a clean rag.

22 Check the mating surfaces of the cylinder block and the cylinder head for nicks, deep scratches and other damage. If slight, they may be removed carefully with a file, but if excessive, machining may be the only alternative to renewal.
23 If warpage of the cylinder head gasket surface is suspected, use a straight-edge to check it for distortion. Refer to Part D of this Chapter if necessary.
24 Clean the threads of the cylinder head bolts or fit new ones (as applicable) and clean out the bolt holes in the block. Screwing a bolt into an oil-filled hole can (in extreme cases) cause the block to fracture, due to the hydraulic pressure.

Refitting

25 Check that the new cylinder head gasket is the same type as the original, and that the "TOP" (or "OBEN") marking is facing upwards. Locate the new cylinder head

7.25 Cylinder head gasket top-face marking ("OBEN")

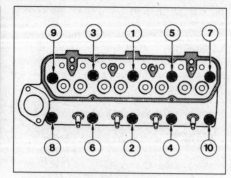

7.27a Cylinder head bolt tightening sequence

7.27b Tightening the cylinder head bolts (Stage 1)

7.27c Cylinder head bolt tightening (Stages 2 and 3) using an angle gauge

gasket onto the top face of the cylinder block and over the dowels. Ensure that it is correctly aligned with the coolant passages and oilways **(see illustration)**.

26 Lower the cylinder head carefully into position, then insert the retaining bolts and hand-tighten them.

27 Tightening of the cylinder head bolts must done in three stages, and in the correct sequence **(see illustration)**. First tighten all of the bolts in the sequence shown to the Stage 1 torque setting **(see illustration)**. When all of the bolts are tightened to the Stage 1 setting, further tighten each bolt (in sequence) through the Stage 2 specified angle of rotation. When the second stage tightening is completed on all of the bolts, further tighten them to the Stage 3 angle setting (in sequence) to complete. Where possible, use an angular torque setting gauge attachment tool for accurate tightening of stages two and three **(see illustration)**.

28 Lubricate the pushrods with clean engine oil, and then insert them into their original locations in the engine.

29 Refit the rocker shaft assembly. As it is fitted, ensure that the rocker adjuster screws engage with their corresponding pushrods.

30 Refit the rocker shaft retaining bolts, hand-tighten them and then tighten them to the specified torque wrench setting. As they are tightened, some of the rocker arms will apply pressure to the ends of the valve stems, and some of the rocker pedestals will not initially be in contact with the cylinder

head - these should pull down as the bolts are tightened. If for any reason they do not, avoid the temptation to overtighten in order to pull them into position; loosen off the bolts, and check the cause of the problem. It may be that the rocker adjuster screws require loosening off in order to allow the assembly to be tightened down as required.

31 Adjust the valve clearances as described in Section 5.

32 Refit the rocker cover as described in Section 4.

33 The remainder of the refitting procedure is a reversal of the removal process. Tighten all fastenings to their specified torque setting (where given). Refer to the appropriate Parts of Chapter 4 for details on reconnecting the fuel and exhaust system components. Ensure that all coolant, fuel, vacuum and electrical connections are securely made.

34 On completion, refill the cooling system and top-up the engine oil (see Chapter 1 and "Weekly Checks"). When the engine is restarted, check for any sign of fuel, oil and/or coolant leakages from the various cylinder head joints.

8 Crankshaft pulley - removal and refitting

Removal

1 Disconnect the battery negative (earth) lead (refer to Chapter 5A, Section 1).

2 Chock the rear wheels then jack up the front of the car and support it on axle stands (see "Jacking and Vehicle Support"). Remove the right-hand front roadwheel.

3 Remove the auxiliary drivebelt as described in Chapter 1.

4 Loosen off the crankshaft pulley retaining bolt. To prevent the crankshaft from turning, unbolt and remove the clutch housing cover plate. Lock the starter ring gear on the flywheel using a large screwdriver or similar tool inserted through the cover plate aperture. Alternatively, remove the starter motor (Chapter 5A) and lock the ring gear through the starter motor aperture.

5 Fully unscrew the crankshaft pulley bolt, and withdraw the pulley from the front end of the crankshaft. If it does not pull off by hand, lever it free using a pair of suitable levers positioned diagonally opposite each other behind the pulley.

6 If required, the crankshaft front oil seal can be renewed at this stage, as described in Section 14.

Refitting

7 Refitting is a reversal of the removal procedure ensuring that the pulley retaining bolt is tightened to the specified torque setting.

8 Refit the auxiliary drivebelt as described in Chapter 1, and lower the vehicle to complete.

9 Timing chain cover - removal and refitting

Removal

1 Remove the sump as described in Section 11.

2 Remove the crankshaft pulley as described in the previous Section.

3 A combined timing cover and water pump gasket is fitted during production; if this is still in position, it will be necessary to drain the cooling system and remove the water pump as described in Chapter 3. If the water pump and/or the timing cover have been removed at any time, the single gasket used originally will have been replaced by an individual gasket for each component, in which case the water pump can remain in position.

4 Unscrew the retaining bolts, and carefully prise free the timing chain cover.

5 Clean the mating faces of the timing chain cover, and the engine.

6 If necessary, renew the crankshaft front oil seal in the timing cover prior to refitting the cover (see Section 14).

Refitting

7 Lightly lubricate the front end of the crankshaft and the radial lip of the timing chain cover oil seal (already installed in the

10.2 Oil slinger removal from crankshaft

10.3 Chain tensioner arm removal from the pivot pin. Note tensioner retaining bolts (arrowed)

cover). Using a new gasket, fit the timing chain cover, centring it with the aid of the crankshaft pulley - lubricate the seal contact surfaces beforehand. Refit and tighten the retaining bolts but, where applicable, leave out the timing cover bolt which also secures the water pump at this stage.

8 Where applicable, refit the water pump as described in Chapter 3.

9 Refit the crankshaft pulley as described in the previous Section.

10 Refit the sump as described in Section 11.

---

10 Timing chain, sprockets and tensioner - removal, inspection and refitting

Removal

1 Remove the timing chain cover as described in the previous Section.

2 Remove the oil slinger from the front face of the crankshaft, noting its orientation **(see illustration)**.

3 Retract the chain tensioner cam back against its spring pressure, then slide the chain tensioner arm from its pivot pin on the front main bearing cap **(see illustration)**.

4 Unbolt and remove the chain tensioner.

5 Bend back the lockplate tabs from the camshaft sprocket bolts, then unscrew and remove the bolts.

6 Withdraw the sprocket complete with the timing chain.

Inspection

7 Examine the teeth on the timing sprockets for any signs of excessive wear or damage.

8 The timing chain should always be renewed during a major engine overhaul. Slack links and pins are indicative of a worn chain. Unless the chain is known to be relatively new, it should be renewed.

9 Examine the rubber cushion on the tensioner spring leaf. If grooved or deteriorated, it must be renewed.

Refitting

10 Commence reassembly by bolting the timing chain tensioner into position. Check that the face of the tensioner cam is parallel with the face of the cylinder block, ideally using a dial gauge. The maximum permissible error between the two measuring points is 0.2 mm. Release and turn the timing chain tensioner as required to achieve this (if necessary). Refer to the Specifications for the correct tightening torque.

11 Turn the crankshaft so that the timing mark on its sprocket is directly in line with the centre of the camshaft sprocket mounting flange.

12 Engage the camshaft sprocket with the timing chain, then engage the chain around the teeth of the crankshaft sprocket. Push the camshaft sprocket onto its mounting flange, and check that the sprocket retaining bolt holes are in alignment **(see illustration)**. Also

check that the timing marks of both sprockets face each other. If required, turn the camshaft/sprocket as required to achieve this. It may also be necessary to remove the camshaft from the chain in order to reposition it in the required location in the chain to align the timing marks. This is a "trial and error" procedure, which must be continued until the exact alignment of the bolt holes and the timing marks is made **(see illustration)**.

13 Insert and tighten the camshaft sprocket retaining bolts to the specified torque wrench setting. Bend up the tabs of the new lockplate to secure **(see illustration)**.

14 Retract the timing chain tensioner cam, and then slide the tensioner arm onto its pivot pin. Release the cam so that it bears on the arm.

15 Refit the oil slinger to the front of the crankshaft sprocket so that its convex side faces the sprocket.

16 Refit the timing chain cover as described in the previous Section.

---

11 Sump - removal and refitting

Removal

1 Disconnect the battery negative (earth) lead (refer to Chapter 5A, Section 1).

2 Refer Chapter 1 and drain the engine oil. Refit the sump drain plug.

3 Undo the retaining nuts and detach the exhaust downpipe from the manifold flange. Note that the flange gasket should be renewed on reassembly. Allowing sufficient clearance for sump removal, tie the exhaust downpipe up with a suitable length of wire or cord to prevent the system straining the insulators. On catalytic converter-equipped vehicles, avoid straining the oxygen sensor wiring; if necessary, disconnect the sensor's multi-plug.

4 Remove the starter motor (see Chapter 5A).

5 Undo the two retaining bolts and remove the clutch housing cover plate and, where fitted, the auxiliary drivebelt lower cover from inside the right-hand wheel arch.

2A

10.12a Fit the timing chain to the crankshaft and camshaft sprockets . . .

10.12b . . . and check that the timing marks on the sprockets are in alignment

10.13 Bend locktabs against the camshaft retaining bolt heads to secure

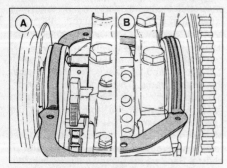

11.8a Sump gasket fitting details at the timing chain cover end (A) and the flywheel end (B)

11.8b Lugs of cork gasket halves to fit under the cut-outs in the rubber gaskets

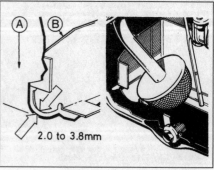

2.0 to 3.8mm

11.9 Sump (A) and oil baffle (B) clearance details

6 Undo the eighteen bolts securing the sump to the base of the engine crankcase, then prise free and lower the sump. If the sump is stuck tight to the engine, cut around the flange gasket with a sharp knife, then lightly tap and prise it free. Keep the sump upright as it is lowered, to prevent spillage of any remaining oil in it. Also be prepared for oil drips from the crankcase when the sump is removed.

7 Remove any dirt and old gasket from the contact faces of the sump and crankcase, and wash the sump out thoroughly before refitting. Check that the mating faces of the sump are not distorted. Check that the oil pick-up strainer is clear, cleaning it if necessary.

Refitting

8 Clean the gasket location faces. Apply a dab of sealing compound to the mating faces where the ends of each cork half-gasket are to be fitted **(see illustration)**. Stick the new cork gaskets into position on the block face, using clean thick grease to retain them, then locate the new rubber gaskets into their slots in the timing chain cover and rear oil seal carrier. The lugs of the cork gasket halves fit under the cut-outs in the rubber gaskets **(see illustration)**.

9 Before offering up the sump, check that the gap between the sump and the oil baffle is between 2.0 and 3.8 mm **(see illustration)**.

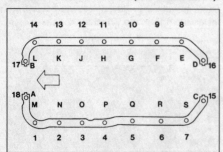

11.10 Sump bolt tightening sequence - arrow indicates crankshaft pulley end of engine

See Specifications for torque wrench settings
Stage 1 - Tighten in alphabetical order
Stage 2 - Tighten in numerical order
Stage 3 - Tighten in alphabetical order

Do not use a dented or damaged sump, as the indicated dimension is important for correct engine lubrication.

10 Fit the sump into position, and fit the retaining bolts. Initially tighten them all finger-tight, then further tighten them in the sequence shown through Stages 1 and 2, to the torque wrench settings specified **(see illustration)**. Note that different tightening sequences are specified for the tightening stages. Final (Stage 3) tightening is carried out after the engine has been started and warmed up.

11 Refit the lower plate to the front face of the clutch housing and refit the auxiliary drivebelt lower cover.

12 Refit the starter motor.

13 Check that the downpipe and manifold mating faces are clean, then locate a new gasket and reconnect the exhaust downpipe to the manifold. Where applicable, use new self-locking nuts, and tighten securely.

14 Check that the sump drain plug is fitted and tightened to the specified torque, then lower the vehicle to the ground.

15 Refill the engine with oil as described in Chapter 1.

16 Reconnect the battery, then start the engine and run it up to its normal operating temperature. Check that no oil leaks are evident around the sump joint.

17 After the engine has warmed up for approximately 15 minutes, switch it off. Tighten the sump bolts to the Stage 3 torque wrench setting given in the Specifications, in the sequence shown in illustration 11.10.

12.4 Unscrewing the oil pump retaining bolts

12 Oil pump - removal and refitting

Removal

1 The oil pump is externally-mounted, on the rear-facing side of the crankcase.

2 Chock the rear wheels then jack up the front of the car and support it on axle stands (see *"Jacking and Vehicle Support"*).

3 Unscrew and remove the oil filter cartridge. It should unscrew by hand, but will probably be tight. Use a strap wrench to loosen it off, if required. Catch any oil spillage in a suitable container.

4 Undo the three retaining bolts and withdraw the oil pump from the engine **(see illustration)**.

5 Clean all traces of the old gasket from the mating surfaces of the pump and engine.

Refitting

6 If the original oil pump has been dismantled and reassembled and is to be re-used, or if a new pump is to be fitted, it must first be primed with engine oil prior to fitting. To do this, turn its driveshaft and simultaneously inject clean engine oil into it.

7 Locate a new gasket into position on the pump mounting flange, then insert the pump, engaging the drivegear as it is fitted **(see illustration)**. Fit the retaining bolts, and tighten to the specified torque wrench setting.

12.7 Refitting the oil pump. Note the new gasket

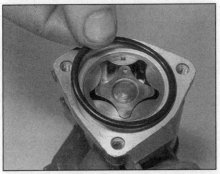

13.1 Extract the O-ring from the groove in the oil pump

13.4a Checking the outer body-to-rotor clearance

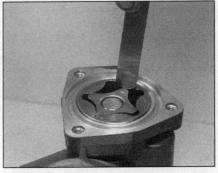

13.4b Checking the inner rotor-to-outer rotor clearance

8 Fit a new oil filter into position on the oil pump body, as described in Chapter 1.
9 Lower the vehicle to the ground, and top-up the engine oil as described in *"Weekly Checks"*.

13 Oil pump - dismantling, inspection and reassembly

Dismantling

1 To inspect the oil pump components for excessive wear, undo the retaining bolts and remove the cover plate from the pump body. Remove the O-ring seal from the cover face **(see illustration)**.
2 Wipe the exterior of the pump housing clean housing.

Inspection

3 Noting their orientation, extract and clean the rotors and the inner body of the pump housing. Inspect them for signs of severe scoring or excessive wear, which if evident will necessitate renewal of the complete pump.
4 Using feeler gauges, check the clearances between the pump body and the outer rotor, the inner-to-outer rotor clearance, and the amount of rotor endfloat **(see illustrations)**.

5 Check the drivegear for signs of excessive wear or damage.
6 If the clearances measured are outside the specified maximum clearances and/or the drivegear is in poor condition, the complete pump unit must be renewed.

Reassembly

7 Refit the rotors into the pump (in their original orientation), lubricate the rotors and the new O-ring seal with clean engine oil, and refit the cover. Tighten the retaining bolts to the specified torque wrench setting.

14 Crankshaft oil seals - renewal

Front oil seal

1 Remove the crankshaft pulley as described in Section 8.
2 Using a suitable claw tool, extract the oil seal from the timing chain cover, but take care not to damage the seal housing. As it is removed, note the fitted orientation of the seal in the cover.
3 Clean the oil seal housing in the timing chain cover. Lubricate the sealing lips of the new seal and the crankshaft stub with clean engine oil.
4 Locate the new seal into position so that it

is squarely located on the crankshaft stub and in the housing, and is correctly orientated. Drift it into position using a large socket, another suitable tool, or the old seal, until the new seal is flush with the edge of the timing chain cover.
5 Lightly lubricate the rubbing surface of the crankshaft pulley, then refit the pulley as described in Section 8.

Rear oil seal

6 Remove the flywheel as described in Section 16.
7 Using a suitable claw tool, lever the seal from the rear seal housing (taking care not to damage the housing). As it is removed, note the fitted orientation of the seal.
8 Clean the seal housing, the crankshaft rear flange face and the flywheel mating surface.
9 One of two possible methods may be used to insert the new oil seal, depending on the tools available.
10 If Ford service tool No 21-011 is available, lubricate the crankshaft flange and the oil seal inner lip with clean engine oil. Position the seal onto the service tool (ensuring correct orientation), then press the seal into its housing.
11 If the service tool is not available, remove the engine sump (Section 11), then unscrew the Torx-head bolts retaining the rear seal housing in position, and remove the seal housing from the rear face of the cylinder block. New gaskets will be required for both the seal housing and the sump when refitting. Clean the seal housing seat and the mating surfaces of the sump and the crankcase. To fit the seal squarely into its housing without damaging either component, place a flat block of wood across the seal, then carefully tap the seal into position in the housing **(see illustration)**. Do not allow the seal to tilt as it is being fitted. Lubricate the crankshaft flange and the oil seal inner lip with clean engine oil, then with a new gasket located on the seal housing/crankcase face, fit the housing into position. Take care not damage the seal lips as it is passed over the crankshaft rear flange

2A

13.4c Checking the rotor endfloat

14.11a Positioning the crankshaft rear oil seal in its housing

14.11b Fitting the rear oil seal housing with a new gasket in position on the rear face of the cylinder block

15.8 Unscrew and remove the engine mounting side bolt (arrowed) from under the wheel arch

15.9 Unscrew and remove the mounting retaining nut and washer from the suspension strut cup retaining plate

(see illustration). Centralise the seal on the shaft, then insert and tighten the housing retaining bolts to the specified torque setting. Refit the sump with reference to Section 11.

12 Check that the crankshaft rear flange and the flywheel mating faces are clean, then refit the flywheel as described in Section 16.

15 Engine/transmission mountings - inspection and renewal

Inspection

1 The engine/transmission mountings seldom require attention, but broken or deteriorated mountings should be renewed immediately, or the added strain placed on the driveline components may cause damage or wear.

2 During the check, the engine/transmission must be raised slightly, to remove its weight from the mountings.

3 Chock the rear wheels then jack up the front of the car and support it on axle stands (see *"Jacking and Vehicle Support"*). Position a jack under the sump, with a large block of wood between the jack head and the sump, then carefully raise the engine/transmission just enough to take the weight off the mountings.

4 Check the mountings to see if the rubber is cracked, hardened or separated from the

metal components. Sometimes, the rubber will split right down the centre.

5 Check for relative movement between each mounting's brackets and the engine/transmission or body (use a large screwdriver or lever to attempt to move the mountings). If movement is noted, lower the engine and check-tighten the mounting fasteners.

Renewal

6 The engine mountings can be removed if the weight of the engine/transmission is supported by one of the following alternative methods.

7 Either support the weight of the assembly from underneath using a jack and a suitable piece of wood between the jack saddle and the sump or transmission (to prevent damage), or from above by attaching a hoist to the engine. A third method is to use a suitable support bar with end pieces which will engage in the water channel each side of the bonnet lid aperture. Using an adjustable

hook and chain connected to the engine, the weight of the engine and transmission can then be taken from the mountings.

Engine right-hand mounting

8 Unscrew and remove the mounting side bolt from under the right-hand wheel arch (see illustration).

9 Unscrew and remove the mounting retaining nut and washer from the suspension strut cup retaining plate (see illustration).

10 Undo the three bolts securing the mounting unit to the cylinder block. The mounting unit and bracket can then be lowered from the engine (see illustration).

11 Unbolt and remove the mounting from its support bracket.

Transmission bearer and mountings

12 Unscrew and remove the two nuts securing the mountings (front and rear) to the transmission bearer (see illustration).

13 Support the transmission bearer, then undo and remove the four retaining bolts from the floorpan, two at the front and two at the

15.10 Undo the three bolts securing the mounting assembly to the cylinder block and withdraw the mounting

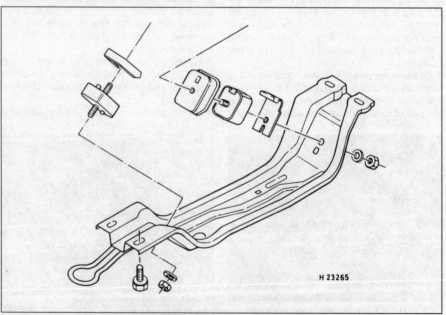

15.12 Exploded view of the transmission bearer mountings

rear, and lower the transmission bearer from the vehicle. Note plate fitment, as applicable, for reassembly.

14 Unscrew the single nut securing each mounting and its retainer to the transmission support bracket, and remove. The transmission support brackets are fixed externally to the transmission casing and do not need to be removed for this operation.

All mountings

15 Refitting of all mountings is a reversal of removal. Make sure that the original sequence of assembly of washers and plates is maintained.

16 Do not fully tighten any mounting bolts until they are all located. As the mounting bolts and nuts are tightened, check that the mounting rubbers do not twist.

16 Flywheel - removal, inspection and refitting

Refitting

1 Remove the transmission as described in Chapter 7A, then remove the clutch as described in Chapter 6.

2 Unscrew the six retaining bolts, and remove the flywheel from the rear end flange of the crankshaft - take care not to drop the flywheel, as it is heavy. A tool similar to that shown in illustration 16.5 can be fitted to prevent the flywheel/crankshaft from rotating as the bolts are removed. If on removal, the retaining bolts are found to be in poor condition (stretched threads, etc) they must be renewed.

Inspection

3 Inspect the starter ring gear on the flywheel for any broken or excessively-worn teeth. If evident, the ring gear must be renewed; this is a task best entrusted to a Ford dealer or a competent garage. Alternatively, obtain a complete new flywheel.

4 The clutch friction surface on the flywheel must be carefully inspected for grooving or hairline cracks (caused by overheating). If these conditions are evident, it may be possible to have the flywheel surface-ground to renovate it, providing that the balance is not upset. Regrinding is a task for an automotive engineer. If surface-grinding is not possible, the flywheel must be renewed.

Refitting

5 Check that the mating faces of the flywheel

16.5 Tightening the flywheel retaining bolts to the specified torque

Note the "peg" tool (arrowed) locking the ring gear teeth to prevent the flywheel/crankshaft from rotating

and the crankshaft are clean before refitting. Lubricate the threads of the retaining bolts with engine oil before they are screwed into position. Locate the flywheel onto the crankshaft, and insert the bolts. Hand-tighten them initially, then tighten them in a progressive sequence to the specified torque wrench setting **(see illustration)**.

6 Refit the clutch as described in Chapter 6 and the transmission as described in Chapter 7A.

2A

Notes

Chapter 2 Part B:
CVH and PTE engine in-car repair procedures

Contents

Auxiliary drivebelt check and renewal . . . . .See Chapter 1
Camshaft oil seal - renewal 10
Camshaft, rocker arms and tappets - removal, inspection
  and refitting 11
Compression test - description and interpretation 2
Crankshaft oil seals - renewal 16
Crankshaft pulley - removal and refitting 6
Cylinder head - removal and refitting 12
Cylinder head rocker cover - removal and refitting 4
Engine oil and filter renewal . . . . .See Chapter 1
Engine oil level check . . . . .See "Weekly Checks"
Engine/transmission mountings - renewal 17

Flywheel/driveplate - removal, inspection and refitting 18
General information 1
Oil pump - dismantling, inspection and reassembly 15
Oil pump - removal and refitting 14
Sump - removal and refitting 13
Timing belt - removal, refitting and adjustment 8
Timing belt covers - removal and refitting 7
Timing belt tensioner and sprockets - removal, inspection
  and refitting 9
Top Dead Centre (TDC) for No 1 piston - locating 3
Valve clearances - general information 5

Degrees of difficulty

Easy, suitable for novice with little experience	Fairly easy, suitable for beginner with some experience 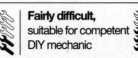	Fairly difficult, suitable for competent DIY mechanic	Difficult, suitable for experienced DIY mechanic	Very difficult, suitable for expert DIY or professional

Specifications

General

Engine type	Four-cylinder, in-line overhead camshaft
Engine code:	
1.4 litre CVH engine:	
Carburettor models	FUF or FUG
CFi fuel injection models	F6E
1.4 litre PTE engine	F4A
1.6 litre CVH engine:	
Carburettor models	LUH
EFi fuel injection models	LJC or LJD
Turbo models	LHA
Capacity:	
1.4 litre CVH and PTE engines	1392 cc
1.6 litre CVH engine	1596 cc
Bore:	
1.4 litre CVH and PTE engines	77.24 mm
1.6 litre CVH engine	79.96 mm
Stroke:	
1.4 litre CVH and PTE engines	74.30 mm
1.6 litre CVH engine	79.52 mm
Compression ratio:	
1.4 litre CVH carburettor engine	9.5:1
1.4 litre CVH CFi fuel injection engine	8.5:1
1.4 litre PTE engine	9.5:1
1.6 litre CVH engine:	
Carburettor models	9.5:1
EFi fuel injection models	9.75:1
Turbo models	8.0:1
Firing order	1-3-4-2 (No 1 cylinder at timing belt end)
Direction of crankshaft rotation	Clockwise (seen from right-hand side of vehicle)

Cylinder head

Hydraulic tappet bore inside diameter . . . . 22.235 to 22.265 mm

Camshaft

Camshaft bearing journal diameter:
    Bearing 1 . . . . 44.75 mm
    Bearing 2 . . . . 45.00 mm
    Bearing 3 . . . . 45.25 mm
    Bearing 4 . . . . 45.50 mm
    Bearing 5 . . . . 45.75 mm
Camshaft bearing journal-to-cylinder head running clearance . . . . 0.033 to 0.058 mm
Camshaft endfloat . . . . 0.05 to 0.13 mm
Camshaft thrust plate thickness . . . . 4.99 to 5.01 mm

Lubrication

Engine oil type/specification . . . . See *"Lubricants, fluids and tyre pressures"*
Engine oil capacity . . . . See *"Lubricants, fluids and tyre pressures"*
Oil pressure:
    Idling . . . . 1.0 bar
    At 2000 rpm . . . . 2.8 bars
Oil pump clearances:
    Outer rotor-to-body . . . . 0.060 to 0.190 mm
    Inner rotor-to-outer rotor . . . . 0.05 to 0.18 mm
    Rotor endfloat . . . . 0.014 to 0.100 mm

Torque wrench settings

	Nm	lbf ft
Oil pump to cylinder block	19	14
Oil pump cover	9	7
Oil pump pick-up to cylinder block	9	7
Oil pump pick-up to pump	9	7
Oil cooler threaded sleeve to cylinder block	57	42
Rear oil seal housing	9	7
Flywheel/driveplate bolts	87	64
Cylinder head bolts:		
Stage 1	30	22
Stage 2	50	37
Stage 3	Angle-tighten a further 90°	
Stage 4	Angle-tighten a further 90°	
Crankshaft pulley bolt	108	80
Camshaft thrust plate	11	8
Camshaft toothed belt sprocket	57	42
Timing belt tensioner	18	13
Rocker studs in cylinder head	20	15
Rocker arms	27	20
Rocker cover	7	5
Timing belt cover	9	7
Sump:		
Stage 1	7	5
Stage 2	7	5
Engine mountings (CVH engines):		
Engine mounting (right-hand):		
Bolt to body (in wheel arch)	41 to 58	30 to 43
Nut to body (by suspension strut)	41 to 58	30 to 43
Bracket to cylinder block	54 to 72	40 to 53
Rubber insulator to bracket	71 to 95	52 to 70
Transmission mounting fasteners	Refer to Chapter 7A or 7B	
Engine mountings (PTE engines):		
Engine mounting (right-hand):		
Bolt to body (in wheel arch)	50	37
Nut to body (by suspension strut)	64	47
Transmission mounting fasteners	Refer to Chapter 7A or 7B	

Note: *Refer to Part D of this Chapter for remaining torque wrench settings.*

1 General information

How to use this Chapter

This Part of Chapter 2 is devoted to repair procedures possible while the engine is still installed in the vehicle, and includes only the Specifications relevant to those procedures. Similar information concerning the 1.3 litre HCS engine, and the 1.6 and 1.8 litre Zetec engines, will be found in Parts A and C of this Chapter respectively. Since these procedures are based on the assumption that the engine is installed in the vehicle, if the engine has been removed from the vehicle and mounted on a stand, some of the preliminary dismantling steps outlined will not apply.

Information concerning engine/transmission removal and refitting, and engine overhaul, can be found in Part D of this Chapter, which also includes the Specifications relevant to those procedures.

Engine description

The engine is a four-cylinder, in-line overhead camshaft type, designated CVH (Compound Valve angle, Hemispherical combustion chamber) or PTE (Pent roof, high Torque, low Emission). The PTE engine was introduced for 1994 and, apart from modifications to the cylinder head, camshaft and intake system, is virtually identical to the CVH engine it replaces. The engine is mounted transversely at the front of the vehicle together with the transmission to form a combined power unit.

The crankshaft is supported in five split-shell type main bearings within the cast-iron crankcase. The connecting rod big-end bearings are split-shell type, and the pistons are attached by interference-fit gudgeon pins. Each piston has two compression rings and one oil control ring.

The cylinder head is of light alloy construction, and supports the camshaft in five bearings. Camshaft drive is by a toothed composite rubber timing belt, which is driven by a sprocket on the front end of the crankshaft. The timing belt also drives the water pump, which is mounted below the cylinder head.

Hydraulic cam followers (tappets) operate the rocker arms and valves. The tappets are operated by pressurised engine oil. When a valve closes, the oil passes through a port in the body of the cam follower, through four grooves in the plunger and into the cylinder feed chamber. From the chamber, the oil flows to a ball-type non-return valve and into the pressure chamber. The tension of the coil spring causes the plunger to press against the valve, and so eliminates any free play. As the cam lifts the follower, the oil pressure in the pressure chamber is increased, and the non-return valve closes off the port feed chamber. This in turn provides a rigid link between the cam follower, the cylinder and the plunger. These then rise as

a unit to open the valve. The cam follower-to-cylinder clearance allows the specified quantity of oil to pass from the pressure chamber, oil only being allowed past the cylinder bore when the pressure is high during the moment of the valve opening. When the valve closes, the escape of oil will produce a small clearance, and no pressure will exist in the pressure chamber. The feed chamber oil then flows through the non-return valve and into the pressure chamber, so that the cam follower cylinder can be raised by the pressure of the coil spring, eliminating free play until the valve is operated again.

As wear occurs between the rocker arm and the valve stem, the quantity of oil that flows into the pressure chamber will be slightly more than the quantity lost during the expansion cycle of the cam follower. Conversely, when the cam follower is compressed by the expansion of the valve, a slightly smaller quantity of oil will flow into the pressure chamber than was lost.

A rotor-type oil pump is mounted on the timing cover end of the engine, and is driven by a gear on the front end of the crankshaft. A full-flow type oil filter is fitted, and is mounted on the side of the crankcase.

Repair operations possible with the engine in the car

The following work can be carried out with the engine in the car:
a) Compression pressure - testing.
b) Rocker cover - removal and refitting.
c) Timing belt - removal, refitting and adjustment.
d) Camshaft oil seal - renewal.
e) Camshaft - removal and refitting.
f) Cylinder head - removal and refitting.
g) Cylinder head and pistons - decarbonising.
h) Crankshaft pulley - removal and refitting.
i) Crankshaft oil seals - renewal.
j) Oil filter renewal.
k) Sump - removal and refitting.
l) Flywheel - removal, inspection and refitting.
m) Mountings - removal and refitting.

Note: It is possible to remove the pistons and connecting rods (after removing the cylinder head and sump) without removing the engine. However, this is not recommended. Work of this nature is more easily and thoroughly completed with the engine on the bench, as described in Chapter 2D.

2 Compression test - description and interpretation

Refer to Section 2 in Part A of this Chapter.

3 Top Dead Centre (TDC) for No 1 piston - locating

1 Top dead centre (TDC) is the highest point of the cylinder that each piston reaches as the crankshaft turns. Each piston reaches its TDC position at the end of its compression stroke, and then again at the end of its exhaust stroke. For the purpose of engine timing, TDC on the compression stroke for No 1 piston is used. No 1 cylinder is at the timing belt end of the engine. Proceed as follows.
2 Remove the upper timing belt cover as described in Section 7.
3 Chock the rear wheels then jack up the front of the car and support it on axle stands (see "Jacking and Vehicle Support").
4 Undo the retaining bolts, and remove the cover from the underside of the crankshaft pulley.
5 Fit a spanner onto the crankshaft pulley bolt, and turn the crankshaft in its normal direction of rotation (clockwise, viewed from the pulley end) to the point where the crankshaft pulley timing notch is aligned with the TDC (0) timing mark on the timing belt cover.

HAYNES HINT *Turning the engine will be easier if the spark plugs are removed first - see Chapter 1.*

6 Although the crankshaft is now in top dead centre alignment, with piston Nos 1 and 4 at the top of their stroke, the No 1 piston may not be on its compression stroke. To confirm that it is, check that the timing pointer on the camshaft sprocket is exactly aligned with the TDC mark on the front face of the cylinder head (see illustrations). If the pointer is not aligned, turn the crankshaft pulley one further

2B

3.6a Crankshaft pulley notch (arrowed) aligned with the TDC (0) mark on the timing belt cover

3.6b Camshaft sprocket timing mark aligned with the TDC mark on the front face of the cylinder head

complete turn, and all the markings should now align.

7 With the engine set at No 1 piston on TDC compression, refit the crankshaft pulley cover, lower the vehicle and refit the upper timing belt cover.

4 Cylinder head rocker cover - removal and refitting

Removal

1 Disconnect the battery negative (earth) lead (refer to Chapter 5A, Section 1).
2 Remove the air cleaner assembly and air inlet components as necessary for access as described in the relevant Part of Chapter 4. Disconnect the crankcase ventilation hose from the rocker cover.
3 Remove the timing belt upper cover as described in Section 7.
4 Referring to the relevant Part of Chapter 4 for details, disconnect the accelerator cable from the throttle linkage and from the adjuster bracket above the rocker cover. Position the cable out of the way.
5 Where applicable, disconnect the choke cable from the carburettor, referring to Chapter 4A for details.
6 Unscrew and remove the rocker cover retaining bolts and washers, then lift the cover from the cylinder head. Note that a new rocker cover gasket will be needed on refitting.

Refitting

7 Before refitting the rocker cover, clean the mating surfaces of both the cylinder head and the cover.
8 Locate the new gasket in position, then fit the cover retaining bolts and washers. Ensure that the grooves in the plate washers are facing upwards as they are fitted **(see illustrations)**. Tighten the cover retaining bolts to the specified torque wrench setting. Refer to Chapter 4 for details on reconnecting the accelerator cable, choke cable, air inlet components and air cleaner (as applicable).
9 Refit the timing belt cover and reconnect the battery earth lead.

5 Valve clearances - general information

It is necessary for a clearance to exist between the tip of each valve stem and the valve operating mechanism, to allow for the expansion of the various components as the engine reaches normal operating temperature.

On most older engine designs, this meant that the valve clearances (also known as "tappet" clearances) had to be checked and adjusted regularly. If the clearances were allowed to be too slack, the engine would be very noisy, its power output would suffer, and its fuel consumption would increase. If the clearances were allowed to be too tight, the engine's power output would be reduced, and the valves and their seats could be severely damaged.

These engines employ hydraulic tappets which use the lubricating system's oil pressure to automatically take up the clearance between each camshaft lobe and its respective valve stem. Therefore, there is no need for regular checking and adjustment of the valve clearances. However, it is **essential** that only good-quality oil of the recommended viscosity and specification is used in the engine, and that this oil is always changed at the recommended intervals. If this advice is not followed, the oilways and tappets may become clogged with particles of dirt, or deposits of burnt (inferior) engine oil, so that the system cannot work properly; ultimately, one or more of the tappets may fail, and expensive repairs may be required.

On starting the engine from cold, there will be a slight delay while full oil pressure builds up in all parts of the engine, especially in the tappets; the valve components, therefore, may well "rattle" for about 10 seconds or so, and then quieten. This is a normal state of affairs, and is nothing to worry about, provided that all tappets quieten quickly and stay quiet.

After the vehicle has been standing for several days, the valve components may "rattle" for longer than usual, as nearly all the oil will have drained away from the engine's top-end components and bearing surfaces. While this is only to be expected, care must be taken not to damage the engine under these circumstances - avoid high-speed running until all the tappets are refilled with oil and operating normally. With the vehicle stationary, hold the engine at no more than a fast idle speed (maximum 2000 to 2500 rpm) for 10 to 15 minutes, or until the noise ceases. Do not run the engine at more than 3000 rpm until the tappets are fully charged with oil and the noise has ceased.

If the valve components are thought to be noisy, or if a light rattle persists from the top end after the engine has warmed up to normal operating temperature, take the vehicle to a Ford dealer for expert advice. Depending on the mileage covered and the usage to which each vehicle has been put, some vehicles may be noisier than others; only a good mechanic experienced in these engines can tell if the noise level is typical for the vehicle's mileage, or if a genuine fault exists. If any tappet's operation is faulty, it must be renewed (Section 11).

6 Crankshaft pulley - removal and refitting

Removal

1 Disconnect the battery negative (earth) lead (refer to Chapter 5A, Section 1).
2 Chock the rear wheels then jack up the front of the car and support it on axle stands (see "Jacking and Vehicle Support").
3 Unbolt and remove the cover from the underside of the crankshaft pulley.
4 Remove the auxiliary drivebelt as described in Chapter 1.
5 If timing belt renewal is also intended, set the engine at TDC as described in Section 3 before removing the crankshaft pulley and retaining bolt.
6 To prevent the crankshaft from turning as the pulley bolt is loosened off, remove the starter motor as described in Chapter 5A, and then lock the starter ring gear using a suitable lever **(see illustration)**.

4.8a Fitting a new gasket to the rocker cover

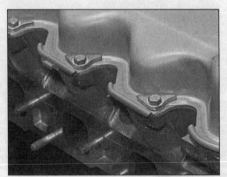

4.8b Rocker cover retaining bolts and plate washers

6.6 Using a suitable bar to lock the flywheel ring gear

6.7 Crankshaft pulley removal

7.3 Upper timing belt cover removal

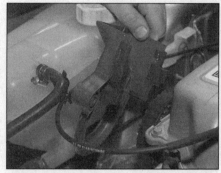

7.5 Lower timing belt cover removal

7 Unscrew and remove the crankshaft pulley retaining bolt and its washer. Withdraw the pulley from the front end of the crankshaft **(see illustration)**. If necessary, lever it free using a pair of diagonally-opposed levers positioned behind the pulley.

Refitting

8 Refit in the reverse order of removal. Tighten the pulley retaining bolt to the specified torque setting, and refer to Chapter 1 for details on refitting the auxiliary drivebelt.
9 On completion, reconnect the battery negative lead.

7 Timing belt covers - removal and refitting

Removal

1 Disconnect the battery negative (earth) lead (refer to Chapter 5A, Section 1).
2 Where applicable, undo the two bolts securing the power steering fluid pipe support clips and ease the pipe away from the upper cover.
3 Undo the two retaining bolts and remove the upper timing belt cover **(see illustration)**.
4 Refer to the previous Section for details, and remove the crankshaft pulley.
5 Unscrew the two bolts securing the lower timing belt cover, and remove it **(see illustration)**.

Refitting

6 Refit in the reverse order of removal. Tighten the cover retaining bolts to the specified torque wrench setting.
7 On completion, reconnect the battery earth lead.

8 Timing belt - removal, refitting and adjustment

Removal

1 Referring to the previous Sections for details, remove the rocker cover, the crankshaft pulley and the timing belt covers.
2 Check that the crankshaft is set with the No 1 piston at TDC (on its compression stroke) before proceeding. If necessary, refer to Section 3 for further details.
3 To check the timing belt for correct adjustment, proceed as described in paragraph 12 below. To remove the belt, proceed as follows.
4 Loosen off the two bolts securing the timing belt tensioner. Using a large screwdriver, prise the tensioner to one side to release the timing belt tension. Secure the tensioner in this position by retightening the bolts **(see illustration)**.
5 If the original timing belt is to be refitted, mark it for direction of travel and also the exact tooth engagement positions on all

sprockets. Slip the belt from the camshaft, water pump and crankshaft sprockets **(see illustration)**. Whilst the timing belt is removed, avoid any excessive movement of the sprockets, otherwise the piston crowns and valves may come into contact and be damaged.
6 If the belt is being removed for reasons other than routine renewal, check it carefully for any signs of uneven wear, splitting, cracks (especially at the roots of the belt teeth) or contamination with oil or coolant. Renew the belt if there is the slightest doubt about its condition. As a safety measure, the belt must be renewed as a matter of course at the intervals given in Chapter 1; if its history is unknown, the belt should be renewed irrespective of its apparent condition whenever the engine is overhauled.

Refitting and adjustment

7 Before refitting the belt, check that the crankshaft is still at the TDC position, with the small projection on the belt sprocket front flange aligned with the TDC mark on the oil pump housing **(see illustration)**. Also ensure that the camshaft sprocket is set with its TDC pointer aligned with the corresponding timing mark on the cylinder head **(see illustration 3.6b)**. If necessary, adjust the sprockets slightly. As previously mentioned, avoid any excessive movement of the sprockets whilst the belt is removed.
8 Engage the timing belt teeth with the teeth

2B

8.4 Timing belt tensioner retaining bolts (arrowed)

8.5 Timing belt removal

8.7 Sprocket and oil pump housing TDC marks in alignment

8.13 Checking the tension of the timing belt

of the crankshaft sprocket, and then pull the belt vertically upright on its right-hand run. Keep it taut, and engage it with the teeth of the camshaft sprocket. If the original belt is being refitted, check that the belt's direction of travel is correct, and realign the belt-to-sprocket marks made during removal, to ensure that the exact original engagement positions are retained. When the belt is fully fitted on the sprockets, check that the sprocket positions have not altered.

9 Carefully manoeuvre the belt around the tensioner, and engage its teeth with the water pump sprocket, again ensuring that the TDC positions of the crankshaft and camshaft are not disturbed as the belt is finally located.

10 Refit the lower timing belt cover, and tighten its retaining bolts to the specified torque setting. Refit the crankshaft pulley, and tighten its retaining bolt to the specified torque setting.

11 To take up belt slack, loosen off the tensioner and move it towards the front of the car to apply an initial tension to the belt. Secure the tensioner in this position, then remove the flywheel ring gear locking device.

12 Rotate the crankshaft through two full revolutions in (the normal direction of travel), returning to the TDC position (camshaft sprocket-to-cylinder head). Check that the crankshaft pulley notch is aligned with the TDC (0) mark on the lower half of the timing belt cover.

13 Grasp the belt between the thumb and forefinger, at the midway point between the crankshaft and camshaft sprockets on the right-hand side. If the belt tension is correct, it should just be possible to twist the belt through 90° at this point **(see illustration)**. To adjust the belt, loosen off the tensioner retaining bolts, move the tensioner as required using a suitable screwdriver as a lever, then retighten the retaining bolts. Rotate the crankshaft to settle the belt, then recheck the tension. It may take two or three attempts to get the tension correct. On completion, tighten the tensioner bolts to the specified torque wrench setting.

14 It should be noted that this setting is approximate, and the belt tension should be rechecked by a Ford dealer with the special

tensioner-setting tool at the earliest opportunity.

15 Refit the starter motor (refer to Chapter 5A).

16 Refit the rocker cover (see Section 4) and the upper timing belt cover (see Section 7).

17 Refit the auxiliary drivebelt, adjust its tension as described in Chapter 1, then refit the crankshaft pulley lower cover.

18 On completion, reconnect the battery earth lead.

---

9 Timing belt tensioner and sprockets - removal, inspection and refitting

Tensioner

1 Set the engine at TDC for No 1 piston on compression as described in Section 3, then refer to Section 7 and remove the timing belt upper cover.

2 Loosen off the two bolts securing the timing belt tensioner. Using a large screwdriver, prise the tensioner to one side to release the timing belt tension.

3 Remove the two tensioner bolts, and withdraw the tensioner from behind the timing belt.

4 Check the condition of the tensioner, ensuring that it rotates smoothly on its bearings, with no signs of roughness or excessive free play. Renew the tensioner if in doubt about its condition.

5 To refit the tensioner, first check that the engine is still positioned at TDC for No 1 piston on compression, with both the camshaft and crankshaft sprocket timing marks correctly aligned as described in Section 3.

6 Refit the tensioner, guiding it in position around the timing belt, and secure with the two bolts. Move the tensioner towards the front of the car, to apply an initial tension to the belt. Secure the tensioner in this position.

7 Adjust the timing belt tension as described in Section 8, paragraphs 12 to 14.

8 Refit the timing belt upper cover on completion.

Camshaft sprocket

9 Set the engine at TDC for No 1 piston on compression as described in Section 3, then refer to Section 7 and remove the timing belt upper cover.

10 Loosen off the two bolts securing the timing belt tensioner. Using a large screwdriver, prise the tensioner to one side to release the timing belt tension. Slip the timing belt off the camshaft sprocket.

11 Pass a bar through one of the holes in the camshaft sprocket to prevent the camshaft from rotating, then unscrew and remove the sprocket retaining bolt. Note that this bolt must be renewed when refitting the camshaft sprocket. Remove the sprocket, noting the Woodruff key fitted to the camshaft; if the key is loose, remove it for safekeeping.

12 Check the condition of the sprocket, inspecting carefully for any wear grooves, pitting or scoring around the teeth.

13 Install the Woodruff key, then fit the camshaft sprocket with a **new** retaining bolt. The threads of the bolt should be smeared with thread-locking compound prior to fitting. Tighten the retaining bolt to the specified torque wrench setting **(see illustrations)**.

14 Check that the engine is still positioned at TDC for No 1 piston on compression, with both the camshaft and crankshaft sprocket timing marks correctly aligned as described in Section 3.

15 Slip the timing belt over the camshaft sprocket, then move the tensioner towards the front of the car to apply an initial tension to the belt. Secure the tensioner in this position.

16 Adjust the timing belt tension as described in Section 8, paragraphs 12 to 14.

17 Refit the timing belt upper cover on completion.

Crankshaft sprocket

18 Remove the timing belt as described in Section 8.

19 The crankshaft sprocket can now be withdrawn. If it is a tight fit on the crankshaft, a puller or two large screwdrivers can be used to release its grip. Withdraw the thrustwasher and the Woodruff key from the crankshaft.

20 Check the condition of the sprocket,

9.13a Refit the camshaft sprocket . . .

9.13b . . . and tighten the retaining bolt to the specified torque whilst retaining the sprocket as shown

inspecting carefully for any wear grooves, pitting or scoring around the teeth.

21 Refit the thrustwasher with its curved side facing outwards, followed by the Woodruff key.

22 Lubricate the oil seal and the crankshaft sprocket with engine oil, then position the sprocket on the crankshaft with its thrust face facing outwards.

23 Using the auxiliary drivebelt pulley and its retaining bolt, draw the sprocket fully into position on the crankshaft. Remove the pulley.

24 Refit the timing belt as described in Section 8.

10 Camshaft oil seal - renewal

1 Remove the camshaft sprocket as described in the previous Section.

2 The oil seal is now accessible for removal. Note its direction of fitting, then using a suitable screwdriver or a tool with a hooked end to lever and extract the seal from its housing (but take care not to damage the housing with the tool) **(see illustration)**.

3 Check that the housing is clean before fitting the new seal. Lubricate the lips of the seal and the running faces of the camshaft with clean engine oil. Carefully locate the seal over the camshaft, and drive it squarely into position using a suitable tube or a socket **(see illustration)**. An alternative method of fitting is

10.2 Camshaft front oil seal removal

10.3 Using a socket to tap the camshaft oil seal into place

to draw it squarely into position using the old sprocket bolt and a suitable distance piece.

4 With the seal fully inserted in its housing, refit the camshaft sprocket as described in the previous Section.

11 Camshaft, rocker arms and tappets - removal, inspection and refitting

Removal

1 Disconnect the battery negative (earth) lead (refer to Chapter 5A, Section 1).

2 Refer to the appropriate earlier Sections in this Chapter, and remove the timing belt upper cover and the rocker cover.

3 On carburettor models, refer to Chapter 4A and remove the fuel pump. On models

equipped with a distributor ignition system, refer to Chapter 5B and remove the distributor. On PTE engines, refer to Chapter 4D and remove the camshaft position sensor.

4 On models equipped with distributorless ignition system, detach, unbolt and remove the ignition coil, its support bracket and the interference capacitor from the end of the cylinder head, as described in Chapter 5B.

5 Undo the retaining nuts and remove the guides, rocker arms and spacer plates **(see illustrations)**. Keep the respective components in their original order of fitting by marking them with a piece of numbered tape, or by using a suitable sub-divided box.

6 Withdraw the hydraulic tappets, again keeping them in their original fitted sequence. The tappets should be placed in an oil bath while removed **(see illustrations)**.

7 Unbolt and remove the lower cover beneath

2B

11.5a Undo the rocker arm retaining nut . . .

11.5b . . . withdraw the guide . . .

11.5c . . . followed by the rocker arm . . .

11.5d . . . and spacer plate

11.6a Removing a hydraulic tappet

11.6b Store tappets in clearly-marked container filled with oil to prevent oil loss

11.10a Undo the two retaining bolts (arrowed) . . .

11.10b . . . and lift out the camshaft thrust plate

11.11a Pierce the centre of the blanking plug . . .

11.11b . . . and lever it out of the cylinder head

the crankshaft pulley, then with a spanner engaged on the crankshaft pulley bolt, turn the crankshaft over to set the engine at TDC for No 1 piston on compression (see Section 3).

8 Remove the camshaft sprocket as described in Section 9.

9 Extract the camshaft oil seal as described in Section 10.

10 Before removing the camshaft and its thrust plate, check and take note of the amount of camshaft endfloat, using a dial gauge or feeler gauges. With the camshaft endfloat measured and noted, unscrew the two retaining bolts and then extract the camshaft thrust plate from its pocket at the front end of the cylinder head **(see illustrations)**.

11 On models with a distributorless ignition system, at the rear end of the cylinder head, pierce the camshaft blanking plug with a suitable tool, and then lever it out of its aperture **(see illustrations)**.

12 Withdraw the camshaft from the cylinder head at the rear (distributor/ignition coil) end **(see illustration)**. Take care not to damage the bearings in the cylinder head as the shaft is withdrawn.

Inspection

13 Clean and inspect the various components removed for signs of excessive wear.

14 Examine the camshaft bearing journals and lobes for damage or wear. If evident, a new camshaft will be required.

15 Compare the previously-measured camshaft endfloat with that specified. If the endfloat is outside of the specified tolerance, the thrust plate must be renewed.

16 The camshaft bearing bore diameters in the cylinder head should be measured and checked against the tolerances specified. A suitable measuring gauge will be required for this, but if this is not available, check for excessive movement between the camshaft journals and the bearings. If the bearings are found to be unacceptably worn, a new cylinder head is the only answer, as the bearings are machined directly into the head.

17 It is seldom that the hydraulic tappets are badly worn in the cylinder head bores but again, if the bores are found to be worn beyond an acceptable level, the cylinder head must be renewed.

18 If the contact surfaces of the cam lobes show signs of depression or grooving, they cannot be renovated by grinding, as the hardened surface will be removed and the overall length of the tappet(s) will be reduced. The self-adjustment point of the tappet will be exceeded as a result, so that the valve adjustment will be affected, resulting in noisy operation. Therefore, renewal of the camshaft is the only remedy in this case.

19 Inspect the rocker arm contact surfaces for excessive wear, and renew if necessary **(see illustration)**.

Refitting

20 Refitting the camshaft and its associated components is a reversal of the removal procedure, but note the following special points.

21 Lubricate the camshaft bearings, the camshaft and the thrust plate with clean engine oil prior to fitting them. As the camshaft is inserted, take care not to damage the bearings in the cylinder head. Tighten the camshaft thrust plate retaining bolts to the specified torque. When the thrust plate bolts are tightened, make a final check to ensure that the camshaft endfloat is as specified.

22 A new front oil seal must be fitted after the camshaft has been installed (see previous Section for details). It will also be necessary to insert a new blanking plug into the rear end of the cylinder head (where applicable). Drive it squarely into position so that it is flush with the head **(see illustration)**.

11.12 Withdraw the camshaft from the cylinder head

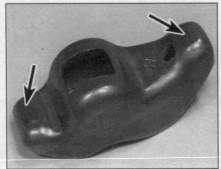

11.19 Inspect the rocker arm contact points indicated for excessive wear

11.22 Driving a new blanking plug into position

23 Refer to the procedure in Section 9 when refitting the camshaft sprocket.

24 Refit and tension the timing belt as described in Section 8.

25 Lubricate the hydraulic tappets with hypoid oil before refitting them into their original locations in the cylinder head.

26 Lubricate and refit the rocker arms and guides in their original sequence, use new nuts and tighten them to the specified torque setting. It is essential, before each rocker arm is installed and its nut tightened, that the respective cam follower is positioned at its lowest point (in contact with the cam base circle). Turn the cam (using the crankshaft pulley bolt) as necessary to achieve this.

27 Refit the rocker cover as described in Section 4.

28 Refit the remaining components with reference to the relevant Sections in this Chapter or elsewhere in the manual.

29 On completion, reconnect the battery negative lead.

12 Cylinder head - removal and refitting

Removal

Note: *The following procedure describes removal and refitting of the cylinder head complete with inlet and exhaust manifolds. If wished, the manifolds may be removed first, as described in the relevant Part of Chapter 4, and the cylinder head then removed on its own.*

1 On fuel-injected engines, depressurise the fuel system as described in Chapter 4B or 4C.

2 Disconnect the battery negative (earth) lead (refer to Chapter 5A, Section 1).

3 Refer to Chapter 1 and drain the cooling system.

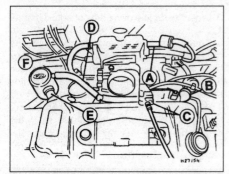

12.8 Vacuum hoses and throttle cable connections on the 1.6 litre EFi fuel injected engine

A Hose to MAP sensor
B Crankcase ventilation breather hose
C Throttle cable and clip
D Oil trap hose and T-piece connector
E Hose to oil trap
F Hose to carbon canister solenoid valve

4 Remove the rocker cover as described in Section 4.

5 Disconnect the accelerator and choke cables as applicable (refer to the relevant Part of Chapter 4).

6 Loosen off the retaining clips and disconnect the upper coolant hose, the expansion tank hose and the heater hose from the thermostat housing. Also disconnect the heater hose from the inlet manifold.

> **HAYNES HiNT** *Whenever you disconnect any vacuum lines, coolant or emissions hoses, wiring connectors and fuel lines, always label them clearly, so that they can be correctly reassembled. Masking tape and/or a touch-up paint applicator work well for marking items. Take instant photos, or sketch the locations of components and brackets.*

7 On CFi models, disconnect the heated coolant hose from the injector unit.

8 On EFi and SEFi models, disconnect the following **(see illustration)**:

a) *The MAP sensor vacuum hose from the inlet manifold upper section (EFi models).*

b) *The carbon canister solenoid valve vacuum hose from the inlet manifold upper section.*

c) *The oil trap vacuum hose at the "T" piece connector.*

d) *The brake servo vacuum hose from the inlet manifold upper section by pressing in the clamp ring and simultaneously pulling the hose free from the connection.*

e) *The coolant hose from the injector intermediate flange and at the thermostat housing.*

9 Disconnect the following fuel supply/return hoses. Plug the hoses and connections, to prevent fuel spillage and the possible ingress of dirt.

a) *On carburettor models, disconnect the fuel supply hose from the pump and the return hose from the carburettor.*

b) *On CFi models, pull free and detach the fuel return hose from the injection unit and the supply hose at the connector.*

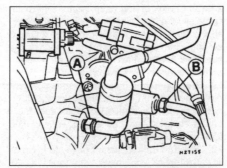

12.10 Vacuum hose to the MAP sensor (A) and the brake servo unit (B) on the 1.4 litre CFi fuel-injected engine

c) *On EFi and SEFi models, detach the fuel supply hose from the fuel rail or at the quick-release coupling (where fitted). Disconnect the return line from the fuel pressure regulator or at the quick-release coupling.*

10 On CFi models, disconnect the brake servo vacuum hose from the inlet manifold, the MAP sensor vacuum hose from the sensor, and the carbon canister connecting hose at the injection unit **(see illustration)**.

11 Noting their connections and routings, disconnect the wiring connectors or multi-plugs from the following items, where applicable:

a) *Temperature gauge sender unit.*
b) *DIS ignition coil.*
c) *Coolant temperature sensor.*
d) *Cooling fan thermostatic switch.*
e) *Carburettor.*
f) *Radio earth lead.*
g) *Road speed sensor.*
h) *Fuel injector wiring loom.*
i) *Intake air temperature sensor.*

12 On CFi models, detach the throttle control motor, throttle position sensor and injector lead multi-plugs **(see illustration)**.

13 On models with a distributorless ignition system, where still attached, disconnect the HT leads from the DIS ignition coil and the spark plugs. On models with a distributor ignition system, remove the distributor as described in Chapter 5B.

14 Position the engine with No 1 piston at TDC on compression as described in Section 3.

15 Loosen off the timing belt tensioner retaining bolts, and move the tensioner to release the tension from the drivebelt. Support the belt, and move it clear of the camshaft sprocket.

16 Chock the rear wheels then jack up the front of the car and support it on axle stands (see *"Jacking and Vehicle Support"*).

17 Unscrew the retaining nuts and detach the exhaust downpipe from the manifold. Remove the gasket; note that a new one must

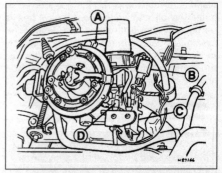

12.12 Wiring connections to be detached on the 1.4 litre CFi fuel injected engine

A Coolant temperature sensor
B Throttle plate control motor
C Throttle position sensor
D Injector

2B

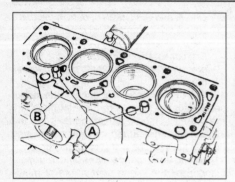

12.21 Cylinder head location dowels (A) and gasket identification teeth (B)

12.27 Fit the cylinder head gasket with the "OBEN/TOP" marking upwards . . .

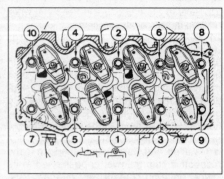

12.28 Cylinder head bolt tightening sequence

be fitted on reassembly. Tie the downpipe up to support it.

18 Before it is released and removed, the cylinder head must first have cooled down to room temperature (about 20ºC).

19 Unscrew the cylinder head retaining bolts progressively in the reverse order to that shown for tightening **(see illustration 12.28)**. The cylinder head bolts must be discarded and new bolts obtained for refitting the cylinder head.

20 Remove the cylinder head complete with its manifolds. If necessary, grip the manifolds and rock it free from the location dowels on the top face of the cylinder block. Do not attempt to tap it sideways or lever between the head and the block top face.

21 Remove the cylinder head gasket. This must always be renewed; it is essential that the correct type is obtained. Save the old gasket, so that the identification marks (teeth) can be used when ordering the new one **(see illustration)**.

Preparation for refitting

22 The mating faces of the cylinder head and cylinder block must be perfectly clean before refitting the head. Use a hard plastic or wood scraper to remove all traces of gasket and carbon; also clean the piston crowns. Take particular care during the cleaning operations, as aluminium alloy is easily damaged. Also, make sure that the carbon is not allowed to enter the oil and water passages - this is particularly important for the lubrication system, as carbon could block the oil supply to the engine's components. Using adhesive tape and paper, seal the water, oil and bolt holes in the cylinder block.

To prevent carbon entering the gap between the pistons and bores, smear a little grease in the gap. After cleaning each piston, use a small brush to remove all traces of grease and carbon from the gap, then wipe away the remainder with a clean rag.

23 Check the mating surfaces of the cylinder block and the cylinder head for nicks, deep scratches and other damage. If slight, they

may be removed carefully with a file, but if excessive, machining may be the only alternative to renewal.

24 If warpage of the cylinder head gasket surface is suspected, use a straight-edge to check it for distortion. Refer to Part D of this Chapter if necessary.

25 Ensure that new cylinder head bolts are used when refitting and clean out the bolt holes in the block. Screwing a bolt into an oil-filled hole can (in extreme cases) cause the block to fracture, due to the hydraulic pressure.

Refitting

26 To prevent the possibility of the valves and pistons coming into contact as the head is fitted, turn the crankshaft over to position No 1 piston approximately 20 mm below its TDC position in the bore.

27 Locate the cylinder head gasket on the top face of the cylinder block, locating it over the dowels. Ensure that the gasket is fitted the correct way up, as indicated by its "OBEN-TOP" marking **(see illustration)**.

28 Lower the cylinder head into position, ensuring that it fits over the locating dowels, then insert the new retaining bolts. Hand-tighten the bolts initially, then tighten them in the order shown in the four stages to the specified torque setting **(see illustration)**. Where possible, use an angular torque setting gauge attachment tool for accurate tightening of stages three and four. Alternatively, after the first two stages, mark the bolt heads with a dab of quick drying paint, so that the paint spots all face the same direction. Now tighten all the bolts in the sequence to the Stage 3 setting, by tightening them through the specified angle. Finally, angle-tighten all the bolts through the Stage 4 angle.

29 The camshaft sprocket should be positioned so that its TDC index mark pointer is in alignment with the TDC index spot mark on the front end face of the cylinder head **(see illustration 3.6b)**.

30 Now turn the crankshaft pulley to bring its TDC notch in alignment with the TDC (0) indicator on the front face of the timing belt cover, taking the shortest route (not *vice-versa*) **(see illustration 3.6a)**.

31 Refit the timing belt over the camshaft sprocket, and then tension the belt as described in Section 8.

32 The remainder of the refitting procedure is a reversal of the removal process. Tighten all fastenings to their specified torque setting (where given). Refer to the appropriate Parts of Chapter 4 for details on reconnecting the fuel and exhaust system components, and to Chapter 5B for details on reconnecting the ignition system components. Ensure that all coolant, fuel, vacuum and electrical connections are securely made.

33 On completion, refill the cooling system and top-up the engine oil (see Chapter 1 and *"Weekly Checks"*). When the engine is restarted, check for any sign of fuel, oil and/or coolant leakages from the various cylinder head joints.

13 Sump - removal and refitting

Removal

1 Disconnect the battery negative (earth) lead (refer to Chapter 5A, Section 1).

2 Drain the engine oil as described in Chapter 1.

3 Chock the rear wheels then jack up the front of the car and support it on axle stands (see *"Jacking and Vehicle Support"*). Remove the auxiliary drivebelt lower cover from inside the right-hand wheel arch.

4 Where fitted, pull free the oxygen sensor lead multi-plug, and disconnect it. If the engine has been recently run, take particular care against burning when working in the area of the catalytic converter.

5 Undo the retaining nuts, and detach the exhaust downpipe from the manifold. The flange gasket must be renewed when reconnecting. Where applicable, also detach the downpipe at the rear of the catalytic converter, and release it from the front mounting.

6 On XR2i models, remove the front suspension crossmember as described in Chapter 10. On all models, undo the nut and

13.7 Removing the clutch cover plate

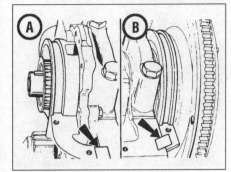

13.11 Sealing compound application points prior to refitting the sump

A *Crankcase-to-oil pump housing*
B *Crankcase-to-rear oil seal carrier*

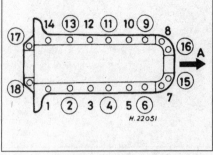

13.14 Sump bolt tightening sequence

A *Crankshaft pulley end of engine*
Circled numbers indicate locations of studs for correct sump alignment (see text)

bolt(s) securing the gearchange mechanism stabiliser bar/exhaust forward mounting bracket (where fitted) and ease it out of the way.

7 Remove the starter motor as described in Chapter 5A, then undo the retaining bolts, and remove the clutch cover plate from the front face of the bellhousing **(see illustration)**.

8 Progressively unscrew the sump retaining bolts and remove them. Support and lower the sump pan, taking care not to spill any oil remaining in it as it is removed. If the sump is stuck to the base of the crankcase, prise it free using a screwdriver, but take care not to damage the sump flange face. If it is really stuck in position, check first that all of the bolts are removed, then cut around the sump gasket with a sharp knife to help in freeing the joint.

9 After the sump is removed, further oil will almost certainly continue to drip down from within the crankcase, some old newspapers positioned underneath will soak up the spillage whilst the sump is removed.

10 Clean the sump of old oil and sludge, using paraffin or a suitable engine cleaner solution. Clean any traces of old gasket and sealer from the mating faces of the sump and the crankcase.

Refitting

11 Smear a suitable sealing compound onto the junctions of the crankcase-to-oil seal

carrier at the rear and the crankcase-to-oil pump housing at the front on each side **(see illustration)**.

12 Insert a new rubber seal in the groove in the rear oil seal carrier and the oil pump case. As an aid to correct sump alignment when refitting it, screw ten M6 studs into the cylinder block, in the positions circled in illustration 13.14.

13 Fit a new gasket over the studs. Fit the sump into position, ensuring that the raised spacers sit in the gasket. Insert the bolts into the available holes, and finger-tighten them only at this stage. Now remove the studs and fit the remaining bolts, again finger-tight.

14 Tighten the sump bolts in a progressive, numerical sequence to the specified torque wrench setting **(see illustration)**.

15 Fit the sump drain plug with a new sealing washer, and tighten it to the specified torque wrench setting.

16 Refit the clutch cover plate, the auxiliary drivebelt lower cover, the front suspension crossmember, the gearchange mechanism stabiliser bar/exhaust forward mounting bracket, and the starter motor with reference to the relevant Sections and Chapters of this manual as applicable.

17 Reconnect the exhaust downpipe as described in Chapter 4E.

18 On completion, lower the vehicle, and fill the engine with oil as described in Chapter 1. Reconnect the battery negative lead.

14 Oil pump - removal and refitting

Removal

1 Disconnect the battery negative (earth) lead (refer to Chapter 5A, Section 1).

2 Remove the auxiliary drivebelt (see Chapter 1).

3 Remove the crankshaft pulley (Section 6), the timing belt covers (Section 7), the timing belt, crankshaft sprocket and thrustwasher (Sections 8 and 9), and the sump (Section 13).

4 Unscrew the retaining nut/bolts and remove the oil pick-up pipe **(see illustration)**.

5 Unbolt and withdraw the oil pump from the front face of the engine. Clean the oil pump for inspection. Refer to Section 15 for the inspection procedures. The oil seal in the oil pump housing should always be renewed (Section 16).

Refitting

6 Before refitting the oil pump and the associated fittings, clean off the respective mating faces. A new oil pump gasket must be obtained, as well as the seals and gaskets for the other associated components to be refitted.

7 When refitting the oil pump, precautionary measures must be taken to avoid the possibility of damaging the new oil seal as it is engaged over the shoulder and onto its journal on the crankshaft. Extract the Woodruff key from the groove in the crankshaft, then cut a thin plastic guide which will furl over and protrude beyond the shoulder of the seal journal on the crankshaft **(see illustration 14.9b)**. This will allow the seal to ride over the step, and avoid damaging the seal lip as it is pushed into position on the crankshaft.

8 If a new oil pump is being fitted or the old pump is to be re-used after cleaning and inspection, first prime the pump by squirting clean engine oil into it, and simultaneously rotating the drivegear a few times **(see illustration)**.

2B

14.4 Removing the oil inlet pipe

14.8 Prime the oil pump prior to fitting

14.9a Refit the oil pump

14.9b With the oil pump refitted, remove the protective guide (arrowed)

9 Align the pump gear flats with those on the crankshaft, then fit the oil pump. Check that the sump mating faces of the oil pump and the base of the crankcase are flush each side, then tighten the retaining bolts to the specified torque setting. Remove the protective guide **(see illustrations)**.

10 Refit the oil pick-up tube to the oil pump, using a new gasket and tighten to the specified torque.

11 Slide the thrustwasher onto the front end of the crankshaft, then insert the Woodruff key into position in the groove in the crankshaft. The key must be located with its flat edge parallel with the line of the crankshaft, to ensure that the crankshaft sprocket slides fully into position as it is being refitted.

12 Refit the sump, crankshaft sprocket, the timing belt, timing belt cover and drivebelt pulley (as described in the appropriate earlier Sections of this Chapter). Refit and adjust the drivebelt as described in Chapter 1.

13 On completion, lower the vehicle and reconnect the battery negative terminal.

---

15 Oil pump - dismantling, inspection and reassembly

Dismantling

1 The oil pump fitted is a low-friction rotor-type, driven from the front end of the crankshaft. Where a high-mileage engine is

being reconditioned, it is recommended that a new oil pump is fitted.

2 To inspect the rotor assembly, first remove the pump from the engine (Section 14), then undo the retaining screws and remove the cover plate **(see illustration)**. Remove the O-ring seal.

Inspection

3 Clean the rotors and the inside of the pump housing, then visually inspect the various components for signs of excessive wear and scoring. Check the pump components for wear using feeler gauges in the same manner as that described in Part A of this Chapter, Section 13. Refer to the Specifications at the start of this Chapter for specific details.

Reassembly

4 When reassembling the pump, ensure that the inner (driving) and outer (driven) rotors are located with the corresponding indented matchmarks facing the same way **(see illustration)**.

---

16 Crankshaft oil seals - renewal

Front oil seal

1 Disconnect the battery negative (earth) lead (refer to Chapter 5A, Section 1).

2 Chock the rear wheels then jack up the

front of the car and support it on axle stands (see *"Jacking and Vehicle Support"*).

3 Remove the auxiliary drivebelt as described in Chapter 1.

4 Remove the crankshaft pulley (Section 6), the timing belt covers (Section 7), the timing belt (Section 8) and crankshaft sprocket, Woodruff key and thrustwasher (Section 9).

5 The oil seal is now accessible for removal from the front face of the oil pump housing **(see illustration)**. To withdraw the seal, a hooked tool will be required; if available, use Ford special tool No 21-096. Take care not to damage the oil pump housing during removal. As it is removed, note the fitted orientation of the seal in its housing.

6 Clean the oil pump housing and the crankshaft stub, then lubricate the lips of the new seal and the crankshaft front stub with clean engine oil.

7 The oil seal should be drawn into position using the Ford special tool No 21-093A. Failing this, use a tube of suitable diameter, with the crankshaft pulley bolt and washers. Do not hammer the seal into position. To protect the seal lips as it is fitted onto the crankshaft, cut a thin sheet of plastic to suit and furl it round the front of the crankshaft, over the journal shoulder.

8 When the seal is fully fitted, remove the special tool (or fabricated tool) and withdraw the plastic protector. Check that the crankshaft is still at the TDC position and refit the Woodruff key, thrustwasher and sprocket. Refit and tension the timing belt, then refit the timing belt cover and crankshaft pulley as described in the appropriate Sections earlier in this Chapter.

9 Refit and adjust the auxiliary drivebelt as described in Chapter 1.

10 On completion, lower the vehicle and reconnect the battery.

Rear oil seal

11 With the engine or transmission removed from the vehicle for access, remove the clutch as described in Chapter 6.

12 Remove the flywheel/driveplate as described in Section 18.

13 If available, use Ford tool No 21-151 or a suitable clawed tool to extract the seal from

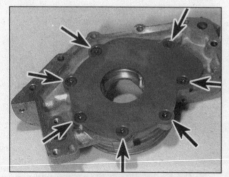

15.2 Oil pump cover plate retaining screws (arrowed)

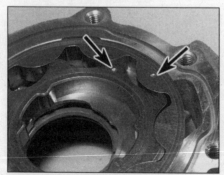

15.4 Inner and outer rotor matchmarks (arrowed)

16.5 Crankshaft front oil seal - seen from below (arrowed)

its housing. If the seal housing is removed from the rear face of the engine, the seal can be removed as described in paragraph 18. As it is removed, note the direction of fitting, and take care not to damage the seal housing as the seal is extracted.

14 Clean the seal housing, the crankshaft rear flange face, and the flywheel/driveplate mating surfaces.

15 One of two possible methods may be used to insert the new oil seal, depending on the tools available.

16 If Ford special service tool No 21-095 is available, lubricate the seal lips of the seal and its running face on the crankshaft with clean engine oil. Position the seal (correctly orientated) into the special tool, then draw the seal into the housing using two flywheel/driveplate securing bolts so that the seal is against the stop.

17 If the correct Ford service tool is not available, it will be necessary to remove the oil seal carrier housing. To do this, first remove the sump as described in Section 13, then unscrew the seal housing retaining bolts and remove the housing from the rear face of the crankcase.

18 Drive the old seal from the housing by carefully tapping it from its aperture using a suitable punch as shown **(see illustration)**. As it is removed, note the direction of fitting, and take care not to damage the seal housing as the seal is extracted.

19 New gaskets will be required for the seal housing and sump during reassembly. Clean the mating faces of the seal housing, the crankcase and sump. Insert the new seal squarely into its housing. To avoid damaging the seal or the housing, place a flat piece of wood across the face of the seal, and carefully tap or draw the seal into place. Do not allow the seal to tilt in the housing as it is being fitted.

20 Lubricate the running surface on the crankshaft and the oil seal lip with clean engine oil. Locate a new gasket onto the rear face of the crankcase, and refit the oil seal housing and seal. To avoid damaging the lips of the seal as it is passed over the end of the crankshaft, cut a thin sheet of plastic to suit and furl it round the rear flange of the crankshaft so that it protrudes, and press the seal over it. With the seal in position, withdraw the plastic protector. Centralise the seal on the shaft, check that the housing-to-sump flange faces are flush to the sump face on the base of the crankcase, then insert and tighten the housing retaining bolts to the specified torque.

21 Refit the sump with reference to Section 13.

22 Refit the flywheel/driveplate as described in Section 18.

23 Refit the clutch as described in Chapter 6.

24 Refit the engine or transmission, as applicable.

17 Engine/transmission mountings - renewal

1 The removal and refitting method for the transmission bearer and mountings is as described for HCS engines in Part A, Section 15. On XR2i models, it will be necessary to remove the front suspension crossmember first (refer to Chapter 10).

2 The engine right-hand mounting is significantly different to that fitted to HCS engines, in that it is a two-piece bracket, and its removal and refitting procedure is detailed below.

3 First of all support the engine/transmission assembly as described in Part A, Section 15, then unscrew and remove the two nuts securing the two halves of the mounting bracket assembly.

4 Unscrew and remove the three bolts securing the engine bracket section to the cylinder block **(see illustration)**.

5 Unscrew and remove the mounting retaining nut and washer from their location near the suspension strut.

6 Unscrew and remove the mounting side bolt from under the right-hand wheel arch.

7 Refitting is a reversal of the removal procedure. Make sure when refitting engine/transmission mountings, that any washers and plates removed during the dismantling process are refitted in their original sequence. Do not fully tighten any mounting bolts until they are all located. As the mounting bolts and nuts are tightened, check that the mounting rubbers do not twist.

2B

16.18 Rear oil seal removal

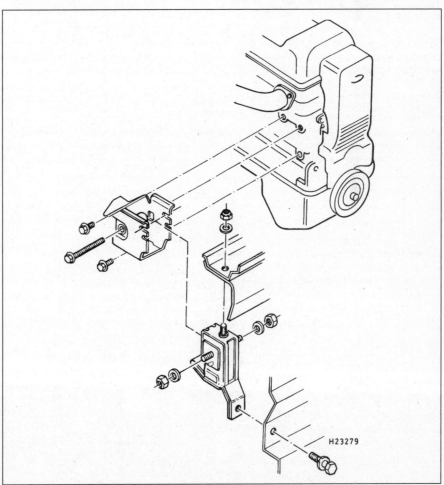

17.4 Exploded view of the right-hand engine mounting

18 Flywheel/driveplate - removal, inspection and refitting

Removal

1 Access to the flywheel (manual transmission) or driveplate (automatic transmission) is gained by first removing the transmission (Chapter 7A or B). On manual transmission models, remove the clutch (Chapter 6).

2 Unscrew and remove the six flywheel/driveplate retaining bolts, and carefully withdraw the flywheel/driveplate from the rear face of the crankshaft. Take care not to drop the flywheel, as it is heavy. Note that the retaining bolts must be renewed when refitting.

Inspection

3 The inspection procedures for the flywheel/driveplate are the same as those described for the HCS engine in Part A of this Chapter, but note that the grinding procedures do not apply to automatic transmission models (the driveplate cannot be reground).

Refitting

4 Check that the mating faces of the flywheel/driveplate and crankshaft are clean before refitting.

5 Smear the new retaining bolt threads with thread-locking compound. Fit the flywheel/driveplate into position on the rear end face of the crankshaft. Check that all of the bolt holes in the flywheel/driveplate are in exact alignment with the corresponding bolt holes in the crankshaft, then insert the **new** bolts and tighten them in a progressive sequence to the specified torque wrench setting.

6 Refit the clutch (manual transmission models) as described in Chapter 6.

7 Refit the transmission (according to type) as described in Chapter 7A or B.

Chapter 2 Part C:
Zetec engine in-car repair procedures

Contents

Auxiliary drivebelt check and renewal . . . . See Chapter 1
Camshaft oil seals - renewal 10
Camshafts and hydraulic tappets - removal, inspection
    and refitting 11
Compression test - description and interpretation 2
Crankshaft oil seals - renewal 15
Crankshaft pulley - removal and refitting 6
Cylinder head - removal and refitting 12
Cylinder head cover - removal and refitting 4
Engine oil and filter renewal . . . . See Chapter 1
Engine oil level check . . . . "Weekly Checks"

Engine/transmission mountings - inspection and renewal 16
Flywheel/driveplate - removal, inspection and refitting 17
General information 1
Oil pump - removal, inspection and refitting 14
Sump - removal and refitting 13
Timing belt - removal, refitting and adjustment 8
Timing belt covers - removal and refitting 7
Timing belt tensioner and sprockets - removal, inspection
    and refitting 9
Top Dead Centre (TDC) for No 1 piston - locating 3
Valve clearances - general information 5

Degrees of difficulty

| Easy, suitable for novice with little experience | | Fairly easy, suitable for beginner with some experience | 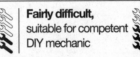 | Fairly difficult, suitable for competent DIY mechanic | | Difficult, suitable for experienced DIY mechanic | | Very difficult, suitable for expert DIY or professional | |

Specifications

General

Engine type	Four-cylinder, in-line, double overhead camshafts
Engine code:	
1.6 litre models	L1G
1.8 litre models	RDB or RQC
Capacity:	
1.6 litre models	1597 cc
1.8 litre models	1796 cc
Bore:	
1.6 litre models	76.0 mm
1.8 litre models	80.6 mm
Stroke - all models	88.0 mm
Compression ratio:	
1.6 litre models	10.3:1
1.8 litre models	10.0:1
Firing order	1-3-4-2 (No 1 cylinder at timing belt end)
Direction of crankshaft rotation	Clockwise (seen from right-hand side of vehicle)

Cylinder head

Hydraulic tappet bore inside diameter	28.395 to 28.425 mm

Camshafts and hydraulic tappets

Camshaft bearing journal diameter	25.960 to 25.980 mm
Camshaft bearing journal-to-cylinder head running clearance	0.020 to 0.070 mm
Camshaft endfloat	0.080 to 0.220 mm

Lubrication

Engine oil type/specification	See "Lubricants, fluids and tyre pressures"
Engine oil capacity	See "Lubricants, fluids and tyre pressures"
Oil pressure:	
Idling	1.3 to 2.5 bar
At 4000 rpm	3.7 to 5.5 bars
Oil pump clearances	Not specified

2C

Torque wrench settings

	Nm	lbf ft
Cylinder head cover bolts:		
Stage 1	2	1.5
Stage 2	7	5
Camshaft sprocket bolts	68	50
Camshaft bearing cap bolts:		
Stage 1	9	7
Stage 2	19	14
Cylinder head bolts:		
Stage 1	24	18
Stage 2	45	33
Stage 3	Angle-tighten a further 105°	
Timing belt cover fasteners:		
Upper-to-middle (outer) cover bolts	4	3
Cover-to-cylinder head or block bolts	7	5
Cover studs-to-cylinder head or block	9	7
Timing belt tensioner bolt	38	28
Timing belt tensioner backplate locating peg	9	7
Timing belt tensioner spring retaining pin	9	7
Timing belt guide pulley bolts	38	28
Water pump pulley bolts	9	7
Auxiliary drivebelt idler pulley	47	35
Front engine lifting eye bolt	16	12
Exhaust manifold heat shield bolts:		
Shield-to-cylinder head	7	5
Shield/dipstick tube	9	7
Shield/coolant pipe-to-manifold	23	17
Crankshaft pulley bolt	115	85
Oil pump-to-cylinder block bolts	10	7
Oil pick-up pipe-to-pump screws	10	7
Oil baffle/pump pick-up pipe nuts	19	14
Oil filter adapter-to-pump	22	16
Oil pressure warning light switch	27	20
Sump bolts	20	15
Coolant pipe-to-sump bolt	9	7
Flywheel/driveplate bolts	110	81
Crankshaft left-hand oil seal carrier bolts	22	16
Engine mountings:		
Engine front right-hand mounting:		
Alternator mounting bracket-to-cylinder block bolts	41 to 58	30 to 43
Mounting bracket-to-alternator mounting bracket bolts	Not available	Not available
Mounting through-bolt	Not available	Not available
Outer bracket-to-mounting bolts	58 to 79	43 to 58
Inner bracket-to-body bolts	58 to 79	43 to 58
Outer bracket-to-body bolts	58 to 79	43 to 58
Engine rear right-hand mounting:		
Bracket-to-cylinder block bolts	76 to 104	56 to 77
Mounting-to-(cylinder block) bracket bolts	71 to 98	52 to 72
Mounting-to-body bolt and nut	102 to 138	75 to 102
Transmission mounting fasteners	Refer to Chapter 7A or 7B	

Note: *Refer to Part D of this Chapter for remaining torque wrench settings.*

1 General information

How to use this Chapter

This Part of Chapter 2 is devoted to repair procedures possible while the engine is still installed in the vehicle, and includes only the Specifications relevant to those procedures. Similar information concerning the 1.3 litre HCS engines, and the 1.4 and 1.6 litre CVH and PTE engines, will be found in Parts A and B of this Chapter respectively. Since these procedures are based on the assumption that the engine is installed in the vehicle, if the engine has been removed from the vehicle and mounted on a stand, some of the preliminary dismantling steps outlined will not apply.

Information concerning engine/transmission removal and refitting, and engine overhaul, can be found in Part D of this Chapter, which also includes the Specifications relevant to those procedures.

Engine description

The Zetec engine, (formerly Zeta), is of sixteen-valve, double overhead camshaft (DOHC), four-cylinder, in-line type, mounted transversely at the front of the vehicle, with the transmission on its left-hand end.

Apart from the plastic timing belt covers and the cast-iron cylinder block/crankcase, all major engine castings are of aluminium alloy.

The crankshaft runs in five main bearings, the centre main bearing's upper half incorporating thrustwashers to control crankshaft endfloat. The connecting rods rotate on horizontally-split bearing shells at their big-ends. The pistons are attached to the connecting rods by gudgeon pins which are an interference fit in the connecting rod small-end eyes. The aluminium alloy pistons are fitted with three piston rings: two compression rings and an oil control ring. After manufacture, the cylinder bores and piston skirts are measured and classified into three grades, which must be carefully matched together, to ensure the correct piston/cylinder clearance; no oversizes are available to permit reboring.

The inlet and exhaust valves are each closed by coil springs; they operate in guides which are shrink-fitted into the cylinder head, as are the valve seat inserts.

Both camshafts are driven by the same toothed timing belt, each operating eight valves via self-adjusting hydraulic tappets, thus eliminating the need for routine checking and adjustment of the valve clearances. Each camshaft rotates in five bearings that are line-bored directly in the cylinder head and the (bolted-on) bearing caps; this means that the bearing caps are not available separately from the cylinder head, and must not be interchanged with caps from another engine.

The water pump is bolted to the right-hand end of the cylinder block, inboard of the timing belt, and is driven with the power steering pump and alternator by a flat "polyvee"-type auxiliary drivebelt from the crankshaft pulley.

When working on this engine, note that Torx-type (both male and female heads) and hexagon socket (Allen head) fasteners are widely used; a good selection of bits, with the necessary adapters, will be required, so that these can be unscrewed without damage and, on reassembly, tightened to the torque wrench settings specified.

Lubrication is by means of an eccentric-rotor trochoidal pump, which is mounted on the crankshaft right-hand end, and draws oil through a strainer located in the sump. The pump forces oil through an externally-mounted full-flow cartridge-type filter - on some versions of the engine, an oil cooler is fitted to the oil filter mounting, so that clean oil entering the engine's galleries is cooled by the main engine cooling system.

Repair operations possible with the engine in the car

The following work can be carried out with the engine in the car:
a) Compression pressure - testing.
b) Cylinder head cover - removal and refitting.
c) Timing belt covers - removal and refitting.
d) Timing belt - renewal.
e) Timing belt tensioner and sprockets - removal and refitting.
f) Camshaft oil seals - renewal.
g) Camshafts and hydraulic tappets - removal and refitting.
h) Cylinder head - removal and refitting.
i) Cylinder head and pistons - decarbonising.
j) Sump - removal and refitting.
k) Crankshaft oil seals - renewal.
l) Oil pump - removal and refitting.

m) Flywheel/driveplate - removal and refitting.
n) Engine/transmission mountings - removal and refitting.
Note: It is possible to remove the pistons and connecting rods (after removing the cylinder head and sump) without removing the engine. However, this is not recommended. Work of this nature is more easily and thoroughly completed with the engine on the bench, as described in Chapter 2D.

2 Compression test - description and interpretation

Refer to Section 2 in Part A of this Chapter.

3 Top Dead Centre (TDC) for No 1 piston - locating

1 Top dead centre (TDC) is the highest point of the cylinder that each piston reaches as the crankshaft turns. Each piston reaches its TDC position at the end of its compression stroke, and then again at the end of its exhaust stroke. For the purpose of engine timing, TDC on the compression stroke for No 1 piston is used. No 1 cylinder is at the timing belt end of the engine. Proceed as follows.
2 Disconnect the battery negative (earth) lead (refer to Chapter 5A, Section 1).
3 Chock the rear wheels then jack up the front of the car and support it on axle stands (see "Jacking and Vehicle Support"). Remove the right-hand roadwheel.
4 Remove the auxiliary drivebelt cover (see Chapter 1) to expose the crankshaft pulley and timing marks.
5 Fit a spanner onto the crankshaft pulley bolt, and turn the crankshaft in its normal direction of rotation (clockwise, viewed from the pulley end).

> **HAYNES HiNT** *Turning the engine will be easier if the spark plugs are removed first - see Chapter 1.*

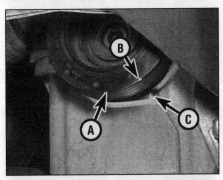

3.6a Do not use crankshaft pulley's first pair of notches "A" - align second pair of notches "B" with raised rib on sump "C" . . .

6 Note the two pairs of notches in the inner and outer rims of the crankshaft pulley. In the normal direction of crankshaft rotation the first pair of notches are irrelevant to the vehicles covered in this manual, while the second pair indicate TDC when aligned with the rear edge of the raised mark on the sump. Rotate the crankshaft clockwise until the second pair of notches align with the edge of the sump mark; use a straight edge extended out from the sump if greater accuracy is required **(see illustrations)**.
7 Nos 1 and 4 cylinders are now at TDC, one of them on the compression stroke. Remove the oil filler cap; if No 4 cylinder exhaust cam lobe is pointing to the rear of the vehicle and slightly downwards, it is No 1 cylinder that is correctly positioned. If the lobe is pointing horizontally forwards, rotate the crankshaft one full turn (360°) clockwise until the pulley notches align again, and the lobe is pointing to the rear and slightly down. No 1 cylinder will then be at TDC on the compression stroke.
8 Once No 1 cylinder has been positioned at TDC on the compression stroke, TDC for any of the other cylinders can then be located by rotating the crankshaft clockwise 180° at a time and following the firing order (see Specifications).
9 With the engine set at No 1 piston on TDC compression, refit the drivebelt cover and the roadwheel, then lower the vehicle and refit the spark plugs.

4 Cylinder head cover - removal and refitting

Removal

1 Disconnect the battery negative (earth) lead (refer to Chapter 5A, Section 1).
2 Remove the air inlet components as necessary for access as described in the Chapter 4D.
3 Disconnect the accelerator cable from the throttle linkage as described in Chapter 4D.
4 On models equipped with power steering, release the high pressure fluid pipe from the

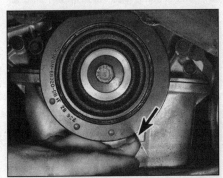

3.6b . . . use a straight edge extended out from the sump (arrowed) if greater accuracy is required

2C

4.6 Disconnecting crankcase breather hose from cylinder head cover union

4.8 Removing cylinder head cover

4.10 Ensure gasket is located correctly in cover groove

clamp brackets and disconnect the pipe joint union over the top of the cylinder head cover. Place absorbent rags beneath the union as it is disconnected to soak up escaping fluid and plug the open unions to prevent dirt entry and further fluid loss. Move the pipe(s) clear just sufficiently to allow removal of the cylinder head cover.

5 Remove the timing belt upper cover (see Section 7).

6 Disconnect the crankcase breather hose from the cylinder head cover union **(see illustration)**.

7 Unplug the HT leads from the spark plugs and withdraw them, unclipping the leads from the cover.

8 Working progressively, unscrew the cylinder head cover retaining bolts, noting the spacer sleeve and rubber seal at each, then withdraw the cover **(see illustration)**.

9 Discard the cover gasket; this *must* be renewed whenever it is disturbed. Check that the sealing faces are undamaged, and that the rubber seal at each retaining bolt is serviceable; renew any worn or damaged seals.

Refitting

10 On refitting, clean the cover and cylinder head gasket faces carefully, then fit a new gasket to the cover, ensuring that it locates correctly in the cover grooves **(see illustration)**.

11 Refit the cover to the cylinder head, then insert the rubber seal and spacer sleeve at each bolt location **(see illustration)**. Start all

bolts finger-tight, ensuring that the gasket remains seated in its groove.

12 Working in a diagonal sequence from the centre outwards, and in two stages (see Specifications), tighten the cover bolts to the specified torque wrench setting.

13 Refit the HT leads, clipping them into place so that they are correctly routed; each is numbered, and can also be identified by the numbering on its respective coil terminal.

14 Reconnect the crankcase breather hose, and refit the timing belt upper cover. Reconnect and adjust the accelerator cable, then refit the air inlet components (see Chapter 4B).

15 On models with power steering, reconnect the high pressure fluid pipe then bleed the system as described in Chapter 10.

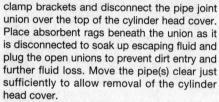

5 Valve clearances - general information

Refer to Section 5 in Part B of this Chapter.

6 Crankshaft pulley - removal and refitting

Removal

1 Remove the auxiliary drivebelt - either remove the drivebelt completely, or just

secure it clear of the crankshaft pulley, depending on the work to be carried out (see Chapter 1).

2 If necessary, rotate the crankshaft until the timing marks align (see Section 3).

3 The crankshaft must now be locked to prevent its rotation while the pulley bolt is unscrewed. To do this, remove the starter motor (Chapter 5A) and lock the starter ring gear teeth using a suitable screwdriver.

4 It should now just be possible to reach between the crankshaft pulley and the body side member to undo and remove the pulley bolt and withdraw the pulley. However, if additional working clearance is needed, proceed as follows.

5 If not already done, chock the rear wheels then jack up the front of the car and support it on axle stands (see *"Jacking and Vehicle Support"*). Remove the front right-hand roadwheel.

6 Support the weight of the engine/transmission using a trolley jack, with a wooden spacer to prevent damage to the sump.

7 From above, unscrew the three bolts securing the engine's front right-hand (Y-shaped) mounting bracket to the alternator mounting bracket. Unfasten the engine's rear right-hand mounting from the body by unscrewing first the single nut (and washer) immediately to the rear of the timing belt cover, then the bolt in the wheel arch

8 With the engine's right-hand mountings unfastened from the body, lower the engine/transmission on the jack until a socket spanner can be fitted to the crankshaft pulley bolt.

9 With the starter ring gear teeth locked, unscrew the crankshaft pulley bolt and withdraw the pulley **(see illustration)**.

Refitting

10 Refitting is the reverse of the removal procedure; ensure that the pulley's keyway is aligned with the crankshaft's locating key, and tighten the pulley bolt to the specified torque wrench setting. If the engine mountings were disturbed, use the jack to adjust the height of the engine/transmission until the bolts (and nut, with washer) can be refitted and screwed

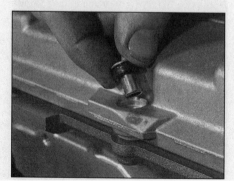

4.11 Ensure rubber seal is fitted to each cover bolt spacer, as shown

6.9 Unscrew pulley bolt to release crankshaft pulley

home by hand, then tighten them securely, to the specified torque wrench settings, where given.

11 Refit the auxiliary drivebelt as described in Chapter 1 on completion.

7 Timing belt covers - removal and refitting

Upper cover

1 Unscrew the cover's two mounting bolts and withdraw it (**see illustration**).
2 Refitting is the reverse of the removal procedure; ensure that the cover edges engage correctly with each other, and note the torque wrench setting specified for the bolts.

Middle cover

3 Slacken the water pump pulley bolts.
4 Remove the timing belt upper cover.
5 Remove the auxiliary drivebelt (see Chapter 1).
6 Unbolt and remove the water pump pulley.
7 Unscrew the middle cover fasteners (one bolt at the front, one at the lower rear, one stud at the top rear) and withdraw the cover.
8 Refitting is the reverse of the removal procedure. Ensure that the cover edges engage correctly with each other, and note the torque wrench settings specified for the various fasteners.

Lower cover

9 Slacken the water pump pulley bolts.
10 Remove the crankshaft pulley (see Section 6) then unbolt and remove the water pump pulley.
11 Unscrew the three cover securing bolts, and withdraw it (**see illustration**).
12 Refitting is the reverse of the removal procedure; ensure the cover edges engage correctly with each other, and note the torque wrench settings specified for the various fasteners.

Inner shield

13 Remove the timing belt, its tensioner components and the camshaft sprockets (see Sections 8 and 9).

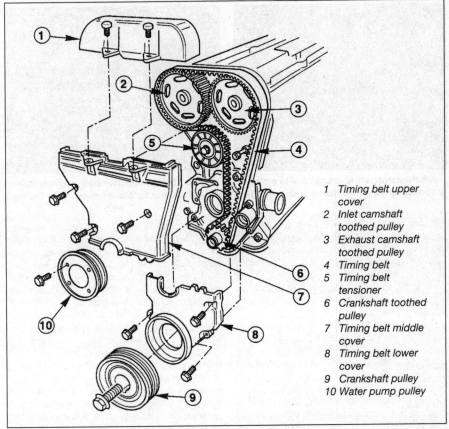

1 Timing belt upper cover
2 Inlet camshaft toothed pulley
3 Exhaust camshaft toothed pulley
4 Timing belt
5 Timing belt tensioner
6 Crankshaft toothed pulley
7 Timing belt middle cover
8 Timing belt lower cover
9 Crankshaft pulley
10 Water pump pulley

7.1 Timing belt and cover details

2C

14 The shield is secured to the cylinder head by two bolts at the top, and by two studs lower down; unscrew these and withdraw the shield (**see illustration**).
15 Refitting is the reverse of the removal procedure; note the torque wrench settings specified for the various fasteners.

8 Timing belt - removal, refitting and adjustment

Note: *To carry out this operation, a new timing belt (where applicable), a new cylinder head cover gasket, and some special tools (see text)*

will be required. If the timing belt is being removed for the first time since the vehicle left the factory, a tensioner spring and retaining pin must be obtained for fitting on reassembly.

Removal

1 Disconnect the battery negative (earth) lead (refer to Chapter 5A, Section 1).
2 Slacken the water pump pulley bolts.
3 Remove the cylinder head cover (see Section 4).
4 Remove the spark plugs, covering their holes with clean rag, to prevent dirt or other foreign bodies from dropping in (see Chapter 1).
5 Remove the auxiliary drivebelt (see Chapter 1).
6 Position the engine with No 1 piston at TDC on compression as described in Section 3.
7 Unbolt and remove the water pump pulley and, where fitted, the auxiliary drivebelt idler pulley.
8 Obtain Ford service tool 21-162, or fabricate a substitute alternative from a strip of metal 5 mm thick (while the strip's thickness *is* critical, its length and width are not, but should be approximately 180 to 230 mm by 20 to 30 mm). Check that Nos 1 and 4 cylinders are at TDC - No 1 on the compression stroke - by resting this tool on the cylinder head mating surface, and sliding

7.11 Removing timing belt lower cover - bolt locations arrowed

7.14 Timing belt inner shield fasteners (arrowed)

8.8 Fit camshaft-aligning tool to ensure engine is locked with Nos 1 and 4 cylinders at TDC

8.12 Slacken tensioner bolt, and use Allen key to rotate tensioner away from timing belt

it into the slot in the left-hand end of both camshafts **(see illustration)**. The tool should slip snugly into both slots while resting on the cylinder head mating surface; if one camshaft is only slightly out of alignment, it is permissible to use an open-ended spanner to rotate the camshaft gently and carefully until the tool will fit.

9 If both camshaft slots (they are machined significantly off-centre) are below the level of the cylinder head mating surface, rotate the crankshaft through one full turn clockwise and fit the tool again; it should now fit as described in the previous paragraph.

10 With the camshaft aligning tool remaining in place, remove the crankshaft pulley. *Do not use the locked camshafts to prevent the crankshaft from rotating - use only the locking method described in Section 6.*

11 Remove the timing belt lower and middle covers (see Section 7).

12 With the camshaft-aligning tool still in place, slacken the tensioner bolt, and use an Allen key inserted into its centre to rotate the tensioner clockwise as far as possible away from the belt; retighten the bolt to secure the tensioner clear of the timing belt **(see illustration)**.

13 If the timing belt is to be re-used, use white paint or similar to mark its direction of rotation, and note from the manufacturer's markings which way round it is fitted. Withdraw the belt. *Do not rotate the crankshaft until the timing belt is refitted.*

14 If the belt is being removed for reasons other than routine renewal, check it carefully for any signs of uneven wear, splitting, cracks (especially at the roots of the belt teeth) or contamination with oil or coolant. Renew the belt if there is the slightest doubt about its condition. As a safety measure, the belt must be renewed as a matter of course at the intervals given in Chapter 1; if its history is unknown, the belt should be renewed irrespective of its apparent condition whenever the engine is overhauled. Similarly, check the tensioner spring (where fitted), renewing it if there is any doubt about its condition. Check also the sprockets for signs of wear or damage, and ensure that the tensioner and guide pulleys rotate smoothly on their bearings; renew any worn or damaged components. If signs of oil or coolant contamination are found, trace the source of the leak and rectify it, then wash down the engine timing belt area and related components, to remove all traces of oil or coolant.

Refitting and adjustment

15 On reassembly, temporarily refit the crankshaft pulley, to check that the crankshaft is still positioned at TDC for No 1 piston on compression, then ensure that both camshafts are aligned at TDC by the special tool (paragraph 8). If the engine is being reassembled after major dismantling, both camshaft sprockets should be free to rotate

on their respective camshafts; if the timing belt alone is being renewed, both sprockets should still be securely fastened.

16 A holding tool will be required to prevent the camshaft sprockets from rotating while their bolts are slackened and retightened; either obtain Ford service tool 15-030A, or fabricate a suitable substitute **(see Tool Tip)**. *Note: Do not use the camshaft-aligning tool (whether genuine Ford or not) to prevent rotation while the camshaft sprocket bolts are slackened or tightened; the risk of damage to the camshaft concerned and to the cylinder head is far too great. Use only a forked holding tool applied directly to the sprockets, as described.*

> **TOOL TIP** *To make a camshaft sprocket holding tool, obtain two lengths of steel strip about 6 mm thick by 30 mm wide or similar, one 600 mm long, the other 200 mm long (all dimensions approximate). Bolt the two strips together to form a forked end, leaving the bolt slack so that the shorter strip can pivot freely. At the end of each "prong" of the fork, bend the strips through 90° about 50 mm from their ends to act as the fulcrums; these will engage with the holes in the sprockets. It may be necessary to grind or cut off their sides slightly to allow them to fit the sprocket holes (see illustration 8.23).*

17 If it is being fitted for the first time, screw the timing belt tensioner spring retaining pin into the cylinder head, tightening it to the specified torque wrench setting. Unbolt the tensioner, hook the spring on to the pin and the tensioner backplate, then refit the tensioner, engaging its backplate on the locating peg **(see illustrations)**.

18 In all cases, slacken the tensioner bolt (if necessary), and use an Allen key inserted into its centre to rotate the tensioner as far as possible against spring tension, then retighten the bolt to secure the tensioner **(see illustration)**.

8.17a Fitting tensioner spring retaining pin

8.17b Hook spring onto tensioner and refit as shown - engage tensioner backplate on locating peg (arrowed) . . .

8.18 . . . then use Allen key to position tensioner so that timing belt can be refitted

8.20 Slacken tensioner bolt to give initial belt tension

8.23 Using forked holding tool while camshaft toothed pulley bolt is tightened

8.24 When setting is correct, tighten tensioner bolt to specified torque wrench setting

19 Fit the timing belt; if the original is being refitted, ensure that the marks and notes made on removal are followed, so that the belt is refitted the same way round, and to run in the same direction. Starting at the crankshaft sprocket, work anti-clockwise around the camshaft sprockets and tensioner, finishing off at the rear guide pulley. The front run, between the crankshaft and the exhaust camshaft sprockets, *must* be kept taut, without altering the position either of the crankshaft or of the camshaft(s) - if necessary, the position of the camshaft sprockets can be altered by rotating each on its camshaft (which remains fixed by the aligning tool). Where the sprocket is still fastened, use the holding tool described above to prevent the sprocket from rotating while its retaining bolt is slackened - the sprocket can then be rotated on the camshaft until the belt will slip into place; retighten the sprocket bolt.

20 When the belt is in place, slacken the tensioner bolt gently until the spring pulls the tensioner against the belt; the tensioner should be retained correctly against the timing belt inner shield and cylinder head, but must be just free to respond to changes in belt tension **(see illustration)**.

21 Tighten both camshaft sprocket bolts (or check that they are tight, as applicable) and remove the camshaft-aligning tool. Temporarily refit the crankshaft pulley, and rotate the crankshaft through two full turns clockwise to settle and tension the timing belt, returning the crankshaft to the TDC position described previously. Refit the camshaft-aligning tool; it should slip into place as described in paragraph 8. If all is well, proceed to paragraph 24 below.

22 If one camshaft is only just out of line, fit the forked holding tool to its sprocket, adjust its position as required, and check that any slack created has been taken up by the tensioner; rotate the crankshaft through two further turns clockwise, and refit the camshaft-aligning tool to check that it now fits as it should. If all is well, proceed to paragraph 24 below.

23 If either camshaft is significantly out of line, use the holding tool to prevent its sprocket from rotating while its retaining bolt

is slackened - the camshaft can then be rotated (gently and carefully, using an open-ended spanner) until the camshaft-aligning tool will slip into place; take care not to disturb the relationship of the sprocket to the timing belt. Without disturbing the sprocket's new position on the camshaft, tighten the sprocket bolt to its specified torque wrench setting **(see illustration)**. Remove the camshaft-aligning tool, rotate the crankshaft through two further turns clockwise, and refit the tool to check that it now fits as it should.

24 When the timing belt has been settled at its correct tension, and the camshaft-aligning tool fits correctly when the crankshaft pulley notches are exactly aligned, tighten the tensioner bolt to its specified torque wrench setting **(see illustration)**. Fitting the forked holding tool to the spokes of each sprocket in turn, check that the sprocket bolts are tightened to their specified torque wrench setting. Remove the camshaft-aligning tool, rotate the crankshaft through two further turns clockwise, and refit the tool to make a final check that it fits as it should.

25 The remainder of the reassembly procedure is the reverse of removal, ensuring that all fasteners are tightened to the specified torque.

---

9 Timing belt tensioner and sprockets - removal, inspection and refitting

Tensioner

Note: *If the tensioner is being removed for the first time since the vehicle left the factory, a tensioner spring and retaining pin must be obtained for fitting on reassembly.*

1 While it is possible to reach the tensioner once the timing belt upper and middle covers only have been removed, the whole procedure outlined below must be followed, to ensure that the valve timing is correctly reset once the belt's tension has been disturbed.

2 Release the tension from the timing belt as described in Section 8, paragraphs 1 to 12.

3 Unscrew the tensioner bolt and withdraw

the tensioner, unhooking the spring, if fitted **(see illustration)**. Check the tensioner spring, and renew it if there is any doubt about its condition.

4 On reassembly, if it is being fitted for the first time, screw the timing belt tensioner spring retaining pin into the cylinder head, tightening it to the specified torque wrench setting. Hook the spring onto the pin and the tensioner backplate, then refit the tensioner, engaging its backplate on the locating peg.

5 Use an Allen key inserted into its centre to rotate the tensioner as far as possible against spring tension, then tighten the bolt to secure the tensioner.

6 Reassemble, checking the camshaft alignment (valve timing) and setting the timing belt tension, as described in paragraphs 20 to 25 of Section 8.

Camshaft and crankshaft sprockets

7 While it may be possible to remove any of these sprockets once the relevant belt covers have been removed, the complete timing belt removal/refitting procedure (see Section 8) must be followed, to ensure that the valve timing is correctly reset once the belt's tension has been disturbed.

8 With the timing belt removed, the camshaft sprockets can be detached once their retaining bolts have been unscrewed as described in paragraph 16 of Section 8. The crankshaft sprocket can be pulled off the end of the crankshaft, once the crankshaft pulley

9.3 Removing timing belt tensioner

2C

9.8 "FRONT" marking on outside face of crankshaft toothed pulley - note which way round thrustwasher behind is fitted

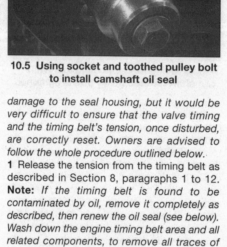

10.5 Using socket and toothed pulley bolt to install camshaft oil seal

the seal into place until it is flush with the housing/bearing cap outer edge. Refit the bearing cap, using sealant and tightening the cap bolts as described in Section 11.

6 For most owners, the simplest answer will be to grease the seal lips, and to slide it onto the camshaft (until it is flush with the housing's outer edge). Refit the bearing cap, using sealant and tightening the cap bolts as described in Section 11 **(see illustration)**. Take care to ensure that the seal remains absolutely square in its housing, and is not distorted as the cap is tightened down.

7 Refit the sprocket to the camshaft, tightening the retaining bolt loosely, then slip the timing belt back onto the sprocket (refer to paragraphs 16 and 19 of Section 8) and tighten the bolt securely.

8 The remainder of the reassembly procedure, including checking the camshaft alignment (valve timing) and setting the timing belt tension, is as described in paragraphs 20 to 25 of Section 8.

---

and the timing belt have been removed. Note the "FRONT" marking identifying the sprocket's outboard face, and the thrustwasher behind it; note which way round the thrustwasher is fitted **(see illustration)**. Note the sprocket-locating Woodruff key; if this is loose, it should be removed for safe storage with the sprocket.

9 Check the sprockets as described in paragraph 14 of Section 8.

10 Refitting is the reverse of the removal procedure.

Timing belt guide pulleys

11 Remove the timing belt covers (see Section 7).

12 Unbolt and withdraw the pulley(s); check their condition as described in paragraph 14 of Section 8.

13 Refitting is the reverse of the removal procedure; tighten the pulley bolts to the specified torque wrench setting.

10 Camshaft oil seals - renewal

Note: *While it is possible to reach either oil seal, once the respective sprocket has been removed (see Section 9) to allow the seal to be prised out, this procedure is not recommended. Not only are the seals very soft, making this difficult to do without risk of*

damage to the seal housing, but it would be very difficult to ensure that the valve timing and the timing belt's tension, once disturbed, are correctly reset. Owners are advised to follow the whole procedure outlined below.

1 Release the tension from the timing belt as described in Section 8, paragraphs 1 to 12. **Note:** *If the timing belt is found to be contaminated by oil, remove it completely as described, then renew the oil seal (see below). Wash down the engine timing belt area and all related components, to remove all traces of oil. Fit a new belt on reassembly.*

2 If the timing belt is still clean, slip it off the sprocket, taking care not to twist it too sharply; use the fingers only to handle the belt. *Do not* rotate the crankshaft until the timing belt is refitted. Cover the belt, and secure it so that it is clear of the working area and cannot slip off the remaining sprocket.

3 Unfasten the sprocket bolt and withdraw the sprocket (see Section 9).

4 Unbolt the camshaft right-hand bearing cap, and withdraw the defective oil seal. Clean the seal housing, and polish off any burrs or raised edges, which may have caused the seal to fail in the first place.

5 To fit a new seal, Ford recommend the use of their service tool 21-009B, with a bolt (10 mm thread size, 70 mm long) and a washer, to draw the seal into place when the camshaft bearing cap is bolted down; a substitute can be made using a suitable socket **(see illustration)**. Grease the seal lips and periphery to ease installation, and draw

11 Camshafts and hydraulic tappets - removal, inspection and refitting

Removal

1 Release the tension from the timing belt as described in Section 8, paragraphs 1 to 12.

2 Either remove the timing belt completely (Section 8, paragraphs 13 and 14) or slip it off the camshaft sprockets, taking care not to twist it too sharply; use the fingers only to handle the belt. Cover the belt, and secure it so that it is clear of the working area. *Do not* rotate the crankshaft until the timing belt is refitted.

3 Unfasten the sprocket bolts as described in Section 8, paragraph 16, and withdraw the sprockets; while both are the same and could be interchanged, it is good working practice to mark them so that each is refitted only to its original location **(see illustration)**.

4 Working in the sequence shown, slacken progressively, by half a turn at a time, the camshaft bearing cap bolts **(see illustration)**. Work only as described, to release gradually

10.6 Alternatively, seal can be inserted when camshaft bearing cap is unbolted

11.3 Using forked holding tool while camshaft toothed pulley bolt is slackened

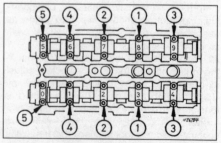

11.4 Camshaft bearing cap slackening sequence

Note: *Viewed from front of vehicle, showing bearing cap numbers*

11.5a Note locating dowels when removing camshaft bearing caps

11.5b Inlet camshaft has lobe for camshaft position sensor

and evenly the pressure of the valve springs on the caps.

5 Withdraw the caps, noting their markings and the presence of the locating dowels, then remove the camshafts and withdraw their oil seals. The inlet camshaft can be identified by the reference lobe for the camshaft position sensor; therefore, there is no need to mark the camshafts **(see illustrations)**.

6 Obtain sixteen small, clean containers, and number them 1 to 16. Using a rubber sucker, withdraw each hydraulic tappet in turn, invert it to prevent oil loss, and place it in its respective container, which should then be filled with clean engine oil **(see illustrations)**. Do not interchange the hydraulic tappets, or the rate of wear will be much increased. Do not allow them to lose oil, or they will take a long time to refill on restarting the engine, resulting in incorrect valve clearances.

Inspection

7 With the camshafts and hydraulic tappets removed, check each for signs of obvious wear (scoring, pitting etc) and for ovality, and renew if necessary.

8 Measure the outside diameter of each tappet **(see illustration)** - take measurements at the top and bottom of each tappet, then a second set at right-angles to the first; if any measurement is significantly different from the others, the tappet is tapered or oval and must

be renewed. If the necessary equipment is available, measure the inside diameter of the corresponding cylinder head bore. Compare the measurements obtained to those given in the Specifications Section of this Chapter; if the tappets or the cylinder head bores are excessively worn, new tappets and/or a new cylinder head will be required.

9 If the engine's valve components have sounded noisy, particularly if the noise persists after initial start-up from cold, there is reason to suspect a faulty hydraulic tappet. Only a good mechanic experienced in these engines can tell whether the noise level is typical, or if renewal of one or more of the tappets is warranted. If faulty tappets are diagnosed, and the engine's service history is unknown, it is always worth trying the effect of renewing the engine oil and filter (see Chapter 1), using *only* good-quality engine oil of the recommended viscosity and specification, before going to the expense of renewing any of the tappets - refer also to the advice in Section 5 of this Chapter.

10 Visually examine the camshaft lobes for score marks, pitting, galling (wear due to rubbing) and evidence of overheating (blue, discoloured areas). Look for flaking away of the hardened surface layer of each lobe. If any such signs are evident, renew the component concerned.

11 Examine the camshaft bearing journals and the cylinder head bearing surfaces for signs of obvious wear or pitting. If any such signs are evident, renew the component concerned.

12 Using a micrometer, measure the diameter of each journal at several points. If the diameter of any one journal is less than the specified value, renew the camshaft.

13 To check the bearing journal running clearance, remove the hydraulic tappets, use a suitable solvent and a clean lint-free rag to clean carefully all bearing surfaces, then refit the camshafts and bearing caps with a strand of Plastigauge across each journal. Tighten the bearing cap bolts to the specified torque wrench setting (do not rotate the camshafts), then remove the bearing caps and use the scale provided to measure the width of the compressed strands. Scrape off the Plastigauge with your fingernail or the edge of a credit card - don't scratch or nick the journals or bearing caps.

14 If the running clearance of any bearing is found to be worn to beyond the specified service limits, fit a new camshaft and repeat the check; if the clearance is still excessive, the cylinder head must be renewed.

15 To check camshaft endfloat, remove the hydraulic tappets, clean the bearing surfaces carefully, and refit the camshafts and bearing

11.6a Removing hydraulic tappets

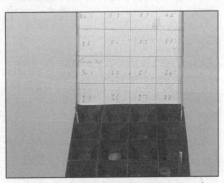

11.6b Hydraulic tappets must be stored as described in text

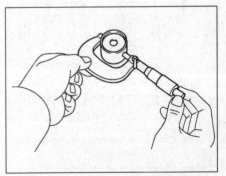

11.8 Use a micrometer to measure diameter of hydraulic tappets

2C

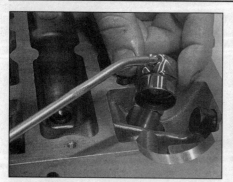

11.17 Oil liberally when refitting hydraulic tappets

11.19 Apply sealant to mating surface of camshaft right-hand bearing caps

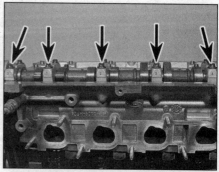

11.20 Etched marks on camshaft bearing caps must be arranged as shown, and face outwards

caps. Tighten the bearing cap bolts to the specified torque wrench setting, then measure the endfloat using a DTI (Dial Test Indicator, or dial gauge) mounted on the cylinder head so that its tip bears on the camshaft right-hand end.

16 Tap the camshaft fully towards the gauge, zero the gauge, then tap the camshaft fully away from the gauge, and note the gauge reading. If the endfloat measured is found to be at or beyond the specified service limit, fit a new camshaft and repeat the check; if the clearance is still excessive, the cylinder head must be renewed.

Refitting

17 On reassembly, liberally oil the cylinder head hydraulic tappet bores and the tappets **(see illustration)**. Note that if new tappets are being fitted, they must be charged with clean engine oil before installation. Carefully refit the tappets to the cylinder head, ensuring that each tappet is refitted to its original bore, and is the correct way up. Some care will be required to enter the tappets squarely into their bores.

18 Liberally oil the camshaft bearings and lobes. Ensuring that each camshaft is in its original location, refit the camshafts, locating each so that the slot in its left-hand end is approximately parallel to, and just above, the cylinder head mating surface.

19 Ensure that the locating dowels are

pressed firmly into their recesses, and check that all mating surfaces are completely clean, unmarked and free from oil. Apply a thin film of suitable sealant (Ford recommend Loctite 518) to the mating surfaces of each camshaft's right-hand bearing cap **(see illustration)**. Referring to paragraph 6 of Section 10, some owners may wish to fit the new camshaft oil seals at this stage.

20 All camshaft bearing caps have a single-digit identifying number etched on them **(see illustration)**. The exhaust camshaft's bearing caps are numbered in sequence 0 to 4, the inlet's 5 to 9; see illustration 11.21a for details. Each cap is to be fitted so that its numbered side faces outwards, to the front (exhaust) or to the rear (inlet).

21 Ensuring that each cap is kept square to the cylinder head as it is tightened down, and working in the sequence shown, tighten the camshaft bearing cap bolts slowly and by one turn at a time, until each cap touches the cylinder head **(see illustration)**. Next, go round again in the same sequence, tightening the bolts to the first stage torque wrench setting specified, then once more, tightening them to the second stage setting. Work only as described, to impose gradually and evenly the pressure of the valve springs on the caps. Fit the camshaft-aligning tool; it should slip into place as described in paragraph 8 of Section 8 **(see illustration)**.

22 Wipe off all surplus sealant, so that none is left to find its way into any oilways. Follow

the sealant manufacturer's instructions as to the time needed for curing; usually, at least an hour must be allowed between application of the sealant and starting the engine.

23 If using Ford's recommended procedure, fit new oil seals to the camshafts as described in paragraph 5 of Section 10.

24 Using the marks and notes made on dismantling to ensure that each is refitted to its original camshaft, refit the sprockets to the camshafts, tightening the retaining bolts loosely. Slip the timing belt back onto the sprockets (refer to paragraph 19 of Section 8) and tighten the bolts securely - use the forked holding tool described in paragraph 16 of Section 8.

25 The remainder of the reassembly procedure, including checking the camshaft alignment (valve timing) and setting the timing belt tension, is as described in paragraphs 15 to 25 of Section 8.

---

12 Cylinder head - removal and refitting

Removal

Note: *The following text assumes that the cylinder head will be removed with both inlet and exhaust manifolds attached. This simplifies the procedure, but makes it a bulky and heavy assembly to handle - an engine hoist will be required, to prevent the risk of injury, and to prevent damage to any delicate components as the assembly is removed and refitted. If it is wished first to remove the manifolds, refer to Chapter 4D, then amend the following procedure accordingly.*

1 Depressurise the fuel system (see Chapter 4D).

2 Disconnect the battery negative (earth) lead (refer to Chapter 5A, Section 1).

3 Refer to Chapter 4D and remove the air inlet components.

4 Equalise the pressure in the fuel tank by removing the filler cap, then undo the fuel feed and return lines connecting the engine to the chassis (see Chapter 4D). Plug or cap all open fittings.

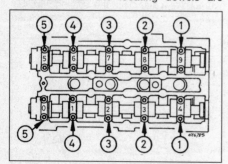

11.21a Camshaft bearing cap tightening sequence

Note: View from front of vehicle - locate bearing caps according to etched numbers, aligned as described in text

11.21b Fit camshaft-aligning tool to set TDC position while camshaft toothed pulleys are refitted

12.7a Unplug engine wiring loom connector alongside the inlet manifold

12.7b Unplug connectors (arrowed) to disconnect ignition coil wiring

12.13 Disconnect all coolant hoses from thermostat housing

> **HAYNES HiNT**
>
> *Whenever you disconnect any vacuum lines, coolant or emissions hoses, wiring connectors and fuel lines, always label them clearly, so that they can be correctly reassembled. Masking tape and/or a touch-up paint applicator work well for marking items. Take instant photos, or sketch the locations of components and brackets.*

5 Disconnect the accelerator cable from the throttle linkage as described in Chapter 4D. Secure the cable clear of the engine/transmission.

6 Remove the auxiliary drivebelt (see Chapter 1).

7 Remove the three screws securing the wiring "rail" to the rear of the manifold. Releasing its wire clip, unplug the large electrical connector (next to the fuel pressure regulator) to disconnect the engine wiring from the main loom **(see illustration)**. Unplug the electrical connectors on each side of the ignition coil, and the single connector from beneath the front of the thermostat housing, to disconnect the coil and coolant temperature gauge sender wiring **(see illustration)**.

8 Marking or labelling them as they are unplugged, disconnect the vacuum hoses as follows:

a) *One from the rear of the throttle housing (only the one hose - there is no need to disconnect the second hose running to the fuel pressure regulator).*

b) *One from the union on the inlet manifold's left-hand end.*

c) *The braking system vacuum servo unit hose (see Chapter 9 for details).*

9 Unbolt the engine earth lead from the cylinder head lifting eye.

10 Unbolt both parts of the exhaust manifold heat shield. Either remove the dipstick and tube, or swing them out of the way.

11 Unscrew the pulse-air filter housing retaining bolt, then disconnect its vacuum hose.

12 Drain the cooling system (see Chapter 1).

13 Disconnect all coolant hoses from the thermostat housing **(see illustration)**.

14 Unscrew the two nuts to disconnect the exhaust system front downpipe from the manifold (Chapter 4B); disconnect the oxygen sensor wiring, so that it is not strained by the weight of the exhaust system.

15 Remove the timing belt and both camshafts (see Sections 8 and 11); if the cylinder head is to be dismantled, withdraw the hydraulic tappets.

16 Remove the timing belt inner shield (see Section 7.

17 Working in the *reverse* of the sequence shown in illustration 12.28a, slacken the ten cylinder head bolts progressively and by one turn at a time; a Torx key (TX 55 size) will be required. Remove each bolt in turn, and ensure that new replacements are obtained for reassembly; these bolts are subjected to severe stresses and so **must** be renewed, regardless of their apparent condition, whenever they are disturbed.

18 Lift the cylinder head away; use assistance if possible, as it is a heavy assembly. If necessary, grip the manifolds and rock it free from the location dowels on the top face of the cylinder block. Do not attempt to tap it sideways or lever between the head and the block top face. Remove the gasket, noting the two dowels, and discard it.

Preparation for refitting

19 The mating faces of the cylinder head and cylinder block must be perfectly clean before

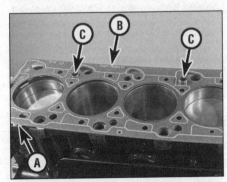

12.23 Ensuring protruding tooth (or teeth) "A" are at front and marking "B" is upwards, locate new cylinder head gasket on dowels "C"

refitting the head. Use a hard plastic or wood scraper to remove all traces of gasket and carbon; also clean the piston crowns. Take particular care during the cleaning operations, as aluminium alloy is easily damaged. Also, make sure that the carbon is not allowed to enter the oil and water passages - this is particularly important for the lubrication system, as carbon could block the oil supply to the engine's components. Using adhesive tape and paper, seal the water, oil and bolt holes in the cylinder block.

> **HAYNES HiNT**
>
> *To prevent carbon entering the gap between the pistons and bores, smear a little grease in the gap. After cleaning each piston, use a small brush to remove all traces of grease and carbon from the gap, then wipe away the remainder with a clean rag.*

20 Check the mating surfaces of the cylinder block and the cylinder head for nicks, deep scratches and other damage. If slight, they may be removed carefully with a file, but if excessive, machining may be the only alternative to renewal.

21 If warpage of the cylinder head gasket surface is suspected, use a straight-edge to check it for distortion. Refer to Part D of this Chapter if necessary.

Refitting

22 Wipe clean the mating surfaces of the cylinder head and cylinder block. Check that the two locating dowels are in position in the cylinder block, and that all cylinder head bolt holes are free from oil.

23 Position a new gasket over the dowels on the cylinder block surface, so that the "TOP/OBEN" mark is uppermost, and with the tooth (or teeth, according to engine size) protruding from the front edge **(see illustration)**.

24 Temporarily refit the crankshaft pulley, and rotate the crankshaft anti-clockwise so that No 1 cylinder's piston is lowered to approximately 20 mm before TDC, thus avoiding any risk of valve/piston contact and damage during reassembly.

2C

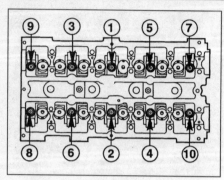

12.28a Cylinder head bolt tightening sequence

Note: View from rear of vehicle

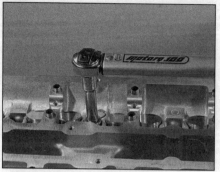

12.28b Tightening cylinder head bolts (Stages 1 and 2) using torque wrench . . .

12.28c . . . and to Stage 3 using angle gauge

25 As the cylinder head is such a heavy and awkward assembly to refit with manifolds, it is helpful to make up a pair of guide studs from two 10 mm (thread size) studs approximately 90 mm long, with a screwdriver slot cut in one end - two old cylinder head bolts with their heads cut off would make a good starting point. Screw these guide studs, screwdriver slot upwards to permit removal, into the bolt holes at diagonally-opposite corners of the cylinder block surface (or into those where the locating dowels are fitted); ensure that approximately 70 mm of stud protrudes above the gasket.

26 Refit the cylinder head, sliding it down the guide studs (if used) and locating it on the dowels. Unscrew the guide studs (if used) when the head is in place.

27 Fit the new cylinder head bolts dry (*do not oil* their threads); carefully enter each into its hole and screw it in, by hand only, until finger-tight.

28 Working progressively and in the sequence shown, use first a torque wrench, then an ordinary socket extension bar and an angle gauge, to tighten the cylinder head bolts in the stages given in the Specifications Section of this Chapter **(see illustrations)**. **Note:** *Once tightened correctly, following this procedure, the cylinder head bolts do not require check-tightening, and must* **not** *be re-torqued.*

29 Refit the hydraulic tappets (if removed), the camshafts, their oil seals and sprockets (see Sections 11, 10 and 9, as appropriate). Temporarily refit the crankshaft pulley, and rotate the crankshaft clockwise to return the pulley notches to the TDC position described in Section 3.

30 Refit the earth lead to the lifting eye

31 Refit the timing belt and covers, checking the camshaft alignment (valve timing) and setting the timing belt tension, as described in Section 8.

32 The remainder of reassembly is the reverse of the removal procedure, noting the following points:

a) *Tighten all fasteners to the torque wrench settings specified.*

b) *Refill the cooling system, and top-up the*

engine oil (see Chapter 1 and "Weekly Checks").

c) *Check all disturbed joints for signs of oil or coolant leakage, once the engine has been restarted and warmed-up to normal operating temperature.*

d) *If the power steering hoses where disconnected, bleed the system as described in Chapter 10 after reconnection.*

13 Sump - removal and refitting

Removal

Note: *The full procedure outlined below must be followed, so that the mating surfaces can be cleaned and prepared to achieve an oil-tight joint on reassembly, and so that the sump can be aligned correctly; depending on your skill and experience, and the tools and facilities available, it may be that this task can be carried out only with the engine removed from the vehicle. Note that the sump gasket must be renewed whenever it is disturbed.*

1 Disconnect the battery negative (earth) lead (refer to Chapter 5A, Section 1).

2 Drain the engine oil, then clean and refit the engine oil drain plug, tightening it to the specified torque wrench setting. Although not strictly necessary as part of the dismantling procedure, owners are advised to remove and discard the oil filter, so that it can be renewed with the oil (see Chapter 1).

3 Refer to Chapter 5A and remove the starter motor.

4 Remove the auxiliary drivebelt cover (see Chapter 1).

5 Unplug the electrical connector(s) to disconnect the oxygen sensor.

6 Unscrew the nuts to disconnect the exhaust system front downpipe from the manifold, then either unhook all the system's rubber mountings and withdraw the complete exhaust system from under the vehicle, or remove only the downpipe/catalytic converter (see Chapter 4E for details).

7 Unscrew the sump-to-transmission bolts, also any securing the engine/transmission lower adapter plate.

8 Progressively unscrew the sump retaining bolts. Break the joint by striking the sump with the palm of the hand, then lower the sump and withdraw it with the engine/transmission lower adapter plate (where fitted); note the presence of any shims between the sump and transmission.

9 Remove and discard the sump gasket; this must be renewed as a matter of course whenever it is disturbed.

10 While the sump is removed, take the opportunity to remove the oil pump pick-up/strainer pipe and to clean it (see Section 14).

Refitting

11 On reassembly, thoroughly clean and degrease the mating surfaces of the cylinder block/crankcase and sump, then use a clean rag to wipe out the sump and the engine's interior. If the oil pump pick-up/strainer pipe was removed, fit a new gasket and refit the pipe, tightening its screws to the specified torque wrench setting. Fit the new gasket to the sump mating surface so that the gasket fits into the sump groove **(see illustration)**.

12 If the sump is being refitted with the engine/transmission still connected and in the vehicle, proceed as follows:

a) *Check that the mating surfaces of the sump, the cylinder block/crankcase and*

13.11 Ensure gasket is located correctly in sump groove

13.13a Apply sealant (arrowed) as directed when refitting sump

13.13b Checking alignment of sump with cylinder block/crankcase

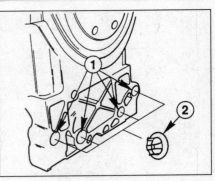

13.13c Sump-to-cylinder block/crankcase alignment shims

1 Fitting points on sump   2 Shim

the transmission are absolutely clean and flat. Any shims found on removal of the sump must be refitted in their original locations.

b) Apply a thin film of suitable sealant (Ford recommend Hylosil 102) to the junctions of the cylinder block/crankcase with the oil pump and the crankshaft left-hand oil seal carrier. Without delay - the sump bolts must be fully tightened within 10 to 20 minutes of applying the sealant - offer up the sump and engine/transmission lower adapter plate, and refit the bolts, tightening them lightly at first.

c) Ensuring that the engine/transmission lower adapter plate is correctly located, firmly press the sump against the transmission, and tighten the transmission-to-sump (ie, engine) bolts to the specified torque wrench setting.

d) Without disturbing the position of the sump, and working in a diagonal sequence from the centre outwards, tighten the sump bolts to the specified torque wrench setting.

e) Proceed to paragraph 14.

13 If the sump is being refitted with the engine and transmission separated (in or out of the vehicle), proceed as follows:

a) Apply a thin film of suitable sealant (Ford recommend Hylosil 102) to the junctions of the cylinder block/crankcase with the oil pump and the crankshaft left-hand oil

seal carrier (see illustration). Without delay - the sump bolts must be fully tightened within 10 to 20 minutes of applying the sealant - offer up the sump to the cylinder block/crankcase, and insert the sump bolts, tightening them lightly at first.

b) Using a suitable straight edge to check alignment across the flat-machined faces of each, move the sump as necessary so that its left-hand face - including any shims found on removal - is flush with that of the cylinder block/crankcase (see illustration). Without disturbing the position of the sump, and working in a diagonal sequence from the centre outwards, tighten the sump bolts to the specified torque wrench setting.

c) Check again that both faces are flush before proceeding; if necessary, unbolt the sump again, clean the mating surfaces, and repeat the full procedure to ensure that the sump is correctly aligned.

d) If it is not possible to achieve exact alignment by moving the sump, shims are available in thicknesses of 0.25 mm (colour-coded yellow) or 0.50 mm (colour-coded black) to eliminate the discrepancy (see illustration).

14 The remainder of reassembly is the reverse of the removal procedure, noting the following points.

a) Tighten all fasteners to the torque wrench settings specified.

b) Always renew any self-locking nuts disturbed on removal.

c) Refill the cooling system (see Chapter 1).

d) Refill the engine with oil, remembering that you are advised to fit a new filter (see Chapter 1).

e) Check for signs of oil or coolant leaks once the engine has been restarted and warmed-up to normal operating temperature.

14 Oil pump - removal, inspection and refitting

Removal

Note: While this task is theoretically possible when the engine is in place in the vehicle, in practice, it requires so much preliminary dismantling, and is so difficult to carry out due to the restricted access, that owners are advised to remove the engine from the vehicle first. Note, however, that the oil pump pressure relief valve can be removed with the engine in situ - see paragraph 8.

1 Remove the timing belt (see Section 8).
2 Withdraw the crankshaft sprocket and the thrustwasher behind it, noting which way round the thrustwasher is fitted (see Section 9).
3 Remove the sump (see Section 13).
4 Undo the screws securing the oil pump pick-up/strainer pipe to the pump, then unscrew the nut and withdraw the oil pump pick-up/strainer pipe. Discard the gasket.
5 Unbolt the pump from the cylinder block/crankcase (see illustration). Withdraw and discard the gasket, and remove the crankshaft right-hand oil seal. Thoroughly clean and degrease all components, particularly the mating surfaces of the pump, the sump, and the cylinder block/crankcase.

Inspection

6 Unscrew the Torx screws, and remove the pump cover plate; noting any identification marks on the rotors, withdraw the rotors (see illustration).

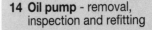

14.5 Unscrew bolts (arrowed) to remove oil pump   **14.6 Withdrawing oil pump inner rotor**

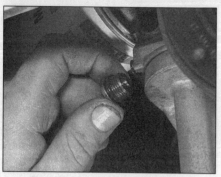

14.9a Unscrew threaded plug - seen through right-hand wheel arch . . .

14.9b . . . to withdraw oil pressure relief valve spring and plunger

14.12 Use new gasket when refitting oil pump

7 Inspect the rotors for obvious signs of wear or damage, and renew if necessary; if either rotor, the pump body, or its cover plate are scored or damaged, the complete oil pump assembly must be renewed.

8 The oil pressure relief valve can be dismantled, if required, without disturbing the pump. Chock the rear wheels then jack up the front of the car and support it on axle stands (see *"Jacking and Vehicle Support"*). Remove the front right-hand roadwheel and auxiliary drivebelt cover (see Chapter 1) to provide access to the valve.

9 Unscrew the threaded plug, and recover the valve spring and plunger **(see illustrations)**. If the plug's sealing O-ring is worn or damaged, a new one must be obtained, to be fitted on reassembly.

10 Reassembly is the reverse of the

dismantling procedure; ensure the spring and valve are refitted the correct way round, and tighten the threaded plug securely.

Refitting

11 The oil pump must be primed on installation, by pouring clean engine oil into it, and rotating its inner rotor a few turns.

12 Using grease to stick the new gasket in place on the cylinder block/crankcase, and rotating the pump's inner rotor to align with the flats on the crankshaft, refit the pump and insert the bolts, tightening them lightly at first **(see illustration)**.

13 Using a suitable straight edge and feeler gauges, check that the pump is both centred *exactly* around the crankshaft, and aligned squarely so that its (sump) mating surface is exactly the same amount - between 0.3 and 0.8 mm - below that of the cylinder block/crankcase on each side of the crankshaft **(see illustration)**. Being careful not to disturb the gasket, move the pump into the correct position, and tighten its bolts to the specified torque wrench setting.

14 Check that the pump is correctly located; if necessary, unbolt it again, and repeat the full procedure to ensure that the pump is correctly aligned.

15 Fit a new crankshaft right-hand oil seal (see Section 15).

16 Using grease to stick the gasket in place on the pump, refit the pick-up/strainer pipe, tightening its screws and nut to their specified torque wrench settings **(see illustration)**.

17 The remainder of reassembly is the reverse of the removal procedure, referring to the relevant text for details where required.

15 Crankshaft oil seals - renewal

Note: *Don't try to prise these seals out without removing the oil pump or seal carrier - the seals are too soft, and the amount of space available is too small, for this to be possible without considerable risk of damage to the seal housing and/or the crankshaft journal. Follow exactly the procedure given below.*

Right-hand seal

1 Remove the oil pump (see Section 14).

2 Drive the oil seal out of the pump from behind **(see illustration)**.

3 Clean the seal housing and crankshaft, polishing off any burrs or raised edges, which may have caused the seal to fail in the first place.

4 Refit the oil pump (see Section 14). Grease the lips and periphery of the new seal, to ease installation.

5 To fit a new seal, Ford recommend the use of their service tool 21-093A, with the crankshaft pulley bolt, to draw the seal into place; an alternative can be arranged using a socket of suitable size, with a washer to match the crankshaft pulley bolt **(see illustration)**.

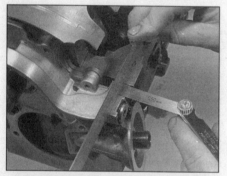

14.13 Oil pump must be positioned accurately

14.16 Use new gasket when refitting oil pick-up pipe to pump

15.2 Driving out crankshaft right-hand oil seal

15.5 Socket of correct size can be used to replace Ford service tool, drawing new seal into place as described

15.6 If seal is tapped into place as shown, exercise great care to prevent seal from being damaged or distorted

15.12 Unscrew bolts (arrowed) to remove crankshaft left-hand oil seal carrier . . .

15.13 . . . and ensure that carrier is properly supported when driving out used oil seal - note notches provided in carrier for drift

6 If such tools are not available, press the seal squarely into place by hand; tap it in until it is flush with the pump housing, using a soft-faced mallet and a socket with an outside diameter only slightly smaller than the seal's **(see illustration)**. This approach requires great care, to ensure that the seal is fitted squarely, without distortion or damage.

7 Wash off any traces of oil. The remainder of reassembly is the reverse of the removal procedure, referring to the relevant text for details where required. Check for signs of oil leakage when the engine is restarted.

Left-hand seal

8 Remove the transmission (see the relevant Part of Chapter 7).

9 Where appropriate, remove the clutch (Chapter 6).

10 Unbolt the flywheel/driveplate (see Section 17).

11 Remove the sump (see Section 13).

12 Unbolt the oil seal carrier **(see illustration)**. Remove and discard its gasket.

13 Supporting the carrier evenly on wooden blocks, drive the oil seal out of the carrier from behind **(see illustration)**.

14 Clean the seal housing and crankshaft, polishing off any burrs or raised edges, which may have caused the seal to fail in the first place. Clean also the mating surfaces of the cylinder block/crankcase and carrier, using a

scraper to remove all traces of the old gasket - be careful not to scratch or damage the material of either - then use a suitable solvent to degrease them.

15 Use grease to stick the new gasket in place on the cylinder block/crankcase, then offer up the carrier **(see illustration)**.

16 Using a suitable straight edge and feeler gauges, check that the carrier is both centred *exactly* around the crankshaft, and aligned squarely so that its (sump) mating surface is exactly the same amount - between 0.3 and 0.8 mm - below that of the cylinder block/crankcase on each side of the crankshaft **(see illustration)**. Being careful not to disturb the gasket, move the carrier into the correct position, and tighten its bolts to the specified torque wrench setting.

17 Check that the carrier is correctly located; if necessary, unbolt it again, and repeat the full procedure to ensure that the carrier is correctly aligned.

18 Ford's recommended method of seal fitting is to use service tool 21-141, with two flywheel bolts to draw the seal into place. If this is not available, make up a guide from a thin sheet of plastic or similar, lubricate the lips of the new seal and the crankshaft shoulder with grease, then offer up the seal, with the guide feeding the seal's lips over the crankshaft shoulder **(see illustration)**. Press the seal evenly into its housing by hand only,

and use a soft-faced mallet gently to tap it into place until it is flush with the surrounding housing.

19 Wipe off any surplus oil or grease; the remainder of the reassembly procedure is the reverse of dismantling, referring to the relevant text for details where required. Check for signs of oil leakage when the engine is restarted.

16 Engine/transmission mountings - inspection and renewal

Inspection

1 The engine/transmission mountings seldom require attention, but broken or deteriorated mountings should be renewed immediately, or the added strain placed on the driveline components may cause damage or wear.

2 During the check, the engine/transmission must be raised slightly, to remove its weight from the mountings.

3 Chock the rear wheels then jack up the front of the car and support it on axle stands (see *"Jacking and Vehicle Support"*). Position a jack under the sump, with a large block of wood between the jack head and the sump, then carefully raise the engine/transmission just enough to take the weight off the mountings.

2C

15.15 Use new gasket when refitting left-hand oil seal carrier

15.16 Oil seal carrier must be positioned accurately

15.18 Using guide made from thin sheet of plastic to slide oil seal lips over crankshaft shoulder

4 Check the mountings to see if the rubber is cracked, hardened or separated from the metal components. Sometimes, the rubber will split right down the centre.

5 Check for relative movement between each mounting's brackets and the engine/transmission or body (use a large screwdriver or lever to attempt to move the mountings). If movement is noted, lower the engine and check-tighten the mounting fasteners.

Renewal

6 The engine mountings can be removed if the weight of the engine/transmission is supported by one of the following alternative methods.

7 Either support the weight of the assembly from underneath using a jack and a suitable piece of wood between the jack saddle and the sump or transmission (to prevent damage), or from above by attaching a hoist to the engine. A third method is to use a suitable support bar with end pieces which will engage in the water channel each side of the bonnet lid aperture. Using an adjustable hook and chain connected to the engine, the weight of the engine and transmission can then be taken from the mountings.

Engine front right-hand mounting

8 This mounting consists of a two-piece bracket bolted to the inner wing panel, connected by the bonded-rubber mounting itself to a (Y-shaped) bracket, bolted (via the alternator mounting bracket) to the cylinder block **(see illustration)**.

9 Unscrew the three bolts securing the front right-hand mounting bracket to the alternator mounting bracket.

10 Unscrew the bolts securing the mounting bracket to the inner wing panel and chassis rail and withdraw the mounting assembly.

16.8 Engine front right-hand mounting

Engine rear right-hand mounting

11 This mounting consists of the bonded-rubber mounting secured to the inner wing panel by a (horizontal) bolt, accessible from within the wheel arch, and a (vertical) stud, the retaining nut of which is accessible from the engine compartment. The mounting is bolted to a bracket, which is in turn bolted to the cylinder block.

12 Unbolt the mounting from the body by unscrewing first the single nut (and washer) immediately to the rear of the timing belt cover, then the bolt in the wheel arch.

13 Unbolt the mounting from the cylinder block bracket and withdraw the mounting assembly.

Transmission bearer and mountings

14 On XR2i models, remove the front suspension crossmember as described in Chapter 10.

15 Unscrew and remove the two nuts securing the mountings (front and rear) to the transmission bearer

16 Support the transmission bearer, then undo and remove the four retaining bolts from the floorpan, two at the front and two at the rear, and lower the transmission bearer from the vehicle. Note plate fitment, as applicable, for reassembly.

17 To remove the mountings from the transmission, unscrew the upper bolt and lower stud (front mounting) or the three nuts (rear mounting) and withdraw the relevant mounting and bracket assembly from the transmission.

All mountings

18 Refitting of all mountings is a reversal of removal. Make sure that the original sequence of assembly of washers and plates is maintained.

19 Do not fully tighten any mounting bolts until they are all located. As the mounting bolts and nuts are tightened, check that the mounting rubbers do not twist.

17 Flywheel/driveplate - removal, inspection and refitting

Removal

1 Remove the transmission (see the relevant Part of Chapter 7).

2 Where appropriate, remove the clutch (Chapter 6).

3 Use a centre-punch or paint to make alignment marks on the flywheel/driveplate and crankshaft, to ensure correct alignment during refitting.

4 Prevent the flywheel/driveplate from turning by locking the ring gear teeth, or by bolting a strap between the flywheel/driveplate and the cylinder block/crankcase. Slacken the bolts evenly until all are free.

5 Remove each bolt in turn, and ensure that new replacements are obtained for reassembly; these bolts are subjected to severe stresses, and so must be renewed, regardless of their apparent condition, whenever they are disturbed.

6 Noting the reinforcing plate (automatic transmission models only), withdraw the flywheel/driveplate; do not drop it - it is very heavy.

Inspection

7 Clean the flywheel/driveplate to remove grease and oil. Inspect the surface for cracks, rivet grooves, burned areas and score marks. Light scoring can be removed with emery cloth. Check for cracked and broken ring gear teeth. Lay the flywheel/driveplate on a flat surface, and use a straight edge to check for warpage.

8 Clean and inspect the mating surfaces of the flywheel/driveplate and the crankshaft. If the crankshaft left-hand seal is leaking, renew it (see Section 15) before refitting the flywheel/driveplate.

9 While the flywheel/driveplate is removed, clean carefully its inboard (right-hand) face, particularly the recesses which serve as the reference points for the crankshaft speed/position sensor. Clean the sensor's tip, and check that the sensor is securely fastened.

Refitting

10 On refitting, ensure that the engine/transmission adapter plate is in place (where necessary), then fit the flywheel/driveplate to the crankshaft so that all bolt holes align - it will fit only one way - check this using the marks made on removal. Do not forget the reinforcing plate (automatic transmission models).

11 Lock the flywheel/driveplate by the method used on dismantling. Working in a diagonal sequence to tighten them evenly, and increasing to the final amount in two or three stages, tighten the new bolts to the specified torque wrench setting.

12 The remainder of reassembly is the reverse of the removal procedure, referring to the relevant text for details where required.

Chapter 2 Part D:
Engine removal and overhaul procedures

Contents

Camshaft and tappets - removal, inspection and refitting
  (HCS engines) 10
Crankshaft - refitting and main bearing running clearance
  check 17
Crankshaft - removal and inspection 12
Cylinder block/crankcase - cleaning and inspection 13
Cylinder head - dismantling 7
Cylinder head - reassembly 9
Cylinder head and valve components - cleaning and inspection ... 8
Engine - initial start-up after overhaul 19
Engine - removal and refitting (HCS engines) 3
Engine overhaul - preliminary information 6

Engine overhaul - reassembly sequence 15
Engine/transmission removal - preparation and precautions 2
Engine/transmission - removal and refitting (CVH and
  PTE engines) 4
Engine/transmission - removal and refitting (Zetec engines) 5
General information 1
Main and big-end bearings - inspection 14
Piston/connecting rod assemblies - refitting and big-end
  bearing running clearance check 18
Piston/connecting rod assemblies - removal and inspection 11
Piston rings - refitting 16

Degrees of difficulty

| Easy, suitable for novice with little experience | Fairly easy, suitable for beginner with some experience 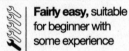 | Fairly difficult, suitable for competent DIY mechanic | Difficult, suitable for experienced DIY mechanic | Very difficult, suitable for expert DIY or professional 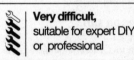 |

Specifications

HCS engines

Cylinder head

Maximum permissible gasket surface distortion (measured over
full length) .... 0.15 mm
Valve seat angle (inlet and exhaust) .... 45°
Valve seat width (inlet and exhaust) .... 1.18 to 1.75 mm*
The inlet and exhaust valves have special inserts which cannot be recut using conventional tools.

Valves - general

	Inlet	Exhaust
Valve length	103.7 to 104.4 mm	104.2 to 104.7 mm
Valve head diameter:		
1.0 and 1.1 litre engines	32.90 to 33.10 mm	28.90 to 29.10 mm
1.3 litre engines	34.40 to 34.60 mm	28.90 to 29.10 mm
Valve stem diameter	7.0 mm	7.0 mm
Valve stem-to-guide clearance	0.020 to 0.069	0.046 to 0.095

Cylinder block

Cylinder bore diameter:
1.0 and 1.1 litre engines:
   Standard class 1 (or A) .... 68.68 to 68.69 mm
   Standard class 2 (or B) .... 68.69 to 68.70 mm
   Standard class 3 (or C) .... 68.70 to 68.71 mm
   Oversize 0.5 mm .... 69.20 to 69.21 mm
   Oversize 1.0 mm .... 69.70 to 69.71 mm
1.3 litre engines:
   Standard class 1 .... 73.94 to 73.95 mm
   Standard class 2 .... 73.50 to 73.96 mm
   Standard class 3 .... 73.96 to 73.97 mm
   Oversize 0.5 mm .... 74.50 to 74.51 mm
   Oversize 1.0 mm .... 75.00 to 75.01 mm

Pistons and piston rings

Piston diameter:
  1.0 and 1.1 litre engines:
    Standard class 1 (or A) . . . . 68.65 to 68.66 mm
    Standard class 2 (or B) . . . . 68.66 to 68.67 mm
    Standard class 3 (or C) . . . . 68.67 to 68.68 mm
    Standard (service) . . . . 68.67 to 68.70 mm
    Oversize 0.5 mm . . . . 69.16 to 69.19 mm
    Oversize 1.0 mm . . . . 69.66 to 69.69 mm
  1.3 litre engines:
    Standard class 1 . . . . 73.91 to 73.92 mm
    Standard class 2 . . . . 73.92 to 73.93 mm
    Standard class 3 . . . . 73.93 to 73.94 mm
    Oversize 0.5 mm . . . . 74.46 to 74.49 mm
    Oversize 1.0 mm . . . . 74.96 to 74.99 mm
Piston-to-cylinder bore clearance . . . . 0.015 to 0.050 mm
Piston ring end gap - installed:
  Top compression ring . . . . 0.25 to 0.45 mm
  Second compression ring:
    1.0 and 1.1 litre engines . . . . 0.25 to 0.45 mm
    1.3 litre engines . . . . 0.45 to 0.75 mm
  Oil control ring . . . . 0.20 to 0.40 mm
Piston ring-to-groove clearance:
  Compression rings . . . . 0.20 mm (maximum)
  Oil control ring . . . . 0.10 mm (maximum)
Ring gap position:
  Top compression ring . . . . Offset 180° from oil control ring gap
  Second compression ring . . . . Offset 90° from oil control ring gap
  Oil control ring . . . . Aligned with gudgeon pin

Gudgeon pin

Length:
  1.0 and 1.1 litre engines . . . . 58.6 to 59.4 mm
  1.3 litre engines . . . . 63.3 to 64.6 mm
Diameter:
  White colour code . . . . 18.026 to 18.029 mm
  Red colour code . . . . 18.029 to 18.032 mm
  Blue colour code . . . . 18.032 to 18.035 mm
  Yellow colour code . . . . 18.035 to 18.038 mm
Clearance in piston . . . . 0.008 to 0.014 mm
Interference fit in connecting rod . . . . 0.016 to 0.048 mm

Crankshaft and bearings

Main bearing journal diameter:
  1.0 and 1.1 litre engines:
    Standard . . . . 56.990 to 57.000 mm
    Standard (with yellow line) . . . . 56.980 to 56.990 mm
    0.254 mm undersize (with green line) . . . . 56.726 to 56.746 mm
    0.508 mm undersize (service) . . . . 56.472 to 56.492 mm
    0.762 mm undersize (service) . . . . 56.218 to 56.238 mm
  1.3 litre engines:
    Standard . . . . 56.980 to 57.000 mm
    0.254 mm undersize (with green line) . . . . 56.726 to 56.746 mm
    0.508 mm undersize (service) . . . . 56.472 to 56.492 mm
    0.762 mm undersize (service) . . . . 56.218 to 56.238 mm
Main bearing journal-to-shell running clearance:
  1.0 and 1.1 litre engines . . . . 0.009 to 0.046 mm
  1.3 litre engines . . . . 0.009 to 0.056 mm
Crankpin (big-end) bearing journal diameter:
  Standard . . . . 40.99 to 41.01 mm
  0.254 mm undersize . . . . 40.74 to 40.76 mm
  0.508 mm undersize . . . . 40.49 to 40.51 mm
  0.762 mm undersize . . . . 40.24 to 40.26 mm
Crankpin (big-end) bearing journal-to-shell running clearance . . . . . . 0.006 to 0.060 mm
Crankshaft endfloat . . . . 0.100 to 0.250 mm
Thrustwasher thickness:
  Standard . . . . 2.80 to 2.85 mm
  Oversize . . . . 2.99 to 3.04 mm

Camshaft
Endfloat . . . .   0.02 to 0.19 mm

Torque wrench settings

	Nm	lbf ft
Main bearing cap	95	70
*Crankpin (big-end) bearing cap bolts:		
Stage 1	4	3
Stage 2	Angle-tighten a further 90°	
Engine-to-transmission bolts	41	30

*New bolts must be used
Note: *Refer to Part A of this Chapter for remaining torque wrench settings.*

CVH and PTE engines

Cylinder head
Maximum permissible gasket surface distortion (measured over
full length) . . . .   0.15 mm
Camshaft bearing bore diameters in cylinder head (standard):
   Bearing 1 . . . .   44.783 to 44.808 mm
   Bearing 2 . . . .   45.033 to 45.058 mm
   Bearing 3 . . . .   45.283 to 45.308 mm
   Bearing 4 . . . .   45.533 to 45.558 mm
   Bearing 5 . . . .   45.783 to 45.808 mm
Camshaft bearing bore diameters in cylinder head (oversize):
   Bearing 1 . . . .   45.188 to 45.163 mm
   Bearing 2 . . . .   45.438 to 45.413 mm
   Bearing 3 . . . .   45.668 to 45.663 mm
   Bearing 4 . . . .   45.938 to 45.913 mm
   Bearing 5 . . . .   46.188 to 46.163 mm
Valve tappet bore diameter (standard) . . . .   22.235 to 22.265 mm
Valve tappet bore diameter (oversize) . . . .   22.489 to 22.519 mm
Valve seat angle (inlet and exhaust) . . . .   44° 30' to 45° 30'
Valve seat width (inlet and exhaust) . . . .   1.75 to 2.32 mm*

*The cylinder head has valve seat rings on the exhaust side. These valve seats cannot be recut with conventional tools.

Valves - general

	Inlet	Exhaust
Valve length:		
1.4 litre engine	136.29 to 136.75 mm	132.97 to 133.43 mm
1.6 litre engine	134.54 to 135.00 mm	131.57 to 132.03 mm
Valve head diameter:		
1.4 litre engine	39.90 to 40.10 mm	33.90 to 34.10 mm
1.6 litre engine	41.90 to 42.10 mm	36.90 to 37.10 mm
Valve stem diameter (standard)	8.025 to 8.043 mm	7.999 to 8.017 mm
Valve stem diameter (0.2 mm oversize)	8.225 to 8.243 mm	8.199 to 8.217 mm
Valve stem diameter (0.4 mm oversize)	8.425 to 8.443 mm	8.399 to 8.417 mm
Valve stem-to-guide clearance	0.020 to 0.063 mm	0.046 to 0.089 mm

Cylinder block
Cylinder bore diameter:
  1.4 litre engine:
    Standard 1 . . . .   77.22 to 77.23 mm
    Standard 2 . . . .   77.23 to 77.24 mm
    Standard 3 . . . .   77.24 to 77.25 mm
    Standard 4 . . . .   77.25 to 77.26 mm
    Oversize A . . . .   77.51 to 77.52 mm
    Oversize B . . . .   77.52 to 77.53 mm
    Oversize C . . . .   77.53 to 77.54 mm
  1.6 litre engine:
    Standard 1 . . . .   79.94 to 79.95 mm
    Standard 2 . . . .   79.95 to 79.96 mm
    Standard 3 . . . .   79.96 to 79.97 mm
    Standard 4 . . . .   79.97 to 79.98 mm
    Oversize A . . . .   80.23 to 80.24 mm
    Oversize B . . . .   80.24 to 80.25 mm
    Oversize C . . . .   80.25 to 80.26 mm

Pistons and piston rings

Piston diameter (production):

1.4 litre engine:

Standard 1	77.190 to 77.200 mm
Standard 2	77.200 to 77.210 mm
Standard 3	77.210 to 77.220 mm
Standard 4	77.220 to 77.230 mm
Oversize A	77.480 to 77.490 mm
Oversize B	77.490 to 77.500 mm
Oversize C	77.500 to 77.510 mm

1.6 litre carburettor engine and turbocharged engine:

Standard 1	79.910 to 79.920 mm
Standard 2	79.920 to 79.930 mm
Standard 3	79.930 to 79.940 mm
Standard 4	79.940 to 79.950 mm
Oversize A	80.200 to 80.210 mm
Oversize B	80.210 to 80.220 mm
Oversize C	80.220 to 80.230 mm

1.6 litre EFi (non-turbo) fuel injection engine:

Standard 1	79.915 to 79.925 mm
Standard 2	79.925 to 79.935 mm
Standard 3	79.935 to 79.945 mm
Standard 4	79.945 to 79.955 mm
Oversize A	80.205 to 80.215 mm
Oversize B	80.215 to 80.225 mm
Oversize C	80.225 to 80.235 mm

Piston-to-cylinder bore clearance:

1.4 litre engine	0.020 to 0.040 mm
1.6 litre carburettor engine and turbocharged engine	0.020 to 0.040 mm
1.6 litre EFi (non-turbo) fuel injection engine	0.015 to 0.035 mm

Piston ring end gaps - installed:

Compression rings	0.30 to 0.50 mm

Oil control rings:

1.4 litre engine	0.40 to 1.40 mm
1.6 litre carburettor engine and turbocharged engine	0.40 to 1.40 mm
1.6 litre EFi (non-turbo) fuel injection engine	0.25 to 0.40 mm

Gudgeon pins

Length:

1.4 litre engine	63.000 to 63.800 mm
1.6 litre carburettor engine	66.200 to 67.000 mm
1.6 litre EFi (non-turbo) fuel injection engine	63.000 to 63.800 mm
1.6 litre turbocharged engine	63.600 to 64.400 mm

Diameter:

White colour code	20.622 to 20.625 mm
Red colour code	20.625 to 20.628 mm
Blue colour code	20.628 to 20.631 mm
Yellow colour code	20.631 to 20.634 mm
Clearance in piston	0.005 to 0.011 mm
Interference fit in connecting rod	0.013 to 0.045 mm

Crankshaft and bearings

Main bearing journal diameter:

Standard	57.98 to 58.00 mm
0.25 mm undersize	57.73 to 57.75 mm
0.50 mm undersize	57.48 to 57.50 mm
0.75 mm undersize	57.23 to 57.25 mm
Main bearing journal-to-shell running clearance	0.011 to 0.058 mm

Crankpin (big-end) bearing journal diameter:

Standard	47.89 to 47.91 mm
0.25 mm undersize	47.64 to 47.66 mm
0.50 mm undersize	47.39 to 47.41 mm
0.75 mm undersize	47.14 to 47.16 mm
1.00 mm undersize	46.89 to 46.91 mm
Crankpin (big-end) bearing journal-to-shell running clearance	0.006 to 0.060 mm
Crankshaft endfloat	0.09 to 0.30 mm

Thrustwasher thickness:

Standard	2.301 to 2.351 mm
Oversize	2.491 to 2.541 mm

Torque wrench settings

	Nm	lbf ft
Main bearing caps	95	70
Crankpin (big-end) bearing caps	33	24
Engine-to-transmission bolts	41	30

Note: *Refer to Part B of this Chapter for remaining torque wrench settings.*

Zetec engines

Cylinder head

Maximum permissible gasket surface distortion	0.10 mm
Valve seat included angle	90°
Valve guide bore	6.060 to 6.091 mm

Valves - general

	Inlet	Exhaust
Valve length	96.870 to 97.330 mm	96.470 to 96.930 mm
Valve head diameter:		
1.6 litre engine	26.0 mm	24.5 mm
1.8 litre engine	32.0 mm	28.0 mm
Valve stem diameter	6.028 to 6.043 mm	6.010 to 6.025 mm
Valve stem-to-guide clearance	0.017 to 0.064 mm	0.035 to 0.081 mm

Cylinder block

Cylinder bore diameter:	
1.6 litre engine:	
Class 1	76.000 to 76.010 mm
Class 2	76.010 to 76.020 mm
Class 3	76.020 to 76.030 mm
1.8 litre engine:	
Class 1	80.600 to 80.610 mm
Class 2	80.610 to 80.620 mm
Class 3	80.620 to 80.630 mm

Pistons and piston rings

Piston diameter	
1.6 litre engine:	
Class 1	75.975 to 75.985 mm
Class 2	75.985 to 75.995 mm
Class 3	75.995 to 76.005 mm
1.8 litre engine:	
Class 1	80.570 to 80.580 mm
Class 2	80.580 to 80.590 mm
Class 3	80.590 to 80.600 mm
Oversizes - all engines	None available
Piston-to-cylinder bore clearance	Not specified
Piston ring end gaps - installed:	
Compression rings	0.30 to 0.50 mm
Oil control ring:	
1.6 litre engine	0.25 to 1.00 mm
1.8 litre engine	0.38 to 1.14 mm

Gudgeon pin

Diameter:	
White colour code/piston crown marked "A"	20.622 to 20.625 mm
Red colour code/piston crown marked "B"	20.625 to 20.628 mm
Blue colour code/piston crown marked "C"	20.628 to 20.631 mm
Clearance in piston	0.010 to 0.016 mm
Interference fit in connecting rod	0.011 to 0.042 mm

Crankshaft and bearings

Main bearing journal standard diameter	57.980 to 58.000 mm
Main bearing journal-to-shell running clearance	0.011 to 0.058 mm
Main bearing shell undersizes available	0.02 mm, 0.25 mm
Crankpin (big-end) bearing journal standard diameter	46.890 to 46.910 mm
Crankpin (big-end) bearing journal-to-shell running clearance	0.016 to 0.070 mm
Big-end bearing shell undersizes available	0.02 mm, 0.25 mm
Crankshaft endfloat	0.090 to 0.310 mm

2D

Torque wrench settings

	Nm	lbf ft
Main bearing cap bolts and nuts	80	59
Crankpin (big-end) bearing cap bolts:		
Stage 1	18	13
Stage 2	Angle-tighten a further 90°	
Piston-cooling oil jet/blanking plug Torx screws	9	7
Cylinder block and head oilway blanking plugs:		
M6 x 10	9	7
M10 x 11.5 - in block	23	17
1/4 PTF plug - in block	24	18
Engine-to-transmission bolts	41	30

Note: *Refer to Part C of this Chapter for remaining torque wrench settings.*

1 General information

Included in this Part of Chapter 2 are details of removing the engine/transmission from the car and general overhaul procedures for the cylinder head, cylinder block/crankcase and all other engine internal components.

The information given ranges from advice concerning preparation for an overhaul and the purchase of replacement parts, to detailed step-by-step procedures covering removal, inspection, renovation and refitting of engine internal components.

After Section 6, all instructions are based on the assumption that the engine has been removed from the car. For information concerning in-car engine repair, as well as the removal and refitting of those external components necessary for full overhaul, refer to Part A, B or C of this Chapter (as applicable) and to Section 6. Ignore any preliminary dismantling operations described in Part A, B or C that are no longer relevant once the engine has been removed from the car.

2 Engine/transmission removal - preparation and precautions

If you have decided that an engine must be removed for overhaul or major repair work, several preliminary steps should be taken.

Locating a suitable place to work is extremely important. Adequate work space, along with storage space for the car, will be needed. If a workshop or garage is not available, at the very least, a flat, level, clean work surface is required.

If possible, clear some shelving close to the work area and use it to store the engine components and ancillaries as they are removed and dismantled. In this manner the components stand a better chance of staying clean and undamaged during the overhaul. Laying out components in groups together with their fixing bolts, screws etc will save time and avoid confusion when the engine is refitted.

Clean the engine compartment and engine/transmission before beginning the removal procedure; this will help visibility and help to keep tools clean.

On three of the engines covered in this manual (CVH, PTE, and Zetec), the unit can only be withdrawn by removing it complete with the transmission; the vehicle's body must be raised and supported securely, sufficiently high that the engine/transmission can be unbolted as a single unit and lowered to the ground; the engine/transmission unit can then be withdrawn from under the vehicle and separated. On all engines, an engine hoist or A-frame will be necessary. Make sure the equipment is rated in excess of the combined weight of the engine and transmission.

The help of an assistant should be available; there are certain instances when one person cannot safely perform all of the operations required to remove the engine from the vehicle. Safety is of primary importance, considering the potential hazards involved in this kind of operation. A second person should always be in attendance to offer help in an emergency. If this is the first time you have removed an engine, advice and aid from someone more experienced would also be beneficial.

Plan the operation ahead of time. Before starting work, obtain (or arrange for the hire of) all of the tools and equipment you will need. Access to the following items will allow the task of removing and refitting the engine/transmission to be completed safely and with relative ease: an engine hoist - rated in excess of the combined weight of the engine/transmission, a heavy-duty trolley jack, complete sets of spanners and sockets as described in *"Tools and working facilities"* at the rear this manual, wooden blocks, and plenty of rags and cleaning solvent for mopping up spilled oil, coolant and fuel. A selection of different sized plastic storage bins will also prove useful for keeping dismantled components grouped together. If any of the equipment must be hired, make sure that you arrange for it in advance, and perform all of the operations possible without it beforehand; this may save you time and money.

Plan on the vehicle being out of use for quite a while, especially if you intend to carry out an engine overhaul. Read through the whole of this Section and work out a strategy based on your own experience and the tools, time and workspace available to you. Some of the overhaul processes may have to be carried out by a Ford dealer or an engineering works - these establishments often have busy schedules, so it would be prudent to consult them before removing or dismantling the engine, to get an idea of the amount of time required to carry out the work.

When removing the engine from the vehicle, be methodical about the disconnection of external components. Labelling cables and hoses as they removed will greatly assist the refitting process.

Always be extremely careful when lifting the engine/transmission assembly from the engine bay. Serious injury can result from careless actions. If help is required, it is better to wait until it is available rather than risk personal injury and/or damage to components by continuing alone. By planning ahead and taking your time, a job of this nature, although major, can be accomplished successfully and without incident.

3 Engine - removal and refitting (HCS engines)

 Warning: Petrol is extremely flammable, so take extra precautions when disconnecting any part of the fuel system. *Don't smoke, or allow naked flames or bare light bulbs, in or near the work area, and don't work in a garage where a natural-gas appliance (such as a clothes dryer or water heater) is installed. If you spill petrol on your skin, rinse it off immediately. Have a fire extinguisher rated for petrol fires handy, and know how to use it.* **Note:** *Read through the entire Section, as well as reading the advice in the preceding Section, before beginning this procedure. The engine is removed separately from the transmission and is lifted upwards and out of the engine compartment.*

Removal

1 On fuel injection engines, refer to Chapter 4B and depressurise the fuel system.
2 Disconnect the battery negative (earth) lead (refer to Chapter 5A, Section 1).

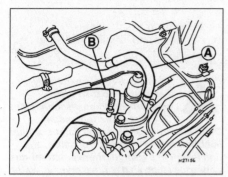

3.6a Disconnect the overflow hose (A) and the top hose (B) from the thermostat housing

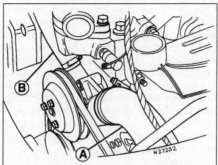

3.6b Disconnect the bottom hose (A) and the heater hose (B) from the water pump

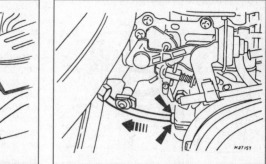

3.8 Detach the servo vacuum hose from the manifold

3 Referring to Chapter 1 for details, drain the coolant and engine oil. Refit the drain plug to the sump on completion.

4 Remove the bonnet as described in Chapter 11.

5 Remove the air cleaner assembly as described in the relevant Part of Chapter 4.

6 Release the retaining clips and detach the

HAYNES HINT

Whenever you disconnect any vacuum lines, coolant or emissions hoses, wiring connectors and fuel lines, always label them clearly, so that they can be correctly reassembled. Masking tape and/or a touch-up paint applicator work well for marking items. Take instant photos, or sketch the locations of components and brackets.

following coolant hoses. Allow for coolant spillage as the hoses are detached **(see illustrations)**:

a) *All hoses at the thermostat housing.*
b) *Bottom hose from the radiator to the water pump.*
c) *Heater hoses at the bulkhead and water pump.*
d) *Inlet manifold coolant supply hose (where applicable).*

7 Disconnect the fuel trap vacuum hose from the inlet manifold.

8 Disconnect the brake servo unit vacuum hose from the inlet manifold, by pushing the hose retainer in towards the manifold and simultaneously pulling free the hose **(see illustration)**.

9 Refer to the relevant Part of Chapter 4 for details, and detach the accelerator cable. Where applicable, detach the choke cable from the carburettor.

10 Compress the quick-release couplings at the sides, and detach the fuel supply hose and return hose from the fuel pump, CFi unit or fuel rail **(see illustration)**. Allow for fuel spillage as the hoses are disconnected, and plug the exposed ends to prevent further

spillage and the ingress of dirt. Position the hoses out of the way.

11 Note their locations and disconnect the wiring connectors from the following **(see illustrations)**:

a) *Coolant temperature gauge sender unit.*
b) *The oil pressure switch.*
c) *The radio earth lead.*
d) *The cooling fan thermostatic switch.*
e) *The DIS/E-DIS ignition coil.*
f) *The crankshaft speed/position sensor.*
g) *The engine coolant temperature sensor.*
h) *The idle cut-off valve.*

12 Disconnect the remaining wiring multi-plugs from the engine sensors at the inlet manifold and from the oxygen sensor (where fitted) in the exhaust manifold or downpipe.

13 Chock the rear wheels then jack up the front of the car and support it on axle stands (see *"Jacking and Vehicle Support"*).

14 Unscrew the retaining nuts, and detach the exhaust downpipe from the exhaust manifold. Remove the seal from the joint flange.

15 Refer to Chapter 5A for details, and remove the starter motor.

16 Undo the two retaining bolts, and remove the clutch lower cover plate.

17 Unscrew the retaining bolt, and detach the gearshift stabiliser from the transmission.

18 Unscrew and remove the engine/

2D

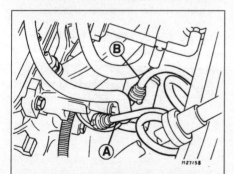

3.10 Fuel supply (A) and return (B) hose connections at the fuel pump

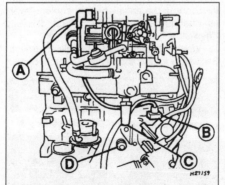

3.11a Wiring connections to the HCS engine

A *Idle cut-off valve*
B *DIS ignition coil*
C *Engine coolant temperature sensor*
D *Oil pressure switch*

3.11b Engine crankshaft position sensor and multi-plug

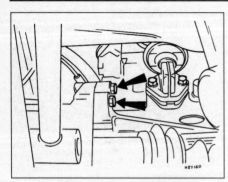

3.18 Engine-to-transmission flange attachment bolts (arrowed)

transmission flange attachment bolts **(see illustration)**.

19 Check that the appropriate underside attachments are disconnected and out of the way, then lower the vehicle to the ground.

20 Unbolt and remove the heat shield from the exhaust manifold.

21 Attach a suitable hoist to the engine. It is possible to fabricate lifting eyes to connect the hoist to the engine, but make sure that they are strong enough, and connect them to the inlet and exhaust manifold at diagonally-opposite ends of the engine.

22 With the hoist securely connected, take the weight of the engine. Unscrew and remove the right-hand engine mounting side bolt from under the right-hand wheel arch. Unscrew and remove the mounting retaining nut and washer from the suspension strut cup retaining plate, and the three bolts securing the mounting unit to the cylinder block.

23 Locate a jack under the transmission, and raise it to take the weight of the transmission.

24 Unscrew and remove the remaining engine-to-transmission retaining bolts on the upper flange.

25 Check around the engine to ensure that all of the relevant fixings and attachments are disconnected and out of the way for the removal.

26 Enlist the aid of an assistant, then move the engine sideways and away from the transmission, whilst simultaneously raising the transmission. When the engine is separated from the transmission, carefully guide it up and out of the engine compartment. Do not allow the weight of the engine to hang on the transmission input shaft at any point during the removal (or refitting) of the engine. When the engine sump is clear of the vehicle, swing the power unit out of the way, and lower it onto a trolley (if available). Unless a mobile hoist is being used, it will be necessary to move the vehicle rearwards and out of the way in order to allow the engine to be lowered for removal. In this instance, ensure that the weight of the transmission is well supported as the vehicle is moved.

27 While the engine is removed, check the mountings; renew them if they are worn or damaged. Similarly, check the condition of all coolant and vacuum hoses and pipes (see

Chapter 1); components that are normally hidden can now be checked properly, and should be renewed if there is any doubt at all about their condition. Also, take the opportunity to overhaul the clutch components (see Chapter 6). It is regarded by many as good working practice to renew the clutch assembly as a matter of course, whenever major engine overhaul work is carried out. Check also the condition of all components disturbed on removal, and renew any that are damaged or worn.

Refitting

28 Refitting is in general, a reversal of the removal procedure, but the following special points should be noted.

29 Before coupling the engine to the transmission, apply a thin smear of high-melting-point grease onto the transmission input shaft splines. If the clutch has been removed, ensure that the clutch disc is centralised, and disconnect the clutch cable from the release lever on the transmission casing.

30 Tighten all fixings to their recommended torque wrench settings.

31 Check that the mating faces are clean, and fit a new exhaust downpipe-to-manifold gasket and self-locking nuts when reconnecting this joint.

32 Ensure that all wiring connections are correctly and securely made.

33 Remove the plugs from the fuel lines before reconnecting them correctly and securely.

34 Reconnect and adjust the accelerator and choke cables as described in the relevant Part of Chapter 4. The refitting details for the air cleaner components are also given in that Chapter.

35 Renew any coolant hoses (and/or retaining clips) that are not in good condition.

36 Refer to Chapter 6 for details on reconnecting the clutch cable.

37 When the engine is fully refitted, check that the various hoses are connected, and then top-up the engine oil and coolant levels as described in Chapter 1 and *"Weekly Checks"*.

38 When engine refitting is completed, refer to Section 19 for the engine start-up procedures.

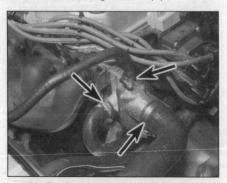

4.6a Coolant hose connections to the thermostat (arrowed)

4 Engine/transmission - removal and refitting (CVH and PTE engines)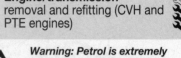

 Warning: Petrol is extremely flammable, so take extra precautions when disconnecting any part of the fuel system.
Don't smoke, or allow naked flames or bare light bulbs, in or near the work area, and don't work in a garage where a natural-gas appliance (such as a clothes dryer or water heater) is installed. If you spill petrol on your skin, rinse it off immediately. Have a fire extinguisher rated for petrol fires handy, and know how to use it.
Note: *Read through the entire Section, as well as reading the advice in Section 2, before beginning this procedure. The engine and transmission are removed as a unit, lowered to the ground and removed from underneath, then separated outside the vehicle.*

Removal

1 On all fuel injection engines, refer to Chapter 4B, C or D as applicable and depressurise the fuel system.

2 Disconnect the battery negative (earth) lead (refer to Chapter 5A, Section 1).

3 Referring to Chapter 1 for details, drain the coolant and the engine oil. Refit the drain plug to the sump on completion.

4 Refer to Chapter 11 for details, and remove the bonnet.

5 Remove the air cleaner assembly and air inlet components as described in the relevant Part of Chapter 4.

6 Release the retaining clips and detach the coolant top hose, the heater hose and the radiator overflow hose from the thermostat housing. Disconnect the coolant hose from the inlet manifold, and the bottom hose from the water pump and/or the radiator **(see illustrations)**. On 1.4 litre CFi fuel injection models, also disconnect the coolant hose from the injection unit. On EFi and SEFi fuel injection models, detach the heater hose Y-connector. Allow for coolant spillage as the hoses are detached. On turbocharged engines, disconnect the coolant return hose from the turbocharger connecting pipe.

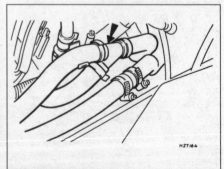

4.6b Heater coolant hoses and Y-connector on 1.6 litre EFi fuel injection models

4.11 Vacuum hose to MAP sensor (A) and brake servo (B)

4.12a Disconnect the wiring at the temperature gauge sender unit . . .

4.12b . . . the oil pressure switch . . .

> **HAYNES HINT**
>
> *Whenever you disconnect any vacuum lines, coolant or emissions hoses, wiring connectors and fuel lines, always label them clearly, so that they can be correctly reassembled. Masking tape and/or a touch-up paint applicator work well for marking items. Take instant photos, or sketch the locations of components and brackets.*

7 Refer to the relevant Part of Chapter 4 for details, and disconnect the accelerator cable from the throttle linkage and support/adjuster bracket. Where applicable, also disconnect the choke cable. Position the cable(s) out of the way.

8 On carburettor models, disconnect the fuel supply hose from the fuel pump, and the return hose from the carburettor.

9 On CFi models, detach the fuel hose at the injector/pressure regulator unit, and the return line, by compressing the couplings whilst pulling the hoses free from their connections. On EFi and SEFi models, unscrew the union nut to detach the fuel line from the fuel rail; release the retaining clip to detach the return pipe from the pressure regulator. Plug the exposed ends of the hoses and connections, to prevent fuel spillage and the ingress of dirt. Position the hoses out of the way.

10 Press the clamp ring inwards, and simultaneously pull free the brake servo hose

from the inlet manifold. Position it out of the way.

11 On CFi and EFi models, detach the vacuum hose from the MAP sensor, and the hose between the carbon canister and the fuel injection unit **(see illustration)**.

12 Note their connections and routings, and detach the following wiring connections, according to model **(see illustrations)**:
a) Coolant temperature sender unit.
b) Oil pressure switch.
c) E-DIS ignition coil unit. or distributor.
d) Coolant temperature sensor.
e) Cooling fan thermostatic switch.
f) Carburettor.
g) Earth lead (radio).
h) Reversing light switch (from transmission).
i) Crankshaft position sensor.
j) Earth leads from the transmission and engine.

13 Disconnect the wiring at the following additional items specific to fuel injection models only.
a) Inlet air temperature sensor.
b) Vehicle speed sensor.
c) Throttle plate control motor (CFi models).
d) Throttle position sensor.
e) Injector harness connector.
f) Idle speed control valve (EFi and SEFi models).

14 Unscrew the retaining bolt and detach the bracket locating the wiring and coolant hoses above the transmission.

15 Disconnect the speedometer drive cable from the transmission.

16 On manual transmission models, disconnect the clutch cable from the release lever at the transmission (see Chapter 6 for details). Position the cable out of the way.

17 On vehicles fitted with the anti-lock braking system, refer to Chapter 9 and release the left-hand modulator from its mounting bracket, without disconnecting the rigid brake pipes or return hose. Tie the modulator securely to the bulkhead.

18 Chock the rear wheels then jack up the front of the car and support it on axle stands (see *"Jacking and Vehicle Support"*). Allow sufficient clearance under the vehicle to withdraw the engine and transmission units from under the front end.

19 On XR2i models, refer to Chapter 10 and remove the front suspension crossmember.

20 Where applicable on catalytic converter-equipped vehicles, release the multi-plug from the bracket and disconnect the wiring connector from the oxygen sensor in the exhaust downpipe.

21 Undo the three retaining bolts, detach the exhaust downpipe from the manifold, and collect the gasket from the flange joint. Now disconnect the exhaust downpipe from the rest of the system, and remove it from the vehicle.

22 Where fitted, undo the four retaining nuts and two bolts securing the front part of the exhaust heat shield to the floor, then remove the heat shield.

23 Refer to Chapter 5A and remove the alternator and starter motor. On models with power steering, refer to Chapter 10 and remove the power steering pump.

Manual transmission models

24 On 4-speed models, select 2nd gear; on 5-speed models, select 4th gear, to assist in correct adjustment of the gearchange during reassembly. If it is likely that the gear lever will be moved from this position before refitting, mark the relative position of the transmission shift rod and the selector shaft before separating them. Undo the clamp bolt, and then pull free and detach the shift rod from the selector shaft **(see illustration)**.

4.12c . . . and the crankshaft position sensor

4.24 Manual transmission shift rod clamp bolt (A), stabiliser-to-transmission bolt (B) and washer (C)

2D

25 Unscrew the retaining bolt, and detach the shift rod stabiliser from the transmission. As it is detached, note the washer located between the stabiliser and the transmission. Tie the stabiliser and the shift rod up out of the way.

Automatic transmission models

26 Unclip and detach the wiring connector from the starter inhibitor switch (on the transmission housing).

27 Referring to the relevant Part of Chapter 4 for details, unhook the accelerator (cam plate) cable from the carburettor or fuel injection unit (as applicable) at the transmission end of the cable. Undo the retaining bolt and detach the cable sheath bracket from the transmission. Detach the cam plate cable from the link.

28 Undo the two nuts from the selector cable bracket which connects it to the lever on the selector shaft. Disconnect the yoke from the lever on the selector shaft and the cable from the lever.

29 Unscrew the union nuts, and disconnect the oil cooler feed and return pipes from the transmission. Allow for a certain amount of spillage, and plug the connections to prevent the ingress of dirt.

All models

30 Unscrew the retaining nut and withdraw the Torx-type clamp bolt securing the lower suspension arm to the spindle carrier on each side.

31 Refer to Chapter 10 for details, and detach the right-hand and left-hand track rod end balljoints from the spindle carriers.

32 On vehicles fitted with the anti-lock braking system, refer to Chapter 9 and release the right-hand modulator from its mounting bracket without disconnecting the rigid brake pipes or return hose. Tie the modulator securely to the bulkhead. Additionally, undo the three bolts securing the modulator bracket.

33 Insert a suitable lever between the right-hand driveshaft inner joint and the transmission housing, and prise free the driveshaft from the transmission; be prepared for oil spillage from the transmission case through the vacated driveshaft aperture. As it is being prised free, simultaneously pull the roadwheel outwards on that side, to enable the driveshaft inboard end to separate from the transmission. Once it is free, suspend and support the driveshaft from the steering gear, to prevent unnecessary strain being placed on the driveshaft joints.

34 Insert a suitable plastic plug (or if available, an old driveshaft joint), into the transmission driveshaft aperture, to immobilise the gears of the differential unit.

35 Proceed as described above in paragraphs 33 and 34, and disconnect the left-hand driveshaft from the transmission.

36 Connect a suitable lift hoist and sling to the engine, connecting to the lifting eyes.

When securely connected, take the weight of the engine/transmission unit so that the tension is relieved from the mountings.

37 Undo the retaining bolts and nuts and detach the right-hand engine mounting from the vehicle body.

38 Undo the four bolts securing the transmission bearer to the underside of the vehicle body. The transmission bearer is removed with the engine/transmission assembly.

39 Unscrew the three retaining bolts, and remove the auxiliary drivebelt cover from under the crankshaft pulley.

40 The engine/transmission unit should now be ready for removal from the vehicle. Check that all of the associated connections and fittings are disconnected from the engine and transmission, and positioned out of the way.

41 Enlist the aid of an assistant to help steady and guide the power unit down through the engine compartment as it is removed. If available, position a suitable engine trolley or crawler board under the engine/transmission so that when lowered, the power unit can be withdrawn from the front end of the vehicle, and then moved to the area where it is to be cleaned and dismantled. On automatic transmission models, particular care must be taken not to damage the transmission fluid pan (sump) during the removal and subsequent refitting processes.

42 Carefully lower the engine and transmission unit, ensuring that no fittings become snagged. Detach the hoist and remove the power unit from under the vehicle.

43 Referring to the relevant Part of Chapter 7, separate the transmission from the engine.

44 While the engine/transmission is removed, check the mountings; renew them if they are worn or damaged. Similarly, check the condition of all coolant and vacuum hoses and pipes (see Chapter 1). Components that are normally hidden can now be checked properly, and should be renewed if there is any doubt at all about their condition. Where the vehicle is fitted with manual transmission, take the opportunity to inspect the clutch components (see Chapter 6). It is regarded by many as good working practice to renew the clutch assembly as a matter of course, whenever major engine overhaul work is carried out. Check also the condition of all components (such as the transmission oil seals) disturbed on removal, and renew any that are damaged or worn.

Refitting

45 Refitting is a reversal of removal, however note the following additional points:

a) *Refer to the applicable Chapters and Sections as for removal.*

b) *Fit new spring clips to the grooves in the inboard end of the right- and left-hand driveshaft joints. Lubricate the splines with transmission oil prior to fitting.*

c) *Renew the exhaust flange gasket when reconnecting the exhaust. Ensure that all wires are routed clear of the exhaust system and, on catalytic converter models, ensure that the heat shields are securely and correctly fitted.*

d) *Ensure that all earth lead connections are clean and securely made.*

e) *Tighten all nuts and bolts to the specified torque.*

f) *Fit a new oil filter, and refill the engine and transmission with oil, with reference to Chapter 1.*

g) *Refill the cooling system with reference to Chapter 1.*

h) *Refit the alternator and starter motor with reference to Chapter 5A.*

i) *Where applicable, refit the power steering pump with reference to Chapter 10.*

46 When engine and transmission refitting is complete, refer to the procedures described in Section 19 before restarting the engine.

---

5 Engine/transmission - removal and refitting (Zetec engines)

⚠️ *Warning: Petrol is extremely flammable, so take extra precautions when disconnecting any part of the fuel system.* **Don't smoke, or allow naked flames or bare light bulbs, in or near the work area, and don't work in a garage where a natural-gas appliance (such as a clothes dryer or water heater) is installed. If you spill petrol on your skin, rinse it off immediately. Have a fire extinguisher rated for petrol fires handy, and know how to use it.** **Note:** *Read through the entire Section, as well as reading the advice in Section 2, before beginning this procedure. The engine and transmission are removed as a unit, lowered to the ground and removed from underneath, then separated outside the vehicle.*

Removal

1 Park the vehicle on firm, level ground, apply the handbrake firmly, and slacken the nuts securing both front roadwheels.

2 Depressurise the fuel system as described in Chapter 4D.

3 Disconnect the battery negative (earth) lead (refer to Chapter 5A, Section 1).

4 Place protective covers on the wings, then remove the bonnet (see Chapter 11).

5 Drain the cooling system and the engine oil (see Chapter 1).

6 Remove the air inlet components and the complete air cleaner assembly as described in Chapter 4D.

7 Equalise the pressure in the fuel tank by removing the filler cap, then release the fuel feed and return quick-release couplings, and pull the hoses off the fuel pipes. Plug or cap all open fittings.

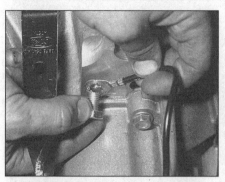

5.11 Unbolt the engine/transmission-to-body earth lead from the transmission

5.14a Disconnect the wiring multi-plug from the ignition coil . . .

5.14b . . . the radio interference suppressor . . .

> **HAYNES HiNT**
>
> *Whenever you disconnect any vacuum lines, coolant or emissions hoses, wiring connectors and fuel lines, always label them clearly, so that they can be correctly reassembled. Masking tape and/or a touch-up paint applicator work well for marking items. Take instant photos, or sketch the locations of components and brackets.*

8 Disconnect the accelerator cable from the throttle linkage as described in Chapter 4D. Secure the cable clear of the engine/transmission.

9 Releasing its wire clip, unplug the wiring connector from the power steering pressure switch (where fitted), then disconnect the earth cable from the engine lifting eye. Refit the bolt after disconnecting the cable.

10 Marking or labelling all components as they are disconnected, disconnect the vacuum hoses as follows:

a) *From the rear of the inlet manifold.*
b) *The braking system vacuum servo unit hose - from the inlet manifold (see Chapter 9 for details).*
c) *While you are there, trace the vacuum line from the pulse-air filter housing, and disconnect it from the pulse-air solenoid valve.*
d) *Secure all these hoses so that they won't get damaged as the engine/transmission is removed.*

11 Unbolt the engine/transmission-to-body

earth lead from the transmission **(see illustration)**. Disconnect the speedometer drive cable (see Chapter 12) and secure it clear of the engine/transmission.

12 Disconnect the earth strap at the top of the engine/transmission flange, and the adjacent bolt securing the wiring harness clip.

13 Where the vehicle is fitted with manual transmission, disconnect the clutch cable (see Chapter 6).

14 Marking or labelling all components as they are disconnected, disconnect the engine wiring connectors as follows **(see illustrations)**:

a) *The multi-plug from the E-DIS ignition coil.*
b) *The radio interference suppressor from the DIS ignition coil.*
c) *The reversing light switch multi-plug.*
d) *The engine main wiring loom multi-plug behind the E-DIS ignition coil.*
e) *The crankshaft speed/position sensor and vehicle speed sensor multi-plugs.*
f) *The oxygen sensor multi-plug.*

15 Unbolt the exhaust manifold heat shield, and lift it clear.

16 Remove the auxiliary drivebelt (see Chapter 1).

17 Marking or labelling all components as they are disconnected and catching as much as possible of the escaping coolant in the drain tray, disconnect the cooling system hoses and pipes as follows:

a) *The coolant hoses at the thermostat housing.*

b) *The coolant hose at the metal cross pipe lower connection.*
c) *The radiator top and bottom hoses.*

18 Where applicable, detach the power steering pump pressure pipe clips, release the unions and disconnect the pump pressure and return lines. Collect the fluid in a suitable container, and plug the disconnected unions.

19 On vehicles fitted with the anti-lock braking system, refer to Chapter 9 and release the left-hand modulator from its mounting bracket, without disconnecting the rigid brake pipes or return hose. Tie the modulator securely to the bulkhead.

20 Chock the rear wheels then jack up the front of the car and support it on axle stands (see *"Jacking and Vehicle Support"*). Remove the front roadwheels.

21 Refer to Chapter 5 if necessary, and disconnect the wiring from the starter motor and alternator.

22 Disconnect the oil pressure switch wiring connector.

23 On automatic transmission models, disconnect the starter inhibitor switch wiring and disconnect the selector cable (see Chapter 7B). Secure the cable clear of the engine/transmission.

24 Where the vehicle is fitted with manual transmission, disconnect the gearchange linkage and transmission support rod from the rear of the transmission - make alignment marks as they are disconnected **(see illustrations)**.

2D

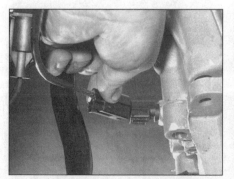

5.14c . . . and the reversing light switch

5.24a Disconnect the gearchange linkage . . .

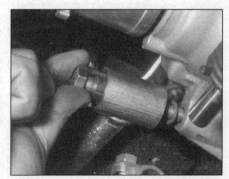

5.24b . . . and transmission support rod

25 On automatic transmission models, clean around the unions, then disconnect the fluid pipes from the transmission. Plug the openings in the transmission and the pipe unions after removal.

26 Refer to Chapter 10 and remove the front suspension crossmember.

27 Unscrew the nuts to disconnect the exhaust system front downpipe from the manifold. Undo the nuts securing the catalytic converter to the rear part of the exhaust system, and remove the converter and downpipe assembly.

28 On vehicles fitted with the anti-lock braking system, refer to Chapter 9 and release the right-hand modulator from its mounting bracket without disconnecting the rigid brake pipes or return hose. Tie the modulator securely to the bulkhead. Additionally, undo the three bolts securing the modulator bracket.

29 Disconnect both anti-roll bar links from their respective suspension struts, and both track rod end ball joints from their spindle carriers (see Chapter 10).

30 Unscrew the retaining nut and withdraw the Torx-type clamp bolt securing the lower suspension arm to the spindle carrier on each side.

31 Insert a suitable lever between the right-hand driveshaft inner joint and the transmission housing, and prise free the driveshaft from the transmission; be prepared for oil spillage from the transmission case through the vacated driveshaft aperture. As it is being prised free, simultaneously pull the roadwheel outwards on that side to enable the driveshaft inboard end to separate from the transmission. Once it is free, suspend and support the driveshaft from the steering gear, to prevent unnecessary strain being placed on the driveshaft joints.

32 Insert a suitable plastic plug (or if available, an old driveshaft joint), into the transmission driveshaft aperture, to immobilise the gears of the differential unit.

33 Proceed as described above in paragraphs 31 and 32, and disconnect the left-hand driveshaft from the transmission.

34 Remove the oil filter, referring to Chapter 1 if necessary.

35 Connect a suitable lift hoist and sling to the engine, connecting to the lift eyes. When securely connected, take the weight of the engine/transmission unit so that the tension is relieved from the mountings.

36 Unbolt the engine rear right-hand mounting from the body (one bolt in the wheel arch, one nut in the engine compartment), then unbolt the engine front right-hand mounting from the alternator mounting bracket. Unbolt the transmission bearer from the underbody.

37 The engine/transmission unit should now be hanging on the hoist only, with all components which connect it to the rest of the vehicle disconnected or removed, and secured well clear of the unit. Make a final check that this is the case.

38 Lower the engine/transmission to the ground, and withdraw it from under the vehicle.

39 Referring to the relevant Part of Chapter 7, separate the transmission from the engine.

40 While the engine/transmission is removed, check the mountings; renew them if they are worn or damaged. Similarly, check the condition of all coolant and vacuum hoses and pipes (see Chapter 1); components that are normally hidden can now be checked properly, and should be renewed if there is any doubt at all about their condition. Where the vehicle is fitted with manual transmission, take the opportunity to overhaul the clutch components (see Chapter 6). It is regarded by many as good working practice to renew the clutch assembly as a matter of course, whenever major engine overhaul work is carried out. Check also the condition of all components (such as the transmission oil seals) disturbed on removal, and renew any that are damaged or worn.

Refitting

41 Refitting is a reversal of removal, however note the following additional points:

a) Refer to the applicable Chapters and Sections as for removal.

b) Fit new spring clips to the grooves in the inboard end of the right- and left-hand driveshaft joints. Lubricate the splines with transmission oil prior to fitting.

c) Renew the exhaust flange gaskets when reconnecting the exhaust. Ensure that all wires are routed clear of the exhaust system, and that the heat shields are securely and correctly fitted.

d) Ensure that all earth lead connections are clean and securely made.

e) Tighten all nuts and bolts to the specified torque.

f) Fit a new oil filter, and refill the engine and transmission with oil, with reference to Chapter 1.

g) Refill the cooling system with reference to Chapter 1.

h) Bleed the power steering system with reference to Chapter 10.

42 When engine and transmission refitting is complete, refer to the procedures described in Section 19 before restarting the engine.

6 Engine overhaul - preliminary information

It is much easier to dismantle and work on the engine if it is mounted on a portable engine stand. These stands can often be hired from a tool hire shop. Before the engine is mounted on a stand, the flywheel/driveplate should be removed so that the stand bolts can be tightened into the end of the cylinder block/crankcase.

If a stand is not available, it is possible to dismantle the engine with it suitably supported on a sturdy, workbench or on the floor. Be careful not to tip or drop the engine when working without a stand.

If you intend to obtain a reconditioned engine, all ancillaries must be removed first, to be transferred to the replacement engine (just as they will if you are doing a complete engine overhaul yourself). These components include the following:

a) Alternator/power steering pump and mounting brackets.

b) DIS/E-DIS ignition coil unit (and mounting bracket), distributor, HT leads and spark plugs.

c) The thermostat and housing cover.

d) Carburettor/fuel injection system components.

e) Inlet and exhaust manifolds.

f) Oil filter.

g) Fuel pump.

h) Engine mountings.

i) Flywheel/driveplate.

j) Water pump.

Note: When removing the external components from the engine, pay close attention to details that may be helpful or important during refitting. Note the fitted positions of gaskets, seals, washers, bolts and other small items.

If you are obtaining a "short" engine (cylinder block/crankcase, crankshaft, pistons and connecting rods all assembled), then the cylinder head, timing chain/belt (together with tensioner, tensioner and idler pulleys and covers) sump and oil pump will have to be removed also.

If a complete overhaul is planned, the engine can be dismantled in the order given below, referring to Part A, B or C of this Chapter unless otherwise stated.

a) Inlet and exhaust manifolds.

b) Timing chain/belt, tensioner and sprockets.

c) Cylinder head.

d) Flywheel/driveplate.

e) Sump.

f) Oil pump.

g) Pistons (with connecting rods).

h) Crankshaft.

i) Camshaft and tappets (HCS engines).

7 Cylinder head - dismantling

Note: New and reconditioned cylinder heads are available from the manufacturers, and from engine overhaul specialists. Due to the fact that some specialist tools are required for the dismantling and inspection procedures, and new components may not be readily available, it may be more practical and economical for the home mechanic to purchase a reconditioned head, rather than to dismantle, inspect and recondition the original head.

1 Remove the cylinder head as described in Part A, B or C of this Chapter (as applicable).

7.6 Compress the valve spring to remove the collets

7.7a Remove the valve spring retainer and spring . . .

7.7b . . . followed by the valve

2 If not already done, remove the inlet and exhaust manifolds with reference to the relevant Part of Chapter 4.

3 Proceed as follows according to engine type.

HCS engines

4 Valve removal should commence with No 1 valve (nearest the timing chain end).

5 To remove the valve springs and valves from the cylinder head, a standard valve spring compressor will required. Fit the spring compressor to the first valve and spring to be removed. Take care not to damage the valve stem with the compressor, and do not over-compress the spring, or the valve stem may bend. When tightening the compressor, it may be found that the spring retainer does not release and the collets are then difficult to remove. In this instance, remove the compressor, then press a piece of tube (or a socket of suitable diameter) so that it does not interfere with the removal of the collets, against the retainer's outer rim. Tap the tube (or socket) with a hammer to unsettle the components.

6 Refit the compressor, and wind it in to enable the collets to be extracted **(see illustration)**.

7 Loosen off the compressor, and remove the retainer and spring. Withdraw the valve from the cylinder head **(see illustrations)**.

8 Prise up and remove the valve stem seal.

9 Repeat the removal procedure with each of the remaining seven valve assemblies in turn. As they are removed, keep the individual valves and their components together, and in their respective order of fitting, by placing them in a separate labelled bag **(see illustration)**.

CVH and PTE engines

10 Remove the camshaft, rocker arms and tappets as described in Part B of this Chapter, being careful to store the hydraulic tappets as described.

11 Valve removal should commence with No 1 valve (nearest the timing belt end).

12 Using a standard valve spring compressor, compress the valve spring (and upper retainer) just enough to enable the split collets to be released from the groove in the top of the valve stem, then separate and extract the split collets from the valve. Do not compress the spring any further than is necessary, or the valve stem may bend. If the valve spring retainer does not release from the collets as the spring is compressed, remove the compressor, and position a piece of suitable tube over the end of the retainer, so that it does not impinge on the collets. Place a small block of wood under the valve head (with the head resting face down on the workbench), then tap the end of the tube with a hammer. Now refit the compressor tool, and compress the valve spring. The collets should release.

13 Extract the split collets, then slowly unscrew, release and remove the compressor.

14 Withdraw the upper retainer and the valve spring from the valve stem, then remove the valve from the underside of the cylinder head. Use a suitable screwdriver or pliers to prise free and remove the valve stem oil seal from the guide **(see illustration)**.

15 Remove the lower retainer.

16 Repeat the removal procedure with each of the remaining valve assemblies in turn. As they are removed, keep the valves and their associated components together, and in the originally-installed order, by placing them in a separate labelled bag **(see illustration 7.9)**.

Zetec engines

17 Remove the camshafts and hydraulic tappets as described in Part C of this Chapter, being careful to store the hydraulic tappets as described.

18 Using a valve spring compressor, compress each valve spring in turn until the split collets can be removed. A special valve spring compressor will be required, to reach into the deep wells in the cylinder head without risk of damaging the hydraulic tappet bores; such compressors are now widely available from most good motor accessory shops. Release the compressor, and lift off the spring upper seat and spring.

19 If, when the valve spring compressor is screwed down, the spring upper seat refuses to free and expose the split collets, gently tap the top of the tool, directly over the upper seat, with a light hammer. This will free the seat.

20 Withdraw the valve through the combustion chamber. If it binds in the guide (won't pull through), push it back in, and de-burr the area around the collet groove with a fine file or whetstone; take care not to mark the hydraulic tappet bores.

21 Ford recommend the use of their service tool 21-160 to extract the valve spring lower seat/stem oil seals; while this is almost indispensable if the seals are to be removed without risk of damage to the cylinder head, a serviceable substitute can be made from a strong spring of suitable size. Screw on the tool or spring so that it bites into the seal, then

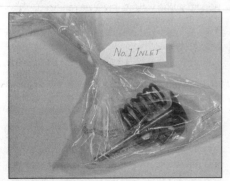

7.9 Use a labelled plastic bag to store and identify valve components

7.14 Prise off the valve stem oil seal

2D

7.21a Ford service tool in use to remove valve spring lower seat/stem oil seals . . .

7.21b . . . can be replaced by home-made tool if suitable spring can be found

7.23 Cylinder head oil-retaining valve (arrowed)

draw the seal off the valve guide **(see illustrations)**.

22 It is essential that the valves are kept together with their collets, spring seats and springs, and in their correct sequence (unless they are so badly worn that they are to be renewed). If they are going to be kept and used again, place them in a labelled polythene bag or similar small container **(see illustration 7.9)**. Note that No 1 valve is nearest to the timing belt end of the engine.

23 If the oil-retaining valve is to be removed (to flush out the cylinder head oil galleries thoroughly), seek the advice of a Ford dealer as to how it can be extracted; it may be that the only course of action involves destroying the valve as follows. Screw a self-tapping screw into its ventilation hole, and use the screw to provide purchase with which the valve can be drawn out; a new valve must be purchased and pressed into place on reassembly **(see illustration)**.

8 Cylinder head and valve components - cleaning and inspection

1 Thorough cleaning of the cylinder head and valve components, followed by a detailed inspection, will enable you to decide how much valve service work must be carried out during the engine overhaul. **Note:** *If the*

engine has been severely overheated, it is best to assume that the cylinder head is warped, and to check carefully for signs of this.

Cleaning

2 Scrape away all traces of old gasket material and sealing compound from the cylinder head.

3 Scrape away the carbon from the combustion chambers and ports, then wash the cylinder head thoroughly with paraffin or a suitable solvent.

4 Scrape off any heavy carbon deposits that may have formed on the valves, then use a power-operated wire brush to remove deposits from the valve heads and stems.

Inspection

Note: *Be sure to perform all the following inspection procedures before concluding that the services of a machine shop or engine overhaul specialist are required. Make a list of all items that require attention.*

Cylinder head

5 Inspect the head very carefully for cracks, evidence of coolant leakage, and other damage. If cracks are found, a new cylinder head should be obtained.

6 Use a straight edge and feeler blade to check that the cylinder head gasket surface is not distorted **(see illustration)**. If it is, it may be possible to re-surface it.

7 Examine the valve seats in each of the combustion chambers. If they are severely

pitted, cracked or burned, then they will need to be renewed or re-cut by an engine overhaul specialist. If they are only slightly pitted, this can be removed by grinding-in the valve heads and seats with fine valve-grinding compound, as described below.

8 If the valve guides are worn, indicated by a side-to-side motion of the valve, new guides must be fitted. Measure the diameter of the existing valve stems (see below) and the bore of the guides, then calculate the clearance, and compare the result with the specified value; if the clearance is excessive, renew the valves or guides as necessary.

9 The renewal of valve guides is best carried out by an engine overhaul specialist.

10 If the valve seats are to be re-cut, this must be done *only after* the guides have been renewed.

Valves

11 Examine the head of each valve for pitting, burning, cracks and general wear, and check the valve stem for scoring and wear ridges. Rotate the valve, and check for any obvious indication that it is bent. Look for pits and excessive wear on the tip of each valve stem. Renew any valve that shows any such signs of wear or damage.

12 If the valve appears satisfactory at this stage, measure the valve stem diameter at several points, using a micrometer **(see illustration)**. Any significant difference in the readings obtained indicates wear of the valve stem. Should any of these conditions be apparent, the valve(s) must be renewed.

13 If the valves are in satisfactory condition, they should be ground (lapped) into their respective seats, to ensure a smooth gas-tight seal. If the seat is only lightly pitted, or if it has been re-cut, fine grinding compound *only* should be used to produce the required finish. Coarse valve-grinding compound should *not* be used unless a seat is badly burned or deeply pitted; if this is the case, the cylinder head and valves should be inspected by an expert, to decide whether seat re-cutting, or even the renewal of the valve or seat insert, is required.

14 Valve grinding is carried out as follows. Place the cylinder head upside-down on a

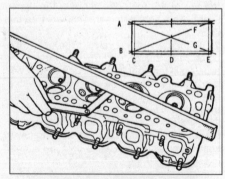

8.6 Check the cylinder head gasket surfaces for warpage, in the planes indicated (A to G)

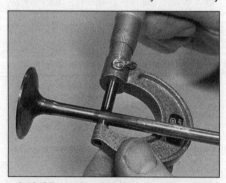

8.12 Measuring the diameter of a valve stem

8.15 Grinding-in a valve seat

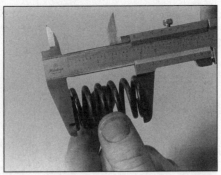

8.18 Checking the valve spring free length

bench, with a block of wood at each end to give clearance for the valve stems.

15 Smear a trace of (the appropriate grade of) valve-grinding compound on the seat face, and press a suction grinding tool onto the valve head. With a semi-rotary action, grind the valve head to its seat, lifting the valve occasionally to redistribute the grinding compound **(see illustration)**. A light spring placed under the valve head will greatly ease this operation.

16 If coarse grinding compound is being used, work only until a dull, matt even surface is produced on both the valve seat and the valve, then wipe off the used compound, and repeat the process with fine compound. When a smooth unbroken ring of light grey matt finish is produced on both the valve and seat, the grinding operation is complete. *Do not grind in the valves any further than absolutely necessary, or the seat will be prematurely sunk into the cylinder head.*

17 When all the valves have been ground-in, carefully wash off *all* traces of grinding compound, using paraffin or a suitable solvent, before reassembly of the cylinder head.

Valve components

18 Examine the valve springs for signs of damage and discolouration, and also measure their free length **(see illustration)**. If possible, compare each of the existing springs with a new component.

19 Stand each spring on a flat surface, and check it for squareness. If any of the springs

are damaged, distorted, or have lost their tension, obtain a complete set of new springs.

20 Check the spring upper seats and collets for obvious wear and cracks. Any questionable parts should be renewed, as extensive damage will occur if they fail during engine operation. Any damaged or excessively-worn parts must be renewed; the valve spring lower seat/stem oil seals must be renewed as a matter of course whenever they are disturbed.

21 Check the rocker gear components and hydraulic tappets as described in earlier parts of this Chapter according to engine type.

9 Cylinder head - reassembly

1 Before reassembling the cylinder head, first ensure that it is perfectly clean, and that no traces of grinding paste are left in the head or on the valves and guides. Use compressed air, if available, to blow out all the oil holes and passages.

2 Commence reassembly of the cylinder head by lubricating the valve stems and guides with clean engine oil.

HCS engines

3 Insert the first valve into its guide. Wipe the oil from the top of the valve stem, then wind some insulation tape over the split collet location groove, to protect the new valve stem seal as it is fitted over the valve and into

position. As the seal is fitted, support the valve to prevent it from falling out; push the seal down the valve, and locate it flush to the valve guide. Press the seal down firmly and evenly using a suitable diameter tube or socket, and take care not to distort the seal as it is located. Check that the seal spring is correctly located to ensure that it seals correctly, then remove the tape from the valve stem **(see illustrations)**.

4 Locate the valve spring and its retainer over the valve stem, and engage the valve spring compressor. Compress the spring and retainer just enough to allow the split collets to be inserted in the location groove in the valve stem. Holding the collets in position, slowly release and remove the valve spring compressor.

A little grease applied to the collet groove will help retain them in position.

5 Repeat the operation on the remaining valves, ensuring that each valve is fitted in its appropriate location.

6 On completion, support the cylinder head on a suitable piece of wood, and lightly strike the end of each valve stem in turn with a plastic- or copper-faced hammer to fractionally open the valve and seat the valve components.

CVH and PTE engines

7 Working on one valve at a time, fit the lower retainer into position **(see illustration)**.

8 Check for correct orientation, then fit the new oil seal into position over the guide. Drive

9.3a Tape the end of the valve stem before fitting the valve stem seal

9.3b Press the seal into position using a suitable socket

9.7 Fit the lower retainer

2D

9.8 Locate the seal, and tap it into position over the guide

9.9 Insert the valve into its guide

9.11 Insert the split collets into the groove in the valve stem

or press the seal squarely into place, using a suitable tube or socket **(see illustration)**.

9 To protect the seal lips from being damaged by the collet grooves in the valve stem as it is passed through the seal, wipe any oil from the stem at the top, and mask the split collet groove on the stem with insulating tape. Lubricate the lips of the valve stem seal, and insert the valve **(see illustration)**.

10 Remove the tape from the grooved section of the valve stem, then locate the spring and the upper retainer over the valve.

11 Locate the valve spring compressor into position, and compress the spring and cup down the valve stem so that the collet's groove is exposed above the upper retainer. Lightly grease the collet's groove in the stem, (to retain the collets in position) then locate the split collets into the groove in the stem. Slowly release and remove the valve spring compressor. As the compressor is released, ensure that the collets remain fully seated in the groove, and the upper retainer rides up over them to secure them in position **(see illustration)**.

12 Repeat the above operations on the remaining valves, ensuring that each valve assembly is returned to its original position, or where new valves have been fitted, onto the seat to which it was ground.

13 When all of the valves have been fitted, support the cylinder head on a wooden block, and using a plastic or copper-faced hammer, lightly tap the end of each valve stem in turn to seat the respective valve assemblies.

14 Refit the camshaft, tappets and rocker arms to the cylinder head as described in Part B of this Chapter.

Zetec engines

15 Beginning at one end of the head, lubricate and install the first valve. Apply molybdenum disulphide-based grease or clean engine oil to the valve stem, and refit the valve. Where the original valves are being re-used, ensure that each is refitted in its original guide. If new valves are being fitted, insert them into the locations to which they have been ground.

16 Fit the plastic protector supplied with new valve spring lower seat/stem oil seals to the end of the valve stem, then put the new seal squarely on top of the guide, and leave it there; the action of refitting the valve spring presses the lower seat/stem oil seal into place **(see illustration)**.

17 Refit the valve spring and upper seat.

18 Compress the spring with a valve spring compressor, and carefully install the collets in the stem groove. Apply a small dab of grease to each collet to hold it in place if necessary. Slowly release the compressor, and make sure the collets seat properly.

19 When the valve is installed, place the cylinder head flat on the bench and, using a hammer and interposed block of wood, tap the end of the valve stem gently, to settle the components.

20 Repeat the procedure for the remaining valves. Be sure to return the components to

their original locations - don't mix them up!

21 Refit the hydraulic tappets as described in Part C of this Chapter.

10 Camshaft and tappets - removal, inspection and refitting (HCS engines)

Removal

1 Refer to the applicable Sections in Part A of this Chapter and remove the cylinder head, timing chain and camshaft sprocket, and the sump.

2 Invert the engine so that it is supported on its cylinder head face (on a clean work area). This is necessary to make all of the tappets slide to the top of their stroke, thus allowing the camshaft to be withdrawn. Rotate the camshaft through a full turn, to ensure that all of the tappets slide up their bores, clear of the camshaft.

3 Before removing the camshaft, check its endfloat using a dial gauge mounted on the front face of the engine or feeler gauges. Pull the camshaft fully towards the front (timing chain) end of the engine, then insert feeler gauges between the camshaft sprocket flange and the camshaft thrust plate to assess the endfloat clearance **(see illustration)**. The camshaft endfloat must be as specified.

4 Undo the two retaining bolts, and remove the camshaft thrust plate.

5 Carefully withdraw the camshaft from the front end of the engine **(see illustration)**.

9.16 Valve spring pressure is sufficient to seat lower seat/stem oil seals on reassembly

10.3 Checking the camshaft endfloat

10.5 Withdrawing the camshaft from the front of the engine

6 Extract each tappet in turn. Keep them in order of fitting by inserting them in a card with eight holes in it, numbered 1 to 8 (from the timing chain end of the engine). A valve grinding suction tool will be found to be useful for the removal of tappets (see illustration).

Inspection

7 Examine the camshaft bearing journals and lobes for damage or excessive wear. If evident, the camshaft must be renewed.
8 Examine the camshaft bearing internal surfaces for signs of damage or excessive wear. If evident, the bearings must be renewed by a Ford dealer.
9 If not carried out on removal, check the camshaft endfloat as described in paragraph 3. If the endfloat is exceeds the specified tolerance, renew the thrust plate.
10 It is seldom that the tappets wear excessively in their bores, but it is likely that after a high mileage, the cam lobe contact surfaces will show signs of depression or grooving.
11 Where this condition is evident, renew the tappets. Grinding out the grooves and wear marks will reduce the thickness of the surface hardening, and will accelerate further wear.

Refitting

12 To refit the tappets and the camshaft, it is essential that the crankcase is inverted.
13 Lubricate their bores and the tappets. Insert each tappet fully into its original bore in the cylinder block.
14 Lubricate the camshaft bearings, camshaft and thrust plate, then insert the camshaft into the crankcase from the timing case end.
15 Fit the thrust plate and tighten the retaining bolts to the specified torque setting (see illustration). Check that the camshaft is able to rotate freely, and that the endfloat is as specified.

11 Piston/connecting rod assemblies - removal and inspection

Removal

HCS engines

1 Refer to Part A of this Chapter and remove the cylinder head and sump, then remove the oil pick-up pipe and strainer.
2 Temporarily refit the crankshaft pulley, so that the crankshaft can be rotated. Check that the connecting rod big-end caps have adjacent matching numbers facing towards the camshaft side of the engine. If no marks can be seen, make your own before disturbing any of the components, so that you can be certain of refitting each piston/connecting rod assembly the right way round, to its correct (original) bore, with the cap also the right way round.

10.6 Tappet withdrawal using a valve grinding tool suction cup

10.15 Refitting the camshaft thrust plate

CVH and PTE engines

3 Refer to Part B of this Chapter and remove the cylinder head and sump, then remove the oil pick-up pipe and strainer.
4 Temporarily refit the crankshaft pulley, so that the crankshaft can be rotated. Check that the connecting rods have identification numbers - these should be found on the exhaust side of the big-ends. No 1 assembly is at the timing belt end of the engine. If no marks can be seen, make your own before disturbing any of the components, so that you can be certain of refitting each piston/ connecting rod assembly the right way round, to its correct (original) bore, with the cap also the right way round.

Zetec engines

5 Refer to Part C of this Chapter and remove the cylinder head and sump.
6 Undo the screws securing the oil pump pick-up/strainer pipe to the pump, then unscrew the four nuts, and withdraw the oil pump pick-up/strainer pipe and oil baffle (see illustration).
7 Temporarily refit the crankshaft pulley, so that the crankshaft can be rotated. Note that each piston/connecting rod assembly can be identified by its cylinder number (counting from the timing belt end of the engine) etched into the flat-machined surface of both the connecting rod and its cap. The numbers are visible from the front (exhaust side) of the engine (see illustration). Furthermore, each

piston has an arrow stamped into its crown, pointing towards the timing belt end of the engine. If no marks can be seen, make your own before disturbing any of the components, so that you can be certain of refitting each piston/connecting rod assembly the right way round, to its correct (original) bore, with the cap also the right way round.

All engines

8 Use your fingernail to feel if a ridge has formed at the upper limit of ring travel (about a quarter-inch down from the top of each cylinder). If carbon deposits or cylinder wear have produced ridges, they must be completely removed with a special tool. Follow the tool manufacturer's instructions provided. Failure to remove the ridges before attempting to remove the piston/connecting rod assemblies may result in piston ring breakage.
9 Slacken each of the big-end bearing cap bolts half a turn at a time, until they can be removed by hand. Remove the No 1 cap and bearing shell. Don't drop the shell out of the cap.
10 Remove the upper bearing shell, and push the connecting rod/piston assembly out through the top of the engine. Use a wooden hammer handle to push on the connecting rod's bearing recess. If resistance is felt, double-check that all of the ridge was removed from the cylinder.
11 Repeat the procedure for the remaining cylinders.

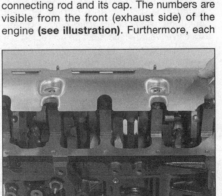

11.6 Removing the oil baffle to provide access to crankshaft and bearings

11.7 Each connecting rod and big-end bearing cap will have a flat-machined surface with the cylinder number etched in it

2D

11.14 Using feeler gauge blades to remove piston rings

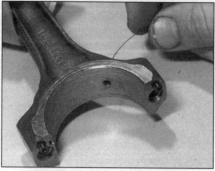

11.24 Check that the connecting rod oilway on CVH engines is clear

12.1 Checking crankshaft endfloat with a dial gauge

12 After removal, reassemble the big-end bearing caps and shells on their respective connecting rods, and refit the bolts finger-tight. Leaving the old shells in place until reassembly will help prevent the bearing recesses from being accidentally nicked or gouged. New shells should be used on reassembly.

Inspection

13 Before the inspection process can begin, the piston/connecting rod assemblies must be cleaned, and the original piston rings removed from the pistons.

14 Carefully expand the old rings over the top of the pistons. The use of two or three old feeler blades will be helpful in preventing the rings dropping into empty grooves (see illustration). Be careful not to scratch the piston with the ends of the ring. The rings are brittle, and will snap if they are spread too far. They are also very sharp - protect your hands and fingers. Note that the third ring may incorporate an expander. Always remove the rings from the top of the piston. Keep each set of rings with its piston if the old rings are to be re-used.

15 Scrape away all traces of carbon from the top of the piston. A hand-held wire brush (or a piece of fine emery cloth) can be used, once the majority of the deposits have been scraped away.

16 Remove the carbon from the ring grooves in the piston using an old ring. Break the ring in half to do this (be careful not to cut your fingers - piston rings are sharp). Be careful to remove only the carbon deposits - do not remove any metal, and do not nick or scratch the sides of the ring grooves.

17 Once the deposits have been removed, clean the piston/connecting rod assembly with paraffin or a suitable solvent, and dry thoroughly. Make sure that the oil return holes in the ring grooves are clear.

18 If the pistons and cylinder liners/bores are not damaged or worn excessively, the original pistons can be refitted. Normal piston wear shows up as even vertical wear on the piston thrust surfaces, and slight looseness of the top ring in its groove. New piston rings should always be used when the engine is reassembled.

19 Carefully inspect each piston for cracks around the skirt, around the gudgeon pin holes, and at the piston ring "lands" (between the ring grooves).

20 Look for scoring and scuffing on the piston skirt, holes in the piston crown, and burned areas at the edge of the crown. If the skirt is scored or scuffed, the engine may have been suffering from overheating, and/or abnormal combustion which caused excessively high operating temperatures. The cooling and lubrication systems should be checked thoroughly. Scorch marks on the sides of the pistons show that blow-by has occurred. A hole in the piston crown, or burned areas at the edge of the piston crown, indicates that abnormal combustion (pre-ignition, knocking, or detonation) has been occurring. If any of the above problems exist, the causes must be investigated and corrected, or the damage will occur again. The causes may include incorrect ignition timing, or a carburettor or fuel injection system fault.

21 Corrosion of the piston, in the form of pitting, indicates that coolant has been leaking into the combustion chamber and/or the crankcase. Again, the cause must be corrected, or the problem may persist in the rebuilt engine.

22 Check the piston-to-rod clearance by twisting the piston and rod in opposite directions. Any noticeable play indicates excessive wear, which must be corrected. The piston/connecting rod assemblies should be taken to a Ford dealer or engine reconditioning specialist to have the pistons, gudgeon pins and rods checked, and new components fitted as required.

23 *Don't* attempt to separate the pistons from the connecting rods (even if non-genuine replacements are found elsewhere). This is a task for a Ford dealer or similar engine reconditioning specialist, due to the special heating equipment, press, mandrels and supports required to do the job. If the piston/connecting rod assemblies do require this sort of work, have the connecting rods checked for bend and twist, since only such engine repair specialists will have the facilities for this purpose.

24 Check the connecting rods for cracks and other damage. Also on CVH engines, check that the oilway in the base of the connecting rod is clear by probing with a piece of wire (see illustration). Temporarily remove the big-end bearing caps and the old bearing shells, wipe clean the rod and cap bearing recesses, and inspect them for nicks, gouges and scratches. After checking the rods, replace the old shells, slip the caps into place, and tighten the bolts finger-tight.

12 Crankshaft - removal and inspection

Removal

Note: *The crankshaft can be removed only after the engine has been removed from the vehicle. It is assumed that the transmission, flywheel/driveplate, timing belt/chain, cylinder head, sump, oil pump pick-up/strainer, oil baffle, oil pump, and piston/connecting rod assemblies, have already been removed. The crankshaft left-hand oil seal carrier/housing must be unbolted from the cylinder block/crankcase before proceeding with crankshaft removal.*

1 Before the crankshaft is removed, check the endfloat. Mount a DTI (Dial Test Indicator, or dial gauge) with the stem in line with the crankshaft and just touching the crankshaft (see illustration).

2 Push the crankshaft fully away from the gauge, and zero it. Next, lever the crankshaft towards the gauge as far as possible, and check the reading obtained. The distance that the crankshaft moved is its endfloat; if it is greater than specified, check the crankshaft thrust surfaces for wear. If no wear is evident, new thrustwashers should correct the endfloat.

3 If no dial gauge is available, feeler gauges can be used. Gently lever or push the crankshaft all the way towards the right-hand end of the engine. Slip feeler gauges between the crankshaft and the main bearing incorporating the thrustwashers to determine the clearance.

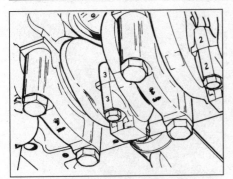

12.4 Connecting rod big-end bearing cap and main bearing cap markings

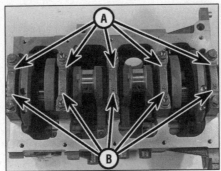

12.12 Crankshaft main bearing cap arrows point to timing belt end of engine (A), and bearing numbers (B) are consecutive from timing belt end

12.22 Measure the diameter of each crankshaft journal at several points, to detect taper and out-of-round conditions

2D

HCS engines

4 Check that the main bearing caps have marks to indicate their respective fitted positions in the block. They also have arrow marks pointing towards the timing chain cover end of the engine to indicate correct orientation **(see illustration)**.

5 Unscrew the retaining bolts, and remove the main bearing caps. If the caps are reluctant to separate from the block face, lightly tap them free using a plastic- or copper-faced hammer. If the bearing shells are likely to be used again, keep them with their bearing caps for safekeeping. However, unless the engine is known to be of low mileage, it is recommended that they be renewed.

6 Lift the crankshaft out from the crankcase, then extract the upper bearing shells and side thrustwashers. Keep them with their respective caps for correct repositioning if they are to be used again.

7 Remove the crankshaft oil seals from the timing cover and the rear oil seal housing.

CVH and PTE engines

8 Check that each main bearing cap is numerically marked for position. Each cap should also have an arrow marking to indicate its direction of fitting (arrow points to the timing belt end).

9 Unscrew the retaining bolts, and remove the main bearing caps. As they are removed, keep each bearing shell with its cap (in case they are to used again). Note that the bearing shells in the main bearing caps are plain (no groove). It is recommended that the shells be renewed, unless the engine is known to be of low mileage.

10 Lift out the crankshaft from the crankcase.

11 Remove each bearing shell in turn from the crankcase, and keep them in order of fitting. Note that the upper shell halves are grooved. Also remove the semi-circular thrustwasher from each side of the central main bearing web, and keep them in their order of fitting.

Zetec engines

12 Check the main bearing caps, to see if

they are marked to indicate their locations **(see illustration)**. They should be numbered consecutively from the timing belt end of the engine - if not, mark them with number-stamping dies or a centre-punch. The caps will also have an embossed arrow pointing to the timing belt end of the engine. Noting the different fasteners (for the oil baffle nuts) used on caps 2 and 4, slacken the cap bolts a quarter-turn at a time each, starting with the left- and right-hand end caps and working toward the centre, until they can be removed by hand.

13 Gently tap the caps with a soft-faced hammer, then separate them from the cylinder block/crankcase. If necessary, use the bolts as levers to remove the caps. Try not to drop the bearing shells if they come out with the caps.

14 Carefully lift the crankshaft out of the engine.

15 Remove each bearing shell in turn from the cylinder block/crankcase, and keep them in order of fitting.

Inspection

16 Clean the crankshaft, and dry it with compressed air if available.

 Warning: Wear eye protection when using compressed air! Be sure to clean the oil holes with a pipe cleaner or similar probe.

17 Check the main and crankpin (big-end) bearing journals for uneven wear, scoring, pitting and cracking.

18 Big-end bearing wear is accompanied by distinct metallic knocking when the engine is running (particularly noticeable when the engine is pulling from low speed) and some loss of oil pressure.

19 Main bearing wear is accompanied by severe engine vibration and rumble - getting progressively worse as engine speed increases - and again by loss of oil pressure.

20 Check the bearing journal for roughness by running a finger lightly over the bearing surface. Any roughness (which will be accompanied by obvious bearing wear) indicates that the crankshaft requires regrinding (where possible) or renewal.

21 Remove all burrs from the crankshaft oil holes with a stone, file or scraper.

22 Using a micrometer, measure the diameter of the main bearing and crankpin (big-end) journals, and compare the results with the Specifications at the beginning of this Chapter **(see illustration)**.

23 By measuring the diameter at a number of points around each journal's circumference, you will be able to determine whether or not the journal is out-of-round. Take the measurement at each end of the journal, near the webs, to determine if the journal is tapered.

24 If the crankshaft journals are damaged, tapered, out-of-round, or worn beyond the limits specified in this Chapter, the crankshaft must be taken to an engine overhaul specialist, who will regrind it, and who can supply the necessary undersize bearing shells.

25 Check the oil seal journals at each end of the crankshaft for wear and damage. If either seal has worn an excessive groove in its journal, consult an engine overhaul specialist, who will be able to advise whether a repair is possible, or whether a new crankshaft is necessary.

13 Cylinder block/crankcase - cleaning and inspection

Cleaning

1 Prior to cleaning, remove all external components and senders. On HCS engines, make sure that the camshaft and tappets are removed before carrying out thorough cleaning of the block. On the CVH and PTE engines, remove the engine ventilation cap from the recess in the rear corner of the cylinder block and if still fitted, undo the retaining screw and withdraw the engine speed sensor from the bellhousing face. On Zetec engines, unbolt the piston-cooling oil jets or blanking plugs (as applicable); note that Ford state that the piston-cooling oil jets (where fitted) must be renewed whenever the

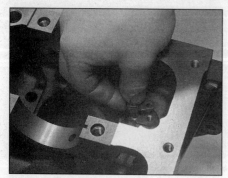

13.1a Unbolt blanking plugs (where fitted) to clean out oilways . . .

13.1b . . . but note that piston-cooling oil jets (where fitted) must be renewed whenever engine is overhauled - Zetec engines

13.6 All bolt holes in the block should be cleaned and restored with a tap

engine is dismantled for full overhaul **(see illustrations)**.

2 Remove all oil gallery plugs (where fitted). The plugs are usually very tight - they may have to be drilled out, and the holes re-tapped. Use new plugs when the engine is reassembled. Drill a small hole in the centre of each core plug, and pull them out with a car bodywork dent puller.
Caution: The core plugs (also known as freeze or soft plugs) may be difficult or impossible to retrieve if they are driven into the block coolant passages.

3 If any of the castings are extremely dirty, all should be steam-cleaned.

4 After the castings are returned from steam-cleaning, clean all oil holes and oil galleries one more time. Flush all internal passages with warm water until the water runs clear, then dry thoroughly, and apply a light film of oil to all machined surfaces, to prevent rusting. If you have access to compressed air, use it to speed the drying process, and to blow out all the oil holes and galleries.

 Warning: Wear eye protection when using compressed air!

5 If the castings are not very dirty, you can do an adequate cleaning job with hot soapy water (as hot as you can stand!) and a stiff brush. Take plenty of time, and do a thorough job. Regardless of the cleaning method used, be sure to clean all oil holes and galleries very

thoroughly, and to dry all components completely; protect the machined surfaces as described above, to prevent rusting.

6 All threaded holes must be clean and dry, to ensure accurate torque readings during reassembly; now is also a good time to clean and check the threads of all principal bolts - however, note that some, such as the cylinder head and flywheel/driveplate bolts, are to be renewed as a matter of course whenever they are disturbed. Run the proper-size tap into each of the holes, to remove rust, corrosion, thread sealant or sludge, and to restore damaged threads **(see illustration)**. If possible, use compressed air to clear the holes of debris produced by this operation; a good alternative is to inject aerosol-applied water-dispersant lubricant into each hole, using the long spout usually supplied.

 Warning: Wear eye protection when cleaning out these holes in this way, and be sure to dry out any excess liquid left in the holes.

7 When all inspection and repair procedures are complete (see below) and the block is ready for reassembly, apply suitable sealant to the new oil gallery plugs, and insert them into the holes in the block. Tighten them securely. After coating the sealing surfaces of the new core plugs with suitable sealant, install them in the cylinder block/crankcase. Make sure they are driven in straight and

seated properly, or leakage could result. Special tools are available for this purpose, but a large socket with an outside diameter that will just slip into the core plug, used with an extension and hammer, will work just as well.

8 On Zetec engines, refit the blanking plugs or (new) piston-cooling oil jets (as applicable), tightening their Torx screws to the torque wrench setting specified. On all engines, refit all other external components removed, referring to the relevant Chapter of this manual for further details where required. Refit the main bearing caps, and tighten the bolts finger-tight.

9 If the engine is not going to be reassembled right away, cover it with a large plastic bag to keep it clean; protect the machined surfaces as described above, to prevent rusting.

Inspection

10 Visually check the castings for cracks and corrosion. Look for stripped threads in the threaded holes. If there has been any history of internal coolant leakage, it may be worthwhile having an engine overhaul specialist check the cylinder block/crankcase for cracks with special equipment. If defects are found, have them repaired, if possible, or renew the assembly.

11 Check each cylinder bore for scuffing and scoring.

12 The cylinder bores must be measured with all the crankshaft main bearing caps bolted in place (without the crankshaft and bearing shells), and tightened to the specified torque wrench settings. Measure the diameter of each cylinder at the top (just under the ridge area), centre and bottom of the cylinder bore, parallel to the crankshaft axis. Next, measure each cylinder's diameter at the same three locations across the crankshaft axis **(see illustration)**. Note the measurements obtained.

13 Measure the piston diameter at right-angles to the gudgeon pin axis, just above the bottom of the skirt; again, note the results **(see illustration)**.

14 If it is wished to obtain the piston-to-bore clearance, measure the bore and piston skirt as described above, and subtract the skirt

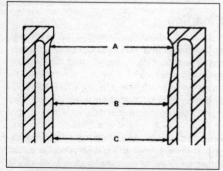

13.12 Measure the diameter of each cylinder just under the wear ridge (A), at the centre (B) and at the bottom (C)

13.13 Measure the piston skirt diameter at right-angles to the gudgeon pin axis, just above the base of the skirt

diameter from the bore measurement. If the precision measuring tools shown are not available, the condition of the pistons and bores can be assessed, though not quite as accurately, by using feeler gauges as follows. Select a feeler gauge of thickness equal to the specified piston-to-bore clearance, and slip it into the cylinder along with the matching piston. The piston must be positioned exactly as it normally would be. The feeler gauge must be between the piston and cylinder on one of the thrust faces (at right-angles to the gudgeon pin bore). The piston should slip through the cylinder (with the feeler gauge in place) with moderate pressure; if it falls through or slides through easily, the clearance is excessive, and a new piston will be required. If the piston binds at the lower end of the cylinder, and is loose toward the top, the cylinder is tapered. If tight spots are encountered as the piston/feeler gauge is rotated in the cylinder, the cylinder is out-of-round (oval).

15 Repeat these procedures for the remaining pistons and cylinder bores.

16 Compare the results with the Specifications at the beginning of this Chapter; if any measurement is beyond the dimensions specified for that class (check the piston crown marking to establish the class of piston fitted), or if any bore measurement is significantly different from the others (indicating that the bore is tapered or oval), the piston or bore is excessively-worn.

17 Worn pistons must be renewed; on some engines, the pistons are available as Ford replacement parts only as part of the complete piston/connecting rod assembly. See a Ford dealer or engine reconditioning specialist for advice.

18 If any of the cylinder bores are badly scuffed or scored, or if they are excessively-worn, out-of-round or tapered, the usual course of action would be to have the cylinder block/crankcase rebored, and to fit new, oversized, pistons on reassembly. See a Ford dealer or engine reconditioning specialist for advice.

19 If the bores are in reasonably good condition and not excessively-worn, then it may only be necessary to renew the piston rings.

20 If this is the case, the bores should be honed, to allow the new rings to bed in correctly and provide the best possible seal. Honing is an operation that will be carried out for you by an engine reconditioning specialist.

21 After all the machining operations have been carried out, the entire block/crankcase must be washed very thoroughly with warm soapy water to remove all traces of abrasive grit produced during the machining operations. When completely clean, rinse it thoroughly and dry it, then lightly oil all exposed machined surfaces to prevent rusting.

22 The cylinder block/crankcase should now be completely clean and dry, with all

components checked for wear or damage, and repaired or overhauled as necessary. Refit as many ancillary components as possible, for safekeeping. If reassembly is not to start immediately, cover the block with a large plastic bag to keep it clean.

14 Main and big-end bearings - inspection

1 Even though the main and big-end bearing shells should be renewed during the engine overhaul, the old shells should be retained for close examination, as they may reveal valuable information about the condition of the engine **(see illustration)**.

2 Bearing failure occurs because of lack of lubrication, the presence of dirt or other foreign particles, overloading the engine, and corrosion. Regardless of the cause of bearing failure, it must be corrected before the engine is reassembled, to prevent it from happening again.

3 When examining the bearing shells, remove them from the cylinder block/crankcase and main bearing caps, and from the connecting rods and the big-end bearing caps, then lay them out on a clean surface in the same general position as their location in the engine. This will enable you to match any bearing problems with the corresponding crankshaft journal. Do not touch any shell's bearing surface with your fingers while checking it, or the delicate surface may be scratched.

4 Dirt or other foreign matter gets into the engine in a variety of ways. It may be left in the engine during assembly, or it may pass through filters or the crankcase ventilation system. It may get into the oil, and from there into the bearings. Metal chips from machining operations and normal engine wear are often present. Abrasives are sometimes left in engine components after reconditioning, especially when parts are not thoroughly cleaned using the proper cleaning methods. Whatever the source, these foreign objects often end up embedded in the soft bearing material, and are easily recognised. Large particles will not embed in the material, and will score or gouge the shell and journal. The best prevention for this cause of bearing failure is to clean all parts thoroughly, and to keep everything spotlessly-clean during engine assembly. Frequent and regular engine oil and filter changes are also recommended.

5 Lack of lubrication (or lubrication breakdown) has a number of inter-related causes. Excessive heat (which thins the oil), overloading (which squeezes the oil from the bearing face) and oil leakage (from excessive bearing clearances, worn oil pump or high engine speeds) all contribute to lubrication breakdown. Blocked oil passages, which usually are the result of misaligned oil holes in a bearing shell, will also starve a

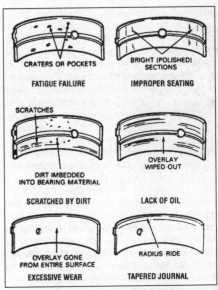

14.1 Typical bearing failures

bearing of oil, and destroy it. When lack of lubrication is the cause of bearing failure, the bearing material is wiped or extruded from the shell's steel backing. Temperatures may increase to the point where the steel backing turns blue from overheating.

6 Driving habits can have a definite effect on bearing life. Full-throttle, low-speed operation (labouring the engine) puts very high loads on bearings, which tends to squeeze out the oil film. These loads cause the shells to flex, which produces fine cracks in the bearing face (fatigue failure). Eventually, the bearing material will loosen in pieces, and tear away from the steel backing.

7 Short-distance driving leads to corrosion of bearings, because insufficient engine heat is produced to drive off condensed water and corrosive gases. These products collect in the engine oil, forming acid and sludge. As the oil is carried to the engine bearings, the acid attacks and corrodes the bearing material.

8 Incorrect shell refitting during engine assembly will lead to bearing failure as well. Tight-fitting shells leave insufficient bearing running clearance, and will result in oil starvation. Dirt or foreign particles trapped behind a bearing shell result in high spots on the bearing, which lead to failure.

9 Do not touch any shell's bearing surface with your fingers during reassembly; there is a risk of scratching the delicate surface, or of depositing particles of dirt on it.

15 Engine overhaul - reassembly sequence

1 Before reassembly begins ensure that all new parts have been obtained and that all necessary tools are available. Read through the entire procedure to familiarise yourself with the work involved, and to ensure that all items necessary for reassembly of the engine are at hand. In addition to all normal tools and materials, jointing and thread locking compound will be needed during engine reassembly. For general-purpose applications, it is recommended that Loctite 275 setting sealer or Hylomar PL32M non-setting sealer be used for joints where required, and Loctite 270 for stud and bolt thread-locking. For specific applications on Zetec engines, Hylosil 102 for the cylinder block/crankcase-to-sump/oil pump/oil seal carrier joints, and Loctite 518 for the camshaft right-hand bearing caps should be used. These are recommended by, and obtained from, Ford dealers. In all other cases, provided the relevant mating surfaces are clean and flat, new gaskets will be sufficient to ensure joints are oil-tight. *Do not* use any kind of silicone-based sealant on any part of the fuel system or inlet manifold, and *never* use exhaust sealants upstream of the catalytic converter.

2 In order to save time and avoid problems, engine reassembly can be carried out in the following order (as applicable):

a) *Engine ventilation cap (CVH and PTE engines).*
b) *Tappets and camshaft (HCS engines).*
c) *Crankshaft and main bearings.*
d) *Pistons and connecting rods.*
e) *Oil pump.*
f) *Sump.*
g) *Flywheel/driveplate.*
h) *Cylinder head.*
i) *Timing sprockets and chain/belt.*
j) *Engine external components.*

3 Ensure that everything is clean prior to reassembly. As mentioned previously, dirt and metal particles can quickly destroy bearings and result in major engine damage. Use clean engine oil to lubricate during reassembly.

16 Piston rings - refitting

1 Before installing new piston rings, check the end gaps. Lay out each piston set with a piston/connecting rod assembly, and keep

16.6 Look for etched markings ("STD" - indicating a standard-sized ring - shown here) identifying piston ring top surface

them together as a matched set from now on.
2 Insert the top compression ring into the first cylinder, and square it up with the cylinder walls by pushing it in with the top of the piston. The ring should be near the bottom of the cylinder, at the lower limit of ring travel.
3 To measure the end gap, slip feeler gauges between the ends of the ring, until a gauge equal to the gap width is found. The feeler gauge should slide between the ring ends with a slight amount of drag. Compare the measurement to the value given in the Specifications in this Chapter; if the gap is larger or smaller than specified, double-check to make sure you have the correct rings before proceeding. If you are assessing the condition of used rings, have the cylinder bores checked and measured by a Ford dealer or similar engine reconditioning specialist, so that you can be sure of exactly which component is worn, and seek advice as to the best course of action to take.
4 If the end gap is still too small, it must be opened up by careful filing of the ring ends using a fine file. If it is too large, this is not as serious, unless the specified limit is exceeded, in which case very careful checking is required of the dimensions of all components, as well as of the new parts.
5 Repeat the procedure for each ring that will be installed in the first cylinder, and for each ring in the remaining cylinders. Remember to keep rings, pistons and cylinders matched up.
6 Refit the piston rings as follows. Where the original rings are being refitted, use the marks or notes made on removal, to ensure that each ring is refitted to its original groove and the same way up. New rings generally have their top surfaces identified by markings (often an indication of size, such as "STD", or the word "TOP") - the rings must be fitted with such markings uppermost **(see illustration)**. **Note:** *Always follow the instructions printed on the ring package or box - different manufacturers may require different approaches. Do not mix up the top and second compression rings, as they usually have different cross-sections.*
7 The oil control ring (lowest one on the piston) is usually installed first. It is composed of three separate elements. Slip the spacer/expander into the groove. If an anti-rotation tang is used, make sure it is inserted into the drilled hole in the ring groove. Next, install the lower side rail. Don't use a piston ring installation tool on the oil ring side rails, as they may be damaged. Instead, place one end of the side rail into the groove between the spacer/expander and the ring land, hold it firmly in place, and slide a finger around the piston while pushing the rail into the groove. Next, install the upper side rail in the same manner.
8 After the three oil ring components have been installed, check that both the upper and lower side rails can be turned smoothly in the ring groove.
9 The second compression (middle) ring is

installed next, followed by the top compression ring - ensure their marks are uppermost, and be careful not to confuse them. Don't expand either ring any more than necessary to slide it over the top of the piston.
10 On HCS engines, when all of the rings are fitted to each piston, arrange them so that the gaps are positioned as described in the Specifications at the start of this Chapter.
11 On the CVH and PTE engines, when all of the rings are fitted to each piston, arrange them so that the gaps are spaced at 120° intervals, with no gaps positioned above the gudgeon pin hole.
12 On Zetec engines, when all the rings are fitted to each piston, space the ring gaps (including the elements of the oil control ring) uniformly around the piston at 120° intervals.

17 Crankshaft - refitting and main bearing running clearance check

1 It is assumed at this point that the cylinder block/crankcase and crankshaft have been cleaned, inspected and repaired or reconditioned as necessary. Position the engine upside-down.
2 Remove the main bearing cap bolts, and lift out the caps. Lay the caps out in the proper order, to ensure correct installation.
3 If they're still in place, remove the old bearing shells from the block and the main bearing caps. Wipe the bearing recesses of the block and caps with a clean, lint-free cloth. They must be kept spotlessly-clean!

Main bearing running clearance check

HCS engines

4 Wipe clean the main bearing shell seats in the crankcase, and clean the backs of the bearing shells. Insert the respective upper shells (dry) into position in the crankcase. Note that the upper shells have grooves in them (the lower shells are plain, and have a wider location lug). Where the old main bearings are being refitted, ensure that they are located in their original positions. Make sure that the tab on each bearing shell fits into the notch in the block or cap.
Caution: Don't hammer the shells into place, and don't nick or gouge the bearing faces. No lubrication should be used at this time.
5 Place the crankshaft thrustwashers into position in the crankcase, so that their oil grooves are facing outwards (away from the central web) (see illustration).

CVH and PTE engines

6 Wipe clean the main bearing shell seats in the crankcase, and clean the backs of the bearing shells. Insert the respective upper shells (dry) into position in the crankcase. Note that with the exception of the front main bearing, the upper shells have grooves in

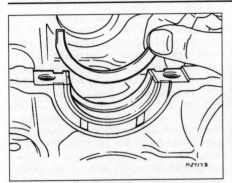

17.5 Place the crankshaft thrustwashers into position in the crankcase so that their oil grooves are facing outwards

17.6 Fit the bearing shells to the main bearing housings in the crankcase

17.7 Fit the crankcase ventilation cap and its retaining spring

them (the lower half bearings are plain). The upper and lower front shells are narrower in section, and both have an oil groove in them. Where the old main bearings are being refitted, ensure that they are located in their original positions (see illustration). Make sure that the tab on each bearing shell fits into the notch in the block or cap.
Caution: Don't hammer the shells into place, and don't nick or gouge the bearing faces. No lubrication should be used at this time.

7 Relocate the crankcase ventilation cap and its retaining spring into position in the crankcase (see illustration).

8 Place the crankshaft thrustwashers into position in the crankcase so that their oil grooves are facing outwards (away from the central web).

Zetec engines

9 Wipe clean the main bearing shell seats in the crankcase, and clean the backs of the new main bearing shells. Fit the shells with an oil groove in each main bearing location in the block; note the thrustwashers integral with the No 3 (centre) main bearing upper shell. Fit the other shell from each bearing set in the corresponding main bearing cap. Make sure the tab on each bearing shell fits into the notch in the block or cap. Also, the oil holes in

the block must line up with the oil holes in the bearing shell (see illustration).
Caution: Don't hammer the shells into place, and don't nick or gouge the bearing faces. No lubrication should be used at this time.

All engines

10 Clean the bearing surfaces of the shells in the block, and the crankshaft main bearing journals with a clean, lint-free cloth. Check or clean the oil holes in the crankshaft, as any dirt here can go only one way - straight through the new bearings.

11 Once you're certain the crankshaft is clean, carefully lay it in position in the main bearings. Trim several pieces of the appropriate-size Plastigauge (they must be slightly shorter than the width of the main bearings), and place one piece on each crankshaft main bearing journal, parallel with the crankshaft centre-line (see illustration).

12 Clean the bearing surfaces of the cap shells, and install the caps in their respective positions (don't mix them up) with the arrows pointing to the timing chain/belt end of the engine. Don't disturb the Plastigauge.

13 Working on one cap at a time, from the centre main bearing outwards (and ensuring that each cap is tightened down squarely and evenly onto the block), tighten the main bearing cap bolts to the specified torque

wrench setting. Don't rotate the crankshaft at any time during this operation!

14 Remove the bolts, and carefully lift off the main bearing caps. Keep them in order. Don't disturb the Plastigauge or rotate the crankshaft. If any of the main bearing caps are difficult to remove, tap them gently from side-to-side with a soft-faced mallet to loosen them.

15 Compare the width of the crushed Plastigauge on each journal with the scale printed on the Plastigauge envelope to obtain the main bearing running clearance (see illustration). Check the Specifications to make sure that the clearance is correct.

16 If the clearance is not as specified, seek the advice of a Ford dealer or similar engine reconditioning specialist - if the crankshaft journals are in good condition, it may be possible simply to renew the shells to achieve the correct clearance. If this is not possible, the crankshaft must be reground by a specialist who can supply the necessary undersized shells. First though, make sure that no dirt or oil was between the bearing shells and the caps or block when the clearance was measured. If the Plastigauge is noticeably wider at one end than the other, the journal may be tapered.

17 Carefully scrape all traces of the Plastigauge material off the main bearing journals and the bearing surfaces. Be very

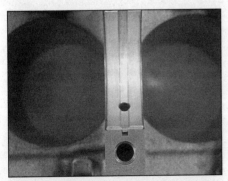

17.9 Tab on each bearing shell must engage with notch in block or cap, and oil holes in upper shells must align with block oilways

17.11 Lay the Plastigauge strips (arrowed) on the main bearing journals, parallel to the crankshaft centre-line

17.15 Compare the width of the crushed Plastigauge to the scale on the envelope to determine the main bearing running clearance

2D

17.20 Refit the crankshaft after checking bearing clearances

careful not to scratch the bearing - use your fingernail or the edge of a credit card.

Final crankshaft refitting

18 Carefully lift the crankshaft out of the engine. Clean the bearing surfaces of the shells in the block, then apply a thin, uniform layer of clean molybdenum disulphide-based grease, engine assembly lubricant, or clean engine oil to each surface. Coat the thrustwasher surfaces as well.

19 Lubricate the crankshaft oil seal journals with molybdenum disulphide-based grease, engine assembly lubricant, or clean engine oil.

20 Make sure the crankshaft journals are clean, then lay the crankshaft back in place in the block **(see illustration)**. Clean the bearing surfaces of the shells in the caps, then lubricate them. Install the caps in their respective positions, with the arrows pointing to the timing belt/chain end of the engine.

21 Working on one cap at a time, from the centre main bearing outwards (and ensuring that each cap is tightened down squarely and evenly onto the block), tighten the main bearing cap bolts to the specified torque wrench setting.

22 Rotate the crankshaft a number of times by hand, to check for any obvious binding.

23 Check the crankshaft endfloat (see Section 12). It should be correct if the crankshaft thrust faces aren't worn or damaged.

24 Refit the crankshaft left-hand oil seal carrier, and install a new seal (see Part A, B or C of this Chapter according to engine type).

18 Piston/connecting rod assemblies - refitting and big-end bearing running clearance check

Note: On HCS engines, **new** big-end bearing cap retaining bolts will be required for reassembly.

1 Before refitting the piston/connecting rod assemblies, the cylinder bores must be perfectly clean, the top edge of each cylinder must be chamfered, and the crankshaft must be in place.

2 Remove the big-end bearing cap from No 1 cylinder connecting rod (refer to the marks noted or made on removal). Remove the original bearing shells, and wipe the bearing recesses of the connecting rod and cap with a clean, lint-free cloth. They must be kept spotlessly-clean!

Big-end bearing running clearance check

3 Clean the back of the new upper bearing shell, fit it to the connecting rod, then fit the other shell of the bearing set to the big-end bearing cap. Make sure that the tab on each shell fits into the notch in the rod or cap recess **(see illustration)**.

Caution: Don't hammer the shells into place, and don't nick or gouge the bearing face. Don't lubricate the bearing at this time.

4 It's critically important that all mating surfaces of the bearing components are perfectly clean and oil-free when they're assembled.

5 Position the piston ring gaps as described in Section 16, lubricate the piston and rings with clean engine oil, and attach a piston ring compressor to the piston. Leave the skirt protruding about a quarter-inch, to guide the piston into the cylinder bore. The rings must be compressed until they're flush with the piston.

6 Rotate the crankshaft until No 1 crankpin (big-end) journal is at BDC (Bottom Dead Centre), and apply a coat of engine oil to the cylinder walls.

7 Arrange the No 1 piston/connecting rod assembly so that the arrow on the piston

crown points to the timing belt/chain end of the engine. Gently insert the assembly into the No 1 cylinder bore, and rest the bottom edge of the ring compressor on the engine block.

8 Tap the top edge of the ring compressor to make sure it's contacting the block around its entire circumference.

9 Gently tap on the top of the piston with the end of a wooden hammer handle **(see illustration)**, while guiding the connecting rod's big-end onto the crankpin. The piston rings may try to pop out of the ring compressor just before entering the cylinder bore, so keep some pressure on the ring compressor. Work slowly, and if any resistance is felt as the piston enters the cylinder, stop immediately. Find out what's binding, and fix it before proceeding. Do not, for any reason, force the piston into the cylinder - you might break a ring and/or the piston.

10 To check the big-end bearing running clearance, cut a piece of the appropriate-size Plastigauge slightly shorter than the width of the connecting rod bearing, and lay it in place on the No 1 crankpin (big-end) journal, parallel with the crankshaft centre-line **(see illustration 17.11)**.

11 Clean the connecting rod-to-cap mating surfaces, and refit the big-end bearing cap. Tighten the cap bolts evenly - on the HCS and Zetec engines, first use a torque wrench to tighten the bolts to the Stage 1 torque setting, then use an ordinary socket extension bar and an angle gauge to tighten the bolts further through the Stage 2 angle **(see illustration)**. On the CVH and PTE engines, tighten the bolts progressively to the specified torque; further angle-tightening is not required on these engines. Use a thin-wall socket, to avoid erroneous torque readings that can result if the socket is wedged between the cap and nut. If the socket tends to wedge itself between the nut and the cap, lift up on it slightly until it no longer contacts the cap. Don't rotate the crankshaft at any time during this operation!

12 Unscrew the bolts and detach the cap, being very careful not to disturb the Plastigauge.

13 Compare the width of the crushed

18.3 Tab on each big-end bearing shell must engage with notch in connecting rod or cap

18.9 The piston can be driven gently into the cylinder bore with the end of a wooden or plastic hammer handle

18.11 Angle-tightening the big-end bolts using the correct tool

Plastigauge to the scale printed on the Plastigauge envelope, to obtain the running clearance (see illustration 17.15). Compare it to the Specifications, to make sure the clearance is correct.

14 If the clearance is not as specified, seek the advice of a Ford dealer or similar engine reconditioning specialist - if the crankshaft journals are in good condition it may be possible simply to renew the shells to achieve the correct clearance. If this is not possible, the crankshaft must be reground by a specialist, who can also supply the necessary undersized shells. First though, make sure that no dirt or oil was trapped between the bearing shells and the connecting rod or cap when the clearance was measured. Also, recheck the crankpin diameter. If the Plastigauge was wider at one end than the other, the crankpin journal may be tapered.

15 Carefully scrape all traces of the Plastigauge material off the journal and the bearing surface. Be very careful not to scratch the bearing - use your fingernail or the edge of a credit card.

Final piston/connecting rod refitting

16 Make sure the bearing surfaces are perfectly clean, then apply a uniform layer of clean molybdenum disulphide-based grease, engine assembly lubricant, or clean engine oil, to both of them. You'll have to push the piston into the cylinder to expose the bearing surface of the shell in the connecting rod.

17 Slide the connecting rod back into place on the crankpin (big-end) journal, refit the big-end bearing cap, and then tighten the bolts as described above.

18 Repeat the entire procedure for the remaining piston/connecting rod assemblies.

19 The important points to remember are:

a) Keep the backs of the bearing shells and the recesses of the connecting rods and caps perfectly clean when assembling them.

b) Make sure you have the correct piston/rod assembly for each cylinder - use the etched cylinder numbers to identify the front-facing side of both the rod and its cap.

c) The arrow on the piston crown must face the timing belt/chain end of the engine.

d) Lubricate the cylinder bores with clean engine oil.

e) Lubricate the bearing surfaces when refitting the big-end bearing caps after the running clearance has been checked.

20 After all the piston/connecting rod assemblies have been properly installed, rotate the crankshaft a number of times by hand, to check for any obvious binding.

21 On HCS engines, if the oil pick-up pipe and strainer was removed, this is a good time to refit it. First clean the joint area, then coat the area indicated with the specified activator (available from Ford dealers) (see illustration). Wait for a period of ten minutes, then smear the shaded area with the specified adhesive and immediately press the inlet pipe into position in the crankcase.

19 Engine - initial start-up after overhaul

1 With the engine refitted in the vehicle, double-check the engine oil and coolant levels. Make a final check that everything has been reconnected, and that there are no tools or rags left in the engine compartment.

2 With the spark plugs removed and the ignition system disabled by unplugging the ignition coil's electrical connector, remove the fuel pump fuse (fuel injection engines) to disconnect the fuel pump (see Chapter 12). Turn the engine on the starter until the oil pressure warning light goes out.

3 Refit the spark plugs, and connect all the spark plug (HT) leads (Chapter 1). Reconnect the ignition coil. On fuel injection engines, refit the fuel pump fuse, switch on the ignition and listen for the fuel pump; it will run for a little longer than usual, due to the lack of pressure in the system.

4 Start the engine, noting that this also may take a little longer than usual, due to the fuel system components being empty.

5 While the engine is idling, check for fuel, coolant and oil leaks. Don't be alarmed if there are some odd smells and smoke from parts getting hot and burning off oil deposits. If the hydraulic tappets (where applicable) have been disturbed, some valve gear noise may be heard at first; this should disappear as the oil circulates fully around the engine, and normal pressure is restored in the tappets.

6 Keep the engine idling until hot water is felt circulating through the top hose, check that it idles reasonably smoothly and at the usual speed, then switch it off.

7 After a few minutes, recheck the oil and coolant levels, and top-up as necessary (Chapter 1).

8 If they were tightened as described, there is no need to re-tighten the cylinder head bolts once the engine has first run after reassembly - in fact, Ford state that the bolts must not be re-tightened.

9 If new components such as pistons, rings or crankshaft bearings have been fitted, the engine must be run-in for the first 500 miles (800 km). Do not operate the engine at full-throttle, or allow it to labour in any gear during this period. It is recommended that the oil and filter be changed at the end of this period.

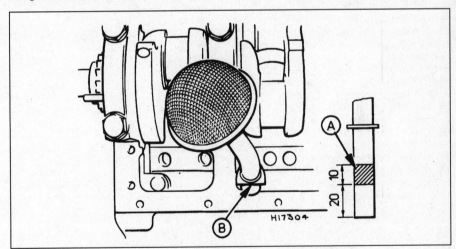

18.21 Oil inlet pipe refitting details on the HCS engine

A Area of sealant application - dimensions in mm
B Edge must be parallel with engine longitudinal axis

2D

Notes

Chapter 3
Cooling, heating and ventilation systems

Contents

Antifreeze - general information 2
Auxiliary drivebelt check and renewal .... See Chapter 1
Coolant level check .... See "Weekly Checks"
Cooling system - draining .... See Chapter 1
Cooling system - filling .... See Chapter 1
Cooling system - flushing .... See Chapter 1
Cooling system electrical switches and sensors - testing, removal
  and refitting 6
Cooling system hoses - disconnection and renewal 3
General information and precautions 1

Heater/ventilation components - removal and refitting 11
Radiator and expansion tank - removal, inspection and refitting ... 7
Radiator electric cooling fan assembly - testing, removal and
  refitting 5
Thermostat - removal, testing and refitting 4
Underbonnet check for fluid leaks and hose condition .. See Chapter 1
Water pump (CVH and PTE engines) - removal and refitting 9
Water pump (HCS engines) - removal and refitting 8
Water pump (Zetec engines) - removal and refitting 10

3

Degrees of difficulty

Easy, suitable for novice with little experience	**Fairly easy,** suitable for beginner with some experience	**Fairly difficult,** suitable for competent DIY mechanic	**Difficult,** suitable for experienced DIY mechanic	**Very difficult,** suitable for expert DIY or professional

Specifications

Coolant

Mixture type .... See Chapter 1
Cooling system capacity .... See Chapter 1

System pressure

Pressure test .... 1.2 bars - should hold this pressure for at least 10 seconds

Expansion tank filler cap

Pressure rating .... 1.0 to 1.4 bars approximately - see cap for actual value

Thermostat

Starts to open .... 85°C to 89°C

Coolant temperature sensor

Resistance:
  At 0°C .... 89 to 102 kilohms
  At 20°C .... 35 to 40 kilohms
  At 100°C .... 1.9 to 2.5 kilohms
  At 120°C .... 1.0 to 1.4 kilohms

Torque wrench settings

	Nm	lbf ft
Thermostat housing to cylinder head:		
HCS engines	17 to 21	13 to 16
CVH engines	9 to 12	7 to 9
PTE engines	9	7
Zetec engines	17 to 21	13 to 16
Water outlet to thermostat housing (Zetec engines)	9 to 12	7 to 9
Water pump pulley	10	7.5
Water pump retaining bolts:		
HCS, CVH and PTE engines	8	6
Zetec engines	18	13
Coolant temperature gauge sender	6	4
Coolant temperature sensor:		
HCS engines	23	17
CVH engines:		
1.4 litre models	19	14
1.6 litre models	15	11
PTE engines	15	11
Zetec engines	15	11
Radiator mounting bolts	20 to 27	15 to 20
Radiator cooling fan shroud retaining bolt	3 to 5	2 to 4
Radiator cooling fan motor to shroud nuts	9 to 12	7 to 9
Automatic transmission fluid cooling pipe connections to radiator	17 to 21	13 to 16

1 General information and precautions

Engine cooling system

The cooling system is of the pressurised type consisting of a belt-driven pump, aluminium crossflow radiator, expansion tank, electric cooling fan and a thermostat. The system functions as follows. Cold coolant in the bottom of the radiator passes through the bottom hose to the water pump, where it is pumped around the cylinder block and head passages. After cooling the cylinder bores, combustion surfaces and valve seats, the coolant reaches the underside of the thermostat, which is initially closed. The coolant passes through the heater and inlet manifold and is returned to the water pump.

When the engine is cold, the coolant circulates through the cylinder block, cylinder head, heater and inlet manifold. When the coolant reaches a predetermined tempera-ture, the thermostat opens, and the coolant then passes through the top hose to the radiator. As the coolant circulates through the radiator, it is cooled by the inrush of air when the car is in forward motion. Airflow is supplemented by the action of the electric cooling fan when necessary. Upon reaching the bottom of the radiator, the coolant is now cooled, and the cycle is repeated.

When the engine is at normal operating temperature, the coolant expands, and some of it is displaced into the expansion tank. This coolant collects in the tank, and is returned to the radiator when the system cools.

The electric cooling fan, mounted behind the radiator, is controlled by a thermostatic switch. At a predetermined coolant temperature, the switch contacts close, thus actuating the fan.

Heating/ventilation system

The heating system consists of a blower fan and heater matrix (radiator) located in the heater unit, with hoses connecting the heater matrix to the engine cooling system. Hot engine coolant is circulated through the heater matrix. Air is forced through the matrix by the three-speed fan, dispersing the heat into the vehicle interior. Fresh air enters the vehicle through the grille slats between the windscreen and the rear edge of the bonnet, and passes through to the heater casing. Depending on the position of the heater slide controls, which actuate cable-controlled flap valves within the heater casing, the air is distributed, either heated or unheated, via the ducting to outlet vents. The main outlet vents in the facia are adjustable. The airflow passes through the passenger compartment to exit at the rear of the vehicle.

Precautions

 Warning: DO NOT attempt to remove the expansion tank filler cap, or to disturb any part of the cooling system, while it or the engine is hot, as there is a very great risk of scalding. If the expansion tank filler cap must be removed before the engine and radiator have fully cooled down (even though this is not recommended) the pressure in the cooling system must first be released. Cover the cap with a thick layer of cloth, to avoid scalding, and slowly unscrew the filler cap until a hissing sound can be heard. When the hissing has stopped, showing that pressure is released, slowly unscrew the filler cap further until it can be removed; if more hissing sounds are heard, wait until they have stopped before unscrewing the cap completely. At all times, keep well away from the filler opening.

 Warning: Do not allow antifreeze to come in contact with your skin, or with the painted surfaces of the vehicle. Rinse off spills immediately with plenty of water. Never leave antifreeze lying around in an open container, or in a puddle in the driveway or on the garage floor. Children and pets are attracted by its sweet smell, but antifreeze can be fatal if ingested.

 Warning: If the engine is hot, the electric cooling fan may start rotating even if the engine is not running, so be careful to keep hands, hair and loose clothing well clear when working in the engine compartment.

2 Antifreeze - general information

Note: *Refer to the warnings given in Section 1 of this Chapter before proceeding.*

The cooling system should be filled with a water/ethylene glycol-based antifreeze solution, of a strength which will prevent freezing down to at least -25°C, or lower if the local climate requires it. Antifreeze also provides protection against corrosion, and increases the coolant boiling point.

The cooling system should be maintained according to the schedule described in Chapter 1. If antifreeze is used that is not to Ford's specification, old or contaminated coolant mixtures are likely to cause damage, and encourage the formation of corrosion and scale in the system. Use distilled water with the antifreeze, if available - if not, be sure to use only soft water. Clean rainwater is suitable.

Before adding antifreeze, check all hoses and hose connections, because antifreeze tends to leak through very small openings. Engines don't normally consume coolant, so if the level falls regularly, find the cause and correct it.

The exact mixture of antifreeze-to-water which you should use depends on the relative weather conditions. The mixture should contain at least 40% antifreeze, but not more than 70%. Consult the mixture ratio chart on the antifreeze container before adding coolant. Hydrometers are available at most automotive accessory shops to test the coolant. Use only good-quality ethylene-glycol-based antifreeze which meets the vehicle manufacturer's specifications.

3 Cooling system hoses - disconnection and renewal

Note: *Refer to the warnings given in Section 1 of this Chapter before starting work.*
1 If the checks described in Chapter 1 reveal a faulty hose, it must be renewed as follows.
2 First drain the cooling system (see Chapter 1); if the antifreeze is not due for renewal, the drained coolant may be re-used, if it is collected in a clean container.
3 To disconnect any hose, use a pair of pliers to release the spring clamps (or a screwdriver to slacken screw-type clamps), then move them along the hose clear of the union. Carefully work the hose off its stubs. The hoses can be removed with relative ease when new - on an older car, they may have stuck.
4 If a hose proves stubborn, try to release it by rotating it on its unions before attempting to work it off. Gently prise the end of the hose with a blunt instrument (such as a flat-bladed screwdriver), but do not apply too much force, and take care not to damage the pipe stubs or hoses. Note in particular that the radiator hose unions are fragile; do not use excessive force when attempting to remove the hoses.

 HAYNES HINT *If all else fails, cut the hose with a sharp knife, then slit it so that it can be peeled off in two pieces. Although this may prove expensive if the hose is otherwise undamaged, it is preferable to buying a new radiator.*

5 When refitting a hose, first slide the clamps onto the hose, then work the hose onto its unions.

HAYNES HINT *If the hose is stiff, use a little soapy water as a lubricant, or soften the hose by soaking it in hot water. Do not use oil or grease, which may attack the rubber.*

4.4a Thermostat housing hose attachments on the CVH engine

4.6 Removing the thermostat housing from a CVH engine

6 Work each hose end fully onto its union, then check that the hose is settled correctly and is properly routed. Slide each clip along the hose until it is behind the union flared end, before tightening it securely.
7 Refill the system with coolant (see Chapter 1).
8 Check carefully for leaks as soon as possible after disturbing any part of the cooling system.

4 Thermostat - removal, testing and refitting

Note: *Refer to the warnings given in Section 1 of this Chapter before starting work.*

Removal
1 Disconnect the battery negative (earth) lead (refer to Chapter 5A, Section 1).
2 Drain the cooling system (see Chapter 1).
3 Refer to the relevant Part of Chapter 4 and remove the air cleaner or air inlet hoses, according to engine type as necessary, to gain access to the thermostat housing.

HCS, CVH and PTE engines
4 Loosen the clips, and disconnect the radiator top hose, expansion tank hose and, where applicable, the heater hose from the thermostat housing **(see illustrations)**.

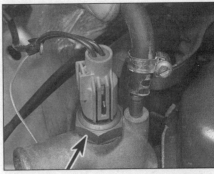
4.4b Disconnecting the expansion tank top hose from the thermostat housing (HCS engine). Radiator cooling fan thermal switch (arrowed)

4.7a Removing the gasket and thermostat from an HCS engine

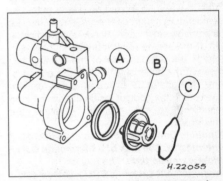
4.7b Exploded view of thermostat and housing (CVH and PTE engines)
A Sealing ring   C Retaining clip
B Thermostat

5 Disconnect the thermostatic switch wire multi-plug from the thermostat housing.
6 Unscrew the retaining bolts, and remove the thermostat housing **(see illustration)**.
7 Remove the gasket from the mating face of the thermostat housing, then using suitable pliers, compress the thermostat retaining clip (where applicable) and remove it from the housing. Extract the thermostat from the housing (noting its direction of fitting) and where applicable, remove the O-ring seal **(see illustrations)**.

Zetec engines
8 Disconnect the expansion tank hose and

4.8 Disconnect the coolant hoses from the water outlet on a Zetec engine

4.10 Zetec engine thermostat removal

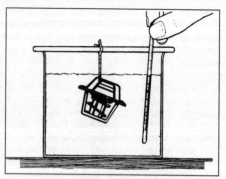

4.16 Testing the thermostat

the radiator top hose from the thermostat housing's water outlet **(see illustration)**.

9 Unscrew the retaining bolts, and remove the water outlet from the thermostat housing.

10 Withdraw the thermostat from the housing noting the position of the air bleed valve, and how the thermostat is installed (which end is facing outwards) **(see illustration)**.

Testing

General check

11 Before assuming the thermostat is to blame for a cooling system problem, check the coolant level, auxiliary drivebelt tension and condition (see Chapter 1) and temperature gauge operation.

12 If the engine seems to be taking a long time to warm up (based on heater output or temperature gauge operation), the thermostat is probably stuck open. Renew the thermostat.

13 If the engine runs hot, use your hand to check the temperature of the radiator top hose. If the hose isn't hot, but the engine is, the thermostat is probably stuck closed, preventing the coolant inside the engine from escaping to the radiator - renew the thermostat.

Caution: Don't drive the vehicle without a thermostat. The lack of a thermostat will slow warm-up time. The engine management system's ECU will then stay in warm-up mode for longer than necessary, causing emissions and fuel economy to suffer.

14 If the radiator top hose is hot, it means that the coolant is flowing and the thermostat is open. Consult the *"Fault finding"* section at the end of this manual to assist in tracing possible cooling system faults.

Thermostat test

15 If the thermostat remains in the open position at room temperature, it is faulty, and must be renewed as a matter of course.

16 To test it fully, suspend the (closed) thermostat on a length of string in a container of cold water, with a thermometer beside it; ensure that neither touches the side of the container **(see illustration)**.

17 Heat the water, and check the temperature at which the thermostat begins to open; compare this value with that specified. It's not possible to check the fully-open temperature, because this occurs above the boiling point of water at normal atmospheric pressure. If the temperature at which the thermostat began to open was as specified, then it is most likely that the thermostat is working properly at all temperatures. Remove the thermostat, and allow it to cool down; check that it closes fully.

18 If the thermostat does not open and close as described, if it sticks in either position, or if it does not open at the specified temperature, it must be renewed.

Refitting

All models

19 Refitting is a reversal of removal. Clean the mating surfaces carefully, and renew the

thermostat's O-ring seal or housing gasket, as applicable.

20 On Zetec engines, ensure that the thermostat is fitted with its air bleed valve uppermost.

21 Tighten the thermostat housing/water outlet bolts to the specified torque.

22 Refill the cooling system (see Chapter 1).

23 Refit the air cleaner or air inlet components, as applicable, if removed for access.

24 Start the engine and allow it to reach normal operating temperature, then check for leaks and proper thermostat operation.

5 Radiator electric cooling fan assembly - testing, removal and refitting

Note: *Refer to the warnings given in Section 1 of this Chapter before starting work.*

Testing

1 If it is suspected that the cooling fan is not operating when high engine temperature would normally require it to do so, first check the relevant fuses and relays (see Chapter 12).

2 Detach the wiring multi-plug from the thermostat switch, which is located either in the thermostat housing or at the right-hand end of the radiator, next to the bottom hose **(see illustration)**. Using a suitable piece of wire, bridge the two connections within the plug. Switch the ignition on and check if the cooling fan operates. If the fan now operates, the thermostatic switch is at fault, and should be renewed as described in Section 6. Remove the bridging wire from the plug, and reconnect the wiring connector to complete the test.

3 If the fan failed to operate in the previous test, either the fan motor is at fault, or there is a fault in the wiring loom (see Chapter 12 for testing details).

Removal

All models except Turbo

4 Disconnect the battery negative (earth) lead (refer to Chapter 5A, Section 1).

5 Detach the wiring multi-plug from the fan motor and unclip the wiring from the retaining clips on the shroud **(see illustration)**.

5.2 Radiator cooling fan thermostatic switch location on CVH engine thermostat housing

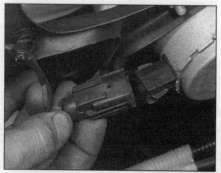

5.5 Disconnecting the multi-plug from the radiator cooling fan motor

6 Unscrew the nut securing the cooling fan shroud to the radiator, noting the insulating washer arrangement, then lift the fan shroud and motor assembly from the vehicle **(see illustration)**.

7 To separate the fan from the motor shaft, first remove its retaining clip and washer, then withdraw the fan **(see illustration)**. A new clip will be needed upon reassembly. Remove the three nuts securing the motor to the shroud and separate the two components.

Turbo models

8 Disconnect the battery negative (earth) lead (refer to Chapter 5A, Section 1).

9 Undo the two retaining screws and move the HT lead bracket clear of the working area, disconnecting the HT leads as required.

10 Disconnect the fan motor wiring multi-plug and the two auxiliary lamp wiring multi-plugs. Unclip the wiring from any local retaining clips.

11 Remove the front bumper as described in Chapter 11.

12 Undo the two lower fan shroud retaining bolts, release the shroud upper locating tongue from the radiator and withdraw the assembly from the front of the car.

13 To separate the fan from the motor shaft, pull off the fan guard from the shroud, flatten back the raised lockwasher tab, and unscrew **clockwise** (a left-hand thread is employed) the nut securing the fan to the motor shaft. Remove the fan then undo the three nuts securing the motor to the shroud and separate the two components.

Refitting

All models

14 Refitting is a reversal of the removal procedure. On non-Turbo models, ensure that the locating tags on the base of the shroud locate correctly in their slots in the body crossmember. On Turbo models, if the fan was removed, use a new lockwasher when refitting. On all models, ensure that the wiring connections are cleanly and securely made, and locate the loom in the retaining clips.

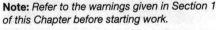

6 Cooling system electrical switches and sensors - testing, removal and refitting

Note: *Refer to the warnings given in Section 1 of this Chapter before starting work.*

Coolant temperature gauge sender

Testing

1 If the coolant temperature gauge is inoperative, check the fuses first (see Chapter 12).

2 If the gauge indicates overheating at any time, consult the *"Fault finding"* section at the end of this manual, to assist in tracing possible cooling system faults.

5.6 Radiator cooling fan shroud securing nut (arrowed)

3 If the gauge indicates overheating shortly after the engine is started from cold, disconnect the temperature gauge sender's wiring multi-plug. The sender is located below the thermostat housing on HCS engines, adjacent to the thermostat housing on CVH and PTE engines, and on the forward-facing side of the thermostat housing on Zetec engines. If the gauge reading now drops, renew the sender. If the reading remains high, the wire to the gauge may be shorted to earth, or the gauge is faulty.

4 If the gauge fails to indicate after the engine has been warmed up (approximately 10 minutes) and the fuses are known to be sound, switch off the engine. Disconnect the sender's wiring multi-plug, and use a jumper wire to ground the connector to a clean earth point (bare metal) on the engine. Switch on the ignition without starting the engine. If the gauge now indicates Hot, renew the sender.

5 If the gauge still does not work, the circuit may be open, or the gauge may be faulty. See Chapter 12 for additional information.

Removal

6 Refer to the relevant Part of Chapter 4 and remove the air cleaner or air inlet hoses, according to engine type as necessary, to gain access to the sender unit.

7 Drain the cooling system (see Chapter 1).

8 On Zetec engines, disconnect the expansion tank coolant hose and the radiator top hose from the thermostat housing's water outlet.

9 Disconnect the wiring multi-plug from the sender unit.

10 Unscrew the sender and withdraw it.

Refitting

11 Clean as thoroughly as possible the sender unit location, then apply a light coat of sealant to the sender's threads. Screw in the sender, tighten it to the specified torque, and reconnect the wiring multi-plug.

12 Reconnect the hoses, and refit any components disconnected for access. Refill or top-up the cooling system (see *"Weekly Checks"* or Chapter 1) and run the engine. Check for leaks and proper gauge operation.

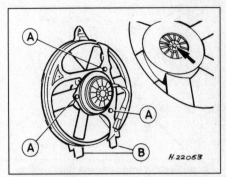

5.7 Nuts securing fan motor to shroud (A), and shroud to body crossmember locating tags (B). Inset shows fan to motor shaft retaining clip (arrowed)

Engine coolant temperature sensor

Testing

13 Disconnect the battery negative (earth) lead (see Chapter 5A, Section 1).

14 Locate the coolant temperature sensor, which will be found below the inlet manifold on HCS engines, on the side or centre of the inlet manifold on CVH and PTE engines, or on top of the thermostat housing on Zetec engines. Once located, refer to the relevant Part of Chapter 4 and remove the air cleaner or air inlet hoses, according to engine type as necessary, to improve access to the sensor unit.

15 Disconnect the wiring multi-plug from the sensor.

16 Using an ohmmeter, measure resistance between the sensor terminals. Depending on the temperature of the sensor tip, the resistance measured will vary, but should be within the broad limits given in the *Specifications* of this Chapter. If the sensor's temperature is varied - by removing it (see below) and placing it in a freezer for a while, or by warming it gently - its resistance should alter accordingly.

17 If the results obtained show the sensor to be faulty, renew it.

18 On completion, reconnect the wiring multi-plug and refit any components removed for access, then reconnect the battery.

Removal

19 Disconnect the battery negative (earth) lead (see Chapter 5A, Section 1).

20 Locate the sensor as described previously, and remove any components as necessary for access.

21 Drain the cooling system (see Chapter 1).

22 Disconnect the wiring multi-plug from the sensor.

23 Unscrew the sensor and withdraw it.

Refitting

24 Clean as thoroughly as possible the sensor location, then apply a light coat of sealant to the sensor's threads. Refit and tighten the sensor to the specified torque

3

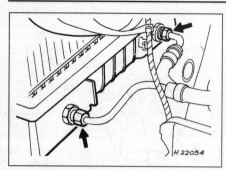

7.4 Automatic transmission fluid cooling pipe connections (arrowed) at the radiator

7.6a Radiator securing bolt, insulator and washer

7.6b Rubber insulator on radiator locating lug

wrench setting, and reconnect the multi-plug.

25 Refit any components disconnected for access then refill the cooling system (see Chapter 1).

Radiator electric cooling fan thermostatic switch

Testing

26 Refer to the procedures contained in Section 5.

Removal

27 Disconnect the battery negative (earth) lead (refer to Chapter 5A, Section 1).
28 Drain the cooling system (see Chapter 1).
29 Disconnect the wiring multi-plug from the thermostatic switch, and then unscrew the switch from the thermostat housing or radiator side tank, as applicable. Remove the sealing washer.

Refitting

30 Refitting is a reversal of removal, but fit a new sealing washer and tighten the switch securely. Refill the cooling system as described in Chapter 1, then reconnect the battery.

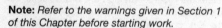

7 Radiator and expansion tank
- removal, inspection and refitting

Note: *Refer to the warnings given in Section 1 of this Chapter before starting work.*

Radiator

HAYNES HiNT *If leakage is the reason for removing the radiator, bear in mind that minor leaks can often be cured using a radiator sealant with the radiator in situ.*

Removal (all models except Turbo)

1 Disconnect the battery negative (earth) lead (refer to Chapter 5A, Section 1).
2 Drain the cooling system (see Chapter 1).
3 Remove the radiator cooling fan assembly as described in Section 5.
4 Release the hose clips and disconnect the hoses from the radiator. Additionally, on

automatic transmission models, disconnect the transmission fluid cooling pipe connections fitting blanking plugs to prevent excessive fluid loss **(see illustration)**.
5 On Zetec engine models, disconnect the wiring multi-plug from the cooling fan thermostatic switch
6 Remove the radiator securing bolts and lift the radiator out of its locating slots in the body crossmember. Note rubber insulators fitted to the locating lugs on the base of the radiator **(see illustrations)**.
7 With the radiator removed, it can be inspected for leaks and damage. If it needs repair, have a radiator specialist or dealer service department perform the work, as special techniques are required.
8 Insects and dirt can be removed from the radiator with a garden hose or a soft brush. Don't bend the cooling fins as this is done.

Removal (Turbo models)

9 Disconnect the battery negative (earth) lead (refer to Chapter 5A, Section 1).
10 Drain the cooling system (see Chapter 1).
11 Remove the radiator cooling fan assembly as described in Section 5.
12 Release the hose clips and disconnect the hoses from the radiator.
13 Disconnect the turbocharger coolant feed by slackening its clamp and pulling the hose (at the radiator rear right-hand side) off the turbocharger's metal pipe.
14 Remove the intercooler, as described in Chapter 4C.
15 Remove its three retaining screws, and withdraw the exhaust manifold heat shield.

7.22a Remove the single bolt retaining the expansion tank . . .

16 Lift the radiator out of its locating slots in the body crossmember. Note rubber insulators fitted to the locating lugs on the base of the radiator.
17 Clean and inspect the radiator with reference to paragraphs 7 and 8 above.

Refitting (all models)

18 Refitting is a reversal of removal, but check the rubber insulators, and if necessary renew them. Refill the cooling system with reference to Chapter 1. On automatic transmission models check, and if necessary top-up, the automatic transmission fluid level (Chapter 1).

Expansion tank

Removal

19 Partially drain the cooling system, so that the coolant level drops below the expansion tank. Refer to Chapter 1 for details.
20 Before disconnecting the coolant hoses from the expansion tank, it is advisable to clamp them just short of their connections to the expansion tank, to prevent spillage of coolant and the ingress of air when they are detached.
21 Loosen off the coolant hose clips at the expansion tank, and detach the hoses from it. If they are not clamped, secure them so that their ends are raised, to minimise coolant spillage.
22 Remove the single bolt retaining the expansion tank, and slide the other side of the tank free from its retaining bracket **(see illustrations)**.

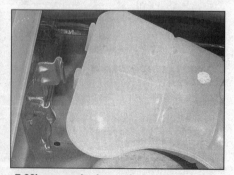

7.22b . . . and release the expansion tank from its retaining bracket

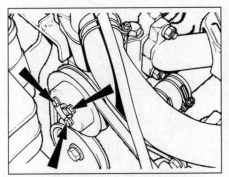

8.3 HCS engine water pump pulley retaining bolts (arrowed)

8.6 HCS engine water pump removal

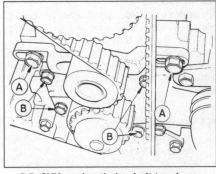

9.5 CVH engine timing belt tensioner retaining bolts (A) and water pump securing bolts (B)

Refitting

23 Refit in the reverse order of removal. Top-up the cooling system as described in *"Weekly Checks"*.

8 Water pump (HCS engines) - removal and refitting

Note: *Refer to the warnings given in Section 1 of this Chapter before starting work.*

Removal

1 Disconnect the battery negative (earth) lead (refer to Chapter 5A, Section 1).
2 Drain the cooling system (see Chapter 1).
3 Slacken the water pump pulley retaining bolts, then remove the auxiliary drivebelt as described in Chapter 1 **(see illustration)**.
4 Remove the retaining bolts, and remove the drivebelt pulley from the water pump.
5 Loosen off the coolant hose securing clips, and disconnect the hoses from the water pump.
6 Unscrew the retaining bolts, and withdraw the water pump from the engine **(see illustration)**.
7 No provision is made for the repair of the water pump; if it is noisy or defective in any way, it must be renewed.

Refitting

8 Clean all traces of gasket from the engine and the water pump mating faces. Ensure that the mating faces are clean and dry. Note that the water pump gasket fitted during production is integral with the timing cover gasket, and this will need to be cut away using a sharp knife, keeping as close to the timing cover as possible.
9 Refitting is a reversal of the removal procedure. Use a new gasket, lightly smeared with jointing compound, and tighten the retaining bolts to the specified torque.
10 Refit and adjust the auxiliary drivebelt as described in Chapter 1.
11 Refill the cooling system as described in Chapter 1, and reconnect the battery.

9 Water pump (CVH and PTE engines) - removal and refitting

Note: *Refer to the warnings given in Section 1 of this Chapter before starting work.*

Removal

1 Disconnect the battery negative (earth) lead (refer to Chapter 5A, Section 1).
2 Drain the cooling system (see Chapter 1).
3 Remove the timing belt and tensioner (see Chapter 2B). If the belt is fouled with coolant, it must be renewed as a matter of course.
4 Loosen off the coolant hose retaining clip, and detach the coolant hose from the water pump.
5 Unscrew and remove the four bolts securing the water pump to the front end face of the cylinder block, and then withdraw the pump from the vehicle **(see illustration)**.

Refitting

6 Clean the engine water pump mating faces. Ensure that the mating faces are clean and dry.
7 No provision is made for the repair of the water pump; if it is noisy or defective in any way, it must be renewed.
8 Refitting is a reversal of the removal procedure. Tighten the retaining bolts to the specified torque, and ensure that the coolant hose connection to the water pump is securely made.

10.5a Unscrew the bolts (arrowed) . . .

9 Refit the timing belt and tensioner as described in Chapter 2B.
10 Refill the cooling system as described in Chapter 1, and reconnect the battery.

10 Water pump (Zetec engines) - removal and refitting

Note: *Refer to the warnings given in Section 1 of this Chapter before starting work.*

Removal

1 Disconnect the battery negative (earth) lead (refer to Chapter 5A, Section 1).
2 Drain the cooling system (see Chapter 1).
3 Remove the timing belt and tensioner (see Chapter 2C). If the belt is fouled with coolant, it must be renewed as a matter of course.
4 Disconnect the radiator bottom hose from the pump union.
5 Unbolt and remove the water pump **(see illustrations)**. If the pump is to be renewed, unbolt the timing belt guide pulleys, and transfer them to the new pump.

Refitting

6 Clean the mating surfaces carefully; the gasket must be renewed whenever it is disturbed.
7 On refitting, use grease to stick the new gasket in place, refit the pump, and tighten the pump bolts to the specified torque.
8 The remainder of refitting is a reversal of the

10.5b . . . and remove the Zetec engine water pump

3

removal procedure. Refit the timing belt and tensioner as described in Chapter 2C, noting that a new tensioner spring and retaining pin must be fitted if the timing belt has been removed for the first time. Tighten all fasteners to the specified torque, and refill the system with coolant as described in Chapter 1.

11 Heater/ventilation components - removal and refitting

Heater controls

1 Disconnect the battery negative (earth) lead (refer to Chapter 5A, Section 1).
2 Refer to Chapter 12 and remove the radio.
3 Pull off the heater fan motor control knob, then move the air distribution and temperature controls fully to the right. Unclip and remove the heater slide facia towards the left-hand side of the vehicle, removing the slide control knobs only as necessary, and disconnecting its bulbholder (bayonet type) as it is withdrawn.
4 Squeeze the two release tabs together on the heater fan motor control switch, and remove it, disconnecting its multi-plug as it is withdrawn.
5 Disconnect the heater control cables from the heater casing assembly by releasing the outer cable abutments and disengaging the

11.5 Disengaging heater control cable from its flap operating mechanism on the heater casing

cable inner cores from their flap operating mechanisms **(see illustration)**.
6 Undo the three heater control panel securing screws, and remove the control panel (with its cables attached) from behind the facia **(see illustration)**.
7 Disconnect the heater control cables from their control panel levers, as required, by releasing their outer cable clamping covers and inner cable core securing clips **(see illustrations)**.
8 If renewing a heater control panel, note that the new unit, is supplied with control cables and assembly aids fitted **(see illustration)**. The assembly aids ensure correct heater control adjustments during fitting, and must be removed thereafter.

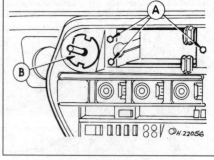

11.6 Heater control panel securing screws (A), and fan motor control switch (B)

9 Refitting is a reversal of the removal procedure, adjusting the heater control cables to complete. The adjustment is made automatically by moving the heater slide control levers from their left-hand stop to their right-hand stop. When moving the control levers, a considerable amount of resistance may be encountered, which must be overcome.

Heater fan motor and resistor assembly

10 Disconnect the battery negative (earth) lead (refer to Chapter 5A, Section 1).
11 Depending on engine type, refer to the relevant Part of Chapter 4 and remove the air cleaner if necessary, to gain access to the bulkhead panel in the engine compartment.
12 Remove the expansion tank as described in Section 7.
13 Undo the retaining bolt and remove the jack and wheelbrace.
14 Disconnect the modules on the bulkhead panel. Release the wiring loom and any connectors, cable-ties and hoses from the bulkhead panel, and remove its rubber seal.
15 Remove the bulkhead panel. The panel is secured by screws, with a nut at either end (behind the panel), and is removed in two sections.
16 Detach and remove the cover from the heater fan motor assembly **(see illustration)**.
17 Disconnect the wiring from the heater fan

11.7a Releasing outer cable clamping cover . . .

11.7b . . . and removing it

11.7c Releasing inner cable core from heater control lever

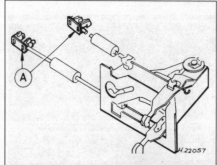

11.8 Heater control panel. Assembly aids (A) fitted to heater casing flap valve end of cables

11.16 Removing the cover from the heater fan motor assembly

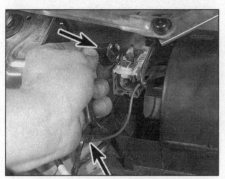

11.17 Disconnecting the wiring from the heater fan motor and resistor assembly (arrowed)

11.20a Releasing the heater fan motor retaining strap from the underside of the assembly

11.20b Removing the heater fan motor

motor and resistor assembly **(see illustration)**.

18 Undo the two nuts securing the assembly to the bulkhead and remove it from the vehicle.

19 Detach the heater fan cover, having released its two retaining clips.

20 Release the heater fan motor retaining strap from underneath, using a flat-bladed screwdriver, and remove it. Remove the resistor assembly and/or heater fan motor, as required **(see illustrations)**.

21 Refitting is a reversal of the removal

procedure, ensuring that the heater fan motor wires are routed under the retaining strap, but are not pinched by it.

Heater matrix

Note: *Refer to the warnings given in Section 1 of this Chapter before starting work.*

22 Disconnect the battery negative (earth) lead (refer to Chapter 5A, Section 1).

23 Drain the cooling system (see Chapter 1).

24 Release the hose clips and disconnect the two heater hoses from their dual heater matrix connector on the bulkhead, at the rear of the engine compartment. Plug the hoses to prevent excessive coolant loss, collecting spillage and any remaining coolant from the heater matrix in a suitable container.

25 Undo the screws securing the heater

matrix connector to the bulkhead, and detach its cover plate and gasket **(see illustration)**.

26 Where fitted, remove the centre console as described in Chapter 11.

27 Unclip and detach the footwell vent from the base of the heater casing **(see illustration)**.

28 Unclip the lower cover from the heater casing and remove the heater matrix, being careful to avoid any residual coolant spillage in the passenger compartment **(see illustrations)**.

29 Refitting is a reversal of the removal procedure. On completion, refill the cooling system as described in Chapter 1.

Heater casing assembly

30 Remove the facia, as described in Chapter 11.

31 Remove the heater matrix, as described previously in this Section.

32 Disconnect the heater control cables from the heater casing assembly as described previously in this Section.

33 Disconnect the side outlet vent ducting from the heater casing. The side outlet ducts can be removed by undoing the screws securing them to the bulkhead, as required.

34 Undo the two heater casing securing nuts and remove the casing from the vehicle **(see illustration)**.

35 Refitting is a reversal of the removal procedure, with reference to the applicable Chapters and Sections of this manual.

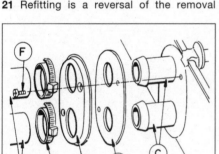

11.25 Exploded view of the heater matrix connections

A *Cover plate*
B *Gasket*
C *Heater matrix connector pipe*
D *Hose clips*
E *Heater hoses*
F *Screw*

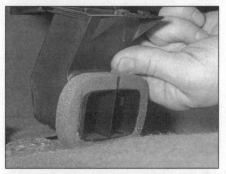

11.27 Removing the footwell vent from the base of the heater casing

3

11.28a Unclipping the lower heater casing cover

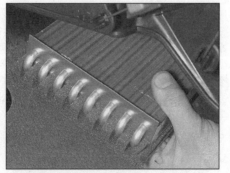

11.28b Withdrawing the heater matrix

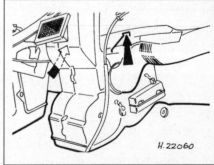

11.34 Heater casing securing nuts (arrowed)

Notes

Chapter 4 Part A:
Fuel system - carburettor engines

Contents

Accelerator cable (CTX automatic transmission models) - adjustment 4
Accelerator cable (manual transmission models) - removal, refitting and adjustment 3
Accelerator pedal - removal and refitting 5
Accelerator pump diaphragm (Weber TLM carburettor) - removal and refitting 16
Air cleaner - removal and refitting 2
Air cleaner element renewal ....See Chapter 1
Automatic choke (Weber TLD carburettor) - adjustment 33
Automatic choke (Weber TLD carburettor) - removal, inspection and refitting 34
Carburettor (Weber DFTM) - description 25
Carburettor (Weber DFTM) - dismantling, cleaning, inspection and reassembly 29
Carburettor (Weber DFTM) - fast-idle speed adjustment 26
Carburettor (Weber DFTM) - removal and refitting 28
Carburettor (Weber TLD) - description 30
Carburettor (Weber TLD) - dismantling, cleaning, inspection and reassembly 36
Carburettor (Weber TLD) - fast-idle speed adjustment 31
Carburettor (Weber TLD) - removal and refitting 35
Carburettor (Weber TLDM) - description 18
Carburettor (Weber TLDM) - dismantling, cleaning, inspection and reassembly 24
Carburettor (Weber TLDM) - fast-idle speed adjustment 19
Carburettor (Weber TLDM) - removal and refitting 23
Carburettor (Weber TLM) - description 12

Carburettor (Weber TLM) - dismantling, cleaning, inspection and reassembly 17
Carburettor (Weber TLM) - fast-idle speed adjustment 13
Carburettor (Weber TLM) - removal and refitting 15
Choke cable - removal, refitting and adjustment 6
Fuel gauge sender unit - removal and refitting 9
Fuel pump - testing, removal and refitting 7
Fuel tank - removal, inspection and refitting 8
Fuel tank filler pipe - removal and refitting 11
Fuel tank ventilation tube - removal and refitting 10
General fuel system checks ....See Chapter 1
General information and precautions 1
Idle speed and mixture check and adjustment ....See Chapter 1
Inlet manifold - removal and refitting 37
Needle valve and float (Weber TLD carburettor) - removal, refitting and adjustment 32
Needle valve and float (Weber TLDM carburettor) - removal, refitting and adjustment 20
Needle valve and float (Weber TLM carburettor) - removal, refitting and adjustment 14
Throttle kicker control solenoid (Weber TLDM carburettor) - removal and refitting 22
Throttle kicker unit (Weber DFTM carburettor) - removal, refitting and adjustment 27
Throttle kicker unit (Weber TLDM carburettor) - removal, refitting and adjustment 21
Underbody fuel/brake line check ....See Chapter 1
Underbonnet check for fluid leaks and hose condition ...See Chapter 1

Degrees of difficulty

Easy, suitable for novice with little experience	**Fairly easy,** suitable for beginner with some experience	**Fairly difficult,** suitable for competent DIY mechanic 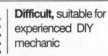

Difficult, suitable for experienced DIY mechanic

Very difficult, suitable for expert DIY or professional

Specifications

General
System type .... Rear-mounted fuel tank, mechanical fuel pump, single Weber carburettor

Carburettor
Type .... Single or twin choke, downdraught
Application:
  1.0 litre HCS engines .... Weber (1V) TLM
  1.1 litre HCS engines .... Weber (2V) TLDM
  1.3 HCS engines .... Weber (2V) TLDM
  1.4 litre CVH engines .... Weber (2V) DFTM
  1.6 litre CVH engines .... Weber (2V) TLD

Fuel grade
Fuel octane requirement:
  Engines without catalytic converter* .... 95 RON unleaded or 97 RON leaded
  Engines with catalytic converter .... 95 RON unleaded (leaded fuel must **not** be used)
Refer to dealer for latest recommendations

Fuel pump

Delivery pressure .... 0.24 to 0.38 bars

Carburettor data

Weber (1V) TLM carburettor - 1.0 litre HCS engines

Idle speed and mixture settings	See Chapter 1
Fast-idle speed	3400 ± 100 rpm
Float height	26.0 ± 1.0 mm
Venturi diameter	23 mm
Main jet	110
Air correction jet	220

Weber (2V) TLDM carburettor - 1.1 litre HCS engines

Idle speed and mixture settings .... See Chapter 1
Fast-idle speed:
   Manual transmission .... 2800 rpm
   CTX automatic transmission .... 2600 rpm
Float height .... 29.0 ± 1.0 mm
Throttle kicker speed:
   Manual transmission .... 1250 to 1350 rpm
   CTX automatic transmission .... 1050 to 1150 rpm

	Primary	Secondary
Venturi diameter	26 mm	28 mm
Main jet:		
Manual transmission	92	122
CTX automatic transmission	92	112
Emulsion tube	F113	F75
Air correction jet	195	155

Weber (2V) TLDM carburettor - 1.3 litre HCS engines

Idle speed and mixture settings .... See Chapter 1
Fast-idle speed .... 2500 rpm
Float height .... 29.0 ± 1.0 mm
Throttle kicker speed .... 1900 ± 100 rpm

	Primary	Secondary
Venturi diameter	19 mm	20 mm
Main jet	90	122
Emulsion tube	F113	F75
Air correction jet	185	130

Weber (2V) DFTM carburettor - 1.4 litre CVH engines

Idle speed and mixture settings .... See Chapter 1
Fast-idle speed .... 2800 ± 100 rpm
Choke pull-down .... 2.7 to 3.2 mm
Float height .... 8.0 ± 0.5 mm
Throttle kicker speed:
   Manual transmission .... 1300 ± 50 rpm
   CTX automatic transmission .... 1100 ± 50 rpm (in Neutral)

	Primary	Secondary
Venturi diameter	21 mm	23 mm
Main jet	100	125
Air correction jet	210	155
Emulsion tube	F22	F60
Idle jet	42	60

Weber (2V) TLD carburettor - 1.6 litre CVH engines

Idle speed and mixture settings .... See Chapter 1
Fast-idle speed .... 1800 ± 50 rpm (on third step of fast-idle cam)
Choke pull-down .... 4.7 ± 0.5 mm
Float height .... 29.0 ± 0.5 mm

	Primary	Secondary
Venturi diameter	21	23
Main jet	117	127
Emulsion tube	F105	F71
Air correction jet	185	125

Torque wrench settings

	Nm	lbf ft
Fuel pump	16 to 20	12 to 15
Inlet manifold	16 to 20	12 to 15

1 General information and precautions

General information

The fuel system on all models with carburettor induction comprises a rear-mounted fuel tank, a mechanical diaphragm fuel pump, a carburettor and an air cleaner.

The fuel tank is mounted at the rear, under the floorpan behind the rear seats. The tank has a "ventilation-to-atmosphere system" through a combined roll-over/anti-trickle fill valve assembly, located in the left-hand rear wheel arch. A filler neck sensing pipe, integral with the fuel tank filler pipe, will shut off the petrol pump filler gun when the predetermined maximum level of fuel is reached in the tank, so preventing spillage and wastage. A conventional fuel level sender unit is mounted in the top face of the fuel tank.

One of two fuel pump types will be fitted, depending on the engine type. On HCS engines, the fuel pump is operated by a pivoting rocker arm; one end rests on an eccentric lobe on the engine camshaft, and the other end is attached to the fuel pump diaphragm. The pump fitted to the CVH engine is operated by a separate pushrod, one end rests on an eccentric lobe on the engine camshaft, and the other rests on the pump actuating rod which operates the diaphragm. Both types of mechanical pump incorporate a nylon mesh filter, and are of sealed type (they cannot be serviced or overhauled).

Four different types of Weber carburettor are featured in the range, further details being given in later Sections of this Chapter.

The air cleaner incorporates a "waxstat" controlled air inlet, supplying either hot air from a shroud mounted around the exhaust manifold, or cool air from a duct in the front of the vehicle.

Precautions

⚠️ *Warning: Petrol is extremely flammable - great care must be taken when working on any part of the fuel system. Do not smoke or allow any naked flames or uncovered light bulbs near the work area. Note that gas powered domestic appliances with pilot flames, such as heaters, boilers and tumble dryers, also present a fire hazard - bear this in mind if you are working in an area where such appliances are present. Always keep a suitable fire extinguisher close to the work area and familiarise yourself with its operation before starting work. Wear eye protection when working on fuel systems and wash off any fuel spilt on bare skin immediately with soap and water. Note that fuel vapour is just as dangerous as liquid fuel; a vessel that has just been emptied of liquid fuel will still contain vapour and can be potentially explosive. Petrol is a highly dangerous and volatile liquid, and the precautions necessary when handling it cannot be overstressed.*

Many of the operations described in this Chapter involve the disconnection of fuel lines, which may cause an amount of fuel spillage. Before commencing work, refer to the above Warning and the information in "Safety first" at the beginning of this manual.

When working with fuel system components, pay particular attention to cleanliness - dirt entering the fuel system may cause blockages which will lead to poor running.

Certain adjustment points in the fuel system are protected by tamperproof caps, plugs or seals. In some territories, it is an offence to drive a vehicle with broken or missing tamperproof seals. Before disturbing a tamperproof seal, first check that no local or national laws will be broken by doing so, and fit a new tamperproof seal after adjustment is complete, where required by law. Do not break tamperproof seals on any vehicle whilst it is still under warranty.

Carburettors are delicate instruments, and care must be taken not to disturb any components unnecessarily. Before attempting work on a carburettor, ensure that the relevant spares are available; it should be noted that a complete strip down of a carburettor is unlikely to cure a fault which is not immediately obvious, without introducing new problems. If persistent problems occur, it is recommended that the services of a Ford dealer or a carburettor specialist are sought. Most dealers will be able to provide carburettor rejetting and servicing facilities. Where necessary, it may be possible to purchase a reconditioned carburettor.

2 Air cleaner - removal and refitting

Note: *Air cleaner element renewal and air cleaner temperature control system checks are described in Chapter 1.*

Removal

1 Disconnect the battery negative (earth) lead (refer to Chapter 5A, Section 1).

2 On CVH engine models, pull free and release the accelerator cable from the locating clip on the side of the air cleaner.

3 Undo the two (HCS engine) or three (CVH engine) retaining screws, and partially lift the air cleaner from the carburettor so that the hose and wiring connections to the underside of the air cleaner body are accessible **(see illustration)**.

4 Note their connections and routings, then detach the wiring multi-plug and hoses from the underside of the air cleaner **(see illustrations)**. On CVH engines, also disconnect the vacuum hose from the inlet manifold.

5 Lift the air cleaner from the carburettor.

6 If required, the inlet air temperature sensor can be unscrewed and removed from the base of the air cleaner (where fitted).

Refitting

7 Refit in the reverse order of removal. Renew any hoses that are perished or cracked, and ensure that all fittings are securely and correctly reconnected.

4A

2.3 Undoing the air cleaner retaining screws (HCS engine shown)

2.4a Disconnecting the oil separator/crankcase ventilation hose from the air cleaner (CVH engine shown)

2.4b Disconnecting the intake air temperature sensor multi-plug (CVH engine shown)

3.5a Remove the accelerator outer cable securing clip . . .

3.5b . . . then release from its support bracket

3 Accelerator cable (manual transmission models) - removal, refitting and adjustment

Removal

1 Disconnect the battery negative (earth) lead (refer to Chapter 5A, Section 1).
2 Working inside the vehicle, disconnect the cable from the top of the accelerator pedal, release the grommet and pull the cable free from the pedal. Withdraw the cable through the engine side of the bulkhead.
3 Refer to Section 2 and remove the air cleaner.
4 Detach the inner cable from the carburettor linkage.
5 Prise free the retaining clip, detach the outer cable from the support bracket, and remove the cable **(see illustrations)**.

Refitting and adjustment

6 To refit the cable, feed the inner cable through the bulkhead, and reconnect the inner cable to the accelerator pedal. Note that a plastic sleeve is supplied with new cables for the purpose of routing through the bulkhead panel.
7 Locate the grommet in the bulkhead, then push the outer cable into it to secure it in the bulkhead.
8 Lubricate the cable grommet at the carburettor end with a mild soapy solution,

then reconnect the cable to the carburettor. Locate the outer cable by pulling it towards the rocker cover.
9 Have an assistant depress the accelerator pedal fully, and hold it in this position. The outer cable should be seen to move in its grommet. Refit the securing clip to the bracket, then release the accelerator pedal.
10 Depress the accelerator pedal, then release it and check that the throttle opens and shuts fully. Further adjust if necessary before refitting the air cleaner and reconnecting the battery.

4 Accelerator cable (CTX automatic transmission models) - adjustment

The system for operating the throttle-plate in the carburettor on CTX automatic transmission equipped vehicles is completely different to that employed on manual transmission vehicles. The cable from the accelerator pedal leads to a linkage mechanism which is bolted to the transmission housing. Two further cables lead from this linkage mechanism, one of which operates the throttle-plate in the carburettor.

As all three cables have to be adjusted at the same time, and access to a Ford special tool is required, it is recommended that a Ford dealer be entrusted with cable adjustments, or renewal.

6.5a Disconnect the inner cable from the choke linkage

6.5b Choke outer cable retaining clip released

5 Accelerator pedal - removal and refitting

Removal

1 Disconnect the battery negative (earth) lead (refer to Chapter 5A, Section 1).
2 Peel back the carpet and insulation from the driver's footwell to allow access to the accelerator pedal.
3 Detach the accelerator cable from the pedal (see Section 3), then release the circlip from the pivot shaft and remove the accelerator pedal.

Refitting

4 Refit in the reverse order of removal. On completion, check the action of the pedal and the cable to ensure that the throttle has full unrestricted movement, and fully returns when released.
5 Reconnect the battery negative lead.

6 Choke cable - removal, refitting and adjustment

Removal

1 Disconnect the battery negative (earth) lead (refer to Chapter 5A, Section 1).
2 Refer to Section 2 and remove the air cleaner.
3 Referring to Chapter 10, Section 20, for further details and illustrations, remove the choke control knob on the side of the steering column shroud by pushing in the pin located on the side of the knob and withdrawing.
4 Detach the steering column lower shroud, disconnect the multi-plug from the choke warning light switch/pull control assembly, and unscrew the collar securing the switch/pull control assembly to the shroud.
5 Disconnect the choke inner cable from its location on the carburettor choke linkage, then release the outer cable retaining clip **(see illustrations)**.
6 Push the bulkhead panel grommet through the bulkhead and remove the cable.

Refitting

7 Route the cable through the bulkhead then secure the bulkhead panel grommet to its location.
8 Reconnect the choke inner cable to its location on the carburettor choke linkage.
9 Refit the choke warning light switch/pull control assembly to the lower steering column shroud and secure with the collar, then reconnect the multi-plug.
10 Refit and secure the lower steering column shroud, then refit the choke control knob.
11 Pull the choke control knob to the fully-on position. Hold the choke in the fully-on

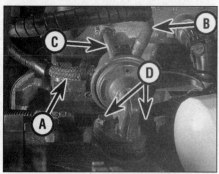

7.1a Fuel pump location on HCS engine (shown from below)

A Fuel inlet hose
B Fuel return hose to tank
C Fuel outlet hose to carburettor
D Pump securing bolts

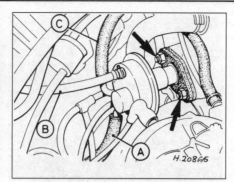

7.1b Fuel pump assembly fitted to CVH engines (securing nuts arrowed)

A Fuel feed from tank
B Fuel return to tank
C Fuel feed to carburettor

position at the carburettor, then secure the outer cable with its retaining clip.

Adjustment

12 To check that the choke cable is correctly adjusted, the control knob must be pulled out to the full-on position and the choke lever must be in contact with its stop. Adjust as required if necessary.

13 Press the choke knob fully in (to the off position), then check that the choke linkage at the carburettor has fully returned to its off position and the choke valve plate in the carburettor is at a right angle (90º) to the venturi.

14 Refit the air cleaner.

15 Reconnect the battery, turn the ignition on, operate the choke and check that the choke warning light operates correctly.

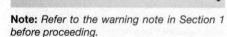

7 Fuel pump - testing, removal and refitting

Note: *Refer to the warning note in Section 1 before proceeding.*

Testing

1 Access to the fuel pump on HCS engine

7.6 Fuel pump and fuel vapour separator arrangement on HCS engine (shown from below)

models is best gained from underneath the vehicle **(see illustrations)**. Apply the handbrake, then raise and support it on axle stands at the front end (see *"Jacking and vehicle support"*).

2 The fuel pump may be tested by disconnecting the fuel feed pipe from the carburettor, and placing the pipe's open end in a suitable container.

3 Detach the multi-plug from the DIS ignition coil, or the LT lead from the negative terminal of the ignition coil, to prevent the engine from firing.

4 Actuate the starter motor. If the fuel pump is in good working order, regular well-defined spurts of fuel should eject from the open end of the disconnected fuel pipe.

5 If this does not occur, and there is fuel in the tank, the pump is defective and must be renewed. The fuel pump is a sealed unit, and cannot be repaired.

Removal

6 Two types of mechanical fuel pump are fitted, the application depending on the engine type. Some models may also be fitted with a fuel vapour separator **(see illustration)**; if this is removed, its hoses should be labelled to avoid the possibility of confusion and incorrect attachment on refitting.

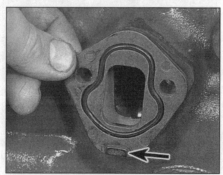

7.11 Gasket/spacer fitment on HCS engine. Note position of the lug (arrowed)

7 To remove the fuel pump, first disconnect the battery negative (earth) lead (refer to Chapter 5A, Section 1).

8 Where applicable, remove the air cleaner to improve access to the fuel pump (see Section 2).

9 Disconnect the fuel hoses from the fuel pump, noting their respective connections for refitting. Where quick-release couplings are used on the fuel hoses, release the protruding locking lugs on each union, by squeezing them together and carefully pulling the coupling apart. Use rag to soak up any spilt fuel. Where the unions are colour-coded, the pipes cannot be confused. Where both unions are the same colour, note carefully which pipe is connected to which, and ensure that they are correctly reconnected on refitting. Plug the hoses to prevent fuel spillage and the ingress of dirt.

10 Unscrew and remove the retaining bolts or nuts (as applicable) and remove the fuel pump.

11 Recover the gasket/spacer **(see illustration)** and if required, withdraw the pump operating pushrod (CVH engines only).

12 Thoroughly clean the mating faces on the pump and engine.

Refitting

13 Refit in the reverse order of removal. Be sure to use a new gasket, and tighten the securing bolts/nuts securely. Ensure that the hoses are correctly and securely reconnected. If they were originally secured with crimped type hose clips, discard them and fit screw type clips. Where quick-release couplings are fitted, press them together until the locking lugs snap into their groove.

14 When the engine is restarted, check the pump connections for any signs of fuel leaks.

8 Fuel tank - removal, inspection and refitting

Note: *Refer to the warning note in Section 1 before proceeding.*

Removal

1 Run the fuel level as low as possible prior to removing the tank.

2 Disconnect the battery negative (earth) lead (refer to Chapter 5A, Section 1).

3 Remove the fuel filler cap, then syphon or pump out the remaining fuel from the fuel tank (there is no drain plug). The fuel must be emptied into a suitable container for storage.

4 Chock the front wheels then jack up the rear of the car and support it on axle stands (see *"Jacking and vehicle support"*). Remove the rear roadwheels.

5 Unclip and disconnect the fuel feed and return hoses located in front of the fuel tank, and allow any residual fuel to drain into a

4A

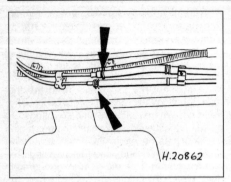

8.5 Fuel feed and return pipe connections (arrowed)

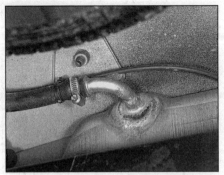

8.6 Filler neck sensing pipe connection at the rear of the fuel tank

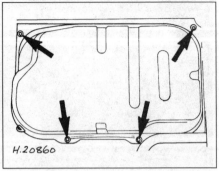

8.7 Fuel tank securing bolts (arrowed)

container which can be sealed **(see illustration)**. Where quick-release couplings are used on the fuel hoses, release the protruding locking lugs on each union, by squeezing them together and carefully pulling the coupling apart. Note that the fuel supply hose couplings are identified by a white colour band and the return hose couplings by a yellow colour band.

6 Disconnect the filler neck sensing pipe connection from the rear of the tank **(see illustration)**.

7 Support beneath the tank to hold it in position and remove its four securing bolts **(see illustration)**.

8 Partially lower the fuel tank and disconnect the ventilation tube from the tank top surface and also disconnect the sender unit multi-plug. The filler pipe should release from its fuel tank seal location as the tank is withdrawn.

Inspection

9 Whilst removed, the fuel tank can be inspected for damage or deterioration. Removal of the sender unit (see Section 9) will allow a partial inspection of the interior. If the tank is contaminated with sediment or water, swill it out with clean petrol. Do not under any circumstances undertake any repairs on a leaking or damaged fuel tank; this work must be carried out by a professional who has experience in this critical and potentially-dangerous work.

10 Whilst the fuel tank is removed from the vehicle, it should not be placed in an area where sparks or open flames could ignite the fumes coming out of the tank. Be especially careful inside garages where a natural-gas type appliance is located, because the pilot light could cause an explosion.

11 Check the condition of the filler pipe seal in the fuel tank, and renew it if necessary.

Refitting

All models

12 Refitting is a reversal of the removal procedure. Apply a light smear of grease to the filler pipe seal, to ease fitting. Ensure that all connections are securely fitted. Where quick-release fuel couplings are fitted, press them

together until the locking lugs snap into their groove. If evidence of contamination was found, do not return any previously-drained fuel to the tank unless it is carefully filtered first.

9 Fuel gauge sender unit - removal and refitting

Note: *Ford specify the use of their service tool 23-014 (a large box spanner with projecting teeth to engage the fuel gauge sender unit retaining ring's slots) for this task. While alternatives are possible, in view of the difficulty experienced in removing and refitting the sender unit, owners are strongly advised to obtain the correct tool before starting work. The help of an assistant will be required. Refer to the warning note in Section 1 before proceeding.*

Removal

1 Remove the fuel tank as described in Section 8.

2 Engage the special tool into the sender unit then carefully turn the sender unit and release it from the top of the tank.

Refitting

3 Refit the sender unit in the reverse order of removal. Be sure to fit a new seal, and lubricate it with a smear of grease to prevent it from distorting when fitting the sender unit.

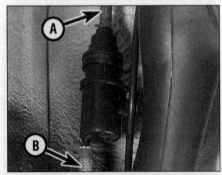

10.1 Combined roll-over anti-trickle-fill valve assembly

A Tube ventilating to atmosphere
B Ventilation tube from fuel tank

10 Fuel tank ventilation tube - removal and refitting

Note: *Refer to the warning note in Section 1 before proceeding.*

Removal

1 The fuel tank ventilation tube runs from the top surface of the fuel tank to the combined roll-over/anti-trickle-fill valve assembly mounted in the left-hand rear wheelarch **(see illustration)**. Its purpose is to eliminate any possibility of vacuum or pressure build-up in the fuel tank.

2 Disconnect the battery negative (earth) lead (refer to Chapter 5A, Section 1).

3 Chock the front wheels then jack up the rear of the car and support it on axle stands (see "Jacking and vehicle support"). Remove the left-hand rear roadwheel.

4 Support the fuel tank from underneath on a suitable jack, using a large thick sheet of board to spread the weight, then undo and remove the four fuel tank securing bolts.

5 Lower the fuel tank slightly in such a manner so as to allow access to disconnect the ventilation tube from the tank top surface. Ensure that the fuel tank does not foul or strain any adjacent components as it is lowered; take appropriate action, as necessary.

6 Disconnect the ventilation tube from the combined roll-over/anti-trickle-fill valve, release the tube from its retaining clips and remove.

Refitting

7 Refitting is a reversal of the removal procedure, ensuring that the fuel tank filler pipe is located correctly with the tank.

11 Fuel tank filler pipe - removal and refitting

Note: *Refer to the warning note in Section 1 before proceeding.*

Removal

1 Remove the fuel tank as described in Section 8.

2 Remove the filler cap surround **(see illustration)**.

3 Disconnect the ventilation tube from the combined roll-over/anti-trickle-fill valve, release the ventilation tube from its retaining clips and detach the valve from the vehicle.

4 Remove the filler pipe securing bolt, then twist and withdraw the filler pipe unit.

5 Prior to refitting, check the condition of the filler pipe seal in the fuel tank and renew if necessary.

Refitting

6 Refitting is a reversal of the removal procedure, but apply a light smear of grease to the filler pipe seal to aid filler pipe entry.

12 Carburettor (Weber TLM) - description

The carburettor is of the single (fixed) venturi downdraught type, featuring a fixed size main jet system with a mechanically-operated accelerator pump and vacuum-operated power valve to provide optimum fuelling.

A manually-operated choke system is fitted, featuring a vacuum-operated pull-down mechanism which brings the choke partially off during conditions of high manifold vacuum.

An anti-dieseling (fuel cut-off) solenoid (where fitted) prevents the possibility of engine run-on when the ignition is switched off.

Idle speed and mixture adjustment procedures are described in Chapter 1, but it is important to note that accurate adjustments can only be made using the necessary equipment.

13 Carburettor (Weber TLM) - fast-idle speed adjustment

Note: *Before carrying out any carburettor adjustments, ensure that the spark plug gaps are set as specified, and that all electrical and vacuum connections are secure. To carry out checks and adjustments, an accurate tachometer and an exhaust gas analyser (CO meter) will be required.*

1 Check the idle speed and mixture settings are as specified (as described in Chapter 1). These must be correct before checking/adjusting the fast-idle speed.

2 With the engine at its normal operating temperature, and a tachometer connected in accordance with the manufacturer's instructions, remove the air cleaner (if not already done) as described in Section 2.

3 Actuate the choke by pulling its control knob fully out, then start the engine.

4 Hold the choke plate open using a 5.0 mm twist drill held between the plate and the

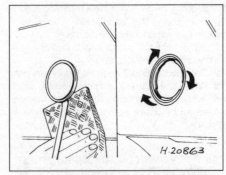

11.2 Removing the filler cap surround

venturi, and record the fast-idle speed achieved. If adjustment is necessary, turn the fast-idle adjusting screw until the specified speed is obtained **(see illustration)**.

5 Re-check the fast-idle and basic idle speeds.

6 On satisfactory completion of the adjustment, stop the engine, disconnect the tachometer and CO meter then refit the air cleaner.

7 Remove the bridging wire from the radiator cooling fan thermal switch multi-plug, and reconnect the multi-plug to the thermal switch.

14 Needle valve and float (Weber TLM carburettor) - removal, refitting and adjustment

Note: *Refer to the warning note in Section 1 before proceeding. New gaskets and a washer (seal) will be required when reassembling. A tachometer and an exhaust gas analyser (CO meter) will also be required to check the idle speed and mixture settings on completion.*

Removal and refitting

1 Disconnect the battery negative (earth) lead (refer to Chapter 5A, Section 1).

2 Remove the air cleaner as described in Section 2.

3 Clean the exterior of the carburettor, then disconnect the fuel feed hose.

4 Disconnect the choke cable and the choke vacuum hose.

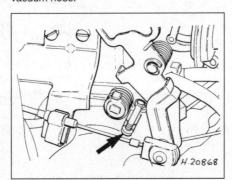

13.4 Fast-idle speed adjusting screw (arrowed) (Weber TLM carburettor)

5 Remove the four screws securing the carburettor upper body (two of these screws are Torx head type), and detach it. Note that the carburettor lower body is now loose on the inlet manifold.

6 Tap out the float retaining pin, remove the float and withdraw the needle valve. Unscrew the needle valve housing, as required, noting washer fitment.

7 Inspect the components for damage and renew as necessary. Check the needle valve for wear, and check the float assembly for leaks by shaking it to see if it contains petrol. Whilst accessible, clean the float chamber and jets (refer to Section 17).

8 Using a new washer, refit the needle valve housing.

9 Refit the needle valve, float and retaining pin, ensuring that the tag on the float engages between the ball and clip on the needle valve.

10 Before refitting the carburettor upper body, check and if necessary adjust the float level as described in paragraph 15 to 18. Also check the float and needle valve for full and free movement.

11 Clean the gasket contact faces (including the inlet manifold) then, using new gaskets for the carburettor upper body and the inlet manifold faces, refit the carburettor upper body and secure the carburettor assembly to the inlet manifold.

12 Reconnect the choke vacuum hose. If the fuel feed hose was originally secured with a crimped type clip, discard this and secure the fuel feed hose with a nut and screw type clip.

13 Reconnect and adjust the choke cable, then refit the air cleaner.

14 Reconnect the battery negative lead, start and warm up the engine then check the idle speed and mixture settings as described in Chapter 1.

Float level adjustment

15 With the carburettor upper body removed as described in paragraphs 1 to 5 inclusive, proceed as follows.

16 Hold the carburettor upper body in the position shown **(see illustration)**, ensuring that the needle valve is shut off. Fit the new upper body gasket to the carburettor upper

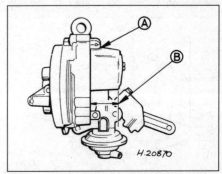

14.16 Float level adjustment (Weber TLM carburettor)

A Adjusting tag
B Float level setting dimension

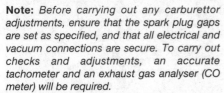

4A

body, then measure the distance between the gasket and the step on the float.

17 If the measurement is not as specified, adjust by bending the tag on the float, then re-check.

18 Refitting should be carried out in accordance with paragraphs 11 to 14 inclusive.

15 Carburettor (Weber TLM) - removal and refitting

Note: Refer to the warning note in Section 1 before proceeding. New gaskets will be required when reassembling. A tachometer and an exhaust gas analyser (CO meter) will also be required to check the idle speed and mixture settings on completion.

Removal

1 Disconnect the battery negative (earth) lead (refer to Chapter 5A, Section 1).

2 Remove the air cleaner as described in Section 2.

3 Disconnect the accelerator inner and outer cable from the carburettor (Section 3).

4 Disconnect the choke inner and outer cable from the carburettor (Section 6).

5 Disconnect the fuel feed hose from the carburettor, and plug its end to avoid spillage and prevent dirt ingress. If a crimped type hose clip is fitted, cut this free taking care to avoid damage to the hose.

6 Where applicable, disconnect the electrical lead from the anti-dieseling (fuel cut-off) solenoid, and all relevant carburettor vacuum pipes (having labelled them for correct subsequent refitting).

7 Remove the two Torx head screws securing the carburettor to the inlet manifold, then withdraw it from the vehicle **(see illustration)**.

Refitting

8 Clean the inlet manifold and carburettor gasket mating faces.

9 Refit in the reverse order of removal. Fit a new gasket, and tighten the retaining screws securely. Ensure that the fuel supply hose connection to the carburettor is securely

fitted, using a new screw type retaining clip.

10 Reconnect the accelerator cable, and adjust it as described in Section 3.

11 Reconnect the choke cable, and adjust it as described in Section 6.

12 Refer to Section 2 and refit the air cleaner.

13 When the battery is reconnected, start and warm up the engine then check the idle speed and mixture settings as described in Chapter 1.

16 Accelerator pump diaphragm (Weber TLM carburettor) - removal and refitting

Note: Refer to the warning note in Section 1 before proceeding.

Removal

1 Remove the carburettor as described in Section 15 and place it on a clean flat work surface.

2 Remove the accelerator pump cover retaining screws and detach the cover.

3 Withdraw the diaphragm and spring. Check the diaphragm for damage, and renew if evident.

Refitting

4 Clean the carburettor and cover mating faces.

5 Refit the spring and diaphragm to the carburettor, aligning the diaphragm with its cover retaining screw holes. Position the actuating lever on its cam, then carefully press the cover against the diaphragm and secure with its retaining screws.

6 Refit the carburettor as described in Section 15.

17 Carburettor (Weber TLM) - dismantling, cleaning, inspection and reassembly

Note: Refer to the warning note in Section 1 before proceeding. Check parts availability before dismantling. If possible, obtain an overhaul kit containing all the relevant gaskets, seals, etc, required for reassembly prior to dismantling the carburettor.

Dismantling

1 Remove the carburettor as described in Section 15 and place it on a clean flat work surface.

2 Clean the exterior of the carburettor, then undo the two retaining screws and lift off the upper carburettor body **(see illustration)**.

3 Remove the float and needle valve from the carburettor upper body, as described in Section 14.

4 Remove the accelerator pump components

A Upper body
B Choke mechanism
C Accelerator pump assembly
D Accelerator pump discharge tube
E Fast-idle speed adjusting screw
F Throttle housing
G Idle speed adjusting screw
H Anti-dieseling (fuel cut-off) solenoid
J Power valve assembly
K Float
L Idle mixture adjusting screw

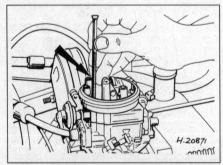

15.7 Removing one of the two Torx head screws (arrowed) securing the carburettor to the inlet manifold (Weber TLM carburettor)

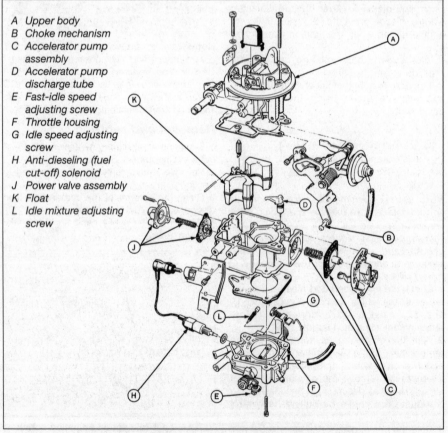

17.2 Exploded view of the carburettor (Weber TLM)

as described in Section 16. The power valve assembly can also be removed in a similar fashion.

5 Prise free the accelerator pump discharge tube, but take care not to damage it or the carburettor body.

6 Remove the jets and emulsion tubes as required, making careful notes of their respective locations for reassembly.

Cleaning and inspection

7 Soak out the fuel in the float chamber using a clean rag; this must be safely disposed of. Clean the float chamber, jets, drillings and passages with clean petrol. The careful use of an air line (or footpump) is ideal to blow out the upper and lower bodies. *Never use a piece of wire for cleaning purposes.*

8 Examine all of the carburettor components for signs of damage or wear, paying particular attention to the diaphragms, throttle spindle and plates, and needle valve. Renew all diaphragms, sealing washers and gaskets as a matter of course.

Reassembly

9 Refit the emulsion tubes and jets to their locations as noted during dismantling.

10 Refit the accelerator pump discharge tube.

11 Refit the accelerator pump and power valve assemblies as described in Section 16.

12 Refit the needle valve and the float, and adjust the float setting as described in Section 14.

13 Locate a new gasket onto the mating face, then refit the carburettor upper body to the main body. As they are reassembled, take care not to snag the float on the carburettor main body. Fit and tighten the retaining screws to secure.

14 On completion, refit the carburettor as described in Section 15.

18 Carburettor (Weber TLDM) - description

The carburettor is of twin venturi, downdraught type, featuring a fixed size main jet system, adjustable idle system, a mechanically-operated accelerator pump, and a vacuum-operated power valve. A manually-operated cold start choke is fitted, and a throttle kicker is used on certain models.

In order to comply with emission control regulations and maintain good fuel consumption, the main jets are calibrated to suit the 1/4 to 3/4 throttle range. The power valve is therefore only used to supply additional fuel during full-throttle conditions.

The accelerator pump is fitted to ensure a smooth transmission from the idle circuit to the main jet system. As the accelerator pedal is depressed, a linkage moves the diaphragm within the accelerator pump, and a small

quantity of fuel is injected into the venturi, to prevent a momentary weak mixture and resultant engine hesitation.

The manually-operated choke features a vacuum-operated pull-down mechanism which controls the single choke plate under certain vacuum conditions.

On CTX automatic transmission models, the throttle kicker acts as an idle speed compensator for when the transmission shift lever positions R, D or L are selected. The throttle kicker is operated by vacuum supplied from the inlet manifold. When the appropriate transmission shift lever position is selected, the throttle kicker control solenoid allows the vacuum to pass to the throttle kicker which maintains the idle speed by means of a diaphragm and mechanical linkage.

On manual transmission models, the throttle kicker (when fitted) acts as a damper by slowing down the closing action of the throttle plate. Under deceleration, this maintains the combustion of the air/fuel mixture entering the cylinders, thus improving the exhaust emission levels. A vacuum sustain valve controls the carburettor-sourced vacuum applied to the throttle kicker unit; this allows the vacuum slowly to decay, allowing normal engine idling speed to be achieved.

An anti-dieseling (fuel cut-off) solenoid is fitted to prevent the possibility of the engine running on after the ignition is switched off.

Idle speed and mixture adjustment procedures are described in Chapter 1, but it is important to note that accurate adjustments can only be made using the necessary equipment.

19 Carburettor (Weber TLDM) - fast-idle speed adjustment

Note: *Before carrying out any carburettor adjustments, ensure that the spark plug gaps are set as specified, and that all electrical and vacuum connections are secure. To carry out checks and adjustments, an accurate tachometer and an exhaust gas analyser (CO meter) will be required.*

1 Check the idle speed and mixture settings

19.4 Fast-idle speed adjusting screw (arrowed) (Weber TLDM carburettor)

are as specified (as described in Chapter 1). These must be correct before checking/adjusting the fast-idle speed.

2 With the engine at its normal operating temperature, and a tachometer connected in accordance with the manufacturer's instructions, switch the engine off, then remove the air cleaner (if not already done) as described in Section 2.

3 Actuate the choke by pulling the control knob fully out, then start the engine and note the engine fast-idle speed. Compare it with the specified speed.

4 If adjustment is required, turn the fast-idle adjusting screw clockwise to decrease, or anti-clockwise to increase, the fast-idle speed **(see illustration)**.

5 Recheck the fast-idle and basic idle speeds.

6 On completion of the adjustment, stop the engine, detach the tachometer and CO meter, reconnect the radiator cooling fan lead, and refit the air cleaner.

20 Needle valve and float (Weber TLDM carburettor) - removal, refitting and adjustment

Note: *Refer to the warning note in Section 1 before proceeding. New gaskets and a washer (seal) will be required when reassembling. A tachometer and an exhaust gas analyser (CO meter) will also be required to check the idle speed and mixture settings on completion.*

Removal and refitting

1 Disconnect the battery negative (earth) lead (refer to Chapter 5A, Section 1).

2 Remove the air cleaner as described in Section 2.

3 Clean the exterior of the carburettor, then disconnect the fuel supply hose and the anti-dieseling solenoid wiring.

4 Disconnect the choke control cable.

5 Undo and remove the six retaining screws (four of which are Torx type) and carefully lift the carburettor upper body clear **(see illustrations)**.

6 Invert and support the upper body of the carburettor for access to the float and pivot.

20.5a Remove the carburettor upper body securing screws . . .

4A

20.5b . . . then detach the carburettor
upper body

20.6a Slide out the float retaining pin . . .

20.6b . . . then detach the float and needle
valve

Lightly tap out the float pivot pin, then
withdraw the float, taking care not to distort
the arms of the float **(see illustrations)**.

7 Unscrew the needle valve housing, and
extract it from the carburettor upper body.
Collect the washer from the threads of the
needle valve housing.

8 Clean and inspect the components for
signs of damage or wear, particularly the pivot
holes in the float arm. Check the float for signs
of leakage, by shaking it to see if it contains
fuel. Clean the float chamber and jets (refer to
Section 24 for details). Renew any
components as necessary.

9 Fit a new washer over the needle valve
housing threads, and then carefully screw the
valve unit into position in the upper body.

10 Refit the needle valve, float and retaining
pin, ensuring that the tag on the float engages
with the ball and clip of the needle valve.

11 Before refitting the upper body to the
carburettor, check and if necessary adjust the
float level as described in paragraphs 16
to 18. Also check the float and needle valve
for free movement.

12 Clean the gasket contact faces, then
locate a new gasket and refit the upper body
to the carburettor.

13 Reconnect the fuel supply hose, anti-
dieseling solenoid wiring and the choke cable.
Adjust the choke cable as described in
Section 6. If the fuel hose was originally
secured with a crimped type clip, discard it
and fit a screw type clip.

14 Refit the air cleaner as described in
Section 2.

15 Reconnect the battery earth lead, then
restart the engine and check the idle speed
and mixture settings. Adjust if necessary as
described in Chapter 1.

Float level adjustment

16 With the carburettor upper body removed
as described in paragraphs 1 to 5 inclusive,
proceed as follows.

17 Support the carburettor upper body
vertically, ensuring that the needle valve is
shut off. Locate the new upper body gasket
onto the carburettor upper body, then
measure the distance between the gasket and
the bottom of the float **(see illustration)**.

18 If the measurement is not as specified,
adjust the setting by carefully bending the tag
on the float as required, then recheck.

19 Refit with reference to paragraphs 12
to 15 inclusive.

**21 Throttle kicker unit (Weber
TLDM carburettor)** - removal,
refitting and adjustment

Note: *A tachometer and exhaust gas analyser
(CO meter) will be required to check and make
any adjustment necessary.*

Removal and refitting

1 Disconnect the battery negative (earth) lead
(refer to Chapter 5A, Section 1).

2 Refer to Section 2 and remove the air
cleaner.

3 Detach the vacuum hose from the kicker
unit. Undo the two retaining screws, detach
the linkage and remove the kicker unit **(see
illustration)**.

4 Refitting the kicker unit is a reversal of the
removal procedure. If the unit is to be
checked for adjustment, loosely locate the air
cleaner, reconnect the inlet air temperature
sensor multi-plug and the battery earth lead,
then proceed as follows.

Adjustment

5 Start and run the engine up to its normal
operating temperature (at which point the
cooling fan will start to operate) then switch
the engine off.

6 Remove the air cleaner again, then detach
the wiring connector of the cooling fan
thermostatic switch. Bridge the terminals in
the connector with a suitable piece of wire to
actuate the cooling fan and keep it running.
Start the engine and run it at 3000 rpm for
30 seconds to stabilise it, then release the
throttle and check (and if necessary adjust)
the idle speed and mixture settings as
described in Chapter 1. Stop the engine.

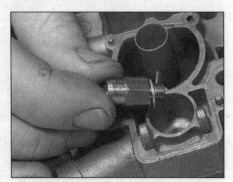

20.6c Remove the needle valve housing
and its washer

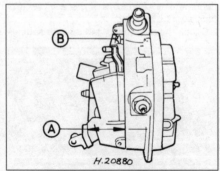

20.17 Float level adjustment (Weber TLDM
carburettor)

A *Float level setting dimension*
B *Adjusting tag*

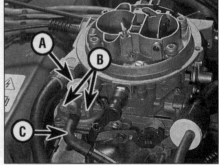

21.3 General view of throttle kicker
arrangement (Weber TLDM carburettor)

A *Tamperproof plug covering adjusting point*
B *Throttle kicker securing screws*
C *Vacuum supply pipe*

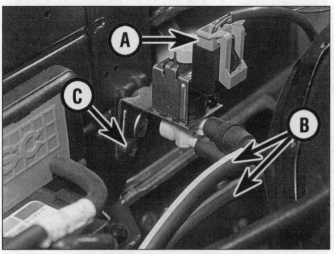

22.2 Throttle kicker control solenoid

A Multi-plug   B Vacuum pipes   C Securing screw

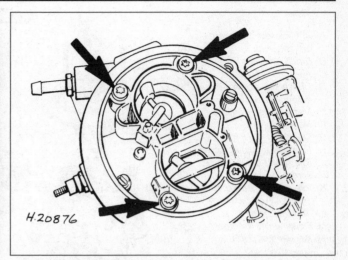

H.20876

23.7 Four Torx head screws (arrowed) secure the carburettor to the inlet manifold (Weber TLDM carburettor)

7 Detach the vacuum hose between the throttle kicker and the inlet manifold at source (but not the vacuum supply to the ignition module). Connect a new length of vacuum hose directly between the manifold and the kicker unit.

8 Restart the engine and check the engine speed. The throttle kicker should increase the engine speed above its normal idle. Check the speed registered against the specified throttle kicker operating speed.

9 If required, the throttle kicker speed can be adjusted by prising free the tamperproof plug and the adjustment screw turned as necessary **(see illustration 21.3)**.

10 When the adjustment is complete, stop the engine, fit a new tamperproof plug, disconnect the temporary vacuum hose (between the manifold and the kicker unit) and reconnect the original hose (between the carburettor and the kicker unit).

11 Remove the bridging wire, and reconnect the cooling fan thermostatic switch multi-plug. Refit and secure the air cleaner, and disconnect the tachometer and CO meter to complete.

22 Throttle kicker control solenoid (Weber TLDM carburettor) - removal and refitting

Removal

1 Disconnect the battery negative (earth) lead (refer to Chapter 5A, Section 1).

2 Disconnect the multi-plug from the solenoid **(see illustration)**.

3 Remove both vacuum pipes, having labelled them for correct subsequent refitting.

4 Remove the screw securing the solenoid and mounting bracket assembly to the bulkhead panel, then withdraw the assembly from the vehicle.

Refitting

5 Refitting is a reversal of the removal procedure, ensuring that the locating lug snaps into position and that the vacuum pipes are connected to their correct terminals.

23 Carburettor (Weber TLDM) - removal and refitting

Note: *Refer to the warning note in Section 1 before proceeding. New gaskets will be required on refitting, and a tachometer and an exhaust gas analyser will be required on completion.*

Removal

1 Disconnect the battery negative (earth) lead (refer to Chapter 5A, Section 1).

2 Remove the air cleaner as described in Section 2.

3 Disconnect the accelerator cable from the carburettor (Section 3).

4 Disconnect the choke cable from the carburettor (Section 6).

5 Disconnect the fuel hose from the carburettor, and plug its end to prevent fuel spillage and the ingress of dirt. If a crimped type hose clip is fitted, cut it free, but take care not to damage the hose. Crimped clips must be discarded and replaced with screw type clips during refitting.

6 Disconnect the wiring from the anti-dieseling solenoid.

7 Unscrew and remove the four carburettor-to-manifold retaining Torx head screws, then carefully lift the carburettor from the manifold **(see illustration)**.

Refitting

8 Clean the carburettor and manifold gasket mating faces.

9 Refit in the reverse order of removal. Fit a new gasket, and tighten the retaining screws securely. Ensure that the fuel supply hose connection to the carburettor is securely fitted, using a new screw type retaining clip.

10 Reconnect the accelerator cable, and adjust it as described in Section 3.

11 Reconnect the choke cable, and adjust it as described in Section 6.

12 Refer to Section 2 and refit the air cleaner.

13 When the battery is reconnected, start and warm up the engine then check the idle speed and mixture settings as described in Chapter 1.

24 Carburettor (Weber TLDM) - dismantling, cleaning, inspection and reassembly

Note: *Refer to the warning note in Section 1 before proceeding. Check parts availability before dismantling. If possible, obtain an overhaul kit containing all the relevant gaskets, seals, etc, required for reassembly prior to dismantling the carburettor.*

Dismantling

1 With the carburettor removed from the vehicle, prepare a clean, flat work surface prior to commencing dismantling. The following procedures may be used for partial or complete dismantling, as required.

2 Clean the exterior of the carburettor, then undo the two retaining screws and lift the upper carburettor body from the lower section **(see illustration overleaf)**.

3 Remove the float and needle valve from the carburettor upper body, as described in Section 20.

4 Unscrew and remove the anti-dieseling solenoid from the upper body, but ensure that

4A

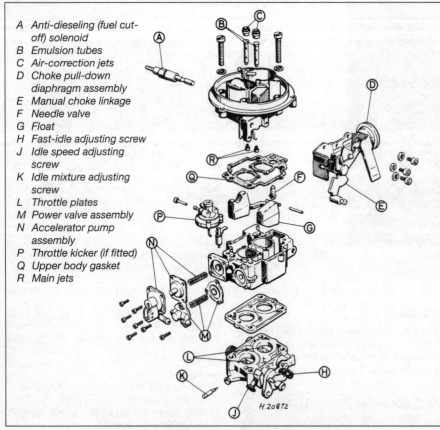

A Anti-dieseling (fuel cut-off) solenoid
B Emulsion tubes
C Air-correction jets
D Choke pull-down diaphragm assembly
E Manual choke linkage
F Needle valve
G Float
H Fast-idle adjusting screw
J Idle speed adjusting screw
K Idle mixture adjusting screw
L Throttle plates
M Power valve assembly
N Accelerator pump assembly
P Throttle kicker (if fitted)
Q Upper body gasket
R Main jets

H.20872

24.2 Exploded view of the carburettor (Weber TLDM)

the seal washer is removed together with the valve **(see illustration)**.

5 Undo the three screws securing the choke mechanism, and detach it **(see illustration)**.

6 Unscrew and remove the two air correction jets from the underside of the upper body. Note the size and location of each, to ensure correct refitting.

7 Invert the upper body so that the emulsion tubes can fall out of their apertures (above the air correction jets). Remove the emulsion tubes from their locations, again having noted the size and location of each.

8 Unscrew and remove the main jets, again having noted their fitted positions.

9 Dismantle the carburettor lower (main) body as follows.

10 Prise free the accelerator pump discharge tube, but take care not to damage it or the carburettor body **(see illustration)**.

11 Undo the four screws securing the accelerator pump; remove the cover, followed by the diaphragm and return spring **(see illustrations)**. The valve should come out on the end of the return spring. Check that the valve is complete and with its O-ring seal (where applicable).

12 Undo the three retaining screws, and remove the power valve unit. Remove the cover and return spring, followed by the diaphragm.

13 Where fitted, undo the retaining screws and remove the throttle kicker unit from the lower (main) body.

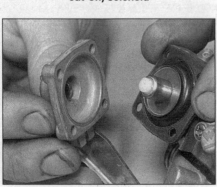

24.4 Withdrawing the anti-dieseling (fuel cut-off) solenoid

24.5 Undo the three screws securing the choke mechanism (arrowed)

24.10 Carefully prising out the accelerator pump discharge tube assembly

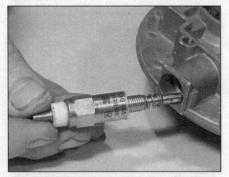

24.11a Remove the accelerator pump cover . . .

24.11b . . . followed by its diaphragm . . .

24.11c . . . and the return spring and valve assembly

14 Prise free and remove the tamperproof seal, then unscrew and remove the idle mixture adjustment screw.

15 Undo the retaining screws, and remove the throttle housing from the carburettor main body.

Cleaning and inspection

16 Wash the carburettor components, drillings and passages with clean petrol, then blow them dry using a low-pressure air line. A high-pressure air line must not be applied to the accelerator pump discharge assembly or the pump supply valve, as they each contain a rubber Vernay valve, and these can easily be damaged under high pressure. *Never use a piece of wire for cleaning purposes.*

17 Examine all of the carburettor components for signs of damage or wear, paying particular attention to the diaphragms, throttle spindle and plates, needle valve and mixture screw; the power valve jet is adjacent to the primary main jet. Renew all diaphragms, sealing washers and gaskets as a matter of course.

Reassembly

18 Refit the throttle housing to the carburettor main body (fitting a new gasket), and secure with its retaining screws.

19 Refit the idle mixture adjustment screw. Make an initial adjustment by screwing it fully in (but do not overtighten or screw it onto its seat), then unscrew it two full turns.

20 Where fitted, reassemble the throttle kicker, ensuring that its diaphragm lies flat, and that the relative position of the operating link to the kicker cover is correct.

21 Fit the power valve, ensuring that its diaphragm lies flat and the vacuum gallery aligns with the diaphragm and housing.

22 Refit the accelerator pump. Take care not damage the valve as it is inserted, and check that the O-ring seal is correctly located on the end of the valve. Check that the valve is not trapped by the spring.

23 Refit the accelerator pump discharge jet. Take care not to damage the valve and/or the O-ring seal, and ensure that they are correctly located.

24 Commence reassembly of the upper body by inserting the emulsion tubes and the air correction jets into their respective ports (as noted during removal).

25 Screw the anti-dieseling solenoid into position. Ensure that the aluminium washer is fitted, and take care not to overtighten the valve.

26 Refit the needle valve and the float, and adjust the float setting as described in Section 20.

27 Refit the choke control mechanism, and secure with its three retaining screws.

28 Locate a new gasket onto the mating face, then refit the carburettor upper body to the main body. As they are reassembled, take care not to snag the float on the carburettor

main body. Fit and tighten the retaining screws to secure.

29 On completion, refit the carburettor as described in Section 23. Where applicable, check and adjust the throttle kicker setting (Section 21) after adjusting the idle speed and mixture settings.

25 Carburettor (Weber DFTM) - description

The carburettor operates in essentially the same manner as TLDM instrument described in Section 18, but the following features should be noted.

A throttle kicker is fitted to both manual transmission, and CTX automatic transmission models, the operation of the unit is described in Section 18.

The secondary venturi (barrel) is vacuum-operated on manual transmission models. On CTX automatic transmission equipped models it is operated sequentially.

A bleed back solenoid (if fitted) is used to control the amount of fuel being delivered to the venturi by the action of the accelerator pump.

Idle speed and mixture adjustment procedures are described in Chapter 1, but it is important to note that accurate adjustments can only be made using the necessary equipment.

26 Carburettor (Weber DFTM) - fast-idle speed adjustment

Refer to the procedure contained in Section 19, but note the following points:

a) *When removing the air cleaner, do not disconnect the vacuum supply or crankcase ventilation hoses; the air cleaner should be positioned clear of the carburettor assembly.*

b) *The fast-idle adjusting screw is located on the side of the linkage (**see illustration**).*

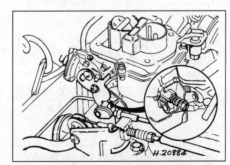

26.1 Manual choke fast-idle adjustment. Inset shows fast-idle adjusting screw (Weber DFTM carburettor)

27 Throttle kicker unit (Weber DFTM carburettor) - removal, refitting and adjustment

Refer to the procedure contained in Section 21.

28 Carburettor (Weber DFTM) - removal and refitting

Note: *Refer to the warning note in Section 1 before proceeding. New gaskets will be required on refitting, and a tachometer and an exhaust gas analyser will be required on completion.*

Removal

1 Disconnect the battery negative (earth) lead (refer to Chapter 5A, Section 1).

2 Remove the air cleaner as described in Section 2.

3 Disconnect the choke cable from the carburettor (Section 6).

4 Carefully prise out the accelerator link retaining clip, remove both securing bolts, then detach the cable and bracket assembly. Position the cable and bracket assembly clear of the carburettor.

5 Disconnect the fuel feed hose at the carburettor, and plug its end to avoid spillage and prevent dirt ingress. If a crimped type hose clip is fitted, cut this free taking care not to damage the hose.

6 Disconnect all relevant vacuum pipes from the carburettor, having labelled them for subsequent refitting.

7 Disconnect the electrical lead from the anti-dieseling (fuel cut-off) solenoid, and the bleed back solenoid (if fitted).

8 Remove the four nuts securing the carburettor to the inlet manifold, then withdraw it from the vehicle.

Refitting

9 Clean the carburettor and manifold gasket mating faces.

10 Refit in the reverse order of removal. Fit a new gasket, and tighten the retaining screws securely. Ensure that the fuel supply hose connection to the carburettor is securely fitted, using a new screw type retaining clip.

11 Reconnect the choke cable, and adjust it as described in Section 6.

12 Refer to Section 2 and refit the air cleaner.

13 When the battery is reconnected, start and warm up the engine then check the idle speed and mixture settings as described in Chapter 1.

4A

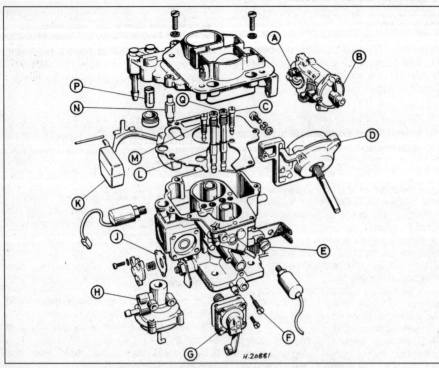

29.3 Exploded view of the carburettor (Weber DFTM)

A	Manual choke assembly	
B	Choke vacuum pull-down	
C	Secondary idle jet	
D	Secondary barrel diaphragm assembly	
E	Idle speed adjusting screw	
F	Idle mixture adjusting screw	
G	Accelerator pump assembly	
H	Throttle kicker	
J	Power valve diaphragm	
K	Float	
L	Primary main jet combined assembly	
M	Primary idle jet	
N	Needle valve	
P	Fuel feed filter	
Q	Secondary main jet combined assembly	

29 Carburettor (Weber DFTM) - dismantling, cleaning, inspection and reassembly

Note: *Refer to the warning note in Section 1 before proceeding. Check parts availability before dismantling. If possible, obtain an overhaul kit containing all the relevant gaskets, seals, etc, required for reassembly prior to dismantling the carburettor.*

Dismantling

1 With the carburettor removed from the vehicle, prepare a clean, flat work surface prior to commencing dismantling. The following procedures may be used for partial or complete dismantling, as required.

2 Clean the exterior of the carburettor and detach all vacuum pipes (where applicable), having noted their fitted location for correct subsequent reassembly.

3 Remove the six screws securing the carburettor upper body, and detach it. Discard the gasket **(see illustration)**.

4 Dismantle the carburettor upper body as described in the following paragraphs.

5 Remove the three screws securing the

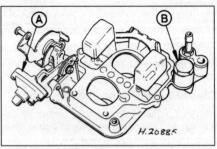

29.5 Choke pull-down assembly (A) and fuel feed filter housing (B) (Weber DFTM carburettor)

choke pull-down diaphragm and detach it **(see illustration)**.

6 Unscrew the brass nut adjacent to the fuel feed connection, and remove the fuel feed filter.

7 Tap out the float retaining pin, then detach the float and needle valve.

8 Unscrew and remove the needle valve housing.

9 Dismantle the carburettor main body as described in the following paragraphs.

10 Remove the main and idle jets, having noted the size and fitted location of each one to ensure correct subsequent reassembly. Note that the main jets are a combined assembly incorporating air correction jets and emulsion tubes. Carefully prise out the accelerator pump discharge tube.

11 Detach the throttle kicker and its mounting bracket assembly.

12 Remove the anti-dieseling (fuel cut-off) solenoid.

13 Remove the four screws securing the accelerator pump assembly, and dismantle the assembly noting the fitment of its components **(see illustration)**.

14 Disconnect the secondary barrel diaphragm operating rod by pulling the lower section of rod downwards and twisting to release it from its retaining socket. Remove its four cover retaining screws and dismantle the assembly **(see illustration)**.

15 Undo the three screws securing the power valve assembly and remove its diaphragm **(see illustration)**.

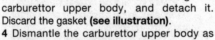

29.13 Accelerator pump renewal (Weber DFTM carburettor)

A Diaphragm   B Housing (cover)

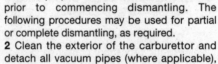

29.14 Exploded view of the secondary barrel diaphragm assembly

A Diaphragm   C Operating rod
B Return spring

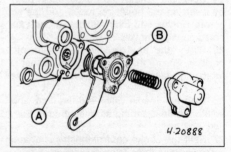

29.15 Exploded view of the power valve assembly (Weber DFTM carburettor)

A Vacuum gallery   B Diaphragm

16 Prise out the tamperproof seal covering the fuel mixture screw, then undo and remove the mixture screw.

Cleaning and inspection

17 Wash the carburettor components, drillings and passages with clean petrol, then blow them dry using a low-pressure air line. A high-pressure air line must not be applied to the accelerator pump discharge assembly or the pump supply valve, as they each contain a rubber Vernay valve, and these can easily be damaged under high pressure. *Never use a piece of wire for cleaning purposes.*
18 Examine all of the carburettor components for signs of damage or wear, paying particular attention to the diaphragms, throttle spindle and plates, needle valve and mixture screw; the power valve jet is adjacent to the primary main jet. Renew all diaphragms, sealing washers and gaskets as a matter of course.

Reassembly

19 Refit the fuel mixture screw by fully winding the screw in, then unwinding three turns to give an approximate setting.
20 Refit the power valve assembly ensuring that the diaphragm lies flat, and that the vacuum gallery lines up correctly with the diaphragm and housing.
21 Reassemble the secondary barrel diaphragm into its housing, ensuring that the diaphragm lies flat and that the vacuum gallery lines up with the diaphragm and housing. Also, to assist with installation, do not reconnect its operating rod until the cover has been secured.
22 Refit the throttle kicker mounting bracket.
23 Refit the anti-dieseling (fuel cut-off) solenoid, using a new sealing washer.
24 Refit the accelerator pump assembly, ensuring that the diaphragm lies flat and is not kinked.
25 Reassemble the throttle kicker, ensuring that the diaphragm lies flat and that the

relative position of the diaphragm operating link to the throttle kicker cover is correct. Fully attach the throttle kicker assembly.
26 Refit the main and idle jets, making reference to the notes taken during dismantling to ensure correct fitted locations.
27 Reassemble the carburettor upper body as described in the following paragraphs.
28 Refit the needle valve housing (using a new washer if applicable).
29 Refit the needle valve and float assembly, having ensured that the float tag locates below the spring clip on the needle valve. Insert the float retaining pin to secure.
30 Adjust the float level as follows. Ensuring that a new gasket is fitted to the carburettor upper body, hold the upper body in the vertical position; the needle valve must be shut off. Measure the distance shown (**see illustration**), and adjust by bending the float tag if the measurement is outside the specification. Recheck the float level adjustment after bending the float tag, as necessary.
31 Refit the choke pull-down diaphragm, ensuring that the diaphragm lies flat and that the vacuum gallery lines up correctly with the diaphragm and housing (**see illustration**).
32 Adjust the choke pull-down as follows. Fully close the choke, then manually push the diaphragm operating rod up to its stop; measure the distance between the downdraught side of the choke plate and the venturi, using a gauge rod or the shank of a twist drill bit (of known size). If the measurement is outside specification, remove the tamperproof seal from the housing, and adjust the now revealed adjustment screw accordingly. Fit a new tamperproof seal after successful adjustment.
33 Refit the fuel feed filter, and secure with its brass nut and sealing washer.
34 Refit the carburettor upper body to the carburettor main body, ensuring that its new gasket seats correctly and that the float does not foul during assembly. Insert and tighten the securing screws.

35 Reconnect any vacuum pipes removed during dismantling (where applicable).
36 On completion, refit the carburettor as described in Section 28. Where applicable, check and adjust the throttle kicker setting (Section 27) after adjusting the idle speed and mixture settings.

30 Carburettor (Weber TLD) - description

This carburettor incorporates many of the features of the TLDM type described in Section 18. The main differences are that a throttle kicker is not used, the secondary venturi (barrel) is vacuum-operated, and that a coolant-heated automatic choke control system is fitted.
The choke system is fully automatic. When the engine is cold, the bi-metal spring which controls the position of the choke plate is fully wound up, and holds the plate closed. As the engine warms up, the bi-metal spring is heated by the coolant and begins to unwind, thereby progressively opening the choke plate. A vacuum-operated pull-down mechanism controls the choke plate under certain operating conditions, and an internal fast-idle system is incorporated.
Idle speed and mixture adjustment procedures are described in Chapter 1, but it is important to note that accurate adjustments can only be made using the necessary equipment.

31 Carburettor (Weber TLD) - fast-idle speed adjustment

Note: *Before carrying out any carburettor adjustments, ensure that the spark plug gaps are set as specified, and that all electrical and vacuum connections are secure. To carry out checks and adjustments, an accurate*

4A

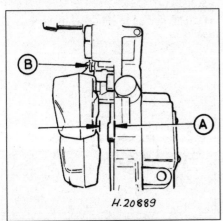

29.30 Float level adjustment (Weber DFTM carburettor)

A *Float level setting dimension*
B *Adjusting tag*

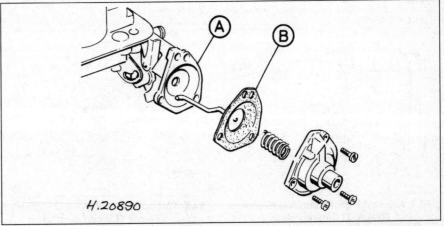

29.31 Exploded view of the choke pull-down assembly (Weber DFTM carburettor)

A *Housing*   B *Diaphragm*

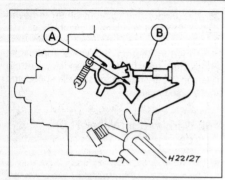

31.3 Fast-idle speed adjustment (Weber TLD carburettor) (Housing cut away for illustration clarity)

A *Fast-idle cam*
B *Fast-idle speed adjusting screw on third step of cam*

tachometer and an exhaust gas analyser (CO meter) will be required.

1 Check that the idle speed and mixture settings are as specified (as described in Chapter 1). These must be correct before checking/adjusting the fast-idle speed.
2 Switch the engine off, then remove the air cleaner as described in Section 2.
3 With the engine at its normal operating temperature and a tachometer connected in accordance with its manufacturer's instructions, hold the throttle linkage partly open, then close the choke plate until the fast-idle adjusting screw aligns with the third (middle) step on the fast-idle cam **(see illustration)**. Release the throttle linkage so that the fast-idle speed adjusting screw rests on the cam. Release the choke plate. The linkage will hold it in the fast-idle setting position, as long as the accelerator pedal is not depressed.
4 Without touching the accelerator pedal, start the engine and record the fast-idle speed achieved. If adjustment is required, turn the fast-idle speed adjusting screw until the specified fast-idle speed is obtained.
5 When the throttle linkage is opened, the choke plate should return to its fully-open position. If this does not happen, either the

engine is not at its normal operating temperature, or the automatic choke mechanism is faulty.
6 Switch off the engine and disconnect the tachometer. Refit the air cleaner.

32 Needle valve and float (Weber TLD carburettor) - removal, refitting and adjustment

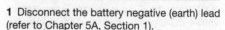

1 Refer to Section 20 and proceed as described, noting the following difference.
2 In paragraph 4, ignore the instruction to detach the choke cable (an automatic choke is fitted to the TLD type carburettor). Instead, clamp the coolant supply and return hoses which lead to the automatic choke unit to minimise coolant loss, then ensure that the cooling system is not pressurised (see Chapter 1). Identify then detach both of the coolant hoses at the automatic choke housing. Catch any coolant spillage in a suitable container.

 Warning: DO NOT attempt to remove the expansion tank filler cap, or to disturb any part of the cooling system, while it or the engine is hot, as there is a very great risk of scalding. If the expansion tank filler cap must be removed before the engine and radiator have fully cooled down (even though this is not recommended) the pressure in the cooling system must first be released. Cover the cap with a thick layer of cloth, to avoid scalding, and slowly unscrew the filler cap until a hissing sound can be heard. When the hissing has stopped, showing that pressure is released, slowly unscrew the filler cap further until it can be removed; if more hissing sounds are heard, wait until they have stopped before unscrewing the cap completely. At all times, keep well away from the filler opening.
3 On completion, reconnect the hoses to the automatic choke unit, and remove the clamps from the hoses. Check and top-up the coolant level on completion (see "Weekly Checks" and Chapter 1).

33 Automatic choke (Weber TLD carburettor) - adjustment

1 Disconnect the battery negative (earth) lead (refer to Chapter 5A, Section 1).
2 Remove the air cleaner as described in Section 2.
3 Disconnect the coolant hoses to the choke unit as described in paragraph 2 of the previous Section.
4 Note the position of the choke coil housing alignment marks, then undo the three retaining screws and withdraw the automatic choke bi-metal coil housing **(see illustration)**.
5 Remove the inner heat shield **(see illustration)**. To check and adjust the choke vacuum pull-down, secure the choke plate lever in the closed position by fitting a rubber band, open the throttle to allow the choke plate to fully close, then release the throttle.
6 Using a screwdriver, push the operating arm to the right against its spring, and measure the clearance between the lower edge of the choke plate and the venturi using a twist drill or other suitable gauge rod **(see illustration)**. Where the clearance is outside that specified, remove the plug from the diaphragm housing, and turn the adjusting screw (now exposed) in the required direction.
7 Fit a new diaphragm housing plug and remove the rubber band.
8 Refit the heat shield so that its slotted hole engages over the choke housing peg.
9 Refit the bi-metal coil housing by first connecting the bi-metal spring to the choke lever (ensuring correct engagement), locate the housing and hand-tighten the three retaining screws. Rotate the housing to align the index line on the housing with the dot mark on the choke main body, then retighten the retaining screws.
10 Reconnect the coolant hoses with reference to paragraph 3 in the previous Section.
11 Refit the air cleaner as described in Section 2.

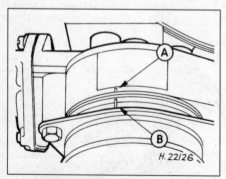

33.4 Automatic choke housing alignment (Weber TLD carburettor)

A *Dot punch mark*
B *Choke housing alignment mark*

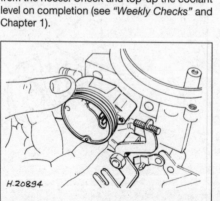

33.5 Automatic choke internal heatshield (Weber TLD carburettor)

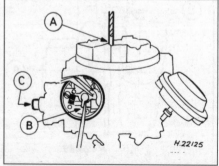

33.6 Choke plate pull-down adjustment (Weber TLD carburettor)

A *Twist drill*   C *Adjusting screw*
B *Diaphragm held fully open*

34 Automatic choke (Weber TLD carburettor) - removal, inspection and refitting

Note: *Refer to the warning note in Section 1 before proceeding. A new carburettor upper body gasket will be required when reassembling. On completion, a tachometer will be required to check the fast-idle speed adjustment.*

Removal

1 Disconnect the battery negative (earth) lead (refer to Chapter 5A, Section 1).
2 Remove the air cleaner as described in Section 2.
3 To prevent excess coolant loss, clamp the coolant supply and return hoses to the automatic choke unit, and ensure that the cooling system is not pressurised (see Chapter 1). Identify then detach both of the coolant hoses at the automatic choke housing. Catch any coolant spillage in a suitable container.

 Warning: DO NOT attempt to remove the expansion tank filler cap, or to disturb any part of the cooling system, while it or the engine is hot, as there is a very great risk of scalding. If the expansion tank filler cap must be removed before the engine and radiator have fully cooled down (even though this is not recommended) the pressure in the cooling system must first be released. Cover the cap with a thick layer of cloth, to avoid scalding, and slowly unscrew the filler cap until a hissing sound can be heard. When the hissing has stopped, showing that pressure is released, slowly unscrew the filler cap further until it can be removed; if more hissing sounds are heard, wait until they have stopped before unscrewing the cap completely. At all times, keep well away from the filler opening.

4 Detach the fuel pipe and the anti-dieseling solenoid wiring connector. Any crimped type hose clips must be replaced with a screw clamp type clips during reassembly.
5 Unscrew and remove the retaining screws

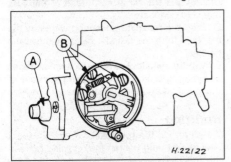

34.7 Automatic choke assembly (Weber TLD carburettor)

A   *Pull-down diaphragm housing*
B   *Securing screws*

(two conventional, and four Torx type), then lift the carburettor upper body clear and remove it.
6 Note the position of the choke housing alignment marks, then undo the three retaining screws and remove the choke bi-metal coil unit. Remove the internal heat shield.
7 To remove the automatic choke unit, undo the three retaining screws and detach the choke link from the operating lever **(see illustration)**.
8 Undo the three retaining screws to remove the vacuum diaphragm unit.
9 If dismantling the choke mechanism any further, note the component fitment as an aid to reassembly, but do not detach the choke spindle.

Inspection

10 Clean and inspect all components for wear, damage and/or distortion. Pay particular attention to the condition of the vacuum (pull-down) diaphragm and the choke housing O-ring. Renew any items that are defective (or suspect).

Refitting

11 Reassemble the automatic choke mechanism, making references to the notes taken during dismantling. Note that no lubricants must be used **(see illustration)**.
12 Refit the vacuum unit, making reference to the notes taken during dismantling. Ensure that the diaphragm is lying flat before tightening the housing retaining screws.
13 Locate the O-ring (ensuring that it is correctly seated), then reconnect the choke link. Refit the automatic choke unit, and secure with the retaining screws. Check and adjust the choke vacuum pull-down as described in the previous Section (paragraphs 5 and 6).
14 Refit the inner heat shield, ensuring that the location peg is securely engaged in its notch.
15 Refit the automatic choke housing and the bi-metal spring unit as described in the previous Section (paragraph 9).
16 Refit the carburettor upper body, ensuring that a new gasket is used and that the mating surfaces are clean. Fit the retaining screws to secure.
17 Reconnect the fuel hose to the carburettor, using new screw type hose clips to secure it.
18 Reconnect the anti-dieseling solenoid wiring connector.
19 Reconnect the coolant hoses to the automatic choke unit, then check and if

necessary top-up the cooling system as described in "Weekly Checks" and Chapter 1.
20 Reconnect the battery negative lead, then check and adjust the fast-idle speed as described in Section 31.
21 Refit the air cleaner (Section 2).

35 Carburettor (Weber TLD) - removal and refitting

Note: *Refer to the warning note in Section 1 before proceeding. New gaskets will be required on refitting and a tachometer and an exhaust gas analyser will be required on completion.*

Removal

1 Disconnect the battery negative (earth) lead (refer to Chapter 5A, Section 1).
2 Remove the air cleaner as described in Section 2.
3 Release any pressure remaining in the cooling system (see Chapter 1), and then detach the two coolant hoses from the automatic choke unit. Catch any coolant spillage in a suitable container. Identify each hose for subsequent refitting, then plug their ends or position them as high as possible to prevent coolant leakage.

Warning: DO NOT attempt to remove the expansion tank filler cap, or to disturb any part of the cooling system, while it or the engine is hot, as there is a very great risk of scalding. If the expansion tank filler cap must be removed before the engine and radiator have fully cooled down (even though this is not recommended) the pressure in the cooling system must first be released. Cover the cap with a thick layer of cloth, to avoid scalding, and slowly unscrew the filler cap until a hissing sound can be heard. When the hissing has stopped, showing that pressure is released, slowly unscrew the filler cap further until it can be removed; if more hissing sounds are heard, wait until they have stopped before unscrewing the cap completely. At all times, keep well away from the filler opening.

4 Disconnect the accelerator cable from the linkage at the carburettor, as described in Section 2.
5 Detach the anti-dieseling solenoid wiring connector.
6 Detach the fuel feed hose at the carburettor.

4A

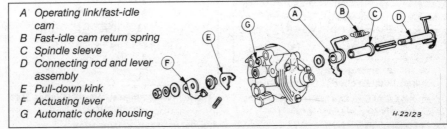

A   *Operating link/fast-idle cam*
B   *Fast-idle cam return spring*
C   *Spindle sleeve*
D   *Connecting rod and lever assembly*
E   *Pull-down kink*
F   *Actuating lever*
G   *Automatic choke housing*

34.11 Exploded view of the automatic choke linkage (Weber TLD carburettor)

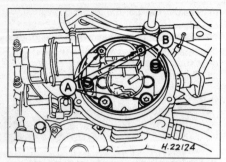

35.8 General view of Weber TLD carburettor

A *Torx head screws securing carburettor to inlet manifold*
B *Standard screws securing upper body to main body*

As it is detached, plug the end of the hose to prevent excessive fuel spillage and the ingress of dirt. Where a crimped type hose clip is fitted, cut it free, taking care not to damage the hose; a new screw type clip will need to be obtained to replace the crimped clip during reassembly.

7 Disconnect the relevant vacuum pipes from the carburettor. As they are detached, label them to ensure correct reassembly.

8 Unscrew and remove the four Torx-type retaining screws, and carefully lift clear the carburettor from the inlet manifold **(see illustration)**. Remove the gasket.

Refitting

9 Clean the carburettor and the inlet manifold mating faces.

10 Refit the carburettor in the reverse order of removal, ensuring that a new gasket is fitted.

11 If they are perished or were damaged during removal, renew the fuel and/or vacuum hoses.

12 Reconnect the automatic choke unit hoses, and then check/top-up the cooling system if required, as described in "Weekly Checks" and Chapter 1.

13 When the battery is reconnected, start and warm up the engine then check the idle speed and mixture settings as described in Chapter 1.

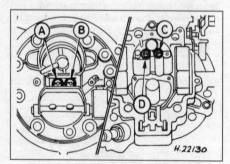

36.1b Jet arrangement in carburettor upper body (Weber TLD carburettor)

A *Primary air correction jet*
B *Secondary air correction jet*
C *Secondary main jet*
D *Primary main jet*

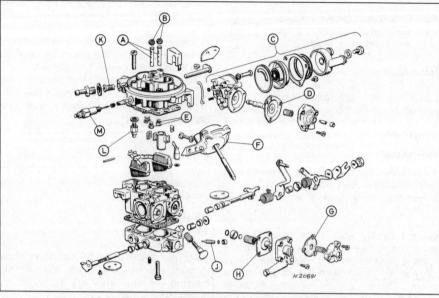

36.1a Exploded view of the carburettor (Weber TLD)

A *Emulsion tubes*
B *Air correction jets*
C *Automatic choke assembly*
D *Choke pull-down diaphragm*
E *Main jets*
F *Secondary barrel diaphragm assembly*
G *Power valve diaphragm*
H *Accelerator pump diaphragm*
J *Idle mixture adjusting screw*
K *Fuel feed filter*
L *Needle valve assembly*
M *Anti-dieseling (fuel cut-off) solenoid*

36 Carburettor (Weber TLD) - dismantling, cleaning, inspection and reassembly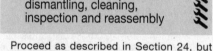

Proceed as described in Section 24, but refer to the appropriate illustrations for the TLD carburettor **(see illustrations)**. The following should also be observed:

a) *When refitting the idle mixture adjustment screw, make the initial adjustment by screwing it fully into position (without overtightening it), then unscrewing it by three full turns.*

b) *Refer to Section 32 to adjust the needle valve and float.*

c) *When the carburettor is reassembled and refitted, check and adjust the idle speed and mixture settings as described in Chapter 1.*

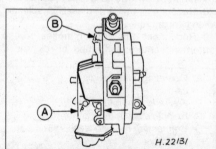

36.1c Float level adjustment (Weber TLD carburettor)

A *Float level setting dimension*
B *Adjusting tag*

37 Inlet manifold - removal and refitting

Note: *Refer to the warning note in Section 1 before proceeding.*

Removal

1 Drain the cooling system as described in Chapter 1.

2 Remove the carburettor as described in the relevant earlier Sections of this Chapter, according to carburettor type.

3 Noting their locations, disconnect the coolant, vacuum and breather hoses from the manifold.

4 Disconnect the wiring multi-plugs from the engine sensors at the inlet manifold. Disconnect the radio earth lead at the inlet manifold connector.

5 Undo the retaining bolts, and withdraw the manifold from the cylinder head. Remove the gasket.

6 With the manifold removed, clean all traces of the old gasket from the mating surfaces of the manifold and the cylinder head.

Refitting

7 Refitting is the reversal of removal. Use a new gasket, and tighten the retaining bolts to the specified torque. Refit the remainder of the components with reference to the appropriate Chapters of this manual. On completion, refill the cooling system as described in Chapter 1.

Chapter 4 Part B:
Fuel system - central fuel injection engines

Contents

Accelerator cable - removal, refitting and adjustment 5
Accelerator pedal - removal and refitting 6
Air cleaner assembly and air inlet components - removal and
  refitting 4
Air cleaner element renewal . . . . See Chapter 1
Fuel cut-off switch - removal and refitting 12
Fuel filter renewal . . . . See Chapter 1
Fuel injection system - checking 13
Fuel injection system components - removal and refitting 14
Fuel lines and fittings - general information 3
Fuel pump/fuel gauge sender unit - removal and refitting 9

Fuel pump/fuel pressure - checking 7
Fuel system - depressurisation 2
Fuel tank - removal, inspection and refitting 8
Fuel tank filler pipe - removal and refitting 11
Fuel tank ventilation tube - removal and refitting 10
General fuel system checks . . . . See Chapter 1
General information and precautions 1
Inlet manifold - removal and refitting 15
Underbody fuel/brake line check . . . . See Chapter 1
Underbonnet check for fluid leaks and hose condition . . See Chapter 1

Degrees of difficulty

| **Easy,** suitable for novice with little experience | | **Fairly easy,** suitable for beginner with some experience | | **Fairly difficult,** suitable for competent DIY mechanic | | **Difficult,** suitable for experienced DIY mechanic | | **Very difficult,** suitable for expert DIY or professional | |

Specifications

General
System type . . . . Central Fuel injection (CFi)
Application . . . . 1.1 and 1.3 litre HCS engines and 1.4 litre CVH engines

Fuel grade
Fuel octane requirement . . . . 95 RON unleaded

Fuel system data
Regulated fuel pressure - engine running at idle speed . . . . 1.0 ± 0.1 bars
Hold pressure - engine stopped after 1 minute . . . . 0.5 bars minimum

Torque wrench settings

	Nm	lbf ft
CFi unit-to-inlet manifold	12 to 15	9 to 11
Inlet manifold	16 to 20	12 to 15
Inlet air temperature sensor	20 to 25	15 to 18
Oxygen sensor	50 to 70	37 to 52

1 General information and precautions

General information

The fuel system consists of a fuel tank (mounted under the body, beneath the rear seats), fuel hoses, an electric fuel pump mounted in the fuel tank, and a central fuel injection (CFi) system.

Fuel is supplied from the tank by an integral electric fuel pump (and combined fuel gauge sender unit). The fuel is passed through an in-line filter within the engine compartment, then to the fuel injection unit. The fuel is maintained at the required operating pressure by a pressure regulator unit.

The CFi unit itself is a relatively simple device when compared with a conventional carburettor. Fuel is injected by a single solenoid valve (fuel injector) which is mounted centrally on top of the unit. It is this feature which gives the system CFi (or Central Fuel injection) its name **(see illustration)**.

The injector is energised by an electrical signal sent from the EEC IV engine management module. When energised, the injector pintle is lifted from its seat, and atomised fuel is delivered into the inlet manifold under pressure. The electrical signals take two forms of current - a high current to open the injector, and a low current to hold it open for the duration required. At idle speed, the injector is pulsed at every other inlet stroke, rather than with every stroke as during normal operation.

The air-to-fuel mixture ratio is regulated by the EEC IV module, based on inputs from the various engine sensors. No adjustments to the fuel mixture are possible.

The throttle plate control motor (mounted on the side of the CFi unit) regulates the idle speed by reacting to the signals sent by the EEC IV module. The signals are calculated by the values and information provided from the engine sensors. When the throttle position sensor indicates that the throttle is closed, the module enters the idle speed mode or dashpot mode (according to engine speed). The module maintains the idle speed at a constant value, making minor adjustments as necessary for different loads and conditions. The base idle speed can only be adjusted by a dealer or fuel injection specialist with the necessary equipment to link up to the engine management module.

To prevent the engine from running on (or dieseling) when it is switched off, the EEC IV module sends a signal to the throttle plate control motor, to fully close the throttle plate and return it to its preset position ready for restarting. When the ignition is switched on to restart the engine, the motor repositions the throttle plate to the position required according to the prevailing conditions.

The EEC IV module is the heart of the entire engine management system, controlling the fuel injection, ignition and emissions control systems. The module receives information from various sensors to determine engine temperature, speed and load, and the quantity of air entering the engine. The sensors also inform the module of throttle position, inlet air temperature and exhaust gas oxygen content. All the information supplied to the module is computed and compared with pre-set values stored in it's memory, to determine the required period of injection.

Information on crankshaft position and engine speed is generated by the distributor on pre-1990 CVH engine models, or by a crankshaft position sensor on all other models. The inductive head of the crankshaft position sensor runs just above the engine flywheel and scans a series of 36 protrusions on the flywheel periphery. As the crankshaft rotates, the sensor transmits a pulse to the system's ignition module every time a protrusion passes it. There is one missing protrusion in the flywheel periphery at a point corresponding to 90° BTDC. The ignition module recognises the absence of a pulse from the crankshaft position sensor at this point to establish a reference mark for crankshaft position. Similarly, the time interval between absent pulses is used to determine engine speed. This information is then fed to the EEC IV module for further processing.

Engine temperature information is supplied by the coolant temperature sensor. This component is an NTC (Negative Temperature Coefficient) thermistor - that is, a semi-conductor whose electrical resistance decreases as its temperature increases. It provides the EEC IV module with a constantly-varying (analogue) voltage signal, corresponding to the temperature of the engine coolant. This is used to refine the calculations made by the module, when determining the correct amount of fuel required to achieve the ideal air/fuel mixture ratio.

Inlet air temperature information is supplied by the inlet air temperature sensor. This component is also an NTC thermistor - see the previous paragraph - providing the EEC IV module with a signal corresponding to the temperature of air passing into the engine.

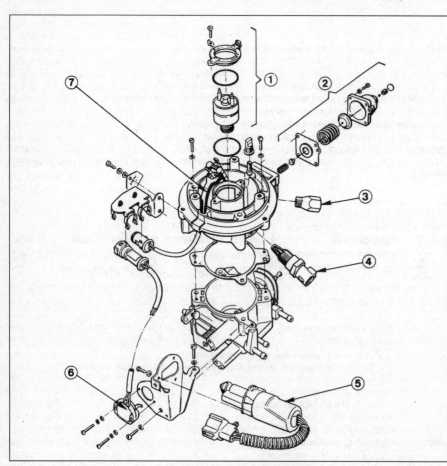

1.3 Exploded view of the CFi unit

1 Fuel injector assembly
2 Fuel pressure regulator assembly
3 Fuel feed connector
4 Intake air temperature sensor
5 Throttle-plate control motor
6 Throttle position sensor
7 Fuel injector wiring

This is used to refine the calculations made by the module, when determining the correct amount of fuel required to achieve the ideal air/fuel mixture ratio.

A throttle position sensor is mounted on the end of the throttle valve spindle, to provide the EEC IV module with a constantly-varying (analogue) voltage signal corresponding to the throttle opening. This allows the module to register the driver's input when determining the amount of fuel required by the engine.

Road speed is monitored by the vehicle speed sensor. This component is a Hall-effect generator, mounted on the transmission's speedometer drive. It supplies the EEC IV module with a series of pulses corresponding to the vehicle's road speed, enabling the module to control features such as the fuel shut-off on overrun.

A manifold absolute pressure sensor measures inlet manifold vacuum, and supplies this information to the module for calculation of engine load at any given throttle position.

Where power steering is fitted, a pressure-operated switch is screwed into the power steering system's high-pressure pipe. The switch sends a signal to the EEC IV module to reduce engine speed should the power steering fluid pressure become excessively high.

Certain later engines may be fitted with a heater in the inlet manifold. This is controlled by the EEC IV module to ensure that, even before the effect of the coolant heating becomes apparent, the manifold is warmed-up. This prevents fuel droplets condensing in the manifold, thus improving driveability and reducing exhaust emissions when the engine is cold.

The oxygen sensor in the exhaust system provides the EEC IV module with constant feedback - "closed-loop" control - which enables it to adjust the mixture to provide the best possible conditions for the catalytic converter to operate.

Precautions

 Warning: Petrol is extremely flammable - great care must be taken when working on any part of the fuel system. Do not smoke or allow any naked flames or uncovered light bulbs near the work area. Note that gas powered domestic appliances with pilot flames, such as heaters, boilers and tumble dryers, also present a fire hazard - bear this in mind if you are working in an area where such appliances are present. Always keep a suitable fire extinguisher close to the work area and familiarise yourself with its operation before starting work. Wear eye protection when working on fuel systems and wash off any fuel spilt on bare skin immediately with soap and water. Note that fuel vapour is just as dangerous as liquid fuel; a vessel that has just been emptied of liquid fuel will still contain

vapour and can be potentially explosive. Petrol is a highly dangerous and volatile liquid, and the precautions necessary when handling it cannot be overstressed.

Many of the operations described in this Chapter involve the disconnection of fuel lines, which may cause an amount of fuel spillage. Before commencing work, refer to the above Warning and the information in "Safety first" at the beginning of this manual.

When working with fuel system components, pay particular attention to cleanliness - dirt entering the fuel system may cause blockages which will lead to poor running.

Note: *Residual pressure will remain in the fuel lines long after the vehicle was last used, when disconnecting any fuel line, it will be necessary to depressurise the fuel system as described in Section 2.*

2 Fuel system - depressurisation

Note: *Refer to the warning note in Section 1 before proceeding.*

 Warning: The following procedure will merely relieve the pressure in the fuel system - remember that fuel will still be present in the system components, and take precautions accordingly before disconnecting any of them.

1 The fuel system referred to in this Chapter is defined as the fuel tank and tank-mounted fuel pump/fuel gauge sender unit, the fuel filter, the fuel injector, fuel pressure regulator, and the metal pipes and flexible hoses of the fuel lines between these components. All these contain fuel, which will be under pressure while the engine is running and/or while the ignition is switched on.

2 The pressure will remain for some time after the ignition has been switched off, and must be relieved before any of these components is disturbed for servicing work.

3 The simplest depressurisation method is to disconnect the fuel pump electrical supply by removing the fuel pump fuse (No 19) and starting the engine; allow the engine to idle until it dies through lack of fuel pressure. Turn the engine over once or twice on the starter to ensure that all pressure is released, then switch off the ignition; do not forget to refit the fuse when work is complete.

4 Note that, once the fuel system has been depressurised and drained (even partially), it will take significantly longer to restart the engine - perhaps several seconds of cranking - before the system is refilled and pressure restored.

3 Fuel lines and fittings - general information

Note: *Refer to the warning note in Section 1 before proceeding.*

Disconnecting and connecting quick-release couplings

1 Quick-release couplings are employed at many of the unions in the fuel feed and return lines.

2 Before disconnecting any fuel system component, relieve the residual pressure in the system (see Section 2), and equalise tank pressure by removing the fuel filler cap.

 Warning: This procedure will merely relieve the increased pressure necessary for the engine to run - remember that fuel will still be present in the system components, and take precautions accordingly before disconnecting any of them.

3 Release the protruding locking lugs on each union, by squeezing them together and carefully pulling the coupling apart. Use rag to soak up any spilt fuel. Where the unions are colour-coded, the pipes cannot be confused. Where both unions are the same colour, note carefully which pipe is connected to which, and ensure that they are correctly reconnected on refitting.

4 To reconnect one of these couplings, press them together until the locking lugs snap into their groove. Switch the ignition on and off five times to pressurise the system, and check for any sign of fuel leakage around the disturbed coupling before attempting to start the engine.

Checking

5 Checking procedures for the fuel lines are included in Chapter 1.

Component renewal

6 If any damaged sections are to be renewed, use original-equipment replacement hoses or pipes, constructed from exactly the same material as the section being replaced. Do not install substitutes constructed from inferior or inappropriate material; this could cause a fuel leak or a fire.

7 Before detaching or disconnecting any part of the fuel system, note the routing of all hoses and pipes, and the orientation of all clamps and clips. Replacement sections must be installed in exactly the same manner.

8 Before disconnecting any part of the fuel system, be sure to relieve the fuel system pressure (see Section 2), and equalise tank pressure by removing the fuel filler cap. Also disconnect the battery negative (earth) lead - see Chapter 5A, Section 1. Cover the fitting being disconnected with a rag, to absorb any fuel that may spray out.

4B

4 Air cleaner assembly and air inlet components - removal and refitting

Note: *Air cleaner element renewal and air cleaner temperature control system checks (where applicable) are described in Chapter 1.*

Air cleaner assembly

1 Disconnect the battery negative (earth) lead (refer to Chapter 5A, Section 1).
2 Undo the retaining bolts and partially lift the air cleaner from the CFi unit, so that the hose and wiring connections to the underside of the air cleaner body are accessible.
3 Note their connections and routings, then detach the wiring and hoses from the underside of the air cleaner.
4 Lift the air cleaner clear from the CFi unit.
5 Refit in the reverse order of removal.
6 Renew any hoses that are perished or cracked, and ensure that all fittings are securely and correctly reconnected.

Air inlet components

7 The air cleaner inlet spout and related components are removed with the air cleaner assembly as described above.

5 Accelerator cable - removal, refitting and adjustment

Removal

1 Disconnect the battery negative (earth) lead (refer to Chapter 5A, Section 1).
2 Fold back the carpet and insulation in the driver's footwell to gain access to the accelerator pedal.
3 Detach the accelerator cable from the pedal.
4 Remove the air cleaner assembly as described in Section 4.
5 Working at the throttle housing end of the cable, pivot the throttle quadrant by hand to release the tension from the cable, then detach the inner cable nipple from the throttle lever.
6 Detach the outer cable from the adjuster/support bracket, then remove the cable.

Refitting and adjustment

7 Refit in the reverse order of removal. When the cable is reconnected at each end, have an assistant depress the accelerator, and check that the throttle fully opens and shuts without binding. Ensure that there is a small amount of slack in the inner cable when the throttle is fully released. If adjustment is required, release the outer cable retaining clip from the cable at the adjustment/support bracket, slide the cable through the adjuster grommet to the point required, then refit the retaining clip to secure it in the set position.

6 Accelerator pedal - removal and refitting

Refer to Part A, Section 5.

7 Fuel pump/fuel pressure - checking

Note: *Refer to the warning note in Section 1 before proceeding.*

Fuel pump operation check

1 Switch on the ignition, and listen for the fuel pump (the sound of an electric motor running, audible from beneath the rear seats). Assuming there is sufficient fuel in the tank, the pump should start and run for approximately one or two seconds, then stop, each time the ignition is switched on. **Note:** *If the pump runs continuously all the time the ignition is switched on, the electronic control system is running in the backup (or "limp-home") mode referred to by Ford as "Limited Operation Strategy" (LOS). This almost certainly indicates a fault in the EEC IV module itself, and the vehicle should therefore be taken to a Ford dealer for a full test of the complete system, using the correct diagnostic equipment; do not waste time or risk damaging the components by trying to test the system without such facilities.*
2 Listen for fuel return noises from the fuel pressure regulator. It should be possible to feel the fuel pulsing in the regulator and in the feed hose from the fuel filter.
3 If the pump does not run at all, check the fuse, relay and wiring (see Chapter 12). Check also that the fuel cut-off switch has not been activated and if so, reset it.

Fuel pressure check

4 A fuel pressure gauge will be required for this check and should be connected in the fuel line between the fuel filter and the CFi unit, in accordance with the gauge maker's instructions.
5 Start the engine and allow it to idle. Note the gauge reading as soon as the pressure stabilises, and compare it with the figures given for regulated fuel pressure in the Specifications. If the pressure is high, check for a restricted fuel return line. If the pressure is low, renew the fuel pressure regulator.

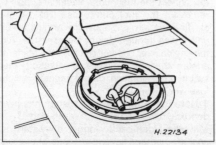

9.2 Ford Special tool engaged on the fuel pump/sender unit

6 Switch off the engine, and check that after one minute, the hold pressure has not fallen below that specified. If it has, check the seals on the fuel injector (see Section 14) and renew them if they appear in any way suspect. If the seals are okay, then the fuel pressure regulator or CFi unit are suspect.
7 Carefully disconnect the fuel pressure gauge, depressurising the system first as described in Section 2.
8 Run the engine, and check that there are no fuel leaks.

8 Fuel tank - removal, inspection and refitting

Proceed as described in Part A, Section 8, but before disconnecting the battery, relieve the residual pressure in the fuel system (see Section 2), and equalise tank pressure by removing the fuel filler cap. Note also that it will be necessary to release any additional ventilation tubes from their retaining clips, and to reposition or remove the underbody heat shields on certain models for access to the tank retaining bolts.

9 Fuel pump/fuel gauge sender unit - removal and refitting

Note: *Refer to the warning note in Section 1 before proceeding. Ford specify the use of their service tool 23-026 (a large box spanner with projecting teeth to engage the fuel pump/sender unit retaining ring's slots) for this task. While alternatives are possible, in view of the difficulty experienced in removing and refitting the pump/sender unit, it is strongly advised that the correct tool is obtained before starting work.*

Removal

1 A combined fuel pump and fuel gauge sender unit are located in the top face of the fuel tank. The combined unit can only be detached and withdrawn from the tank after the tank is released and lowered from under the vehicle. Refer to Section 8 and remove the fuel tank, then proceed as follows.
2 With the fuel tank removed, the pump/sender unit can be unscrewed using the special tool **(see illustration)**.
3 Withdraw the unit upwards from the tank **(see illustration)**, and detach the seal ring.

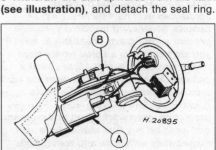

9.3 Fuel pump (A) and sender unit (B)

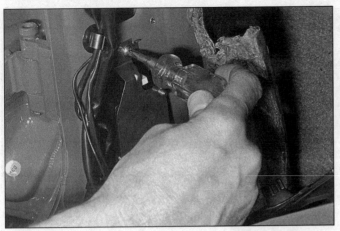

12.3a Remove the screw securing the inertia switch bracket . . .

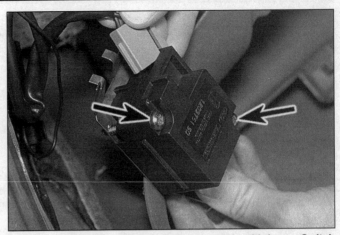

12.3b . . . and disconnect the multi-plug as it is withdrawn. Switch to bracket retaining screws (arrowed)

The seal ring must be renewed whenever the pump/sender unit is withdrawn from the tank.

Refitting

4 Refit in the reverse order of removal. Lightly coat the new unit seal ring with grease to ease fitting, and ensure that the seal is not distorted as the unit is fitted into position. Insert the unit so that the lug of the unit is in engagement with the slot in the tank aperture, then turn the unit to lock and secure.

10 Fuel tank ventilation tube - removal and refitting

Refer to Part A, Section 10, but note that on models with evaporative emission control, the ventilation tube connects to the combined roll-over/anti-trickle-fill valve assembly but, instead of venting to atmosphere, a further tube runs the length of the vehicle to a carbon canister in the front right-hand corner of the engine compartment.

Further information on the evaporative emission control system is contained in Part E of this Chapter.

11 Fuel tank filler pipe - removal and refitting

Refer to Part A, Section 11.

12 Fuel cut-off switch - removal and refitting

Removal

1 Disconnect the battery negative (earth) lead (refer to Chapter 5A, Section 1).
2 Remove the left-hand sill scuff plate as described in Chapter 11, Section 42.

3 Undo the retaining screws and withdraw the cut-off (inertia) switch and bracket assembly. As it is withdrawn, disconnect the wiring multi-plug from the switch **(see illustrations)**.
4 The switch may be separated from the bracket by removing the two securing screws.

Refitting

5 Reconnect the wiring multi-plug to the switch, ensuring that it is felt to snap securely into position.
6 Refit the switch to the bracket then relocate the bracket, and refit the screw to secure it.
7 Reset the switch by pushing the top button down, then refit the sill scuff plate.
8 Reconnect the battery and restart the engine to ensure that the switch has reset.

13 Fuel injection system - checking

Note: Refer to the warning note in Section 1 before proceeding.

If a fault appears in the fuel injection system, first ensure that all the system wiring connectors are securely connected and free of corrosion. Ensure that the fault is not due to poor maintenance; ie, check that the air cleaner filter element is clean, the spark plugs are in good condition and correctly gapped, the valve clearances are correctly adjusted (where adjustable), the cylinder compression pressures are correct, the ignition timing is correct (where adjustable), and that the engine breather hoses are clear and undamaged, referring to Chapters 1, 2 and 5 for further information.

If these checks fail to reveal the cause of the problem, the vehicle should be taken to a suitably-equipped Ford dealer for testing. A wiring block connector is incorporated in the engine management circuit, into which a special electronic diagnostic tester can be plugged. The tester will locate the fault quickly and simply, alleviating the need to test all the

system components individually, which is a time-consuming operation that also carries a risk of damaging the EEC IV engine management module.

14 Fuel injection system components - removal and refitting

Note: Refer to the warning note in Section 1 before proceeding.

Fuel injector

1 Relieve the residual pressure in the fuel system (see Section 2), and equalise tank pressure by removing the fuel filler cap.

> ⚠ *Warning: This procedure will merely relieve the increased pressure necessary for the engine to run - remember that fuel will still be present in the system components, and take precautions accordingly before disconnecting any of them.*

2 Disconnect the battery negative (earth) lead (refer to Chapter 5A, Section 1).
3 Refer to Section 4 and remove the air cleaner.
4 Release the injector feed wiring multi-plug, and detach it from the injector (pulling on the plug - not the wire) **(see illustration)**.

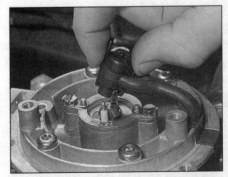

14.4 Disconnect the multi-plug from the injector

4B

14.5a Removing an injector retaining collar securing bolt and its locktab

14.5b Removing the injector retaining collar

14.5c Withdrawing the injector from the CFi unit

14.5d Injector seals in the CFi unit

14.5e Withdrawing the seal from the injector retaining collar

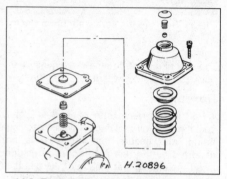

14.8 Exploded view of the fuel pressure regulator assembly

5 Bend over the locking tabs retaining the injector screws, then undo and remove the screws. Withdraw the injector retaining collar, then carefully withdraw the injector from the CFi unit (noting its orientation) followed by its seals. Withdraw the seal from the retaining collar **(see illustrations)**.
6 Refit in the reverse order of removal. Always use new seals in the CFi unit and the retaining collar, and lightly lubricate them with clean engine oil prior to assembly. Take care not to damage the seals as they are fitted and as the injector is fitted, check that the location peg engages correctly.

Fuel pressure regulator

7 Refer to paragraphs 14 to 22 in this Section and remove the CFi unit from the vehicle.
8 Unscrew and remove the four regulator retaining screws, and remove the regulator **(see illustration)**. As they are removed, note the fitting positions and the orientation of the components. **Do not** (unless absolutely necessary) attempt to prise out the plug or adjust the screw in the centre of the housing (if no plug is fitted), as this will alter the system pressure.
9 Examine the components, and renew any that are defective or suspect.
10 To refit, position the regulator on its side, then insert the small spring, the valve, diaphragm (ensuring that it seats correctly), large spring, cup and then the regulator cover. Insert and tighten the retaining screws, but

take care not overtighten them, or the cover will be distorted.
11 Carefully place the ball into position on the spring cup, and ensure that it seats correctly.
12 If removed, fit the central Allen type adjuster screw, hand-tighten it and then unscrew it (from the hand-tight position) three full turns to make a provisional adjustment.
13 Refit the CFi unit in accordance with paragraphs 23 to 25 in this Section, but note that further checks for fuel leaks must be made with the engine running. The fuel system pressure must be checked by a Ford dealer or other suitable specialist at the earliest opportunity.

CFi unit

14 Relieve the residual pressure in the fuel system (see Section 2), and equalise tank pressure by removing the fuel filler cap.

> ⚠ **Warning: This procedure will merely relieve the increased pressure necessary for the engine to run - remember that fuel will still be present in the system components, and take precautions accordingly before disconnecting any of them.**

15 Disconnect the battery negative (earth) lead (refer to Chapter 5A, Section 1).
16 Refer to Section 4 and remove the air cleaner.
17 Position a suitable drain tray under the coolant hose connections to the CFi unit.

Ensure that the cooling system is not pressurised (see Chapter 1), then detach the hoses from the unit. Plug or clamp the hoses to prevent further coolant spillage whilst the hoses are detached.

> ⚠ **Warning: DO NOT attempt to remove the expansion tank filler cap, or to disturb any part of the cooling system, while it or the engine is hot, as there is a very great risk of scalding. If the expansion tank filler cap must be removed before the engine and radiator have fully cooled down (even though this is not recommended) the pressure in the cooling system must first be released. Cover the cap with a thick layer of cloth, to avoid scalding, and slowly unscrew the filler cap until a hissing sound can be heard. When the hissing has stopped, showing that pressure is released, slowly unscrew the filler cap further until it can be removed; if more hissing sounds are heard, wait until they have stopped before unscrewing the cap completely. At all times, keep well away from the filler opening.**

18 Disconnect the fuel return pipe from the CFi unit.
19 Refer to Section 5 and disconnect the accelerator cable from the CFi unit.
20 Disconnect the inlet air temperature sensor, throttle plate control motor and throttle position sensor wiring multi-plug connectors.

14.22 CFi unit securing screws (arrowed)

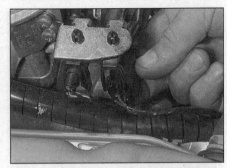

14.28a Release the throttle position sensor multi-plug from its retaining clip and disconnect it

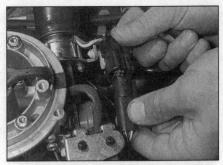

14.28b Disconnecting the throttle plate control motor multi-plug

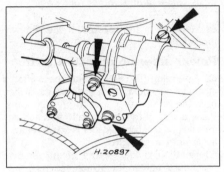

14.29 Throttle-plate control motor and throttle position sensor assembly mounting bracket securing screws (arrowed)

21 Disconnect the vacuum hose from the CFi unit.
22 Unscrew and remove the four retaining screws, and remove the CFi unit from the inlet manifold **(see illustration)**. Remove the gasket.
23 Clean the CFi unit and the inlet manifold mating faces.
24 Refit in the reverse order of removal. Tighten the retaining bolts to the specified torque wrench setting. Check and top-up the cooling system as required (see *"Weekly Checks"* and Chapter 1).
25 When the CFi unit is refitted, turn the ignition on and off at least five times to pressurise the system, and check for leaks.

Throttle plate control motor

26 Disconnect the battery negative (earth) lead (refer to Chapter 5A, Section 1).
27 Refer to Section 4 and remove the air cleaner.
28 Detach the wiring multi-plugs from the throttle position sensor and the throttle plate control motor, and release the retaining clips on the bracket **(see illustrations)**.
29 Undo and remove the motor support bracket screws, and remove the bracket complete with the motor from the CFi unit **(see illustration)**.
30 Undo the motor retaining screws and remove it from the support bracket.
31 Refit in the reverse order of removal, but note the following points:

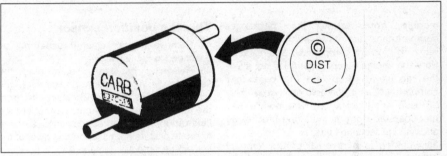

14.34 Fuel trap vacuum connection markings

a) When refitting the motor and its support bracket to the injector unit, the throttle position sensor must locate on the accelerator linkage, and the bracket must align with the pegs.
b) On completion, the idle speed should be checked by a Ford dealer or fuel injection specialist who has the required equipment to link up with the EEC IV engine management module.

Fuel trap

32 A fuel trap is fitted to the manifold absolute pressure sensor vacuum hose on certain models.
33 To remove the fuel trap, disconnect the vacuum hoses from the fuel trap and withdraw it.
34 Refit in the reverse order of removal. It is important to ensure that the trap is correctly orientated, with the "CARB" mark on one end

face towards the inlet manifold, and the "DIST" mark towards the MAP sensor **(see illustration)**.

EEC IV engine management module

Note: *The module is fragile. Take care not to drop it, or subject it to any other kind of impact. Do not subject it to extremes of temperature, or allow it to get wet.*
35 Disconnect the battery negative (earth) lead (refer to Chapter 5A, Section 1).
36 Unscrew and remove the two nuts securing the module cover in the engine compartment, then carefully draw the cover away from its location. Unscrew the module multi-plug retaining bolt and disconnect the multi-plug from the module **(see illustrations)**.
37 The aid of an assistant will be required at this stage, to support and withdraw the

14.36a Undoing the EEC IV engine management module cover retaining nuts (vehicle jack removed for clarity)

14.36b Undoing the EEC IV engine management module multi-plug retaining bolt

4B

14.37 Withdrawing the EEC IV engine management module into the passenger footwell

14.42 Disconnecting the intake air temperature sensor multi-plug

14.45 Throttle position sensor retaining screws (arrowed) (shown with throttle plate control motor removed)

module from inside the passenger compartment as its mounting bracket retaining tags are compressed and released from the engine compartment. Do not allow the module to drop into the passenger compartment as irreparable damage is likely to result **(see illustration)**. The module may be separated from its mounting bracket by undoing the securing bolts.

38 Refitting is a reversal of the removal procedure, ensuring that the module mounting bracket retaining tags are felt to snap into position

Crankshaft position sensor

39 Refer to Chapter 5B.

Coolant temperature sensor

40 Refer to Chapter 3.

Inlet air temperature sensor

41 Remove the air cleaner assembly as described in Section 4.
42 Releasing its clip, unplug the sensor's electrical connector, then unscrew the sensor from the CFi unit **(see illustration)**.
43 Refitting is the reverse of the removal procedure. Tighten the sensor to the specified torque wrench setting; if it is overtightened, its tapered thread may crack the resonator.

Throttle position sensor

44 Remove the air cleaner assembly as described in Section 4.
45 Releasing its wire clip, unplug the sensor's wiring connector. Remove the retaining screws, and withdraw the unit from the throttle plate control motor bracket **(see illustration)**. *Do not* force the sensor's centre to rotate past its normal operating sweep; the unit will be seriously damaged.
46 Refitting is the reverse of the removal procedure, ensuring that the sensor actuating arm is correctly located.

Vehicle speed sensor

47 The sensor is mounted at the base of the speedometer drive cable, and is removed with the speedometer drive pinion. Refer to the relevant Section of Chapter 7A or B, as applicable.

Manifold absolute pressure sensor

48 The sensor is located near the centre of the engine compartment bulkhead.
49 Disconnect the wiring multi-plug, and detach the vacuum hose from the base of the sensor **(see illustration)**.
50 Undo the two retaining screws, and withdraw the sensor from its location.

51 Refitting is the reverse of the removal procedure.

Power steering pressure switch

52 Releasing its clip, unplug the switch's electrical connector, then unscrew the switch from the power steering high pressure pipe. Place a wad of rag underneath, to catch any spilt fluid. If a sealing washer is fitted, renew it if it is worn or damaged.
53 Refitting is the reverse of the removal procedure; tighten the switch securely, then top-up the fluid reservoir (see *"Weekly Checks"*) to replace any fluid lost from the system, and bleed out any trapped air (see Chapter 10).

Oxygen sensor

Note: *The sensor is delicate, and will not work if it is dropped or knocked, if its power supply is disrupted, or if any cleaning materials are used on it.*

54 Release the sensor's electrical connector from its bracket and unplug it to disconnect the sensor **(see illustration)**.
55 Raise and support the front of the vehicle if required to remove the sensor from underneath (*"see Jacking and vehicle support"*). Remove the sensor heat shield then unscrew the sensor from the exhaust system front downpipe; collect the sealing washer (where fitted).
56 On refitting, clean the sealing washer (where fitted) and renew it if it is damaged or

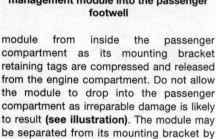

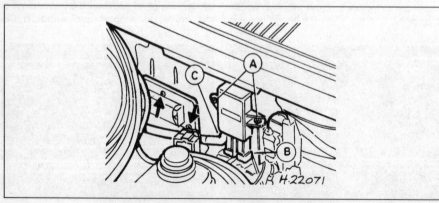

14.49 Manifold absolute pressure sensor location

A Securing screws   *B Multi-plug*   *C Vacuum hose*
Arrows indicate ignition module retaining screws

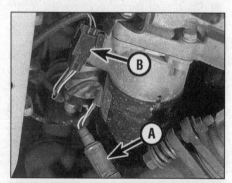

14.54 Oxygen sensor (A) (shown with its heatshield removed), and its multi-plug (B)

worn. Apply a smear of anti-seize compound to the sensor's threads, to prevent them from welding themselves to the downpipe in service. Refit the sensor, tightening it to its specified torque wrench setting; a slotted socket will be required to do this. Reconnect the wiring, and heat shield then refit the connector plug.

Inlet manifold heater

57 The heater is located in a recess in the inlet manifold, directly underneath the CFi unit. While access is possible from underneath, it is preferable, depending on the tools available, to remove the complete manifold (Section 15) to reach the heater.
58 Assuming the work is being carried out without removing the manifold, disconnect the battery negative (earth) lead (refer to Chapter 5A, Section 1).
59 Chock the rear wheels then jack up the front of the car and support it on axle stands (see *"Jacking and vehicle support"*).
60 Disconnect the heater wiring, and extract the circlip retaining the heater **(see illustration)**. Withdraw the heater.
61 Refitting is the reverse of the removal procedure. Ensure that both the heater and its circlip are correctly located in the manifold.

Injector ballast resistor

62 When fitted, this component is located on the engine compartment bulkhead, next to the manifold absolute pressure sensor.
63 Disconnect the battery negative (earth) lead (refer to Chapter 5A, Section 1).
64 Disconnect the resistor wiring at its multi-plug, remove the retaining screw and withdraw the resistor.
65 Refitting is the reverse of the removal procedure.

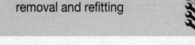

15 Inlet manifold - removal and refitting

Note: *Refer to the warning note in Section 1 before proceeding.*

Removal

1 Drain the cooling system as described in Chapter 1.
2 Remove the CFi unit as described in Section 14.
3 Noting their locations, disconnect the coolant, vacuum and breather hoses from the manifold.
4 Disconnect the wiring multi-plugs from the

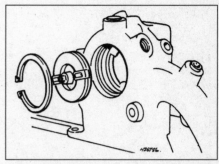

14.60 Inlet manifold heater components

engine sensors at the inlet manifold. Disconnect the radio earth lead at the inlet manifold connector.
5 Undo the retaining bolts, and withdraw the manifold from the cylinder head. Remove the gasket.
6 With the manifold removed, clean all traces of the old gasket from the mating surfaces of the manifold and the cylinder head.

Refitting

7 Refitting is the reversal of removal. Use a new gasket, and tighten the retaining bolts to the specified torque. Refit the remainder of the components with reference to the appropriate Chapters of this manual.

4B

Notes

Chapter 4 Part C:
Fuel system - electronic fuel injection engines

Contents

Accelerator cable - removal, refitting and adjustment 5
Accelerator pedal - removal and refitting 6
Air cleaner assembly and air inlet components - removal and
  refitting 4
Air cleaner element renewal .See Chapter 1
Exhaust system check . . . . .See Chapter 1
Fuel cut-off switch - removal and refitting 12
Fuel filter renewal . . . . .See Chapter 1
Fuel injection system - checking 13
Fuel injection system components - removal and refitting 14
Fuel lines and fittings - general information 3
Fuel pump/fuel gauge sender unit - removal and refitting 9
Fuel pump/fuel pressure - checking 7
Fuel system - depressurisation 2
Fuel tank - removal, inspection and refitting 8
Fuel tank filler pipe - removal and refitting 11
Fuel tank ventilation tube - removal and refitting 10
General fuel system checks . . . . .See Chapter 1
General information and precautions 1
Idle speed and mixture check and adjustment . . . . .See Chapter 1
Idle speed control valve cleaning and maintenance . . . .See Chapter 1
Inlet manifold - removal and refitting 15
Intercooler - removal and refitting 17
Turbocharger - general information and precautions 16
Turbocharger - removal, examination and refitting 20
Turbocharger boost control valve - removal and refitting 18
Turbocharger boost pressure - checking and adjustment 19
Underbody fuel/brake line check . . . . .See Chapter 1
Underbonnet check for fluid leaks and hose condition . .See Chapter 1

Degrees of difficulty

Easy, suitable for novice with little experience	Fairly easy, suitable for beginner with some experience	Fairly difficult, suitable for competent DIY mechanic	Difficult, suitable for experienced DIY mechanic	Very difficult, suitable for expert DIY or professional

Specifications

General
System type . . . . Electronic Fuel injection (EFi) with turbocharger on RS Turbo models
Application . . . . 1.6 litre CVH engines

Fuel grade
Fuel octane requirement:
  Engines without catalytic converter* . . . . 95 RON unleaded or 97 RON leaded
  Engines with catalytic converter . . . . 95 RON unleaded (leaded fuel must **not** be used)
*Refer to dealer for latest recommendations

Fuel system data
Idle speed and mixture settings . . . . See Chapter 1
Fuel pump pressure - engine not running . . . . 3.0 bars minimum
Regulated fuel pressure - engine running at idle speed . . . . 2.3 to 2.5 bars
Hold pressure - engine stopped after two minutes . . . . Not less than 0.8 bars below regulated pressure

Turbocharger
Type . . . . Garrett AiResearch T02
Boost pressure . . . . 0.47 to 0.51 bars

Torque wrench settings

	Nm	lbf ft
Idle speed control valve bolts	4 to 5	3 to 4
Fuel pressure regulator bolts	8 to 12	6 to 9
Fuel rail bolts	20 to 26	15 to 19
Inlet air temperature sensor	20 to 25	15 to 18
Inlet manifold	16 to 20	12 to 15
Oxygen sensor	50 to 70	37 to 52
Intercooler-to-radiator bolts	4 to 6	3 to 5
Boost control valve screws	2.2 to 2.7	1.5 to 2
Exhaust manifold heatshield bolts	21 to 26	16 to 19
Exhaust manifold-to-engine nuts (non-Turbo models)	14 to 17	11 to 13
Exhaust manifold-to-engine nuts (Turbo models)	28 to 31	21 to 23
Exhaust manifold-to-turbocharger bolts	20 to 28	15 to 21
Turbocharger-to-exhaust downpipe nuts	35 to 47	26 to 35
Turbocharger cooling pipe banjo union bolts	22 to 29	17 to 22
Turbocharger oil feed and return line couplings	15 to 20	11 to 15

1 General information and precautions

General information

The fuel system consists of a fuel tank (mounted under the body, beneath the rear seats), fuel hoses, an electric fuel pump mounted in the fuel tank, and an electronic fuel injection system.

Fuel is supplied under pressure from the fuel pump to the fuel distributor rail mounted on top of the inlet manifold (see illustration). The fuel rail acts as a pressurised fuel reservoir for the fuel injectors. The electro-mechanical injectors have only "on" or "off" positions, the volume of fuel being injected to

meet the engine operating conditions being determined by the length of time that the injectors are opened. The volume of fuel required for one power stroke is determined by the EEC IV engine management module, and is divided by two equal amounts. The first half of the required volume is injected into the static air ahead of the inlet valve one complete engine revolution before the inlet valve is due to open. After one further revolution, the inlet valve opens and the required fuel volume is injected into the air flow being drawn into the cylinder. The fuel will therefore be consistently injected to two inlet valves simultaneously at a particular crankshaft position.

The volume of air drawn into the engine is governed by the air filter unit and other variable operating factors. These variables are assessed by the EEC IV module and the

corresponding signals are produced to actuate the injectors accordingly.

The engine base idle speed can be adjusted (if required), by turning the adjuster screw (covered by a tamperproof cap) in the throttle housing. Provision for adjusting the fuel mixture is made by the mixture screw in the potentiometer unit mounted on the bulkhead.

An idle speed control valve, itself controlled by the EEC-IV engine management module, stabilises the engine idle speed under all conditions by the opening of an auxiliary air passage which bypasses the throttle. Apart from a base-idle speed adjustment, no adjustments to the operational idle speed can be made.

The EEC IV module is the heart of the entire engine management system, controlling the fuel injection, ignition and emissions control systems. The module receives information from various sensors to determine engine temperature, speed and load, and the quantity of air entering the engine. The sensors also inform the module of throttle position, inlet air temperature and, on models with catalytic converters, exhaust gas oxygen content. All the information supplied to the module is computed and compared with pre-set values stored in it's memory, to determine the required period of injection.

Information on crankshaft position and engine speed is generated by a crankshaft position sensor. The inductive head of the sensor runs just above the engine flywheel and scans a series of 36 protrusions on the flywheel periphery. As the crankshaft rotates, the sensor transmits a pulse to the system's ignition module every time a protrusion passes it. There is one missing protrusion in the flywheel periphery at a point corresponding to 90° BTDC. The ignition module recognises the absence of a pulse from the crankshaft position sensor at this point to establish a reference mark for crankshaft position. Similarly, the time interval between absent pulses is used to determine engine speed. This information is then fed to the EEC IV module for further processing.

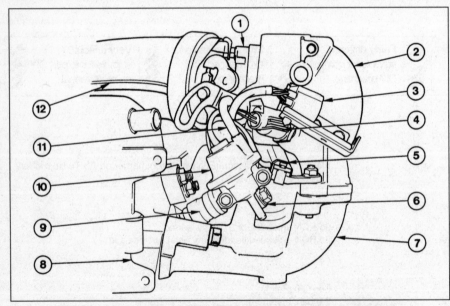

1.2 General view of the 1.6 litre EFi fuel injection system arrangement

1 Throttle housing
2 Upper inlet manifold section
3 Wiring loom connector
4 Intake air temperature sensor
5 Wiring harness ducting
6 Fuel rail
7 Lower section of inlet manifold
8 Cylinder head
9 Fuel injector
10 Fuel pressure regulator
11 Vacuum hose
12 Air inlet duct

Engine temperature information is supplied by the coolant temperature sensor. This component is an NTC (Negative Temperature Coefficient) thermistor - that is, a semi-conductor whose electrical resistance decreases as its temperature increases. It provides the EEC IV module with a constantly-varying (analogue) voltage signal, corresponding to the temperature of the engine coolant. This is used to refine the calculations made by the module, when determining the correct amount of fuel required to achieve the ideal air/fuel mixture ratio.

Inlet air temperature information is supplied by the inlet air temperature sensor. This component is also an NTC thermistor - see the previous paragraph - providing the module with a signal corresponding to the temperature of air passing into the engine. This is used to refine the calculations made by the module, when determining the correct amount of fuel required to achieve the ideal air/fuel mixture ratio.

A throttle position sensor is mounted on the end of the throttle valve spindle, to provide the EEC IV module with a constantly-varying (analogue) voltage signal corresponding to the throttle opening. This allows the module to register the driver's input when determining the amount of fuel required by the engine.

Road speed is monitored by the vehicle speed sensor. This component is a Hall-effect generator, mounted on the transmission's speedometer drive. It supplies the module with a series of pulses corresponding to the vehicle's road speed, enabling the module to control features such as the fuel shut-off on overrun.

A manifold absolute pressure sensor measures inlet manifold vacuum, and supplies this information to the EEC IV module for calculation of engine load at any given throttle position.

Where power steering is fitted, a pressure-operated switch is screwed into the power steering system's high-pressure pipe. The switch sends a signal to the EEC IV module to reduce engine speed should the power steering fluid pressure become excessively high.

On models with a catalytic converter, the oxygen sensor in the exhaust system provides the EEC IV module with constant feedback - "closed-loop" control - which enables it to adjust the mixture to provide the best possible conditions for the catalytic converter to operate.

On turbocharged engines, control of the turbocharger boost pressure is also governed by the EEC IV module, acting through the boost control valve. This allows inlet manifold depression to be applied to the turbocharger wastegate control.

The turbocharger consists of a turbine that is driven by the exhaust gases, to suck air through the air filter and to compress it into the engine. An air-cooled intercooler, mounted next to the radiator, cools the inlet air (heated by its passage through the turbocharger); this increases the density of the compressed fuel/air mixture entering the engine, thus improving the engine's power output.

Precautions

 Warning: Petrol is extremely flammable - great care must be taken when working on any part of the fuel system. Do not smoke or allow any naked flames or uncovered light bulbs near the work area. Note that gas powered domestic appliances with pilot flames, such as heaters, boilers and tumble dryers, also present a fire hazard - bear this in mind if you are working in an area where such appliances are present. Always keep a suitable fire extinguisher close to the work area and familiarise yourself with its operation before starting work. Wear eye protection when working on fuel systems and wash off any fuel spilt on bare skin immediately with soap and water. Note that fuel vapour is just as dangerous as liquid fuel; a vessel that has just been emptied of liquid fuel will still contain vapour and can be potentially explosive. Petrol is a highly dangerous and volatile liquid, and the precautions necessary when handling it cannot be overstressed.

Many of the operations described in this Chapter involve the disconnection of fuel lines, which may cause an amount of fuel spillage. Before commencing work, refer to the above Warning and the information in "Safety first" at the beginning of this manual.

When working with fuel system components, pay particular attention to cleanliness - dirt entering the fuel system may cause blockages which will lead to poor running.

Note: *Residual pressure will remain in the fuel lines long after the vehicle was last used; when disconnecting any fuel line, it will be necessary to depressurise the fuel system as described in Section 2.*

Note: *Refer to Section 16 for specific precautions relating to turbocharged engines.*

2 Fuel system - depressurisation

Refer to Part B, Section 2.

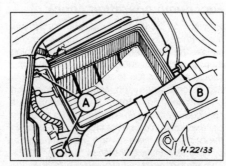

4.6 Air cleaner housing attachments

A Bolts   B Grommet

3 Fuel lines and fittings - general information

Refer to Part B, Section 3.

4 Air cleaner assembly and air inlet components - removal and refitting

Note: *Air cleaner element renewal and air cleaner temperature control system checks (where applicable) are described in Chapter 1.*

Air cleaner assembly

1 Disconnect the battery negative (earth) lead (refer to Chapter 5A, Section 1).
2 If the idle speed control valve is mounted on the air cleaner, disconnect the multi-plug and the air bypass hose from the valve.
3 Disconnect the flexible hose between the air cleaner lid and the air inlet duct or turbocharger air inlet.
4 Disconnect the crankcase breather hose from the front of the air cleaner housing.
5 Unclip and remove the air cleaner lid, then withdraw the element.
6 Remove the two bolts securing the forward end of the air cleaner housing, free the rearward end of the housing from its location and carefully withdraw from the vehicle **(see illustration)**.
7 Refitting is a reversal of the removal procedure.

Air inlet components

8 Disconnect the battery negative (earth) lead (refer to Chapter 5A, Section 1).
9 If the idle speed control valve is mounted on the air cleaner, disconnect the multi-plug and the air bypass hose from the valve **(see illustration)**.
10 Disconnect the HT leads from the spark plugs, labelling them if necessary to avoid confusion on refitting.

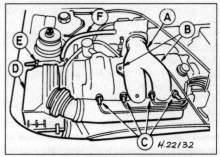

4.9 General view of the air inlet components on non-Turbo models

A Air inlet duct
B Air inlet duct securing bolts
C Spark plug HT lead connectors
D Air cleaner lid
E Idle speed control valve multi-plug
F Air bypass hose

4C

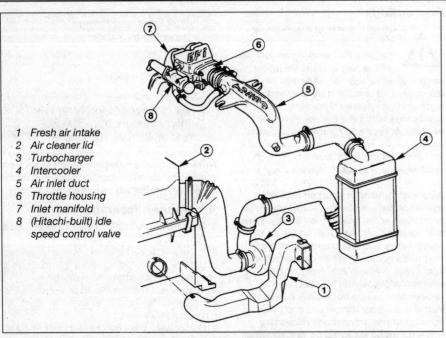

1 Fresh air intake
2 Air cleaner lid
3 Turbocharger
4 Intercooler
5 Air inlet duct
6 Throttle housing
7 Inlet manifold
8 (Hitachi-built) idle
  speed control valve

4.12 Air intake, turbocharger and intercooler details on Turbo models

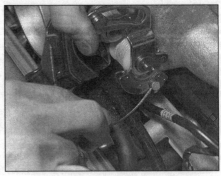

5.45 Accelerator cable retention arrangement at the throttle linkage

11 On non-Turbo models, disconnect the flexible hose between the air cleaner lid and the air inlet duct.

12 On Turbo models, disconnect the idle speed control valve air bypass hose from the air inlet duct and the flexible hose between the air inlet duct and intercooler **(see illustration)**.

13 Undo the two retaining bolts, and remove the air inlet duct from the rocker cover.

14 Refitting is the reverse of the removal procedure.

5 Accelerator cable - removal, refitting and adjustment

Removal

1 Disconnect the battery negative (earth) lead (refer to Chapter 5A, Section 1).

2 Remove the air inlet components as described in Section 4.

3 Fold back the carpet and insulation in the driver's footwell to gain access to the accelerator pedal.

4 Detach the accelerator cable from the pedal.

5 Working at the throttle housing end of the cable, pivot the throttle quadrant by hand to release the tension from the cable, then detach the inner cable nipple from the throttle lever **(see illustration)**.

6 Detach the outer cable from the adjuster/support bracket, then remove the cable.

Refitting and adjustment

7 Refit in the reverse order of removal. When the cable is reconnected at each end, have an assistant depress the accelerator, and check that the throttle fully opens and shuts without binding. Ensure that there is a small amount of slack in the inner cable when the throttle is fully released. If adjustment is required, release the outer cable retaining clip from the cable at the adjustment/support bracket, slide the cable through the adjuster grommet to the point required, then refit the retaining clip to secure it in the set position.

6 Accelerator pedal - removal and refitting

Refer to Part A, Section 5.

7 Fuel pump/fuel pressure - checking

Note: Refer to the warning note in Section 1 before proceeding.

Fuel pump operation check

1 Switch on the ignition, and listen for the fuel pump (the sound of an electric motor running, audible from beneath the rear seats). Assuming there is sufficient fuel in the tank, the pump should start and run for approximately one or two seconds, then stop, each time the ignition is switched on. **Note:** *If the pump runs continuously all the time the ignition is switched on, the electronic control system is running in the backup (or "limp-home") mode referred to by Ford as "Limited Operation Strategy" (LOS). This almost certainly indicates a fault in the EEC IV module itself, and the vehicle should therefore be taken to a Ford dealer for a full test* of the complete system, using the correct diagnostic equipment; do not waste time or risk damaging the components by trying to test the system without such facilities.

2 Listen for fuel return noises from the fuel pressure regulator. It should be possible to feel the fuel pulsing in the regulator and in the feed hose from the fuel filter.

3 If the pump does not run at all, check the fuse, relay and wiring (see Chapter 12). Check also that the fuel cut-off switch has not been activated and if so, reset it.

Fuel pressure check

4 A fuel pressure gauge will be required for this check and should be connected in the fuel line between the fuel filter and the fuel rail, in accordance with the gauge maker's instructions.

5 Disconnect the wiring from the E-DIS ignition coil and the fuel injectors.

6 Switch the ignition on and off twice, and check that the pump pressure is as listed in the *Specifications*.

7 If the pressure is not as specified, check the fuel system for leaks or damage. If the system appears okay, renew the fuel pump.

8 Reconnect the wiring to the ignition coil and fuel injectors.

9 If the pump pressure was satisfactory, start the engine and allow it to idle. Disconnect the vacuum hose at the fuel pressure regulator, and plug the hose. Note the gauge reading as soon as the pressure stabilises, and compare it with the figures given for regulated fuel pressure in the *Specifications*.

10 If the regulated fuel pressure is not as specified, remove the plug from the top of the fuel pressure regulator, and using a suitable Allen key, adjust the pressure regulator as necessary.

11 Switch off the engine, and check that the fuel pressure stays at the specified hold pressure for two minutes after the engine is turned off.

12 Carefully disconnect the fuel pressure gauge, depressurising the system first as described in Section 2. Reconnect the ignition coil and fuel injector wiring.

13 Run the engine, and check that there are no fuel leaks.

8 Fuel tank - removal, inspection and refitting

Proceed as described in Part A, Section 8, but before disconnecting the battery, relieve the residual pressure in the fuel system (see Section 2), and equalise tank pressure by removing the fuel filler cap.

9 Fuel pump/fuel gauge sender unit - removal and refitting

Refer to Part B, Section 9.

10 Fuel tank ventilation tube - removal and refitting

Refer to Part A, Section 10, but note that on models with evaporative emission control, the ventilation tube connects to the combined roll-over/anti-trickle-fill valve assembly but, instead of venting to atmosphere, a further tube runs the length of the vehicle to a carbon canister in the front right-hand corner of the engine compartment.

Further information on the evaporative emission control system is contained in Part E of this Chapter.

11 Fuel tank filler pipe - removal and refitting

Refer to Part A, Section 11.

12 Fuel cut-off switch - removal and refitting

Refer to Part B, Section 12.

13 Fuel injection system - checking

Refer to Part B, Section 13

14 Fuel injection system components - removal and refitting

Note: *Refer to the warning note in Section 1 before proceeding.*

Fuel rail and injectors

Note: *For simplicity, and to ensure that the necessary absolute cleanliness on reassembly, the following procedure describes the removal of the fuel rail assembly, complete with the injectors and pressure regulator, so that the injectors can be serviced individually on a* clean work surface. It is also possible to remove and refit an individual injector, once the fuel system has been depressurised and the battery has been disconnected. If this approach is followed, read through the complete procedure, and work as described in the relevant paragraphs, depending on the amount of preliminary dismantling required. Be careful not to allow any dirt to enter the system.

1 Relieve the residual pressure in the fuel system (see Section 2), and equalise tank pressure by removing the fuel filler cap.

!!! **Warning:** *This procedure will merely relieve the increased pressure necessary for the engine to run - remember that fuel will still be present in the system components, and take precautions accordingly before disconnecting any of them.*

2 Disconnect the battery negative (earth) lead (refer to Chapter 5A, Section 1).

3 Disconnect the HT lead connectors from the spark plugs, and release the leads from their locating grooves in the air inlet duct. Position them out of the way. On Turbo models, undo the two screws and remove the HT lead bracket.

4 Remove the air inlet components as described in Section 4.

5 Unscrew the retaining nuts and the bolt, and detach the accelerator cable support bracket at the throttle housing.

6 Disconnect the wiring connector from the throttle position sensor.

7 Unscrew the four retaining bolts, and remove the throttle housing and its mating face gasket **(see illustration)**.

8 Disconnect the wiring multi-plug from the engine coolant temperature sensor and the inlet air temperature sensor.

9 Disconnect the wiring multi-plugs from the fuel injectors, then undo the two retaining bolts and detach the wiring harness from the fuel rail **(see illustrations)**.

10 Unscrew the fuel supply pipe at the fuel rail. Plug the rail and pipe, to prevent further fuel spillage and the possible ingress of dirt.

11 Disconnect the fuel return and vacuum pipes from the pressure regulator, and catch any fuel spillage in a clean cloth.

12 Unscrew the fuel rail securing bolts, and carefully withdraw the rail (complete with injectors) from the engine **(see illustrations)**.

4C

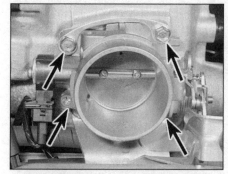

14.7 Throttle housing retaining bolt locations (arrowed)

14.9a Disconnect the wiring multi-plug from each injector . . .

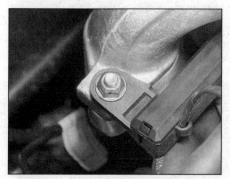

14.9b . . . unbolt the wiring harness . . .

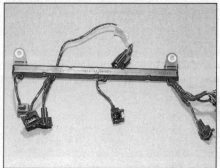

14.9c . . . and remove the complete harness

14.12a Remove the fuel rail retaining bolts . . .

14.12b ... and withdraw the fuel rail and injectors

14.13 Remove the seals from the injectors

13 Detach the fuel injectors from the fuel rail, then remove the upper and lower seal from each injector **(see illustration)**. All seals must be renewed (even if only one injector is to be renewed).

14 Prior to refitting the injectors, ensure that all mating surfaces are perfectly clean. Lubricate the new injector seals with clean engine oil to ease their assembly to the injectors.

15 Refitting is a reversal of the removal procedure. Refer to the *Specifications* at the start of this Chapter for the tightening torques. When refitting the fuel rail, ensure that the injectors are correctly located. Ensure that the mating surfaces of the throttle housing are perfectly clean before assembling.

16 On completion, restart the engine and check the various fuel connections for any signs of leaks.

Fuel pressure regulator

17 Relieve the residual pressure in the fuel system (see Section 2), and equalise tank pressure by removing the fuel filler cap.

 Warning: This procedure will merely relieve the increased pressure necessary for the engine to run - remember that fuel will still be present in the system components, and take precautions accordingly before disconnecting any of them.

18 Disconnect the battery negative (earth) lead (refer to Chapter 5A, Section 1).

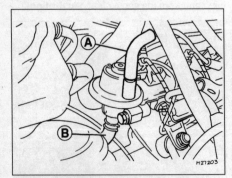

14.20 Fuel pressure regulator showing vacuum pipe (A) and fuel return pipe connection (B)

19 Release the fuel return pipe securing clip, and detach the pipe from the regulator.

20 Pull free the vacuum pipe from the regulator connector **(see illustration)**.

21 Unscrew the two retaining bolts and remove the regulator. Remove the old sealing ring for renewal.

22 Refit in the reverse order of removal. Lubricate the new seal ring with clean engine oil to ease assembly. When the regulator is refitted and the fuel and vacuum lines are reconnected, turn the ignition on and off five times (without cranking the engine) and check for any sign of fuel leaks before restarting the engine.

Idle speed control valve

Note: *The idle speed control valve may be mounted on the air cleaner, on the engine compartment bulkhead, or on the side of the inlet manifold according to valve make and year of manufacture. Valves manufactured by Weber are mounted on the air cleaner and require periodic maintenance (see Chapter 1). Bulkhead and inlet manifold mounted valves are manufactured by Hitachi and are maintenance free.*

23 Disconnect the battery negative (earth) lead (refer to Chapter 5A, Section 1).

24 Disconnect the valve's wiring multiplug **(see illustration)**.

25 Where applicable disconnect the air hose(s) from the valve.

26 Undo the two or four bolts (according to type), and remove the valve from the air cleaner, bulkhead or inlet manifold.

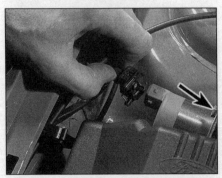

14.24 Disconnect the multi-plug from the idle speed control valve. Upper valve retaining bolt (arrowed)

27 Refitting is a reversal of the removal procedure. Ensure that the mating faces are clean before reassembling.

28 When the valve is refitted, restart the engine and check that there are no induction leaks. Run the engine until its normal operating temperature is reached, and check that the idle speed is stable. Stop the engine, connect up a tachometer in accordance with its maker's instructions, then restart the engine and check that the idle speed is as specified with all electrical items (lights, heater blower motor, etc) switched off, then on. The idle speed should remain the same. Switch off the electrical items, turn the engine off and detach the tachometer to complete the test.

Throttle housing

29 Disconnect the battery negative (earth) lead (refer to Chapter 5A, Section 1).

30 Disconnect the ignition HT lead connectors from the spark plugs, and release the leads from their locating grooves in the air inlet duct. Position them out of the way.

31 Remove the air inlet components as described in Section 4.

32 Unscrew the retaining nuts and the bolt, and detach the accelerator cable support bracket at the throttle housing.

33 Disconnect the wiring connector from the throttle position sensor.

34 Unscrew the four retaining bolts, and remove the throttle housing and its mating face gasket **(see illustration 14.7)**.

35 Refit in the reverse order of removal. Check that the mating faces are clean, and fit a new gasket.

EEC IV engine management module

Note: *The module is fragile. Take care not to drop it, or subject it to any other kind of impact. Do not subject it to extremes of temperature, or allow it to get wet. Refer to Part B, Section 14 for illustrations of the following procedure.*

36 Disconnect the battery negative (earth) lead (refer to Chapter 5A, Section 1).

37 Unscrew and remove the two nuts securing the module cover in the engine compartment, then carefully draw the cover away from its location. Unscrew the module multi-plug retaining bolt and disconnect the multi-plug from the module.

38 The aid of an assistant will be required at this stage, to support and withdraw the module from inside the passenger compartment as its mounting bracket retaining tags are compressed and released from the engine compartment. Do not allow the module to drop into the passenger compartment as irreparable damage is likely to result. The module may be separated from its mounting bracket by undoing the securing bolts.

39 Refitting is a reversal of the removal procedure, ensuring that the module mounting bracket retaining tags are felt to snap into position

14.43 Disconnecting the intake air temperature sensor multi-plug

14.46 Disconnect the multi-plug from the throttle position sensor. Sensor retaining screws (arrowed)

Crankshaft position sensor

40 Refer to Chapter 5B.

Coolant temperature sensor

41 Refer to Chapter 3.

Inlet air temperature sensor

42 Remove the air inlet components as described in Section 4.
43 Releasing its clip, unplug the sensor's electrical connector, then unscrew the sensor from the inlet manifold **(see illustration)**.
44 Refitting is the reverse of the removal procedure.

Throttle position sensor

45 Remove the air inlet components as described in Section 4.
46 Releasing its wire clip, unplug the sensor's electrical connector. Remove the retaining screws, and withdraw the unit from the throttle housing **(see illustration)**. *Do not force the sensor's centre to rotate past its normal operating sweep; the unit will be seriously damaged.*
47 Refitting is the reverse of the removal procedure, noting the following points **(see illustration)**:
a) *Ensure that the potentiometer is correctly orientated, by locating its centre on the D-shaped throttle shaft (throttle closed), and*

aligning the potentiometer body so that the bolts pass easily into the throttle housing.
b) Tighten the screws evenly and securely (but do not overtighten them, or the potentiometer body will be cracked).

Vehicle speed sensor

48 The sensor is mounted at the base of the speedometer drive cable, and is removed with the speedometer drive pinion. Refer to the relevant Section of Chapter 7A or B, as applicable.

Manifold absolute pressure sensor

49 The sensor is located near the centre of the engine compartment bulkhead.
50 Disconnect the wiring multi-plug, and detach the vacuum hose from the base of the sensor.
51 Undo the two retaining screws, and withdraw the sensor from its location.
52 Refitting is the reverse of the removal procedure.

Power steering pressure switch

53 Releasing its clip, unplug the switch's electrical connector, then unscrew the switch from the power steering high pressure pipe. Place a wad of rag underneath, to catch any

spilt fluid. If a sealing washer is fitted, renew it if it is worn or damaged.
54 Refitting is the reverse of the removal procedure; tighten the switch securely, then top-up the fluid reservoir (see *"Weekly Checks"*) to replace any fluid lost from the system, and bleed out any trapped air (see Chapter 10).

Oxygen sensor

Note: *The sensor is delicate, and will not work if it is dropped or knocked, if its power supply is disrupted, or if any cleaning materials are used on it.*
55 Release the sensor's wiring multi-plug from its bracket below the starter motor, and unplug it to disconnect the sensor.
56 Raise and support the front of the vehicle if required to remove the sensor from underneath ("see *Jacking and vehicle support*"). Remove the sensor heat shields then unscrew the sensor from the exhaust system front downpipe; collect the sealing washer (where fitted).
57 On refitting, clean the sealing washer (where fitted) and renew it if it is damaged or worn. Apply a smear of anti-seize compound to the sensor's threads, to prevent them from welding themselves to the downpipe in service. Refit the sensor, tightening it to its specified torque wrench setting; a slotted socket will be required to do this. Reconnect the wiring, and refit the connector plug.

Fuel mixture/CO% adjustment potentiometer

58 The fuel mixture/CO% adjustment potentiometer is located on the engine compartment bulkhead below the ignition module.
59 Disconnect the battery negative (earth) lead (refer to Chapter 5A, Section 1).
60 Disconnect the potentiometer's wiring multiplug **(see illustration)**.
61 Unscrew the retaining screw and remove the potentiometer from the bulkhead.
62 Refitting is the reverse of the removal procedure.

4C

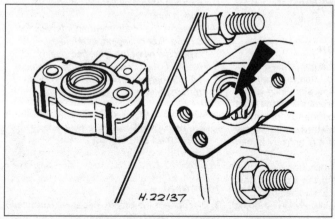

14.47 General view of the throttle position sensor and its "D" shaped throttle spindle location (arrowed)

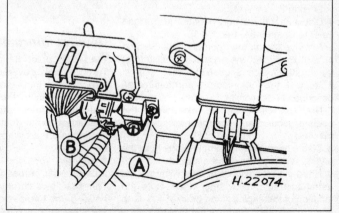

14.60 Fuel mixture/CO% adjustment potentiometer
A Securing screw   B Multi-plug

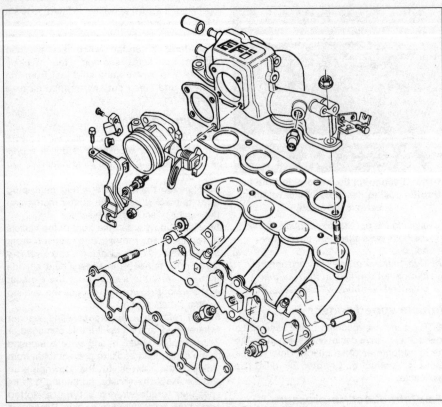

15.1 Exploded view of the inlet manifold arrangement

15 Inlet manifold - removal and refitting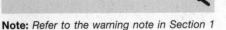

Note: *Refer to the warning note in Section 1 before proceeding.*

Removal

1 The inlet manifold is a two-piece assembly comprising an upper and lower section bolted together **(see illustration)**.
2 Drain the cooling system with reference to Chapter 1.
3 Depressurise the fuel system as described in Section 2.
4 Disconnect the battery negative (earth) lead (refer to Chapter 5A, Section 1).
5 Remove the air inlet components (Section 4) and disconnect the accelerator cable from the throttle linkage (Section 5).
6 Remove the fuel injectors and fuel rail as described in Section 14.
7 Noting their locations, disconnect the coolant, vacuum and breather hoses from the manifold.
8 Disconnect the wiring multi-plugs from the engine sensors at the inlet manifold.
9 Undo the retaining bolts, and withdraw the manifold from the cylinder head. Note the location of the engine lifting bracket and earth lead, where fitted. Remove the gasket.
10 With the manifold removed, clean all traces of the old gasket from the mating surfaces of the manifold and the cylinder head.

Refitting

11 Refitting is the reversal of removal. Use a new gasket, and tighten the retaining bolts to the specified torque **(see illustration)**. Refit the remainder of the components with reference to the appropriate Chapters of this manual. Refill the cooling system as described in Chapter 1 on completion.

16 Turbocharger - general information and precautions

General information

1 A water-cooled turbocharger is used on all Turbo models covered by this manual. The turbocharger increases the efficiency of the engine by raising the pressure in the inlet manifold above atmospheric pressure. Instead of the air/fuel mixture being simply sucked into the cylinders it is actively forced in.
2 Energy for the operation of the turbocharger comes from the exhaust gas. The gas flows through a specially-shaped housing (the turbine housing) and in so doing spins the turbine wheel. The turbine wheel is attached to a shaft, at the other end of which is another vaned wheel known as the compressor wheel. The compressor wheel spins in its own housing and compresses the inducted air on the way to the inlet manifold.
3 After leaving the turbocharger, the compressed air passes through an intercooler, which is an air-to-air heat exchanger mounted with the radiator. Here the air gives up heat which it acquired when being compressed. This temperature reduction improves engine efficiency and reduces the risk of detonation.
4 Boost pressure (the pressure in the inlet manifold) is limited by the turbocharger wastegate control, which diverts the exhaust gas away from the turbine wheel in response to the boost control valve. The valve is controlled by the EEC IV engine management module.
5 The turbo shaft is pressure-lubricated by means of a feed pipe from the engine's main oil gallery. The shaft "floats" on a cushion of oil. A drain pipe returns the oil to the sump.
6 Water cooling reduces the operating temperature of the turbocharger, and in particular, the shaft bearings. Water continues to circulate by convection after the engine has stopped, so cooling the unit if it is hot after a long run.

Precautions

7 The turbocharger operates at extremely high speeds and temperatures. Certain precautions must be observed to avoid premature failure of the turbo or injury to the operator.

a) *Do not operate the turbo with any parts exposed. Foreign objects falling onto the rotating vanes could cause extensive damage and (if ejected) personal injury.*
b) *Do not race the engine immediately after start-up, especially if it is cold. Give the oil a few seconds to circulate.*
c) *Always allow the engine to return to idle speed before switching it off - do not blip the throttle and switch off, as this will leave the turbo spinning without lubrication.*
d) *Allow the engine to idle for several minutes before switching off after a high-speed run.*
e) *Observe the recommended intervals for oil and filter changing, and use a reputable oil of the specified quality. Neglect of oil changing, or use of inferior oil, can cause carbon formation on the turbo shaft and subsequent failure.*

17 Intercooler - removal and refitting

Removal

1 Disconnect the battery negative (earth) lead (refer to Chapter 5A, Section 1).
2 Remove the flexible hose connecting the intercooler to the air inlet duct, then the pipe

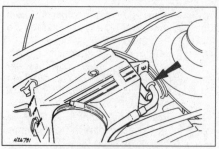

18.2 Location of turbo boost control valve (arrowed)

and flexible hose connecting the turbocharger to the intercooler **(see illustration 4.12)**. Use adhesive tape to seal the turbocharger ports against the entry of dirt.

3 Unbolt the horn nearest the intercooler.

4 Unbolt the radiator/intercooler assembly from the bonnet closure panel and the body crossmember.

5 Move the assembly as far as possible towards the engine, and unbolt the intercooler from the radiator; withdraw the intercooler.

Refitting

6 Refitting is the reverse of the removal procedure, tightening all nuts and bolts to the specified torque settings, and not forgetting to unseal the turbocharger openings before reconnecting the intercooler pipe and hose.

18 Turbocharger boost control valve - removal and refitting

Removal

1 Disconnect the battery negative (earth) lead (refer to Chapter 5A, Section 1).

2 Disconnect the control valve wiring at its multi-plug **(see illustration)**.

3 Marking or labelling the valve hoses so that each can be reconnected to its original union, disconnect the hoses from the valve.

4 Remove the securing screws and withdraw the valve.

Refitting

5 Refitting is the reverse of the removal procedure; tighten the screws to the specified torque setting.

19 Turbocharger boost pressure - checking and adjustment

Accurate checking and adjustment of the turbocharger boost pressure requires

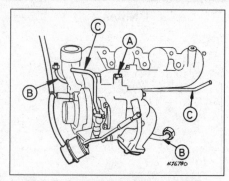

20.4 Turbocharger/exhaust manifold assembly details

A *Exhaust manifold-to-turbocharger bolts*
B *Oil pipes*
C *Coolant pipes (metal)*

considerable skill and experience and the use of Ford special tools and diagnostic test equipment. This work should therefore be entrusted to a Ford dealer or performance engine specialist.

20 Turbocharger - removal, examination and refitting

Removal

1 Disconnect the battery negative (earth) lead (refer to Chapter 5A, Section 1).

2 Drain the cooling system as described in Chapter 1.

3 Remove the air inlet components as described in Section 4.

4 Disconnect the turbocharger coolant feed and return hoses by slackening the clamps and pulling the hoses off the turbocharger's metal pipes **(see illustration)**.

5 Remove the pipe and flexible hoses connecting the turbocharger to the air cleaner and intercooler. Use adhesive tape to seal the turbocharger ports against the entry of dirt.

6 Disconnect the turbocharger oil feed and return pipes by unscrewing the couplings.

7 Remove its three retaining screws and withdraw the exhaust manifold heat shield.

8 Disconnect the exhaust system downpipe from the turbocharger, then disconnect the hose from the boost control valve to the turbocharger wastegate control actuator.

9 Unscrew the exhaust manifold nuts, and withdraw the manifold and turbocharger as an assembly, protecting the radiator with cardboard or similar.

10 To separate the turbocharger from the manifold, flatten back the raised lockwasher

tabs and unscrew the three retaining bolts. Disconnect the turbocharger oil and coolant pipes if required. This is as far as the unit can be dismantled; **do not** disturb the wastegate or its actuator and linkage.

Examination

11 With the turbocharger in the vehicle, check that there are no air leaks around any part of the air inlet components, and that the boost control valve hoses are intact and securely fastened.

12 With the turbocharger removed, check the turbine wheels and blades (as far as possible) for signs of wear or damage. Spin the turbine and check that it rotates smoothly and easily, with no sign of roughness, free play or abnormal noise. If possible, check for axial play (endfloat) of the shaft. Check that the wastegate, its actuator and linkage show no visible signs of wear, damage or stiffness due to dirt and corrosion.

13 If any sign of wear or damage is found, the turbocharger must be renewed.

Refitting

14 Refitting is the reverse of the removal procedure, noting the following points:

a) *Refit the oil and coolant pipes, tightening the unions to the specified torque settings.*

b) *Always use new lockwashers when refitting the turbocharger to the manifold; again, tighten the bolts to their specified torque setting.*

c) *Protect the radiator when refitting the assembly, and always fit a new exhaust manifold gasket.*

d) *Ensure that the oil feed and return pipes are absolutely clean before reconnecting them and tightening them to the specified torque setting.*

e) *Owners are well advised to change the engine oil and filter whenever the turbocharger is disturbed (see Chapter 1).*

f) *When reassembly is complete and the cooling system refilled (see Chapter 1), disable the ignition system by disconnecting the E-DIS ignition coil wiring multi-plug, then turn the engine over on the starter motor until the oil pressure light goes out. This is essential to ensure that the turbocharger oil supply is established BEFORE the engine is started; do not forget to reconnect the coil before attempting to start the engine*

4C

Notes

Chapter 4 Part D: Fuel system - sequential electronic fuel injection engines

Contents

Accelerator cable - removal, refitting and adjustment 5
Accelerator pedal - removal and refitting 6
Air cleaner assembly and air inlet components - removal and
    refitting 4
Air cleaner element renewal . . . . See Chapter 1
Fuel cut-off switch - removal and refitting 12
Fuel filter renewal . . . . See Chapter 1
Fuel injection system - checking 13
Fuel injection system components - removal and refitting 14
Fuel lines and fittings - general information 3
Fuel pump/fuel gauge sender unit - removal and refitting 9

Fuel pump/fuel pressure - checking 7
Fuel system - depressurisation 2
Fuel tank - removal, inspection and refitting 8
Fuel tank filler pipe - removal and refitting 11
Fuel tank ventilation tube - removal and refitting 10
General fuel system checks . . . . See Chapter 1
General information and precautions 1
Inlet manifold - removal and refitting 15
Underbody fuel/brake line check . . . . See Chapter 1
Underbonnet check for fluid leaks and hose condition . . See Chapter 1

Degrees of difficulty

| **Easy,** suitable for novice with little experience | | **Fairly easy,** suitable for beginner with some experience | | **Fairly difficult,** suitable for competent DIY mechanic | | **Difficult,** suitable for experienced DIY mechanic | | **Very difficult,** suitable for expert DIY or professional | |

Specifications

General

System type	Sequential Electronic Fuel injection (SEFi)
Application	1.4 litre PTE engines and 1.6 and 1.8 litre Zetec engines

Fuel grade

Fuel octane requirement	95 RON unleaded

Fuel pressure

Regulated fuel pressure:*

Pressure regulator vacuum hose disconnected	2.7 ± 0.2 bars
With engine running and pressure regulator vacuum hose connected	2.1 ± 0.2 bars
Hold pressure - engine stopped after five minutes*	1.8 bars minimum

*The figures quoted are specific to Zetec engines. No values are quoted by the manufacturer for PTE engines, however they are likely to be similar.

Torque wrench settings

	Nm	lbf ft
PTE engines		
Inlet air duct to cylinder head cover	9	7
Inlet manifold to cylinder head	18	13
Inlet manifold upper to lower sections	18	13
Inlet air temperature sensor	15	11
Fuel rail-to-lower inlet manifold	23	17
Camshaft position sensor	6	4
Oxygen sensor	60	44
Zetec engines		
Throttle housing-to-inlet manifold screws	9	7
Inlet manifold to cylinder head	18	13
Idle speed control valve bolts	6	4
Inlet air temperature sensor	15	11
Fuel pressure regulator bolts	6	4
Fuel injector bolts	6	4
Fuel rail-to-inlet manifold bolts	9	7
Camshaft position sensor	8	6
Oxygen sensor	60	44

4D

1 General information and precautions

General information

The fuel system consists of a fuel tank (mounted under the body, beneath the rear seats), fuel hoses, an electric fuel pump mounted in the fuel tank, and a sequential electronic fuel injection system.

The electric fuel pump supplies fuel under pressure to the fuel rail, which distributes fuel evenly to all injectors. A pressure regulator controls the system pressure in relation to inlet tract depression. From the fuel rail, fuel is injected into the inlet ports, just above the inlet valves, by four fuel injectors. The system also includes features such as the flushing of fresh (ie, cold) fuel around each injector on start-up, thus improving hot starts.

The amount of fuel supplied by the injectors is precisely controlled by the EEC IV engine management module. The module uses the signals derived from the crankshaft position sensor and the camshaft position sensor, to trigger each injector separately in cylinder firing order (sequential injection), with benefits in terms of better fuel economy and lower exhaust emissions.

The EEC IV module is the heart of the entire engine management system, controlling the fuel injection, ignition and emissions control systems. The module receives information from various sensors which is then computed and compared with pre-set values stored in it's memory, to determine the required period of injection.

Information on crankshaft position and engine speed is generated by a crankshaft position sensor. The inductive head of the sensor runs just above the engine flywheel and scans a series of 36 protrusions on the flywheel periphery. As the crankshaft rotates, the sensor transmits a pulse to the system's ignition module every time a protrusion passes it. There is one missing protrusion in the flywheel periphery at a point corresponding to 90° BTDC. The ignition module recognises the absence of a pulse from the crankshaft position sensor at this point to establish a reference mark for crankshaft position. Similarly, the time interval between absent pulses is used to determine engine speed. This information is then fed to the EEC IV module for further processing.

The camshaft position sensor is located in the cylinder head so that it registers with a lobe on the camshaft. The camshaft position sensor functions in the same way as the crankshaft position sensor, producing a series of pulses; this gives the EEC IV module a reference point, to enable it to determine the firing order, and operate the injectors in the appropriate sequence.

The mass air flow sensor is based on a "hot-wire" system, sending the EEC IV module a constantly-varying (analogue) voltage signal corresponding to the mass of air passing into the engine. Since air mass varies with temperature (cold air being denser than warm), measuring air mass provides the module with a very accurate means of determining the correct amount of fuel required to achieve the ideal air/fuel mixture ratio.

Engine temperature information is supplied by the coolant temperature sensor. This component is an NTC (Negative Temperature Coefficient) thermistor - that is, a semi-conductor whose electrical resistance decreases as its temperature increases. It provides the EEC IV module with a constantly-varying (analogue) voltage signal, corresponding to the temperature of the engine coolant. This is used to refine the calculations made by the module, when determining the correct amount of fuel required to achieve the ideal air/fuel mixture ratio.

Inlet air temperature information is supplied by the inlet air temperature sensor. This component is also an NTC thermistor - see the previous paragraph - providing the module with a signal corresponding to the temperature of air passing into the engine. This is used to refine the calculations made by the module, when determining the correct amount of fuel required to achieve the ideal air/fuel mixture ratio.

A throttle position sensor is mounted on the end of the throttle valve spindle, to provide the EEC IV module with a constantly-varying (analogue) voltage signal corresponding to the throttle opening. This allows the module to register the driver's input when determining the amount of fuel required by the engine.

Road speed is monitored by the vehicle speed sensor. This component is a Hall-effect generator, mounted on the transmission's speedometer drive. It supplies the module with a series of pulses corresponding to the vehicle's road speed, enabling the module to control features such as the fuel shut-off on overrun.

Where power steering is fitted, a pressure-operated switch is screwed into the power steering system's high-pressure pipe. The switch sends a signal to the EEC IV module to reduce engine speed should the power steering fluid pressure become excessively high.

The oxygen sensor in the exhaust system provides the module with constant feedback - "closed-loop" control - which enables it to adjust the mixture to provide the best possible conditions for the catalytic converter to operate.

The air inlet side of the system consists of an air cleaner housing, the mass air flow sensor, an inlet hose and duct, and a throttle housing.

The throttle valve inside the throttle housing is controlled by the driver, through the accelerator pedal. As the valve opens, the amount of air that can pass through the system increases. As the throttle valve opens further, the mass air flow sensor signal alters, and the EEC IV module opens each injector for a longer duration, to increase the amount of fuel delivered to the inlet ports.

Both the idle speed and mixture are under the control of the EEC IV module, and cannot be adjusted. Not only can they not be adjusted, they cannot even be checked, except with the use of special Ford diagnostic equipment.

Precautions

⚠️ *Warning: Petrol is extremely flammable - great care must be taken when working on any part of the fuel system. Do not smoke or allow any naked flames or uncovered light bulbs near the work area. Note that gas powered domestic appliances with pilot flames, such as heaters, boilers and tumble dryers, also present a fire hazard - bear this in mind if you are working in an area where such appliances are present. Always keep a suitable fire extinguisher close to the work area and familiarise yourself with its operation before starting work. Wear eye protection when working on fuel systems and wash off any fuel spilt on bare skin immediately with soap and water. Note that fuel vapour is just as dangerous as liquid fuel; a vessel that has just been emptied of liquid fuel will still contain vapour and can be potentially explosive. Petrol is a highly dangerous and volatile liquid, and the precautions necessary when handling it cannot be overstressed.*

Many of the operations described in this Chapter involve the disconnection of fuel lines, which may cause an amount of fuel spillage. Before commencing work, refer to the above Warning and the information in "Safety first" at the beginning of this manual.

When working with fuel system components, pay particular attention to cleanliness - dirt entering the fuel system may cause blockages which will lead to poor running.

Note: *Residual pressure will remain in the fuel lines long after the vehicle was last used, when disconnecting any fuel line, it will be necessary to depressurise the fuel system as described in Section 2.*

2 Fuel system - depressurisation

Refer to Part B, Section 2.

3 Fuel lines and fittings - general information

Refer to Part B, Section 3.

4.2a Disconnect the mass air flow sensor wiring multi-plug . . .

4.2b . . . release the retaining clips . . .

4.2c . . . and withdraw the sensor

4 Air cleaner assembly and air inlet components - removal and refitting

Air cleaner assembly

1 Disconnect the battery negative (earth) lead (refer to Chapter 5A, Section 1).
2 Disconnect the mass air flow sensor wiring multi-plug, then release the clips and withdraw the sensor, complete with inlet hose, from the air cleaner cover **(see illustrations)**. Carefully position the mass air flow sensor and hose assembly to one side.
3 Detach the fresh air inlet duct from the air cleaner housing.
4 Unscrew the air cleaner housing retaining nut, then pull the housing upwards to release the locating pegs from their rubber grommets. As the housing is withdrawn, detach the crankcase breather hose **(see illustration)**. Remove the assembly from the car.
5 Refitting is the reverse of the removal procedure. Ensure that the housing pegs seat fully in their grommets, and that the mass air flow sensor is correctly located.

Air inlet components

6 On PTE engines, disconnect the HT leads from the spark plugs, labelling them if necessary to avoid confusion on refitting.
7 Slacken the hose clip, and detach the

flexible air inlet hose from the mass air flow sensor.
8 On PTE engines, disconnect the ventilation hose from the inlet duct over the top of the engine.
9 On PTE engines undo the two inlet duct retaining bolts; On Zetec engines , undo the two bolts and lift off the air inlet duct retaining strap **(see illustration)**. Withdraw the inlet duct from the throttle housing and remove the duct and flexible hose from the engine.
10 Refitting is the reverse of the removal procedure.

5 Accelerator cable - removal, refitting and adjustment

Removal

1 Disconnect the battery negative (earth) lead (refer to Chapter 5A, Section 1).
2 Fold back the carpet and insulation in the driver's footwell to gain access to the accelerator pedal.
3 Detach the accelerator cable from the pedal.
4 From within the engine compartment, detach the outer cable from the adjuster/support bracket by removing the metal retaining clip **(see illustration)**.

5 Pivot the throttle quadrant by hand, detach the inner cable nipple from the throttle lever and remove the cable.

Refitting

6 Refit in the reverse order of removal. When the cable is reconnected at each end, adjust the cable as follows.

Adjustment

7 Remove the outer cable metal retaining clip at the adjuster/support bracket and lubricate the cable adjuster grommet with soapy water.
8 Remove any slack by pulling the cable outer as far as possible out of the adjuster. Have an assistant depress the accelerator pedal fully - the cable outer will move back into the adjuster - and hold it there while the clip is refitted.
9 Check that the throttle quadrant moves smoothly and easily from the fully-closed to the fully-open position and back again as the assistant depresses and releases the accelerator pedal. Re-adjust the cable if required.

6 Accelerator pedal - removal and refitting

Refer to Part A, Section 5.

4.4 Unscrew front retaining nut and lift the air cleaner housing, disconnecting the breather hose (arrowed)

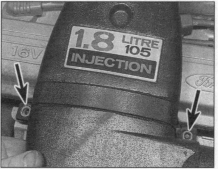

4.9 Unscrew the nuts (arrowed) to release the air intake duct on Zetec engines

5.4 Detach the accelerator outer cable retaining clip (arrowed)

4D

7 Fuel pump/fuel pressure - checking

Note: *Refer to the warning note in Section 1 before proceeding.*

Fuel pump operation check

1 Switch on the ignition, and listen for the fuel pump (the sound of an electric motor running, audible from beneath the rear seats). Assuming there is sufficient fuel in the tank, the pump should start and run for approximately one or two seconds, then stop, each time the ignition is switched on. **Note:** *If the pump runs continuously all the time the ignition is switched on, the electronic control system is running in the backup (or "limp-home") mode referred to by Ford as "Limited Operation Strategy" (LOS). This almost certainly indicates a fault in the EEC IV module itself, and the vehicle should therefore be taken to a Ford dealer for a full test of the complete system, using the correct diagnostic equipment; do not waste time or risk damaging the components by trying to test the system without such facilities.*

2 Listen for fuel return noises from the fuel pressure regulator. It should be possible to feel the fuel pulsing in the regulator and in the feed hose from the fuel filter.

3 If the pump does not run at all, check the fuse, relay and wiring (see Chapter 12). Check also that the fuel cut-off switch has not been activated and if so, reset it.

Fuel pressure check

4 A fuel pressure gauge will be required for this check and should be connected in the fuel line between the fuel filter and the fuel rail, in accordance with the gauge maker's instructions. On Zetec engines, a pressure gauge equipped with an adapter to suit the Schrader-type valve on the fuel rail pressure test/release fitting (identifiable by its blue plastic cap, and located on the union of the fuel feed line and the fuel rail) will be required. If the Ford special tool 29-033 is available, the tool can be attached to the valve, and a conventional-type pressure gauge attached to the tool.

5 If using the service tool, ensure that its tap is turned fully anti-clockwise, then attach it to the valve. Connect the pressure gauge to the service tool. If using a fuel pressure gauge with its own adapter, connect it in accordance with its maker's instructions.

6 Start the engine and allow it to idle. Note the gauge reading as soon as the pressure stabilises, and compare it with the regulated fuel pressure figures listed in the *Specifications*.

a) If the pressure is high, check for a restricted fuel return line. If the line is clear, renew the fuel pressure regulator.

b) If the pressure is low, pinch the fuel return line. If the pressure now goes up, renew

the fuel pressure regulator. If the pressure does not increase, check the fuel feed line, the fuel pump and the fuel filter.

7 Detach the vacuum hose from the fuel pressure regulator; the pressure shown on the gauge should increase. Note the increase in pressure, and compare it with that listed in the *Specifications*. If the pressure increase is not as specified, check the vacuum hose and pressure regulator.

8 Reconnect the regulator vacuum hose, and switch off the engine. Verify that the hold pressure stays at the specified level for five minutes after the engine is turned off.

9 Carefully disconnect the fuel pressure gauge, depressurising the system first as described in Section 2. Be sure to cover the fitting with a rag before slackening it. Mop up any spilt petrol.

10 Run the engine, and check that there are no fuel leaks.

8 Fuel tank - removal, inspection and refitting

Proceed as described in Part A, Section 8, but before disconnecting the battery, relieve the residual pressure in the fuel system (see Section 2), and equalise tank pressure by removing the fuel filler cap.

9 Fuel pump/fuel gauge sender unit - removal and refitting

Refer to Part B, Section 9.

10 Fuel tank ventilation tube - removal and refitting

Refer to Part A, Section 10, but note that the ventilation tube connects to the combined roll-over/anti-trickle-fill valve assembly but, instead of venting to atmosphere, a further tube runs the length of the vehicle to the evaporative emission control system carbon

canister in the front right-hand corner of the engine compartment.

Further information on the evaporative emission control system is contained in Part E of this Chapter.

11 Fuel tank filler pipe - removal and refitting

Refer to Part A, Section 11.

12 Fuel cut-off switch - removal and refitting

Refer to Part B, Section 12.

13 Fuel injection system - checking

Refer to Part B, Section 13

14 Fuel injection system components - removal and refitting

Note: *Refer to the warning note in Section 1 before proceeding.*

Throttle housing

1 Disconnect the battery negative (earth) lead (refer to Chapter 5A, Section 1).

2 Remove the air inlet components as described in Section 4.

3 Disconnect the accelerator cable from the throttle linkage (see Section 5).

4 Disconnect the throttle position sensor multi-plug.

5 Unscrew the retaining bolts, and detach the accelerator cable support bracket at the throttle housing **(see illustration)**.

6 Unscrew the throttle housing-to-manifold retaining bolts **(see illustration)**, and unbolt the throttle housing support bracket bolts (where fitted). Remove the throttle housing

14.5 Unscrew the retaining bolts (arrowed), and detach the accelerator cable support bracket

14.6 Throttle housing retaining bolts (arrowed)

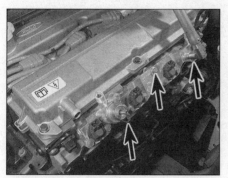

14.17a Unscrewing fuel rail mounting bolts (arrowed)

14.17b Note nose seals (arrowed) between rail and intermediate flange

14.18 Removing an injector from the fuel rail. Note the O-ring seals (arrowed)

and gasket. Discard the gasket - this must be renewed whenever it is disturbed.

7 Refit in the reverse order of removal. Check that the mating faces are clean, and fit a new gasket. Adjust the accelerator cable as described in Section 5 on completion.

Fuel rail and injectors

Note: *The following procedure is applicable mainly to Zetec engines; specific information for the PTE engine was not available at the time of writing. However, apart from minor differences in component attachments, both engine types are very similar in this area.*

8 Relieve the residual pressure in the fuel system (see Section 2), and equalise tank pressure by removing the fuel filler cap.

 Warning: This procedure will merely relieve the increased pressure necessary for the engine to run - remember that fuel will still be present in the system components, and take precautions accordingly before disconnecting any of them.

9 Disconnect the battery negative (earth) lead - see Chapter 5A, Section 1.

10 Remove the air inlet components as described in Section 4.

11 Disconnect the accelerator cable from the throttle linkage (see Section 5).

12 Disconnect the throttle position sensor multi-plug.

13 Remove the throttle housing mounting screws, then detach the throttle housing and

gasket from the inlet manifold. Discard the gasket - this must be renewed whenever it is disturbed.

14 Detach the crankcase breather hose from the cylinder head cover, and the fuel pressure regulator vacuum hose from the inlet manifold.

15 Releasing the wire clips, unplug the four fuel injector multi-plugs and the inlet air temperature sensor multi-plug.

16 Refer to Section 3 and disconnect the fuel feed and return lines at the quick-release couplings, then unclip the fuel hoses from the inlet manifold; use rag to soak up any spilt fuel. **Note:** *Do not disturb the threaded couplings at the fuel rail unions unless absolutely necessary; these are sealed at the factory. The quick-release couplings will suffice for all normal service operations.*

17 Unscrew the three bolts securing the fuel rail **(see illustration)**. Withdraw the rail, carefully prising it out of the inlet manifold, and draining any remaining fuel into a suitable clean container. Note the seals between the rail noses and the manifold; these must be renewed whenever the rail is removed **(see illustration)**.

18 Clamping the rail carefully in a vice fitted with soft jaws, unscrew the two bolts securing each injector, and withdraw the injectors **(see illustration)**. Place each in a clean, clearly-labelled storage container.

19 If the injector(s) are being renewed, discard the old injector, the nose seal and the O-rings. If only the injector O-rings are being

renewed, and it is intended that the same injectors will be re-used, remove the old nose seal and O-rings, and discard them.

20 Refitting is the reverse of the removal procedure, noting the following points:

a) *Lubricate each nose seal and O-ring with clean engine oil on installation.*

b) *Locate each injector carefully in the fuel rail recess, ensuring that the locating tab on the injector head fits into the slot provided in the rail. Tighten the bolts securely.*

c) *Fit a new seal to each fuel rail nose, and ensure that the seals are not displaced as the rail is refitted (see illustration). Ensure that the fuel rail is settled fully in the manifold before tightening the bolts.*

d) *Ensure that the hoses and wiring are routed correctly, and secured on reconnection by any clips or ties provided.*

e) *Adjust the accelerator cable as described in Section 5.*

f) *On completion, switch the ignition on and off five times, to activate the fuel pump and pressurise the system, without cranking the engine. Check for signs of fuel leaks around all disturbed unions and joints before attempting to start the engine.*

Fuel pressure regulator

21 Relieve the residual pressure in the fuel system (see Section 2), and equalise tank pressure by removing the fuel filler cap.

 Warning: This procedure will merely relieve the increased pressure necessary for the engine to run - remember that fuel will still be present in the system components, and take precautions accordingly before disconnecting any of them.

22 Disconnect the battery negative (earth) lead - see Chapter 5A, Section 1.

23 Disconnect the vacuum hose from the regulator.

24 Unscrew the two regulator retaining bolts **(see illustration)** then use a wad of clean rag to soak up any spilt fuel, and withdraw the regulator.

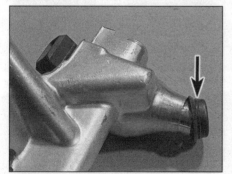

14.20 Fit new nose seals (arrowed) before refitting the fuel rail

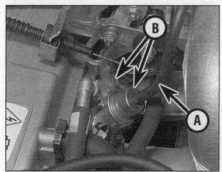

14.24 Fuel pressure regulator vacuum hose (A) and retaining bolts (B)

4D

14.27 Idle speed control valve wiring multi-plug (A) and visible mounting bolts (B)

25 Refitting is the reverse of the removal procedure, noting the following points:

a) Renew the regulator sealing O-ring whenever the regulator is disturbed. Lubricate the new O-ring with clean engine oil on installation.

b) Locate the regulator carefully in the fuel rail recess, and tighten the bolts securely.

c) On completion, switch the ignition on and off five times, to activate the fuel pump and pressurise the system, without cranking the engine. Check for signs of fuel leaks around all disturbed unions and joints before attempting to start the engine.

Idle speed control valve

26 Disconnect the battery negative (earth) lead (refer to Chapter 5A, Section 1).

27 Disconnect the valve's wiring multi-plug **(see illustration)**.

28 Unscrew the three retaining bolts, and withdraw the valve from the inlet manifold.

29 Refitting is the reverse of the removal procedure, noting the following points:

a) Clean the mating surfaces carefully, and always fit a new gasket whenever the valve is disturbed.

b) Once the wiring and battery are reconnected, start the engine and allow it to idle. When it has reached normal operating temperature, check that the idle speed is stable, and that no induction (air) leaks are evident. Switch on all electrical

loads (headlights, heated rear window, etc), and check that the idle speed is still satisfactory.

Mass air flow sensor

30 Releasing its wire clip, unplug the electrical connector from the sensor **(see illustration 4.2a)**.

31 Release the two clips and detach the sensor from the air cleaner cover **(see illustrations 4.2b and 4.2c)**.

32 Slacken the clamp securing the sensor to the air inlet hose, and withdraw the sensor.

33 Refitting is the reverse of the removal procedure. Ensure that the sensor and air cleaner cover are seated correctly and securely fastened, so that there are no air leaks.

EEC IV engine management module

Note: The module is fragile. Take care not to drop it, or subject it to any other kind of impact. Do not subject it to extremes of temperature, or allow it to get wet. Refer to Part B, Section 14 for illustrations of the following procedure.

34 Disconnect the battery negative (earth) lead (refer to Chapter 5A, Section 1).

35 Remove the cooling system expansion tank as described in Chapter 3, for access to the module multi-plug.

36 Unscrew and remove the two nuts securing the module cover in the engine compartment, then carefully draw the cover away from its location. Unscrew the module multi-plug retaining bolt and disconnect the multi-plug from the module.

37 The aid of an assistant will be required at this stage, to support and withdraw the module from inside the passenger compartment as its mounting bracket retaining tags are compressed and released from the engine compartment. Do not allow the module to drop into the passenger compartment as irreparable damage is likely to result. The module may be separated from its mounting bracket by undoing the securing bolts.

38 Refitting is a reversal of the removal procedure, ensuring that the module mounting bracket retaining tags are felt to

snap into position. Refit the expansion tank as described in Chapter 3 on completion.

Crankshaft position sensor

39 Refer to Chapter 5B.

Camshaft position sensor

40 Where applicable, release the fuel feed and return hoses from their clip. On PTE engines, detach the adjacent engine breather hose.

41 Releasing its wire clip, unplug the sensor's wiring multi-plug. Remove the retaining screw, and withdraw the sensor from the cylinder head; be prepared for slight oil loss **(see illustration)**.

42 Refitting is the reverse of the removal procedure, noting the following points:

a) Apply petroleum jelly or clean engine oil to the sensor's sealing O-ring.

b) Locate the sensor fully in the cylinder head, and wipe off any surplus lubricant before securing it.

c) Tighten the screw to the specified torque wrench setting.

Coolant temperature sensor

43 Refer to Chapter 3.

Inlet air temperature sensor

44 Releasing its clip, unplug the sensor's electrical connector, then unscrew the sensor from the inlet manifold **(see illustration)**.

45 Refitting is the reverse of the removal procedure.

Throttle position sensor

46 Releasing its wire clip, unplug the sensor's wiring multi-plug. Remove the retaining screws, and withdraw the unit from the throttle housing **(see illustration)**. Do not force the sensor's centre to rotate past its normal operating sweep; the unit will be seriously damaged.

47 Refitting is the reverse of the removal procedure, noting the following points:

a) Ensure that the sensor is correctly orientated, by locating its centre on the D-shaped throttle shaft (throttle closed), and aligning the sensor body so that the bolts pass easily into the throttle housing.

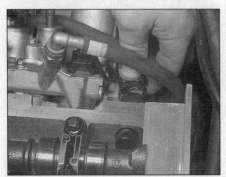

14.41 Disconnecting the camshaft position sensor wiring multi-plug (Zetec engine shown)

14.44 Removing the intake air temperature sensor from the rear of the inlet manifold (Zetec engine shown)

14.46 Throttle position sensor mounting screws (arrowed)

b) *Tighten the screws evenly and securely (but do not overtighten them, or the potentiometer body will be cracked).*

Vehicle speed sensor

48 The sensor is mounted at the base of the speedometer drive cable, and is removed with the speedometer drive pinion. Refer to the relevant Section of Chapter 7A or B, as applicable.

Power steering pressure switch

49 Releasing its clip, unplug the switch's electrical connector, then unscrew the switch from the power steering high pressure pipe. Place a wad of rag underneath, to catch any spilt fluid. If a sealing washer is fitted, renew it if it is worn or damaged.
50 Refitting is the reverse of the removal procedure; tighten the switch securely, then top-up the fluid reservoir (see *"Weekly Checks"*) to replace any fluid lost from the system, and bleed out any trapped air (see Chapter 10).

Oxygen sensor

Note: *The sensor is delicate, and will not work if it is dropped or knocked, if its power supply is disrupted, or if any cleaning materials are used on it.*

51 Raise and support the front of the vehicle if required to remove the sensor from underneath (*"see Jacking and vehicle support"*).
52 Release the sensor's wiring multi-plug from its support bracket, and unplug it to disconnect the sensor **(see illustration)**.
53 Unscrew the sensor from the exhaust system front downpipe; collect the sealing washer (where fitted).
54 On refitting, clean the sealing washer (where fitted) and renew it if it is damaged or worn. Apply a smear of anti-seize compound to the sensor's threads, to prevent them from welding themselves to the downpipe in service. Refit the sensor, tightening it to its specified torque wrench setting; a slotted socket will be required to do this. Reconnect the wiring, and refit the connector plug.

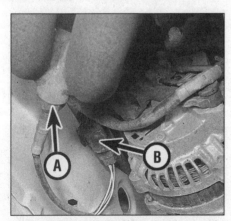

14.52 Oxygen sensor (A) and wiring multi-plug (B) (Zetec engine shown)

15 Inlet manifold - removal and refitting

Note: *Refer to the warning note in Section 1 before proceeding.*

Removal

PTE engines

1 The inlet manifold is a two-piece assembly comprising an upper and lower section bolted together.
2 Drain the cooling system with reference to Chapter 1.
3 Relieve the residual pressure in the fuel system (see Section 2), and equalise tank pressure by removing the fuel filler cap.

⚠ **Warning: This procedure will merely relieve the increased pressure necessary for the engine to run - remember that fuel will still be present in the system components, and take precautions accordingly before disconnecting any of them.**

4 Disconnect the battery negative (earth) lead (refer to Chapter 5A, Section 1).
5 Remove the air inlet components (Section 4) and disconnect the accelerator cable from the throttle linkage (Section 5).
6 Remove the fuel injectors and fuel rail as described in Section 14.
7 Noting their locations, disconnect the coolant, vacuum and breather hoses from the manifold.

8 Disconnect the wiring multi-plugs from the engine sensors at the inlet manifold.
9 Undo the retaining bolts, and withdraw the manifold from the cylinder head. Note the location of the engine lifting bracket and earth lead, where fitted. Remove the gasket.
10 With the manifold removed, clean all traces of the old gasket from the mating surfaces of the manifold and the cylinder head.

Zetec engines

11 Relieve the residual pressure in the fuel system (see Section 2), and equalise tank pressure by removing the fuel filler cap.

⚠ **Warning: This procedure will merely relieve the increased pressure necessary for the engine to run - remember that fuel will still be present in the system components, and take precautions accordingly before disconnecting any of them.**

12 Disconnect the battery negative (earth) lead (refer to Chapter 5A, Section 1).
13 Remove the air inlet components (Section 4) and disconnect the accelerator cable from the throttle linkage (Section 5).
14 Disconnect the crankcase breather hose from the cylinder head cover union.
15 Unbolt the upper part of the exhaust manifold heat shield.
16 Remove the two screws securing the wiring "rail" to the top of the manifold - this is simply so that it can be moved as required to reach the manifold bolts **(see illustration)**.

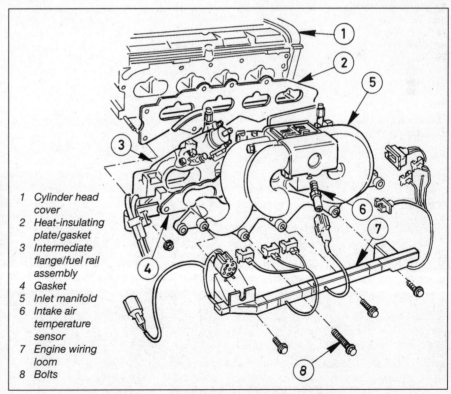

1 Cylinder head cover
2 Heat-insulating plate/gasket
3 Intermediate flange/fuel rail assembly
4 Gasket
5 Inlet manifold
6 Intake air temperature sensor
7 Engine wiring loom
8 Bolts

15.16 Exploded view of the Zetec engine inlet manifold components

4D

Unplug the electrical connectors at the camshaft position sensor and the coolant temperature sensor, then unclip the wiring from the ignition coil bracket, and secure it to the manifold.

17 Remove the three screws securing the wiring "rail" to the rear of the manifold. Releasing its wire clip, unplug the large electrical connector (next to the fuel pressure regulator) to disconnect the wiring of the manifold components from the engine wiring loom.

18 Marking or labelling them as they are unplugged, disconnect the vacuum hoses at the manifold and throttle housing.

19 Undo the fuel feed and return lines connecting the engine to the chassis. Plug or cap all open fittings.

20 Unbolt the earth lead from the cylinder head rear support plate/engine lifting eye, then unscrew the bolt securing the support plate/lifting eye.

21 Unscrew the nuts and bolts securing the manifold to the cylinder head, and withdraw it. Take care not to damage vulnerable components as the manifold assembly is manoeuvred out of the engine compartment.

22 With the manifold removed, clean all traces of the old gasket from the mating surfaces of the manifold and the cylinder head.

Refitting

All engines

23 Refitting is the reverse of the removal procedure, noting the following points:

a) Fit a new gasket, then locate the manifold on the head and install the nuts and bolts.

b) Tighten the nuts/bolts in three or four equal steps to the specified torque, working from the centre outwards, to avoid warping the manifold.

c) Refit the remaining parts in the reverse order of removal - tighten all fasteners to the torque wrench settings specified (where given).

d) Where drained, refill the cooling system as described in Chapter 1.

e) Before starting the engine, check the accelerator cable for correct adjustment and the throttle linkage for smooth operation (Section 5).

f) When the engine is fully warmed-up, check for signs of fuel, inlet and/or vacuum leaks.

Chapter 4 Part E:
Exhaust and emission control systems

Contents

Catalytic converter - general information and precautions 4
Emission control system check .See Chapter 1
Evaporative emissions control system - checking and component
   renewal 6
Exhaust manifold - removal and refitting 3
Exhaust system - renewal 2

Exhaust system check . . . . .See Chapter 1
General information 1
Positive crankcase ventilation system - checking and component
   renewal 5
Pulse-air system - checking and component renewal 7
Underbonnet check for fluid leaks and hose condition . .See Chapter 1

Degrees of difficulty

Easy, suitable for novice with little experience	**Fairly easy,** suitable for beginner with some experience	**Fairly difficult,** suitable for competent DIY mechanic	**Difficult,** suitable for experienced DIY mechanic	**Very difficult,** suitable for expert DIY or professional

Specifications

Torque wrench settings	Nm	lbf ft
Pulse-air system piping sleeve nuts	32	24
Exhaust manifold to cylinder head:		
HCS engines	23	17
CVH engines (non turbocharged)	16	12
CVH engines (turbocharged)	28 to 31	21 to 23
PTE engines	16	12
Zetec engines	16	12

1 General information

Exhaust system

The exhaust system is composed of an exhaust manifold, the front downpipe and catalytic converter (where fitted), and a main section incorporating two silencers. The service replacement exhaust system consists of three sections: the front downpipe/catalytic converter, the intermediate pipe and front silencer, and the tailpipe and rear silencer. The system is suspended throughout its entire length by rubber mountings.

Emission control systems

To minimise pollution of the atmosphere from incompletely-burned and evaporating gases, and to maintain good driveability and fuel economy, a number of emissions control systems are used on these vehicles. They include the following:

a) *The engine management system (comprising both fuel and ignition subsystems) itself.*
b) *Positive Crankcase Ventilation (PCV) system.*
c) *Evaporative emissions control (EVAP) system.*
d) *Pulse-air (PAIR) system.*
e) *Catalytic converter.*

The operation of the systems is described in the following paragraphs.

Positive crankcase ventilation system

The function of the crankcase ventilation system is to reduce the emissions of unburned hydrocarbons from the crankcase, and to minimise the formation of oil sludge. By ensuring that a depression is created in the crankcase under most operating conditions, particularly at idle, and by positively inducing fresh air into the system, the oil vapours and "blow-by" gases collected in the crankcase are drawn from the crankcase, through the air cleaner or oil separator, into the inlet tract, to be burned by the engine during normal combustion.

On HCS engines, the system consists of a vented oil filler cap (with an integral mesh filter) and a hose connecting it to a connector on the underside of the air cleaner housing. A further hose leads from the adapter/filter to the inlet manifold. Under conditions of idle and part-load, the emissions gases are directed into the inlet manifold, and dispensed with in the combustion process. Additional air is supplied through two small orifices next to the mushroom valve in the air cleaner housing, the object of which is to prevent high vacuum build-up. Under full-load conditions, when the inlet manifold vacuum is weak, the mushroom valve opens, and the emissions are directed through the air cleaner housing

4E

into the engine induction system and thence into the combustion chambers. This arrangement eliminates any fuel mixture control problems. The operating principles for the system used on the Endura-E engine are basically the same as just described with revisions to the component locations and hose arrangement.

On CVH and PTE engines, a closed-circuit type crankcase ventilation system is used, the function of which is basically the same as that described for the HCS engine type, but the breather hose connects directly to the rocker cover. The oil filler cap incorporates a separate filter in certain applications.

On Zetec engines, the crankcase ventilation system main components are the oil separator mounted on the front (radiator) side of the cylinder block/crankcase, and the Positive Crankcase Ventilation (PCV) valve set in a rubber grommet in the separator's left-hand upper end. The associated pipework consists of a crankcase breather pipe and two flexible hoses connecting the PCV valve to a union on the left-hand end of the inlet manifold, and a crankcase breather hose connecting the cylinder head cover to the air cleaner assembly. A small foam filter in the air cleaner prevents dirt from being drawn directly into the engine.

Evaporative emissions control system

This system is fitted to minimise the escape of unburned hydrocarbons into the atmosphere. Fuel evaporative emissions control systems are limited on vehicles meeting earlier emissions regulations; carburettor float chambers are vented internally, whilst fuel tanks vent to atmosphere through a combined roll-over/anti-trickle-fill valve. On vehicles meeting the more stringent emissions regulations, the fuel tank filler cap is sealed, and a charcoal canister is used to collect and store petrol vapours generated in the tank when the vehicle is parked. When the engine is running, the vapours are cleared from the canister (under the control of the EEC IV engine management module via the canister-purge solenoid valve) into the inlet tract, to be burned by the engine during normal combustion.

To ensure that the engine runs correctly when it is cold and/or idling, and to protect the catalytic converter from the effects of an over-rich mixture, the canister-purge solenoid valve is not opened by the EEC IV module until the engine is fully warmed-up and running under part-load; the solenoid valve is then switched on and off, to allow the stored vapour to pass into the inlet tract.

Pulse-air system

This system consists of the pulse-air solenoid valve, the pulse-air valve itself, the delivery tubing, a pulse-air filter, and on some models, a check valve. The system injects filtered air directly into the exhaust ports, using the pressure variations in the exhaust gases to draw air through from the filter housing; air will flow into the exhaust only when its pressure is below atmospheric. The pulse-air valve can allow gases to flow only one way, so there is no risk of hot exhaust gases flowing back into the filter.

The system's primary function is raise exhaust gas temperatures on start-up, thus reducing the amount of time taken for the catalytic converter to reach operating temperature. Until this happens, the system reduces emissions of unburned hydrocarbon particles (HC) and carbon monoxide (CO) by ensuring that a considerable proportion of these substances remaining in the exhaust gases after combustion are burned up, either in the manifold itself or in the catalytic converter.

To ensure that the system does not upset the smooth running of the engine under normal driving conditions, it is linked by the pulse-air solenoid valve to the EEC IV module, so that it only functions during engine warm-up, when the oxygen sensor is not influencing the fuel/air mixture ratio.

Catalytic converter

Catalytic converters have been introduced progressively on all models in the range, to meet the various emissions regulations.

The catalytic converter is located in the exhaust system, and operates in conjunction with an exhaust gas oxygen sensor to reduce exhaust gas emissions. The catalytic converter uses precious metals (platinum and palladium or rhodium) as catalysts to speed up the reaction between the pollutants and the oxygen in the vehicle's exhaust gases, CO and HC being oxidised to form H_2O and CO_2 and (in the three-way type of catalytic converter) NO_x being reduced to N_2. **Note**: *The catalytic converter is not a filter in the physical sense; its function is to promote a chemical reaction, but it is not itself affected by that reaction.*

The converter consists of an element (or "substrate") of ceramic honeycomb, coated with a combination of precious metals in such a way as to produce a vast surface area over which the exhaust gases must flow; the whole being mounted in a stainless-steel box. A simple "oxidation" (or "two-way") catalytic converter can deal with CO and HC only, while a "reduction" (or "three-way") catalytic converter can deal with CO, HC and NO_x. Three-way catalytic converters are further sub-divided into "open-loop" (or "unregulated") converters, which can remove 50 to 70% of pollutants and "closed-loop" (also known as "controlled" or "regulated") converters, which can remove over 90% of pollutants.

In order for a closed-loop catalytic converter to operate effectively, the air/fuel mixture must be very accurately controlled, and this is achieved by measuring the oxygen content of the exhaust gas. The oxygen sensor transmits information on the exhaust gas oxygen content to the EEC IV engine management module, which adjusts the air/fuel mixture strength accordingly.

The sensor has a built-in heating element which is controlled by the EEC IV module, in order to bring the sensor's tip to an efficient operating temperature as rapidly as possible. The sensor's tip is sensitive to oxygen, and sends the module a varying voltage depending on the amount of oxygen in the exhaust gases; if the inlet air/fuel mixture is too rich, the sensor sends a high-voltage signal. The voltage falls as the mixture weakens. Peak conversion efficiency of all major pollutants occurs if the inlet air/fuel mixture is maintained at the chemically-correct ratio for the complete combustion of petrol - 14.7 parts (by weight) of air to 1 part of fuel (the "stoichiometric" ratio). The sensor output voltage alters in a large step at this point, the module using the signal change as a reference point, and correcting the inlet air/fuel mixture accordingly by altering the fuel injector pulse width (injector opening time).

Removal and refitting procedures for the oxygen sensor are given in Parts B, C and D of this Chapter according to fuel system type.

2 Exhaust system - renewal

⚠️ *Warning: Inspection and repair of exhaust system components should be done only after enough time has elapsed after driving the vehicle to allow the system components to cool completely. This applies particularly to the catalytic converter, which runs at very high temperatures. Also, when working under the vehicle, make sure it is securely supported on axle stands.*

If the exhaust system components are extremely corroded or rusted together, they will probably have to be cut from the exhaust system. The most convenient way of accomplishing this is to have a quick-fit exhaust repair specialist remove the corroded sections. Alternatively, you can simply cut off the old components with a hacksaw. If you do decide to tackle the job at home, be sure to wear eye protection, to protect your eyes from metal chips, and work gloves, to protect your hands. If the production-fit system is still fitted, it must be cut for the service-replacement system sections to fit. The best way of determining the correct cutting point is to obtain the new centre or rear section first then, with the old system removed, lay the two side by side on the ground. It should now be relatively easy to determine where the old system needs to be cut, and it can be marked accordingly. Remember to allow for the overlap where the two sections will plug together.

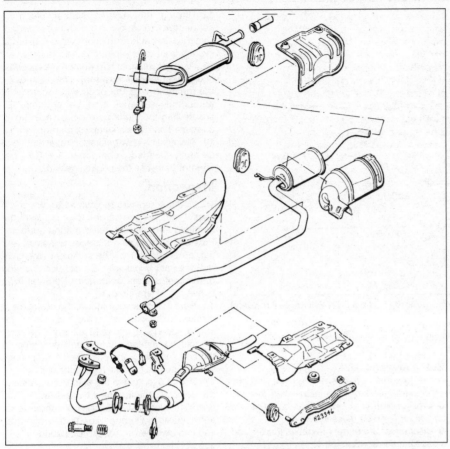

2.2a **Typical exhaust system and heat shield arrangement**
(1.4 litre CVH CFi model shown)

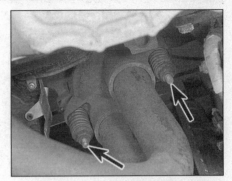

2.2b **Exhaust system downpipe-to-manifold securing nuts (arrowed)**

overheating the floorpan, and possibly damaging the interior carpet and insulation. Pay particularly close attention to the catalytic converter and its heat shield.

⚠️ **Warning: The catalytic converter operates at very high temperatures, and takes a long time to cool. Wait until it's completely cool before attempting to remove the converter. Failure to do so could result in serious burns.**

3 Exhaust manifold - removal and refitting

Removal

Note: *Never work on or near the exhaust system and in particular, the catalytic converter (where fitted), while it is still hot. If this is unavoidable, wear thick gloves, and protect yourself from burns should you accidentally touch a hot exhaust component.*

All engines except Zetec

Note: *On turbocharged engines, removal and refitting procedures for the exhaust manifold, complete with turbocharger are given in Part C, Section 20.*

1 Disconnect the battery negative (earth) lead - see Chapter 5A, Section 1.

4E

Here are some simple guidelines to apply when repairing the exhaust system:

a) *Work from the back to the front when removing exhaust system components* **(see illustration)**.

b) *Apply penetrating fluid to the exhaust system component fasteners, to make them easier to remove.*

c) *Use new gaskets, rubber mountings and clamps.*

d) *Apply anti-seize compound to the threads of all exhaust system fasteners*

e) *Note that on some models, the downpipe*

is secured to the manifold by two bolts, with a coil spring, spring seat and self-locking nut on each. On refitting, tighten the nuts until they stop on the bolt shoulders; the pressure of the springs will then suffice to make a gastight joint. Do not overtighten the nuts to cure a leak - the bolts will shear. Renew the gasket and the springs if a leak is found **(see illustrations)**.

f) *Be sure to allow sufficient clearance between newly-installed parts and all points on the underbody, to avoid*

2.2c **Showing securing bolts - note coil spring, and shoulder on bolt**

2.2d **Renew the exhaust system downpipe-to-manifold gasket to prevent leaks**

2.2e **Release the spring clip to extract the securing bolt from the manifold, when required**

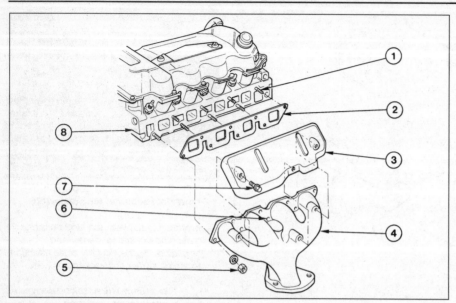

3.2 Exploded view of the exhaust manifold arrangement (1.6 litre CVH EFi engine models)

1 Retaining stud
2 Gasket
3 Heatshield
4 Exhaust manifold
5 Manifold retaining nut
6 Centring hole
7 Heatshield retaining bolt
8 Cylinder head

2 The exhaust manifold is secured the cylinder head by studs and nuts, and is similarly attached to the exhaust downpipe. A shroud/heat shield is bolted to the manifold, to direct exhaust-heated air into the air inlet system when the engine is cold. Access to the exhaust manifold retaining nuts is gained by first removing this shroud **(see illustration)**.

3 On vehicles equipped with a pulse-air system, remove the pulse-air piping as described in Section 7.

4 Support the exhaust downpipe on a jack or suitable blocks, and undo the downpipe-to-manifold retaining nuts. Separate the pipe from the manifold, and remove the gasket. On catalytic converter-equipped vehicles with an oxygen sensor fitted to the exhaust downpipe, take care not to stretch the sensor wiring; if necessary, disconnect the sensor's multi-plug.

5 Undo the retaining nuts, and withdraw the manifold from the cylinder head studs. Remove the manifold gasket.

Zetec engines

Note: *In addition to the new gasket and any other parts, tools or facilities needed to carry out this operation, a new plastic guide sleeve will be required on reassembly.*

6 Disconnect the battery negative (earth) lead - see Chapter 5A, Section 1.

7 Remove the air inlet components as described in Part D of this Chapter.

8 Drain the cooling system (see Chapter 1).

9 Disconnect the coolant hose and the coolant pipe/hose from the thermostat housing; secure them clear of the working area.

10 Unbolt the exhaust manifold heat shield, and withdraw both parts of the shield **(see illustration)**.

11 While the manifold can be removed with the pulse-air system components attached - unbolt the filter housing and disconnect its vacuum hose if this is to be done - it is easier to remove the pulse-air assembly first, as described in Section 7.

12 Unplug the oxygen sensor electrical connector, to avoid straining its wiring. Unscrew the nuts to disconnect the exhaust system front downpipe from the manifold.

13 Remove the nuts and detach the manifold and gasket **(see illustration)**. When removing the manifold with the engine in the vehicle, additional clearance can be obtained by unscrewing the studs from the cylinder head; a female Torx-type socket will be required.

14 Always fit a new gasket on reassembly, to carefully-cleaned components. *Do not attempt to re-use the original gasket.*

Inspection

15 Use a scraper to remove all traces of old gasket material and carbon deposits from the manifold and cylinder head mating surfaces. Provided both mating surfaces are clean and flat, a new gasket will be sufficient to ensure that the joint is gastight. *Do not* use any kind of exhaust sealant upstream of the catalytic converter, where fitted.

16 Note that on some models, the downpipe is secured to the manifold by two bolts, with a coil spring, spring seat and self-locking nut on each. On refitting, tighten the nuts until they stop on the bolt shoulders; the pressure of the springs will then suffice to make a gastight joint.

17 Do not overtighten the nuts to cure a leak - the bolts will shear; renew the gasket and the springs if a leak is found. The bolts themselves are secured by spring clips to the manifold, and can be renewed easily if damaged.

Refitting

18 Refitting is the reverse of the removal procedure, noting the following points:

a) *Position a new gasket over the cylinder head studs, and on Zetec engines, fit a new plastic guide sleeve to the stud nearest to the thermostat housing, so that the manifold will be correctly located* **(see illustration)**. *Do not refit the manifold without this sleeve.*

b) *Refit the manifold, and finger-tighten the mounting nuts.*

c) *Working from the centre out, and in three or four equal steps, tighten the nuts to the torque wrench settings given in the Specifications.*

3.10 Exhaust manifold heat shield bolts (arrowed) (Zetec engine models)

3.13 Exhaust manifold retaining nuts (Zetec engine models)

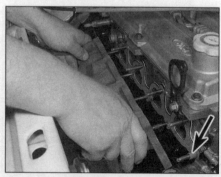

3.18 Fit a new plastic guide sleeve to the stud (arrowed) when refitting the manifold (Zetec engine models)

d) Refit the remaining parts in the reverse order of removal. Tighten all fasteners to the specified torque wrench settings where given.

e) Where drained, refill the cooling system (see Chapter 1).

f) Run the engine, and check for exhaust leaks. Check the coolant level when fully warmed-up to normal operating temperature.

4 Catalytic converter - general information and precautions

The catalytic converter is a reliable and simple device, which needs no maintenance in itself, but there are some facts of which an owner should be aware if the converter is to function properly for its full service life.

a) DO NOT use leaded petrol in a vehicle equipped with a catalytic converter - the lead will coat the precious metals, reducing their converting efficiency, and will eventually destroy the converter.

b) Always keep the ignition and fuel systems well-maintained in accordance with the manufacturer's schedule (see Chapter 1).

c) If the engine develops a misfire, do not drive the vehicle at all (or at least as little as possible) until the fault is cured.

d) DO NOT push - or tow-start the vehicle - this will soak the catalytic converter in unburned fuel, causing it to overheat when the engine does start.

e) DO NOT switch off the ignition at high engine speeds, ie do not "blip" the throttle immediately before switching off.

f) DO NOT use fuel or engine oil additives - these may contain substances harmful to the catalytic converter.

g) DO NOT continue to use the vehicle if the engine burns oil to the extent of leaving a visible trail of blue smoke.

h) Remember that the catalytic converter operates at very high temperatures. DO NOT, therefore, park the vehicle in dry undergrowth, over long grass or piles of dead leaves, after a long run.

l) Remember that the catalytic converter is FRAGILE. Do not strike it with tools during servicing work.

j) In some cases, a sulphurous smell (like that of rotten eggs) may be noticed from the exhaust. This is common to many catalytic converter-equipped vehicles. Once the vehicle has covered a few thousand miles, the problem should disappear. Low quality fuel with a high sulphur content will exacerbate this effect.

k) The catalytic converter used on a well-maintained and well-driven vehicle should last for between 50 000 and 100 000 miles. If the converter is no longer effective, it must be renewed.

5 Positive crankcase ventilation system - checking and component renewal

Checking

1 Checking procedures for the system components are included in Chapter 1.

Component renewal - all engines except Zetec

Air cleaner components

2 See Chapter 1.

Filter/oil separator and hoses

3 All the components relating to the positive crankcase ventilation system, with the exception of the HCS engine filter/adapter located on the underside of the air cleaner, may be removed by simple disconnection and withdrawal (having noted all connections for subsequent refitting).

4 The refitting of all components is a reversal of the removal procedure, ensuring that the connections are correctly made.

Component renewal - Zetec engines

Air cleaner components

5 See Chapter 1.

Positive Crankcase Ventilation (PCV) valve

6 The valve is plugged into the oil separator on Zetec engines **(see illustration)**.

Depending on the tools available, access to the valve may be possible once the pulse-air assembly has been removed (see Section 7). If this is not feasible, proceed as outlined in paragraph 7 below.

Oil separator

7 Remove the exhaust manifold (see Section 3). The positive crankcase ventilation valve can now be unplugged and flushed, or renewed, as required, as described in Chapter 1.

8 Unbolt the oil separator from the cylinder block/crankcase, and withdraw it; remove and discard the gasket.

9 Flush out or renew the oil separator, as required (see Chapter 1).

10 Refitting is the reverse of the removal procedure, but use a new gasket between the oil separator and cylinder block. Refill the cooling system (see Chapter 1). Run the engine, check for exhaust leaks, and check the coolant level when it is fully warmed-up.

6 Evaporative emissions control system - checking and component renewal

Checking

1 Poor idle, stalling and poor driveability can be caused by an inoperative canister-purge solenoid valve, a damaged canister, split or cracked hoses, or hoses connected to the wrong fittings. Check the fuel filler cap for a damaged or deformed gasket.

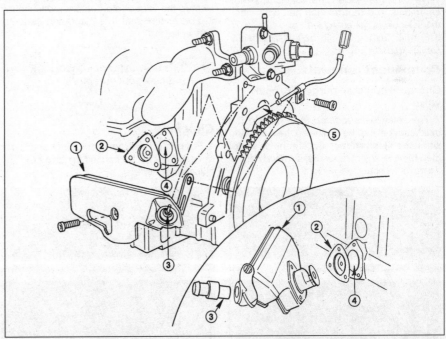

5.6 Crankcase emission control system (Zetec engine models)

1 Oil separator
2 Gasket
3 Positive crankcase ventilation (PCV) valve
4 Cylinder block/crankcase opening
5 Crankcase breather pipe and flexible hoses

4E

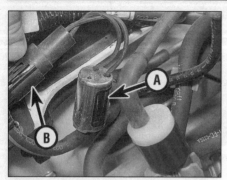

6.7a Canister purge solenoid valve (A) and multi-plug (B) (1.4 litre CVH CFi engine models)

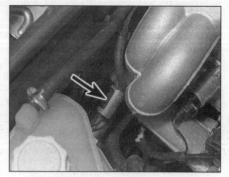

6.7b Canister purge solenoid valve (arrowed) (Zetec engine models)

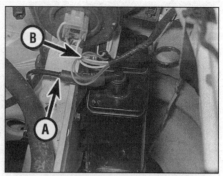

6.12a Fuel vapour pipe (A) and canister retaining screw (B) (1.4 litre CVH CFi engine models)

2 Fuel loss or fuel odour can be caused by liquid fuel leaking from fuel lines, a cracked or damaged canister, an inoperative canister-purge solenoid valve, or disconnected, misrouted, kinked or damaged vapour or control hoses.

3 Inspect each hose attached to the canister for kinks, leaks and cracks along its entire length. Repair or renew as necessary.

4 Inspect the canister. If it is cracked or damaged, renew it. Look for fuel leaking from the bottom of the canister. If fuel is leaking, renew the canister, and check the hoses and hose routing.

5 If the canister-purge solenoid valve is thought to be faulty, unplug its electrical connector and disconnect its vacuum hoses. Connect a battery directly across the valve terminals. Check that air can flow through the valve passages when the solenoid is thus energised, and that nothing can pass when the solenoid is not energised.

6 Further testing should be left to a dealer service department.

Component renewal

Charcoal canister-purge solenoid valve

7 The solenoid is located at or near to the bulkhead, behind the engine on the right-hand side **(see illustrations)**. Locate the solenoid, then remove any components as necessary to improve access.

8 Disconnect the battery negative (earth) lead (refer to Chapter 5A, Section 1), then unplug the valve's electrical connector. Unclip the valve from its location, then disconnect its vacuum hoses and withdraw it.

9 Refitting is the reverse of the removal procedure.

Charcoal canister

10 Disconnect the battery negative (earth) lead (refer to Chapter 5A, Section 1).

11 The canister is located in the front right-hand corner of the engine compartment.

12 Disconnect the vapour pipe from the unit, and plug it to prevent the ingress of dirt **(see illustrations)**.

13 Undo the retaining screw and withdraw the unit upwards, releasing it from its bracket **(see illustration)**.

14 Refit in the reverse order of removal. Unplug the vapour pipe before reconnecting it, and ensure that it is clean and securely connected.

7	Pulse-air system - checking and component renewal

Checking

1 Poor idle, stalling, backfiring and poor driveability can be caused by a fault in the pulse-air system.

2 Inspect the vacuum pipe/hose for kinks, leaks and cracks along its entire length. Repair or renew as necessary.

3 Inspect the filter housing and piping. If either is cracked or damaged, renew it.

4 If the pulse-air solenoid valve is thought to be faulty, unplug its electrical connector and disconnect its vacuum hoses. Connect a battery directly across the valve terminals, and check that air can flow through the valve passages when the solenoid is thus energised, and that nothing can pass when the solenoid is not energised.

5 Further testing should be left to a dealer service department.

Component renewal

Pulse-air valve, filter and housing (HCS engines)

6 Disconnect the battery negative (earth) lead (refer to Chapter 5A, Section 1).

7 Disconnect the vacuum hose from the rear of the pulse-air valve assembly **(see illustration)**.

8 Undo the retaining screws, and withdraw the air-valve, filter and housing assembly from the mounting bracket.

9 To dismantle the filter housing, undo the four screws and separate the top from the base of the housing; extract the foam filter, and clean it in a suitable solvent. If any of the housing's components are worn or damaged, the assembly must be renewed.

6.12b Canister location and fuel vapour pipe (arrowed) (Zetec engine models)

6.13 Undo the retaining screw and withdraw the canister upwards, releasing the tag (arrowed) from its bracket

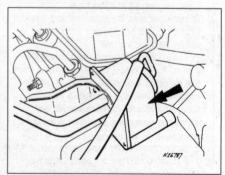

7.7 Location of pulse-air valve (arrowed) (1.3 litre HCS CFi engine models)

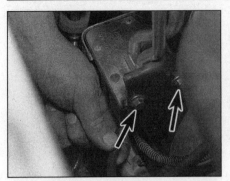

7.13 Disconnecting the vacuum hose from the base of the filter housing - note the housing retaining bolts (arrowed) (Zetec engine models)

7.19 Pulse-air solenoid valve location (arrowed) under ignition module

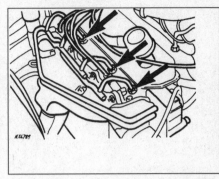

7.25 Pulse-air piping sleeve nuts (3 of 4 arrowed) (1.3 litre HCS CFi engine models)

10 Refitting is the reverse of the removal procedure.

Pulse-air valve, filter and housing (Zetec engines)

11 Disconnect the battery negative (earth) lead (refer to Chapter 5A, Section 1).

12 Chock the rear wheels then jack up the front of the car and support it on axle stands (see *"Jacking and vehicle support"*).

13 Disconnect the vacuum hose from the base of the filter housing (see illustration).

14 Remove the air cleaner air inlet components for access (refer to Part D of this Chapter).

15 Remove the screws securing the filter housing to the piping, unscrew the mounting bolt, then withdraw the housing.

16 To dismantle the filter housing, undo the four screws and separate the top from the base of the housing. Extract the foam filter, and clean it in a suitable solvent. If any of the housing's components are worn or damaged, the assembly must be renewed.

17 Refitting is the reverse of the removal procedure.

Pulse-air solenoid valve

18 Disconnect the battery negative (earth) lead (refer to Chapter 5A, Section 1).

19 Releasing its wire clip, unplug the electrical connector, then release the valve from its mounting bracket. Withdraw the valve, then label and disconnect the two vacuum hoses (see illustration).

20 Refitting is the reverse of the removal procedure; ensure that the hoses are correctly reconnected.

Pulse-air piping (HCS engines)

21 Disconnect the battery negative (earth) lead (refer to Chapter 5A, Section 1).

22 Remove the air cleaner if necessary for improved access (refer to Part B of this Chapter).

23 Disconnect the vacuum hose from the pulse-air valve.

24 Unbolt and detach the air tube from its fixing to the exhaust manifold, cylinder head and transmission, according to engine type.

25 Loosen off the four nuts securing the air delivery tubes to the cylinder head exhaust ports, then carefully withdraw the delivery tubes as a unit (see illustration). Do not apply undue force to the tubes as they are detached.

26 Carefully clean the piping, particularly its threads and those of the manifold. Remove all traces of corrosion, which might prevent the pipes seating properly, causing air leaks when the engine is restarted.

27 On refitting, insert the piping carefully into the cylinder head ports, taking care not to bend or distort it. Apply anti-seize compound to the threads, and tighten the retaining sleeve nuts while holding each pipe firmly in its port.

28 The remainder of the refitting procedure is the reverse of removal.

Pulse-air piping (Zetec engines)

29 Disconnect the battery negative (earth) lead (refer to Chapter 5A, Section 1).

30 Remove the air cleaner air inlet components for access (refer to Part D of this Chapter).

31 Unbolt the exhaust manifold heat shield; unclip the coolant hose to allow the upper part to be withdrawn.

32 Chock the rear wheels then jack up the front of the car and support it on axle stands (see *"Jacking and vehicle support"*).

33 Disconnect the vacuum hose at the base of the pulse-air filter housing.

34 Unscrew the two bolts securing the pipe assembly to the support bracket and the four sleeve nuts securing the pipes into the exhaust manifold (see illustration). Remove the pipes and filter housing as an assembly, taking care not to distort them.

35 Carefully clean the piping, particularly its threads and those of the manifold. Remove all traces of corrosion, which might prevent the pipes seating properly, causing air leaks when the engine is restarted.

36 On refitting, insert the piping carefully into the cylinder head ports, taking care not to bend or distort it. Apply anti-seize compound to the threads, and tighten the retaining sleeve nuts while holding each pipe firmly in its port; if a suitable spanner is available, tighten the sleeve nuts to the specified torque wrench setting.

37 The remainder of the refitting procedure is the reverse of removal.

4E

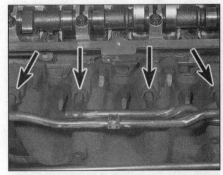

7.34 Pulse-air piping sleeve nuts (arrowed) (Zetec engine models)

Notes

Chapter 5 Part A:
Starting and charging systems

Contents

Alternator - removal and refitting 6
Alternator brushes and voltage regulator - renewal 7
Auxiliary drivebelt check and renewal ....See Chapter 1
Battery - removal and refitting 4
Battery - testing and charging 3
Battery, bulbs and fuses ....See "Weekly Checks"
Charging system - testing 5
Electrical fault finding - general information 2
General information, precautions and battery disconnection 1
Starter motor - removal and refitting 9
Starter motor - testing and overhaul 10
Starting system - testing 8

Degrees of difficulty

Easy, suitable for novice with little experience	Fairly easy, suitable for beginner with some experience	Fairly difficult, suitable for competent DIY mechanic	Difficult, suitable for experienced DIY mechanic	Very difficult, suitable for expert DIY or professional

Specifications

General
System type .... 12 volt, negative earth

Battery
Rating - Cold cranking/Reserve capacity .... 270 A/50 RC, 360 A/60 RC, 500 A/70 RC, 590 A/90 RC or 650 A/130 RC

Charge condition:
Poor .... 12.5 volts
Normal .... 12.6 volts
Good .... 12.7 volts

Alternator
Make/type:
Bosch .... K1-55A, K1-70A, KC-70A or KC-90A
Magneti-Marelli .... A127/55 or 127/70
Mitsubishi .... A5T or A002T
Output (nominal at 13.5 volts with engine speed of 6000 rpm) .... 55, 70 or 90 amps
Regulating voltage at 4000 rpm engine speed and 3 to 7 amp load ... 14.0 to 14.6 volts
Minimum brush length .... 5.0 mm

Starter motor
Make/type:
Bosch .... DM, DW or EV
Magneti-Marelli .... M79 or M80R
Nippondenso .... No type numbers given
Minimum brush length:
Bosch and Magneti-Marelli .... 8.0 mm
Nippondenso .... 9.0 mm

Torque wrench settings	Nm	lbf ft
Alternator mounting bolts	25	18
Alternator adjustment bolt	12	9
Alternator adjustment centre lockbolt	22	16
Adjuster link-to-mounting bracket bolt	12	9
Alternator pulley nut:		
With key	50	37
Without key	60	44
Starter motor mounting bolts	35	26
Starter motor support bracket bolt	25	18

1 General information, precautions and battery disconnection

General information

The engine electrical system consists mainly of the charging and starting systems. Because of their engine-related functions, these components are covered separately from the body electrical devices such as the lights, instruments, etc (which are covered in Chapter 12). Information on the ignition system is covered in Part B of this Chapter.

The electrical system is of the 12-volt negative earth type.

The battery is of the low maintenance or "maintenance-free" (sealed for life) type and is charged by the alternator, which is belt-driven from the crankshaft pulley.

The starter motor is of the pre-engaged type incorporating an integral solenoid. On starting, the solenoid moves the drive pinion into engagement with the flywheel ring gear before the starter motor is energised. Once the engine has started, a one-way clutch prevents the motor armature being driven by the engine until the pinion disengages from the flywheel.

Precautions

Further details of the various systems are given in the relevant Sections of this Chapter. While some repair procedures are given, the usual course of action is to renew the component concerned. The owner whose interest extends beyond mere component renewal should obtain a copy of the *"Automobile Electrical & Electronic Systems Manual"*, available from the publishers of this manual.

It is necessary to take extra care when working on the electrical system to avoid damage to semi-conductor devices (diodes and transistors), and to avoid the risk of personal injury. In addition to the precautions given in *"Safety first!"* at the beginning of this manual, observe the following when working on the system:

Always remove rings, watches, etc before working on the electrical system. Even with the battery disconnected, capacitive discharge could occur if a component's live terminal is earthed through a metal object. This could cause a shock or nasty burn.

Do not reverse the battery connections. Components such as the alternator, electronic control units, or any other components having semi-conductor circuitry could be irreparably damaged.

If the engine is being started using jump leads and a slave battery, connect the batteries *positive-to-positive* and *negative-to-negative* (see *"Jump starting"*). This also applies when connecting a battery charger.

Never disconnect the battery terminals, the alternator, any electrical wiring or any test instruments when the engine is running.

Do not allow the engine to turn the alternator when the alternator is not connected.

Never "test" for alternator output by "flashing" the output lead to earth.

Never use an ohmmeter of the type incorporating a hand-cranked generator for circuit or continuity testing.

Always ensure that the battery negative lead is disconnected when working on the electrical system.

Before using electric-arc welding equipment on the car, disconnect the battery, alternator and components such as the fuel injection/ignition electronic control unit to protect them from the risk of damage.

Battery disconnection

Several systems fitted to the vehicle require battery power to be available at all times, either to ensure that their continued operation (such as the clock) or to maintain control unit memories (such as that in the engine management system's ECU) which would be wiped if the battery were to be disconnected. Whenever the battery is to be disconnected therefore, first note the following, to ensure that there are no unforeseen consequences of this action:

a) *First, on any vehicle with central locking, it is a wise precaution to remove the key from the ignition, and to keep it with you, so that it does not get locked in, if the central locking should engage accidentally when the battery is reconnected.*

b) *On cars equipped with an engine management system, the system's ECU will lose the information stored in its memory - referred to by Ford as the "KAM" (Keep-Alive Memory) - when the battery is disconnected. This includes idling and operating values, and any fault codes detected - in the case of the fault codes, if it is thought likely that the system has developed a fault for which the corresponding code has been logged, the vehicle must be taken to a Ford dealer for the codes to be read, using the special diagnostic equipment necessary for this. Whenever the battery is disconnected, the information relating to idle speed control and other operating values will have to be re-programmed into the unit's memory. The ECU does this by itself, but until then, there may be surging, hesitation, erratic idle and a generally inferior level of performance. To allow the ECU to relearn these values, start the engine and run it as close to idle speed as possible until it reaches its normal operating temperature, then run it for approximately two minutes at 1200 rpm. Next, drive the vehicle as far as necessary - approximately 5 miles of varied driving conditions is usually sufficient - to complete the relearning process.*

c) *If the battery is disconnected while the alarm system is armed or activated, the alarm will remain in the same state when the battery is reconnected. The same applies to the engine immobiliser system (where fitted).*

d) *If a Ford "Keycode" audio unit is fitted, and the unit and/or the battery is disconnected, the unit will not function again on reconnection until the correct security code is entered. Details of this procedure, which varies according to the unit and model year, are given in the "Ford Audio Systems Operating Guide" supplied with the vehicle when new, with the code itself being given in a "Radio Passport" and/or a "Keycode Label" at the same time. Ensure you have the correct code before you disconnect the battery. For obvious security reasons, the procedure is not given in this manual. If you do not have the code or details of the correct procedure, but can supply proof of ownership and a legitimate reason for wanting this information, the vehicle's selling dealer may be able to help.*

Devices known as "memory-savers" (or "code-savers") can be used to avoid some of the above problems. Precise details vary according to the device used. Typically, it is plugged into the cigarette lighter, and is connected by its own wires to a spare battery; the vehicle's own battery is then disconnected from the electrical system, leaving the "memory-saver" to pass sufficient current to maintain audio unit security codes and ECU memory values, and also to run permanently-live circuits such as the clock, all the while isolating the battery in the event of a short-circuit occurring while work is carried out.

 Warning: Some of these devices allow a considerable amount of current to pass, which can mean that many of the vehicle's systems are still operational when the main battery is disconnected. If a "memory-saver" is used, ensure that the circuit concerned is actually "dead" before carrying out any work on it!

2 Electrical fault finding - general information

Refer to Chapter 12.

3 Battery - testing and charging

Standard and low maintenance battery - testing

1 If the vehicle covers a small annual mileage, it is worthwhile checking the specific gravity of the electrolyte every three months to determine the state of charge of the battery. Use a hydrometer to make the check and compare the results with the following table.

	Ambient temperature above 25°C (77°F)	Ambient temperature below 25°C (77°F)
Fully-charged	1.210 to 1.230	1.270 to 1.290
70% charged	1.170 to 1.190	1.230 to 1.250
Fully-discharged	1.050 to 1.070	1.110 to 1.130

Note that the specific gravity readings assume an electrolyte temperature of 15°C (60°F); for every 10°C (18°F) below 15°C (60°F) subtract 0.007. For every 10°C (18°F) above 15°C (60°F) add 0.007.

2 If the battery condition is suspect, first check the specific gravity of electrolyte in each cell. A variation of 0.040 or more between any cells indicates loss of electrolyte or deterioration of the internal plates.

3 If the specific gravity variation is 0.040 or more, the battery should be renewed. If the cell variation is satisfactory but the battery is discharged, it should be charged as described later in this Section.

Maintenance-free battery - testing

4 In cases where a "sealed for life" maintenance-free battery is fitted, topping-up and testing of the electrolyte in each cell is not possible. The condition of the battery can therefore only be tested using a battery condition indicator or a voltmeter.

5 If testing the battery using a voltmeter, connect the voltmeter across the battery and compare the result with those given in the *Specifications* under "charge condition". The test is only accurate if the battery has not been subjected to any kind of charge for the previous six hours. If this is not the case, switch on the headlights for 30 seconds, then wait four to five minutes before testing the battery after switching off the headlights. All other electrical circuits must be switched off, so check that the doors and tailgate are fully shut when making the test.

6 If the voltage reading is less than 12.2 volts, then the battery is discharged, whilst a reading of 12.2 to 12.4 volts indicates a partially discharged condition.

7 If the battery is to be charged, remove it from the vehicle (Section 4) and charge it as described later in this Section.

Standard and low maintenance battery - charging

Note: *The following is intended as a guide only. Always refer to the manufacturer's recommendations (often printed on a label attached to the battery) before charging a battery.*

8 Charge the battery at a rate of 3.5 to 4 amps and continue to charge the battery at this rate until no further rise in specific gravity is noted over a four hour period.

9 Alternatively, a trickle charger charging at the rate of 1.5 amps can safely be used overnight.

10 Specially rapid "boost" charges which are claimed to restore the power of the battery in 1 to 2 hours are not recommended, as they can cause serious damage to the battery plates through overheating.

11 While charging the battery, note that the temperature of the electrolyte should never exceed 37.8°C (100°F).

Maintenance-free battery - charging

Note: *The following is intended as a guide only. Always refer to the manufacturer's recommendations (often printed on a label attached to the battery) before charging a battery.*

12 This battery type takes considerably longer to fully recharge than the standard type, the time taken being dependent on the extent of discharge, but it can take anything up to three days.

13 A constant voltage type charger is required, to be set, when connected, to 13.9 to 14.9 volts with a charger current below 25 amps. Using this method, the battery should be usable within three hours, giving a voltage reading of 12.5 volts, but this is for a partially discharged battery and, as mentioned, full charging can take considerably longer.

14 If the battery is to be charged from a fully discharged state (condition reading less than 12.2 volts), have it recharged by your Ford dealer or local automotive electrician, as the charge rate is higher and constant supervision during charging is necessary.

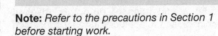

4 Battery - removal and refitting

Note: *Refer to the precautions in Section 1 before starting work.*

Removal

1 The battery is located forward on the left-hand side of the engine compartment, on a platform welded to the vehicle structure.

2 Undo the retaining nut, then detach the earth leads from the stud of the battery negative (earth) terminal post. This is the terminal to disconnect before working on, or disconnecting, any electrical component on the vehicle.

3 Pivot up the plastic cover from the positive terminal, then unscrew the positive lead retaining nut on the terminal. Detach the positive lead from the terminal.

4 Release the clamp securing the battery to its platform and remove it. Lift the battery from its location, keeping it in an upright position to avoid the possibility of corrosive electrolyte spilling onto the paintwork.

5 Clean the battery terminal posts, clamps and the battery casing. If the bulkhead is rusted as a result of battery acid spilling onto it, clean it thoroughly and re-paint with reference to Chapter 1.

6 If you are renewing the battery, make sure that you get one that's identical, with the same dimensions, amperage rating, cold cranking rating, etc. Dispose of the old battery in a responsible fashion. Most local authorities have facilities for the collection and disposal of such items - batteries contain sulphuric acid and lead, and should not be simply thrown out with the household rubbish!

Refitting

7 Refitting is a reversal of removal. Smear the battery terminals with a petroleum-based jelly prior to reconnecting. Always connect the positive terminal clamp first and the negative terminal clamp last.

5 Charging system - testing

Note: *Refer to the precautions in Section 1 before starting work.*

1 If the ignition warning light fails to illuminate when the ignition is switched on, first check the alternator wiring connections for security. If satisfactory, check that the warning light bulb has not blown, and that the bulbholder is secure in its location in the instrument panel. If the light still fails to illuminate, check the continuity of the warning light feed wire from the alternator to the bulbholder. If all is satisfactory, the alternator is at fault and should be renewed or taken to an auto-electrician for testing and repair.

2 If the ignition warning light illuminates when the engine is running, stop the engine and check that the drivebelt is correctly tensioned (see Chapter 1) and that the alternator connections are secure. If all is so far satisfactory, have the alternator checked by an auto-electrician for testing and repair.

3 If the alternator output is suspect even though the warning light functions correctly, the regulated voltage may be checked as follows.

4 Connect a voltmeter across the battery terminals and start the engine.

5 Increase the engine speed until the voltmeter reading remains steady; the reading should be approximately 13.5 to 14.6 volts.

6 Switch on as many electrical accessories (eg, the headlights, heated rear window and heater blower) as possible, and check that the alternator maintains the regulated voltage at around 13 to 14 volts.

7 If the regulated voltage is not as stated, the fault may be due to worn brushes, weak brush springs, a faulty voltage regulator, a faulty diode, a severed phase winding or worn or damaged slip rings. The alternator should be renewed or taken to an auto-electrician for testing and repair.

5A

6.3 Removing the drivebelt splash guard (where fitted)

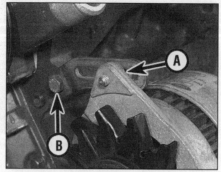

6.5 Alternator sliding arm type adjuster strap

A Adjuster bolt
B Adjuster bracket to engine bolt

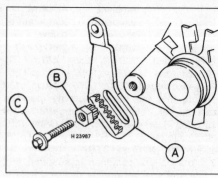

6.6 Rack-and-pinion type drivebelt adjuster

A Adjuster arm   C Central (locking) bolt
B Pinion (adjuster) nut

6 Alternator - removal and refitting

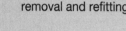

Removal

1 Disconnect the battery negative (earth) lead (refer to Section 1).
2 Chock the rear wheels then jack up the front of the car and support it on axle stands (see *"Jacking and vehicle support"*).
3 Where applicable, undo the retaining bolts and remove the drivebelt splash guard **(see illustration)**.
4 On models with power steering and a separate drivebelt, remove the auxiliary (power steering pump) drivebelt as described in Chapter 1.

Alternator with manual adjustment drivebelt

5 On models fitted with a sliding arm type adjuster strap, unscrew and remove the top (adjuster) bolt from the strap **(see illustration)**.
6 On models fitted with a "rack-and-pinion" type adjuster, unscrew and remove the central (locking) bolt whilst, at the same time, loosening the (adjuster) nut **(see illustration)**.
7 Loosen off, but do not yet remove, the lower mounting bolts, pivot the alternator inwards towards the engine to slacken the tension of the drivebelt, then disengage the drivebelt from the pulleys and remove it.
8 Where applicable, detach and remove the alternator splash cover/heat shield **(see illustration)**.
9 Where applicable, detach and remove the phase terminal and the splash cover.
10 Supporting the weight of the alternator from underneath, unscrew and remove the mounting bolts. Lower the alternator; noting the connections, detach the wiring and remove the alternator from the vehicle **(see illustration)**.

Alternator with automatic adjustment drivebelt

11 Remove the heatshield (if fitted) and disconnect the alternator wiring.
12 Fit a ring spanner onto the drivebelt tensioner, and rotate it clockwise to loosen off the tension from the drivebelt **(see illustration)**. Note the routing of the drivebelt, then disengage the belt from the pulleys and remove it.
13 On pre-1994 model year Zetec engines, disconnect the oxygen sensor wiring multi-plug, then undo the two nuts and separate the exhaust downpipe from the manifold. Support

the downpipe to avoid straining the exhaust system mountings.
14 On all models, unscrew the alternator upper mounting bolts/nuts and disconnect the alternator wiring. Unscrew the lower bolts/nuts and remove the alternator from the engine. On pre-1994 Zetec engines, it will be necessary to de-tension the drivebelt tensioner to provide clearance for removal of the upper mounting bolt nut.

Refitting

15 Refit in the reverse order of removal. Refit the drivebelt, and ensure that it is correctly re-routed around the pulleys. Adjust the tension of the drivebelt (according to type) as described in Chapter 1.

7 Alternator brushes and voltage regulator - renewal

1 Disconnect the battery negative (earth) lead (refer to Section 1).
2 Remove the alternator from the vehicle as described in the previous Section.

Bosch

3 Remove the two screws securing the combined brush box/regulator unit, and

6.8 Removing the splash cover from the inner end of the alternator

6.10 Wiring loom routing on rear of alternator (CVH engine)

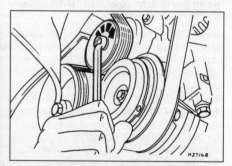

6.12 Automatic drivebelt tensioner

Turn tensioner clockwise to release drivebelt tension

7.3a Undo the retaining screw and . . .

7.3b . . . withdraw the brush box/regulator unit (Bosch alternator)

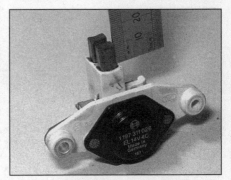

7.4 Measuring the brush lengths (Bosch alternator)

7.7a Removing the regulator and brushbox assembly securing screws (Magneti-Marelli alternator)

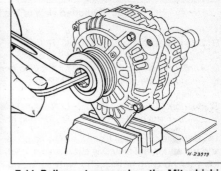

7.7b Disconnecting the field connector (Magneti-Marelli alternator)

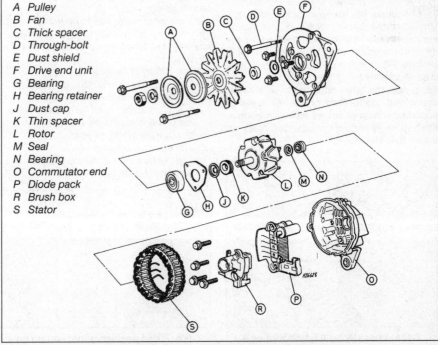

7.11 Pulley nut removal on the Mitsubishi alternator

withdraw the assembly from the rear of the alternator (**see illustrations**).

4 Check the brush lengths (**see illustration**). If either is less than, or close to, the minimum specified length, renew them by unsoldering the brush wiring connectors and withdrawing the brushes and their springs.

5 Clean the slip rings with a solvent-moistened cloth, then check for signs of scoring, burning or severe pitting. If evident, the slip rings should be attended to by an automobile electrician.

6 Refit in the reverse order of removal.

Magneti-Marelli

7 Remove the three screws securing the regulator/brush box unit on the rear face of the alternator, partially withdraw the assembly, detach the field connector, and remove the unit from the alternator (**see illustrations**).

8 If the brushes are worn beyond the minimum allowable length specified, a new regulator and brush box unit must be fitted; the brushes are not available separately.

9 Clean the slip rings with a solvent-moistened cloth, then check for signs of scoring, burning or severe pitting. If evident, the slip rings should be attended to by an automobile electrician.

10 Refit in the reverse order of removal.

Mitsubishi

11 Hold the pulley nut stationary using an 8 mm Allen key, unscrew the pulley nut and remove the washer (**see illustration**).

12 Withdraw the pulley, cooling fan, spacer and dust shield from the rotor shaft.

13 Mark the relative fitted positions of the front housing, stator and rear housing (to ensure

correct re-alignment when reassembling). Unscrew the through-bolts and remove the front housing from the rotor shaft, followed by the dust seal and the thin spacer (**see illustrations**).

5A

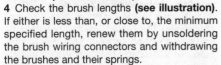

A Pulley
B Fan
C Thick spacer
D Through-bolt
E Dust shield
F Drive end unit
G Bearing
H Bearing retainer
J Dust cap
K Thin spacer
L Rotor
M Seal
N Bearing
O Commutator end
P Diode pack
R Brush box
S Stator

7.13a Exploded view of the Mitsubishi A5T alternator

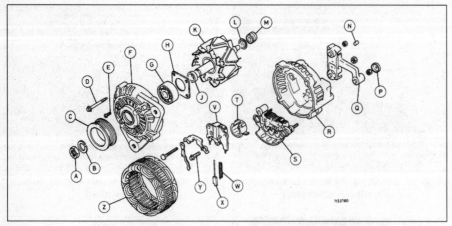

7.13b Exploded view of the AOO2T Mitsubishi alternator

A Pulley nut	J Spacer	S Rectifier
B Spring washer	K Rotor	T Dust cover
C Pulley	L Spacer	V Regulator
D Through-bolt	M Slip ring end bearing	W Brush spring
E Retainer plate screw	N Plug	X Brush
F Drive end housing	P Cap	Y Regulator screw
G Bearing	Q Terminal insulator	Z Stator
H Bearing retaining plate	R Slip ring end housing	

14 Remove the rotor from the rear housing and the stator. If difficulty is experienced, heat the rear housing with a 200-watt soldering iron for three or four minutes.

15 Unbolt the rectifier/brush box and stator assembly from the rear housing **(see illustration)**.

16 Unsolder the stator and brush box from the rectifier, using the very minimum of heat. Use a pair of pliers as a heat sink to reduce the heat transference to the diodes (overheating may cause diode failure).

17 Renew the brushes if they are worn down to, or beyond, the minimum specified length. Unsolder the brush wires at the points indicated **(see illustration)**, then solder the new brush leads so that the wear limit line projects 2 to 3 mm from the end of the holder **(see illustration)**.

18 Clean the slip rings with a solvent-moistened cloth, then check for signs of scoring, burning or severe pitting. If evident, the slip rings should be attended to by an automobile electrician.

19 Refit in the reverse order of removal. Insert a piece of wire through the access hole in the rear housing to hold the brushes in the retracted position as the rotor is refitted **(see illustration)**. Do not forget to release the brushes when assembled.

8 Starting system - testing

Note: *Refer to the precautions in Section 1 before starting work.*

1 If the starter motor fails to operate when the ignition key is turned to the appropriate position, the following possible causes may be to blame.
a) *The battery is faulty.*
b) *The electrical connections between the switch, solenoid, battery and starter motor are somewhere failing to pass the necessary current from the battery through the starter to earth.*
c) *The solenoid is faulty.*
d) *The starter motor is mechanically or electrically defective.*

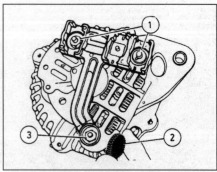

7.15 Rectifier/brush box (1) and regulator unit (3) retaining nuts on the Mitsubishi alternator. Note that cap (2) covers the regulator nut

2 To check the battery, switch on the headlights. If they dim after a few seconds, this indicates that the battery is discharged - recharge (see Section 3) or renew the battery. If the headlights glow brightly, operate the ignition switch and observe the lights. If they dim, then this indicates that current is reaching the starter motor, therefore the fault must lie in the starter motor. If the lights continue to glow brightly (and no clicking sound can be heard from the starter motor solenoid), this indicates that there is a fault in the circuit or solenoid - see following paragraphs. If the starter motor turns slowly when operated, but the battery is in good condition, then this indicates that either the starter motor is faulty, or there is considerable resistance somewhere in the circuit.

3 If a fault in the circuit is suspected, disconnect the battery leads (including the earth connection to the body), the starter/solenoid wiring and the engine/transmission earth strap. Thoroughly clean the connections, and reconnect the leads and wiring, then use a voltmeter or test lamp to check that full battery voltage is available at the battery positive lead connection to the solenoid, and that the earth is sound. Smear petroleum jelly around the battery terminals to prevent corrosion - corroded connections are amongst the most frequent causes of electrical system faults.

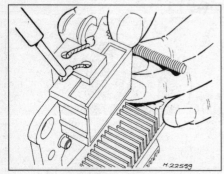

7.17a Unsoldering a brush wire on a Mitsubishi alternator

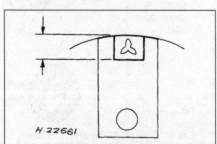

7.17b Fitted position of new brush on a Mitsubishi alternator

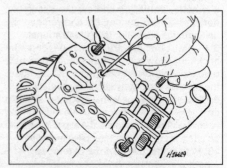

7.19 Use a length of wire rod to hold brushes in the retracted position when reassembling the rotor to the housing on the Mitsubishi alternator

9.4 Disconnecting the wires from the starter motor solenoid

9.5a Starter motor retaining bolts

9.5b Starter motor rear support bracket and fasteners (arrowed)

4 If the battery and all connections are in good condition, check the circuit by disconnecting the wire from the solenoid blade terminal. Connect a voltmeter or test lamp between the wire end and a good earth (such as the battery negative terminal), and check that the wire is live when the ignition switch is turned to the "start" position. If it is, then the circuit is sound - if not the circuit wiring can be checked as described in Chapter 12.

5 The solenoid contacts can be checked by connecting a voltmeter or test lamp between the battery positive feed connection on the starter side of the solenoid, and earth. When the ignition switch is turned to the "start" position, there should be a reading or lighted bulb, as applicable. If there is no reading or lighted bulb, the solenoid is faulty and should be renewed.

6 If the circuit and solenoid are proved sound, the fault must lie in the starter motor. In this event, it may be possible to have the starter motor overhauled by a specialist, but check on the cost of spares before

proceeding, as it may prove more economical to obtain a new or exchange motor.

9 Starter motor - removal and refitting

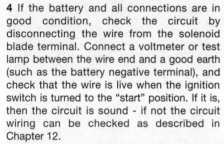

Removal

1 Disconnect the battery negative (earth) lead (refer to Section 1).

2 Chock the rear wheels then jack up the front of the car and support it on axle stands (see *"Jacking and vehicle support"*). Remove the front roadwheels.

3 Undo the two retaining nuts, and remove the starter motor heat shield (where fitted).

4 Prise free the cap, if fitted, then unscrew the nuts to disconnect the wiring from the starter/solenoid terminals. Where applicable, disconnect the oxygen sensor wiring multi-plug from the locating bracket **(see illustration)**.

5 Unscrew and remove the starter motor retaining bolts at the transmission/clutch

housing and, where applicable, also unbolt and detach the support bracket. Withdraw the starter motor from its mounting, and remove it from the vehicle **(see illustrations)**.

Refitting

6 Refitting is a reversal of removal. Tighten the retaining bolts to the specified torque. Ensure that the wiring is securely reconnected to the starter motor (and solenoid) and is routed clear of the exhaust downpipe.

10 Starter motor - testing and overhaul

If the starter motor is thought to be suspect, it should be removed from the vehicle and taken to an auto-electrician for testing. Most auto-electricians will be able to supply and fit brushes at a reasonable cost. However, check on the cost of repairs before proceeding as it may prove more economical to obtain a new or exchange motor.

5A

Notes

Chapter 5 Part B:
Ignition system

Contents

Crankshaft position sensor - removal and refitting 6
Distributor cap and rotor arm - removal and refitting 7
Distributor vacuum diaphragm unit - renewal 9
Distributor - removal and refitting 8
General information and precautions 1
Ignition coil - checking, removal and refitting 3
Ignition module - removal and refitting 5
Ignition system - testing 2
Ignition timing - checking and adjustment 10
Ignition amplifier module (distributor ignition systems) -
    removal and refitting 4
Spark plug renewal . . . . See Chapter 1

Degrees of difficulty

Easy, suitable for novice with little experience	Fairly easy, suitable for beginner with some experience	Fairly difficult, suitable for competent DIY mechanic	Difficult, suitable for experienced DIY mechanic	Very difficult, suitable for expert DIY or professional 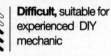

Specifications

General

System type:

1.0, 1.1 and 1.3 litre HCS engines with carburettor	Distributorless ignition system (DIS) controlled by ignition module
1.1 and 1.3 litre HCS engines with CFi fuel injection	Electronic distributorless ignition system (E-DIS) with ignition module controlled by EEC IV engine management module
1.4 litre CVH engines with carburettor:	
Early models	Distributor, with integral ignition amplifier module
Later models	Distributorless ignition system (DIS) controlled by ignition module
1.6 litre CVH engines with carburettor	Distributor, with integral ignition amplifier module
1.4 litre CVH engines with CFi fuel injection:	
Pre-September 1990 models	Distributor, with ignition module, controlled by EEC IV engine management module
September 1990 models onward	Electronic distributorless ignition system (E-DIS) with ignition module controlled by EEC IV engine management module
1.6 litre CVH engines with EFi fuel injection, and all PTE and Zetec engines	Electronic distributorless ignition system (E-DIS) with ignition module controlled by EEC IV engine management module

Firing order:

HCS engines	1-2-4-3
All other engines	1-3-4-2
Location of No 1 cylinder	Crankshaft pulley end

Ignition coil

All engines with distributor ignition systems:

Output	30.0 kilovolts (minimum)
Primary resistance	0.72 to 0.88 ohms
Secondary resistance	4500 to 7000 ohms
All engines with distributorless ignition systems:	
Output	37.0 kilovolts (minimum)
Primary resistance (measured at coil tower)	0.5 to 1.0 ohm

Distributor

Make:

1.4 and 1.6 litre carburettor models	Lucas
1.4 litre CFi fuel injection models (pre-September 1990)	Bosch
Direction of rotor arm rotation	Anti-clockwise (viewed from cap)
Automatic advance method:	
1.4 and 1.6 litre carburettor models	Mechanical and vacuum
1.4 litre CFi fuel injection models (pre-September 1990)	Totally controlled by EEC IV engine management module
Heat sink compound for ignition amplifier module (Lucas distributor) . .	Ford part number 81 SF-12103-AA

5B

Ignition timing

1.4 and 1.6 litre carburettor models with distributor:

For use with 4-star leaded petrol (97 RON)	12° BTDC at idle speed (vacuum pipe disconnected and plugged)
For use with unleaded petrol (95 or 98 RON)	8° BTDC at idle speed (vacuum pipe disconnected and plugged)
1.4 litre CFi fuel injection models with distributor (pre-Sept 1990)	10° BTDC at idle speed (set using STAR test equipment - refer to text)
All other models	Totally controlled by ignition module or EEC IV engine management module

Spark plugs . . . .

See Chapter 1 Specifications

Torque wrench settings

	Nm	lbf ft
Crankshaft position sensor (all engines except Zetec)	3 to 4	2 to 3
Crankshaft position sensor to bracket (Zetec engines)	7 to 9	5 to 7
Crankshaft position sensor bracket to engine (Zetec engines)	18 to 23	13 to 17
DIS/E-DIS ignition coil to bracket	5 to 7	4 to 5
DIS/E-DIS ignition coil bracket to engine (all engines except Zetec) . . .	9 to 12	7 to 9
DIS/E-DIS ignition coil bracket to engine (Zetec engines)	18 to 23	13 to 17

1 General information and precautions

General information

The ignition system is responsible for igniting the air/fuel mixture in each cylinder, at the correct moment in relation to engine speed and load, as the electrical spark generated jumps the spark plug gap.

The ignition system is based on feeding low tension (LT) voltage from the battery to the ignition coil where it is converted to high tension (HT) voltage. The high tension voltage is powerful enough to jump the spark plug gap in the cylinders many times a second under high compression pressures, providing that the system is in good condition.

A number of different ignition systems have been fitted to Fiesta models depending on the year of manufacture, type of fuel system fitted and the emission level that the vehicle has been designed to meet. Broadly speaking the systems can be sub-divided into two categories - distributor ignition systems and distributorless ignition systems.

One version of the distributor ignition system is fitted to all CVH engines with carburettors. A second (more sophisticated) version is fitted to pre-September 1990 CVH engines with CFi fuel injection.

Distributorless ignition systems are fitted to all HCS, PTE and Zetec engines, and to all CVH engines with fuel injection except pre-September 1990 CFi versions.

Distributor ignition systems (CVH engines with carburettor)

The ignition system is divided into two circuits; low tension (primary) and high tension (secondary). The low tension circuit consists of the battery, ignition switch, coil primary windings, ignition amplifier module and the signal generating system inside the distributor. The signal generating system comprises the trigger coil, trigger wheel, stator, permanent magnet and trigger coil to ignition amplifier module connector. The high tension circuit consists of the coil secondary windings, the HT lead from the coil to the distributor cap, the distributor cap, the rotor arm, the HT leads from the distributor cap to the spark plugs and the spark plugs themselves.

When the system is in operation, low tension voltage is changed in the coil into high tension voltage by the action of the electronic amplifier module in conjunction with the signal generating system. Any change in the magnetic field force (flux), created by the movement of the trigger wheel relative to the magnet, induces a voltage in the trigger coil. This voltage is passed to the ignition amplifier module which switches off the ignition coil primary circuit. This results in the collapse of the magnetic field in the coil which generates the high tension voltage. The high tension voltage is then fed, via the coil HT lead and the carbon brush in the centre of the distributor cap, to the rotor arm. The voltage passes across to the appropriate metal segment in the cap and via the spark plug HT lead to the spark plug where it finally jumps the spark plug gap to earth.

The distributor is driven by an offset drive dog locating to a correspondingly offset slot in the end of the camshaft.

The ignition advance is a function of the distributor and is controlled both mechanically and by a vacuum operated system. The mechanical governor mechanism consists of two weights which move out from the distributor shaft as the engine speed rises due to centrifugal force. As they move outwards, they rotate the trigger wheel relative to the distributor shaft and so advance the spark. The weights are held in position by two light springs and it is the tension of the springs which is largely responsible for correct spark advancement.

The vacuum control consists of a diaphragm, one side of which is connected via a small bore hose to the carburettor or throttle housing, and the other side to the distributor. Depression in the inlet manifold and/or carburettor, which varies with engine speed and throttle position, causes the diaphragm to move, so moving the stator and advancing or retarding the spark. A fine degree of control is achieved by a spring in the diaphragm assembly.

Additionally, one or more vacuum valve may be incorporated in the vacuum line between the inlet manifold or carburettor and the distributor. The function of these is to control the vacuum felt at the distributor and to prevent fuel entering along the vacuum line (as applicable).

Distributor ignition systems (pre-September 1990 CVH engines with CFi fuel injection)

The ignition system is divided into two circuits; low tension (primary) and high tension (secondary). The low tension circuit consists of the battery, ignition switch, ignition module, ballast resistor, coil primary windings and "Hall effect" distributor. The high tension circuit consists of the coil secondary windings, coil-to-distributor cap HT lead, distributor cap, rotor arm, spark plug HT leads and spark plugs. The system is under the overall control of the EEC IV engine management module which also controls the fuel injection and emission control equipment.

When the system is in operation the distributor supplies the EEC IV module with a crankshaft position reference signal to enable an initial ignition timing setting to be established. This signal is generated by means of a trigger vane attached to the distributor shaft and which rotates in the gap between a permanent magnet and a sensor. The trigger vane has four cut-outs, one for each cylinder. When one of the trigger vane cut-outs is in line with the sensor, magnetic flux can pass between the magnet and the sensor. When a trigger vane segment is in line with the sensor, the magnetic flux is diverted through the trigger vane, away from the sensor. The sensor detects the change in magnetic flux and sends an impulse to the EEC IV module. Additional data is received from the engine coolant temperature sensor, manifold absolute pressure sensor, inlet air temperature sensor, throttle position sensor and vehicle speed sensor. Using this information the EEC IV module calculates the optimum ignition advance setting and switches off the low tension circuit via the ignition module. This results in the collapse of the magnetic field in the coil which generates the high tension voltage. The high tension voltage is then fed, via the coil HT lead and the carbon brush in the centre of the distributor cap, to the rotor arm. The voltage passes across to the appropriate metal segment in the cap and via the spark plug HT lead to the spark plug where it finally jumps the spark plug gap to earth. It can be seen that the ignition module functions basically as a high current switch by controlling the low tension supply to the ignition coil primary windings.

In the event of failure of a sensor, the EEC IV module will substitute a preset value for that input to allow the system to continue to function. In the event of failure of the EEC IV module, a "limited operation strategy" (LOS) function allows the vehicle to be driven, albeit at reduced power and efficiency. The EEC IV module also has a "keep alive memory" (KAM) function which stores idle and drive values and codes which can be used to indicate any system fault which may occur.

Distributorless ignition systems

The main ignition system components include the ignition switch, the battery, the crankshaft speed/position sensor, the ignition module, the coil, the primary (low tension/LT) and secondary (high tension/HT) wiring circuits, and the spark plugs.

The system used on carburettor models is termed DIS (Distributorless Ignition System), and on fuel injection models E-DIS, (Electronic Distributorless Ignition System). The primary difference between the two is that the DIS system is an independent ignition control system while the E-DIS system operates in conjunction with the EEC IV engine management module which also controls the fuel injection and emission control systems.

With both systems, the main functions of the distributor are replaced by a computerised ignition module and a coil unit. The coil unit combines a double-ended pair of coils - each time a coil receives an ignition signal, two sparks are produced, at each end of the secondary windings. One spark goes to a cylinder on compression stroke and the other goes to the corresponding cylinder on its exhaust stroke. The first will give the correct power stroke, but the second spark will have no effect (a "wasted spark"), occurring as it does during exhaust conditions.

The ignition signal is generated by a crankshaft position sensor which scans a series of 36 protrusions on the periphery of the engine flywheel. The inductive head of the crankshaft position sensor runs just above the flywheel periphery and as the crankshaft rotates, the sensor transmits a pulse to the ignition module every time a protrusion passes it. There is one missing protrusion in the flywheel periphery at a point corresponding to 90° BTDC. The ignition module recognises the absence of a pulse from the crankshaft position sensor at this point to establish a reference mark for crankshaft position. Similarly, the time interval between absent pulses is used to determine engine speed.

On carburettor engines, the ignition module receives signals provided by information sensors which monitor various engine functions (such as crankshaft position, coolant temperature, inlet air temperature, inlet manifold vacuum etc). This information allows the ignition module to generate the optimum ignition timing setting under all operating conditions.

On fuel injection engines, the ignition module operates in conjunction with the EEC IV engine management module, and together with the various additional information sensors and emission control components, provides total control of the fuel and ignition systems to form a complete engine management package.

The information contained in this Chapter concentrates on the ignition-related components of the engine management system. Information covering the fuel, exhaust and emission control components can be found in the applicable Parts of Chapter 4.

Precautions

When working on the ignition system, take the following precautions:

a) *Do not keep the ignition switch on for more than 10 seconds if the engine will not start.*

b) *If a separate tachometer is ever required for servicing work, consult a dealer service department before buying a tachometer for use with this vehicle - some tachometers may be incompatible with these types of ignition systems - and always connect it in accordance with the equipment manufacturer's instructions.*

c) *Never connect the ignition coil terminals to earth. This could result in damage to the coil and/or the ignition module.*

d) *Do not disconnect the battery when the engine is running.*

e) *Make sure that the ignition module is properly earthed.*

f) *Refer to the warning at the beginning of the next Section concerning HT voltage.*

2 Ignition system - testing

  Warning: Voltages produced by an electronic ignition system are considerably higher than those produced by conventional ignition systems. Extreme care must be taken when working on the system with the ignition switched on. Persons with surgically-implanted cardiac pacemaker devices should keep well clear of the ignition circuits, components and test equipment.

Note: *Refer to the precautions given in Section 1 of Part A of this Chapter before starting work. Always switch off the ignition before disconnecting or connecting any component and when using a multi-meter to check resistances.*

1 If the engine turns over but won't start, disconnect the (HT) lead from any spark plug, and attach it to a calibrated tester (available at most automotive accessory shops). Connect the clip on the tester to a good earth - a bolt or metal bracket on the engine. If you're unable to obtain a calibrated ignition tester, have the check carried out by a Ford dealer service department or similar. Any other form of testing (such as jumping a spark from the end of an HT lead to earth) is not recommended, because of the risk of personal injury, or of damage to the ignition module.

2 Crank the engine, and watch the end of the tester to see if bright blue, well-defined sparks occur.

3 If sparks occur, sufficient voltage is reaching the plug to fire it. Repeat the check at the remaining plugs, to ensure that all leads are sound and that the coil is serviceable. However, the plugs themselves may be fouled or faulty, so remove and check them as described in Chapter 1.

4 If no sparks or intermittent sparks occur, the spark plug lead(s) may be defective. Also, on distributor systems, there may be problems with the rotor arm or distributor cap - check all these components as described in Chapter 1.

5 If there's still no spark, check the coil's electrical connector (where applicable), to make sure it's clean and tight. Check for full battery voltage to the coil at the connector's centre terminal. Check the coil itself (see Section 3). Make any necessary repairs, then repeat the check again.

6 The remainder of the system checks should be left to a dealer service department or other qualified repair facility, as there is a chance that the ignition module may be damaged if tests are not performed properly.

5B

3 Ignition coil - checking, removal and refitting

Distributor ignition systems

Checking

1 Accurate checking of the coil output requires the use of special test equipment and should be left to a dealer or suitably equipped automotive electrician. It is however possible to check the primary and secondary winding resistance using an ohmmeter as follows.

2 Disconnect the battery negative (earth) lead (refer to Part A, Section 1).

3 Remove the vehicle jack from its storage position by unscrewing its retainer. The ignition coil is mounted below.

4 To check the primary resistance (with all leads disconnected if the coil is fitted), connect the ohmmeter across the coil positive and negative terminals. The resistance should be as given in the *Specifications* at the beginning of this Chapter.

5 To check the secondary resistance (with all leads disconnected if the coil is fitted), connect one lead from the ohmmeter to the coil negative terminal, and the other lead to the centre HT terminal. Again the resistance should be as given in the *Specifications*.

6 If any of the measured values vary significantly from the figures given in the *Specifications*, the coil should be renewed.

7 If a new coil is to be fitted, ensure that it is of the correct type. The appropriate Ford supplied ignition coil is identified by a red label, and will be one of three different makes, all of which are fully interchangeable. Bosch and Femsa coils are fitted with protective plastic covers, and Polmot coils are fitted with an internal fusible link. Note that contact breaker ignition coils are not interchangeable with the required breakerless type and could cause ignition module failure if used.

Removal

8 If not already done, remove the vehicle jack from its storage position by unscrewing its retainer. The ignition coil is mounted below.

9 Disconnect the battery negative (earth) lead (refer to Part A, Section 1).

10 Disconnect the HT lead and the low tension (LT) connections from the ignition coil. Note that the LT connections on the ignition coil are of different sizes. As an aid to refitting the positive (+) terminal is larger than the negative (-) terminal **(see illustration)**.

11 Remove the two screws or bolts securing the coil mounting bracket to the inner wing panel, and withdraw the coil and mounting bracket assembly.

Refitting

12 Refitting is a reversal of the removal procedure, ensuring correct LT lead polarity.

Distributorless ignition systems

Checking

Note: *The ignition coil is located on the rear facing side of the cylinder block on HCS engines; on the left-hand end of the cylinder head on CVH, PTE and Zetec engines.*

13 Having checked that full battery voltage is available at the centre terminal of the coil's electrical connector (see Section 2), disconnect the battery negative (earth) lead (refer to Part A, Section 1).

14 Unplug the coil's electrical connector, if not already disconnected.

15 Using an ohmmeter, measure the resistance of the coil's primary windings, connecting the meter between the coil's terminal pins as follows. Measure first from one outer pin to the centre pin, then from the other outer pin to the centre. Compare the readings with the coil primary resistance listed in the *Specifications*.

16 Disconnect the spark plug (HT) leads - note their connections or label them carefully, as described in Chapter 1. Use the meter to check that there is continuity between each pair of (HT) lead terminals; Nos 1 and 4 terminals are connected by their secondary winding, as are Nos 2 and 3. Now switch to the highest resistance scale, and check that there is no continuity between either pair of terminals and the other - ie, there should be infinite resistance between terminals 1 and 2, or 4 and 3 - and between any terminal and earth.

17 If either of the above tests yield resistance values outside the specified amount, or results other than those described, renew the coil. Any further testing should be left to a dealer service department or other qualified repair facility.

Removal

Note: *The ignition coil is located on the rear facing side of the cylinder block on HCS engines; on the left-hand end of the cylinder head on CVH, PTE and Zetec engines.*

18 Disconnect the battery negative (earth) lead (refer to Part A, Section 1).

19 Disconnect the coil main electrical connector and (where fitted) the electrical connector to the suppressor.

20 The coil can be removed with the HT leads left attached, in which case disconnect the leads from their respective spark plugs and from the location clips in the rocker cover or air inlet duct (as applicable). If preferred, the HT leads can be disconnected from the coil. First check that both the ignition HT leads and their fitted positions are clearly marked numerically to ensure correct refitting. Spot mark them accordingly if necessary, using quick-drying paint.

21 If disconnecting the leads from the spark plugs, pull them free by gripping on the connector, not the lead. To detach the leads from the ignition coil, compress the retaining arms of each lead connector at the coil, and detach each lead in turn **(see illustration)**.

22 Unscrew the Torx-type retaining screws, and remove the coil from its mounting on the engine **(see illustration)**.

Refitting

23 Refitting is the reverse of the removal procedure. Ensure that the spark plug (HT) leads are correctly reconnected, and tighten the coil screws securely.

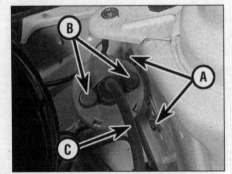

3.10 Ignition coil fitted to distributor ignition systems

A Retaining bolts
B LT connections
C HT lead to distributor cap

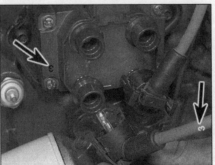

3.21 Removing an HT lead from the distributorless ignition system ignition coil. Note the corresponding markings on the ignition coil and HT lead (arrowed)

3.22 Distributorless ignition system ignition coil and mounting bracket removal (HCS engine shown)

5.3 Disconnecting the vacuum pipe from the ignition module

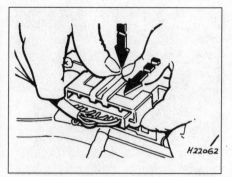

5.4a Disconnecting the ignition module multi-plug

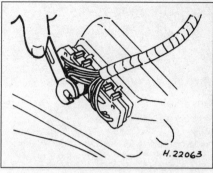

5.4b Undoing the ignition module multi-plug securing bolt

4 Ignition amplifier module (distributor ignition systems) - removal and refitting

Note: *The ignition amplifier module is only fitted to carburettor engine models.*

Removal

1 Disconnect the battery negative (earth) lead (refer to Part A, Section 1).
2 Remove the distributor, as described in Section 8.
3 With the distributor on the workbench, remove both screws securing the module to the distributor body, then slide the module from its trigger coil connector and remove it.
4 Check that the rubber grommet is serviceable. If it is not, it must be renewed but ensure that the correct type is obtained.

Refitting

5 Apply heat sink compound (see *Specifications*) to the module metal face, ensuring a good earth. This is an essential part of the procedure, protecting the module electronic circuitry from excessive heat build-up and subsequent malfunction.
6 Slide the module into its trigger coil connector and secure with both screws.
7 Refit the distributor in accordance with Section 8, then reconnect the battery.

5 Ignition module - removal and refitting

Note: *Various designs of ignition module may be fitted depending on ignition system type. Although the units may differ in appearance from the those shown in the accompanying illustrations, the procedures described below are applicable to all types.*

Removal

1 The ignition module is located on the engine compartment bulkhead.
2 Disconnect the battery negative (earth) lead (refer to Part A, Section 1).
3 Where applicable, detach the vacuum hose from the module **(see illustration)**.
4 According to type, either compress the locktab securing the wiring multi-plug in position, or where applicable, undo the retaining bolt, then withdraw the plug from the module **(see illustrations)**.
5 Undo the retaining screws, and remove the module from the bulkhead **(see illustration)**.

Refitting

6 Refitting is the reverse of the removal procedure.

6 Crankshaft position sensor - removal and refitting

Removal

1 Disconnect the battery negative (earth) lead (refer to Part A, Section 1).
2 Chock the rear wheels then jack up the front of the car and support it on axle stands (see *"Jacking and vehicle support"*).
3 If working on the Zetec engine, remove the starter motor as described in Part A of this Chapter.
4 Compress the retaining clip and pull free the wiring multi-plug connector from the sensor unit, but take care to pull on the connector, not the lead **(see illustration)**.
5 Undo the Torx-type retaining screw, and withdraw the sensor from its location in the cylinder block bellhousing flange.

Refitting

6 Refitting is the reversal of removal.

7 Distributor cap and rotor arm - removal and refitting

Removal

1 Disconnect the battery negative (earth) lead (refer to Part A, Section 1).
2 Disconnect the coil HT lead from the centre of the distributor cap and the spark plug HT leads from the spark plugs, having identified them for subsequent refitting. Pull on the connectors, not the leads. Release the leads from any cable clips or ties.
3 On carburettor models, unclip the suppressor shield (where fitted), remove the distributor cap securing screws and detach the cap.
4 On CFi fuel injection models, disconnect the distributor multi-plug for better access to the rear cap securing clip. Release the distributor cap securing clips by levering with a screwdriver, withdraw the cap assembly

5B

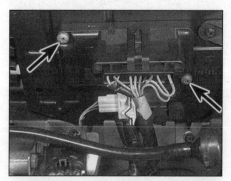

5.5 Ignition module location on bulkhead panel. Note retaining screws (arrowed)

6.4 Crankshaft position sensor removal

A Retaining screw   B Multi-plug

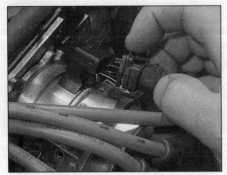

7.4a Disconnecting the distributor multi-plug

7.4b Releasing one of the distributor cap securing clips by carefully levering with a screwdriver

7.4c Withdrawing the distributor cap and suppressor shield assembly

and separate the suppressor shield from the cap **(see illustrations)**.

5 Withdraw the rotor arm from the distributor shaft.

6 Before refitting, wipe clean the distributor cap and leads and carry out a careful inspection as described in Chapter 1.

Refitting

7 Refitting is a reversal of the removal procedure, ensuring that the HT leads are securely connected and in the correct order.

8 Distributor - removal and refitting

Note: *On pre-September 1990 CVH engines with CFi fuel injection, unless the original distributor is to be refitted to the original cylinder head, it will be necessary to take the vehicle to a Ford dealer for accurate adjustment of the ignition timing after refitting.*

Removal

1 Disconnect the battery negative (earth) lead (refer to Part A, Section 1).

2 If the original distributor is to be refitted to the original cylinder head, check that the punch marks on the cylinder head and distributor body are aligned before removing the distributor **(see illustration)**. If no marks are present, make your own using a punch or

small file to ensure correct alignment upon subsequent refitting.

3 Refer to Section 7 and remove the distributor cap.

4 On carburettor equipped CVH engines, disconnect the vacuum pipe from the distributor vacuum diaphragm unit.

5 Disconnect the wiring multi-plug from the distributor.

6 Remove the clamp bolts securing the distributor in position and slide it out **(see illustration)**.

7 Prior to refitting, check the condition of the distributor oil seal and renew it if necessary.

Refitting

CVH engines with carburettor

8 Position the distributor so that its offset drive is engaged with the slot in the end of the camshaft, then loosely insert the two clamp bolts.

9 Where both original punch marks are present, on the cylinder head and distributor body, rotate the distributor body until the punch marks are aligned before fully tightening the clamp bolts.

10 If one or both of the punch marks are missing (due to component renewal), turn the body of the distributor so that the clamp bolts are centrally located in their slots then fully tighten the bolts.

11 Refit the rotor arm (if removed), distributor cap, suppressor shield (as applicable) and HT

leads, making reference to Section 7, then reconnect the wiring multi-plug and vacuum pipe.

12 Reconnect the battery negative lead.

13 If one or both of the punch marks are missing after component renewal, check the ignition timing, as described in Section 10, and adjust as necessary. This will not be required where the original punch marks have been re-aligned.

Pre-September 1990 CVH engines with CFi fuel injection

14 Position the distributor so that its offset drive is engaged with the slot in the end of the camshaft, then loosely insert the two clamp bolts.

15 Where both original punch marks are present, on the cylinder head and distributor body, rotate the distributor body until the punch marks are aligned then fully tighten the clamp bolts.

16 If one or both of the punch marks are missing (due to component renewal), rotate the distributor body until the centre line through the distributor multi-plug connector is at 40° to the vertical **(see illustration)**, before fully tightening the distributor clamp bolts. This will give an approximate (static) ignition timing setting to enable starting of the engine

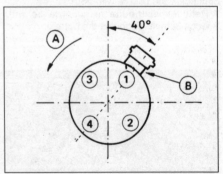

8.16 Distributor orientation when re-fitting if alignment punch marks are missing (Pre-September 1990 CVH engines with CFi fuel injection)

A Direction of rotation
B Centre line through distributor connector (40° to vertical)

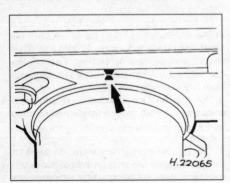

8.2 Distributor alignment punch marks (arrowed)

8.6 Removing the distributor from the cylinder head

Chapter 7 Part A:
Manual transmission

Contents

Gearchange linkage - adjustment	2	Manual transmission overhaul - general	8
Gearchange linkage and gear lever - removal and refitting	3	Oil seals - renewal	5
General information	1	Reversing light switch - removal and refitting	6
Manual transmission - removal and refitting	7	Speedometer drive pinion - removal and refitting	4
Manual transmission oil level check	See Chapter 1		

Degrees of difficulty

| **Easy,** suitable for novice with little experience | | **Fairly easy,** suitable for beginner with some experience | | **Fairly difficult,** suitable for competent DIY mechanic | | **Difficult,** suitable for experienced DIY mechanic | | **Very difficult,** suitable for expert DIY or professional | |

Specifications

Type .... Four or five forward speeds and reverse. Synchromesh on all forward gears

Gear ratios (typical)

1st	3.58:1 or 3.15:1
2nd	2.04:1 or 1.91:1
3rd	1.32:1 or 1.28:1
4th	0.95:1
5th	0.75:1
Reverse	3.77:1 or 3.62 : 1
Final drive	3.82:1, 3.84:1 or 4.06:1 (according to model)

Torque wrench settings

	Nm	lbf ft
Reversing light switch	16 to 20	12 to 15
Engine-to-transmission bolts	35 to 45	26 to 33
Clutch housing cover plate bolts	34 to 46	25 to 34
Gearshift stabiliser rod-to-transmission	50 to 60	37 to 44
Gearshift stabiliser rod-to-gearshift housing	5 to 7	4 to 5
Gearshift linkage clamp bolt	14 to 17	10 to 12
Gearshift housing-to-floor	6 to 8	4 to 6
Rear transmission mounting bracket threaded studs to transmission	21 to 27	15 to 20
Rear transmission mounting bracket retaining nuts	41 to 58	30 to 43
Transmission bearer to body	52	38
Transmission bearer mounting nuts	80 to 100	59 to 74

7A

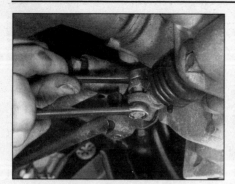

2.3a Loosen off the clamp bolt . . .

2.3b . . . and disengage the gearshift rod from the selector shaft

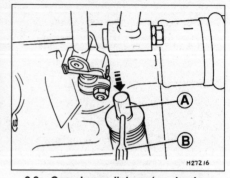

2.3c Gearchange linkage/mechanism adjustment

A Selector shaft   B Rod or punch

1 General information

The manual transmission is a 4- or 5-speed unit with synchromesh gear selection on all forward gears.

The unit consists of a compact, two-piece, lightweight aluminium alloy housing, containing both the transmission and differential assemblies.

The transmission is lubricated independently of the engine, with the transmission and differential both sharing the same lubricating oil. Torque from the transmission output shaft is transmitted to the crownwheel (which is bolted to the differential unit), and then from the differential gears to the driveshafts.

Gearshift is by means of a floor-mounted gear lever, connected by a remote control housing and gearshift rod to the transmission selector shaft.

2 Gearchange linkage - adjustment

1 Chock the rear wheels then jack up the front of the car and support it on axle stands (see *"Jacking and vehicle support"*).
2 On 4-speed models, select 2nd gear; on 5-speed models, select 4th gear.
3 Working from underneath the vehicle, loosen off the gearshift rod-to-gear selector shaft clamp bolt, and disengage the shift rod from the transmission selector shaft **(see illustrations)**. Slide the selector shaft back and forth to find its central position, then turn the selector shaft to the right and left to find the central position in the transverse plane. Hold the selector shaft in the centralised position, then insert a suitable rod (or punch) into the hole in the selector shaft in the transmission, and move it as far forwards as possible **(see illustration)**.
4 Insert a fabricated "lock pin" adjustment tool (from the left-hand side), and secure it in position with a sturdy elastic band or similar **(see illustration)**.
5 Check that the selector shaft coupling surfaces are free of grease, then reconnect the gearshift rod onto the transmission selector shaft, and secure it by tightening the clamp bolt to the specified torque setting.
6 Extract the locking pin, then check for the satisfactory engagement of all gears, selecting each gear in turn to confirm that the mechanism has been correctly reset. Further minor adjustment may be required.
7 With the adjustment correctly made, lower the vehicle to complete.

3 Gearchange linkage and gear lever - removal and refitting

Removal

1 Working inside the car, first engage 2nd gear (4-speed transmission) or 4th gear (5-speed transmission). This will provide the correct re-engagement and adjustment for the gearchange mechanism during reassembly.
2 Unscrew and remove the gearlever knob. Pull up and remove the outer gaiter and retaining frame. Remove the inner gaiter (unless secured).
3 Loosen off the four gear lever retaining nuts.
4 Chock the rear wheels then jack up the front of the car and support it on axle stands (see *"Jacking and vehicle support"*).
5 On XR2i models, remove the one-piece undertray (where fitted) and the front suspension crossmember (see Chapter 10).
6 Release the flexible exhaust pipe mountings, and disconnect the exhaust system from the downpipe. On catalytic converter models, also detach the heat shield from the underside of the floorpan to allow access to the underside of the gear lever for its removal. When detaching the exhaust system refer to Chapter 4E for details.
7 Mark the relative fitted positions of the selector shaft and gearshift rod, then undo the clamp bolt and separate the shaft from the rod.
8 Unscrew and remove the gearshift rod stabiliser retaining bolt. Note the position of the washer as the bolt is withdrawn **(see illustration)**. Support the gear lever assembly from underneath, and have an assistant unscrew and remove the four gear lever retaining nuts within the vehicle, then lower and withdraw the gearchange mechanism from underneath the vehicle.

Refitting

9 Refitting is a reversal of removal, but lubricate the pivot points with grease. Before lowering the vehicle from the axle stands, check and if necessary adjust the gearchange linkage as described in Section 2.

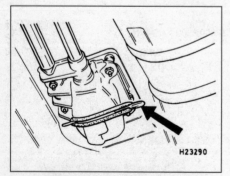

2.4 Gear lever locked in position by fabricated tool with elastic band to secure it

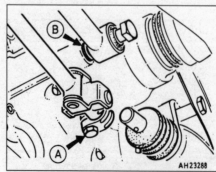

3.8 Gearchange mechanism shift rod clamp bolt (A), and stabiliser bar washer fitment (B)

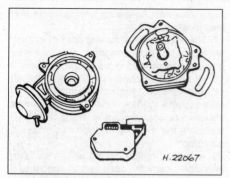

9.3 Distributor body halves separated (ignition amplifier module also shown)

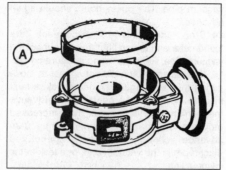

9.4 Remove the plastic spacer ring (A)

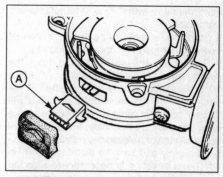

9.5 Trigger coil to ignition amplifier module connector (A) and seal

after the remaining components have been refitted and the relevant connections made.

17 Refit the rotor arm (if removed), distributor cap, suppressor shield (as applicable) and HT leads, making reference to Section 7, then reconnect the wiring multi-plug.

18 Reconnect the battery negative lead.

19 If one or both of the punch marks are missing after component renewal, the vehicle will need to be taken to a Ford dealer for accurate ignition timing checking and, if necessary, adjustment. This can only be carried out with the EEC IV engine management module in "self-test" mode and connected to the Ford specialised test equipment (see Section 10, paragraph 19).

9 Distributor vacuum diaphragm unit - renewal

Note: *Check parts availability before proceeding with this operation.*

1 Remove the distributor, as described in Section 8.

2 With the distributor on the workbench, remove the ignition amplifier module (see Section 4) and the distributor cap and rotor arm (if not already done).

3 Remove the three screws securing the

distributor body halves and separate the assembly **(see illustration)**.

4 Lift out the plastic spacer ring from the upper distributor body half **(see illustration)**.

5 Remove the trigger coil to ignition amplifier module connector and seal, having noted which way the connector fits for subsequent reassembly **(see illustration)**.

6 Lift out the trigger coil, before careful not to damage it or its connectors as it is withdrawn.

7 Remove the stator securing circlip and the upper shim followed by the stator and the lower shim **(see illustration)**.

8 Undo the vacuum diaphragm unit securing screw and detach the unit.

9 This is the limit of dismantling that can be undertaken on these distributors. Should the distributor be worn or unserviceable in any other respect, renewal of the complete unit will be necessary.

10 Reassembling is a reversal of the dismantling procedure. During reassembly, ensure that the pin on the vacuum diaphragm unit arm engaged in the stator as the stator is refitted, and fit the plastic spacer ring so that its cut-out aligns with the trigger coil to ignition amplifier module connector. Additionally, after the distributor body halves' securing screws have been tightened, ensure that the distributor shaft turns easily. Refit the ignition amplifier module in accordance with Section 4.

10 Ignition timing - checking and adjustment

Distributorless ignition systems

1 The ignition timing is controlled entirely by the ignition module (acting in conjunction with the EEC IV engine management module on fuel injection engines), and can only be checked and adjusted when the system is connected to Ford diagnostic equipment.

2 If the timing is thought to be incorrect, this can only be due to a fault in the ignition module or engine management system components and the vehicle should be taken to a Ford dealer for full testing and fault diagnosis.

Distributor ignition systems (CVH engines with carburettor)

Note: *When an engine is timed in production, marks are punched into the cylinder head and the distributor body flange to indicate the correct timing position of the distributor (see illustration 8.2). Therefore, under normal circumstances, ignition timing adjustment will only be necessary if the initial setting has been disturbed. An ignition timing setting for use with unleaded petrol (95 RON) is given in the Specifications*

3 Where the original punch marks are present on the cylinder head and the distributor body flange, correct ignition timing can be set, as necessary, by turning the body of the distributor to align the marks before re-tightening the distributor clamp bolts.

4 If, due to component renewal, one or both of the original punch marks is missing, the following procedure must be carried out.

5 Turn the distributor body so that the clamp bolts are located centrally in their slots then tighten the clamp bolts.

6 Increase the contrast of the notch in the crankshaft pulley and the appropriate mark on the timing cover scale (refer to *Specifications*) by applying a dab of quick-drying white paint **(see illustration)**.

7 Connect a stroboscopic timing light in

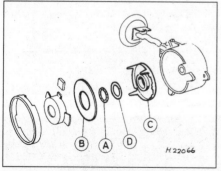

9.7 Stator and shim details

A Circlip   C Stator
B Upper shim   D Lower shim

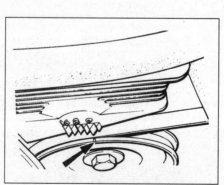

10.6 Crankshaft pulley timing notch (arrowed) and timing marks on the timing cover scale

5B

accordance with the manufacturer's instructions.

8 Start the engine, bring it up to normal operating temperature and allow it to idle.

9 Disconnect the vacuum pipe from the distributor and fit blanking plugs.

10 If the timing light is now directed at the engine timing marks, the pulley notch will appear to be stationary and opposite the specified mark on the scale. If the marks are not in alignment, release the distributor clamp bolts slightly and turn the distributor body in whichever direction is necessary to align the pulley notch to the appropriate scale mark. Tighten the clamp bolts fully when the setting is correct.

11 Using a suitable punch, re-mark the cylinder head and/or the distributor flange to indicate the new distributor timing position for any future repair operations.

12 The operation of the centrifugal advance weights in the distributor can be checked by increasing the engine speed with the timing light pointing at the engine timing marks and observing that the pulley notch advances from its initial position.

13 To check the vacuum advance, run the engine at a fast idle speed and reconnect the vacuum pipe. The pulley notch should again advance.

14 Stop the engine, disconnect the tachometer and timing light and reconnect the vacuum pipe. Refit the timing aperture cover.

15 If the timing notch did not appear to move during the centrifugal advance check, a fault in the distributor centrifugal advance mechanism is indicated. No increased movement of the notch during the vacuum advance check indicate a punctured diaphragm in the vacuum unit, or a leak in the vacuum line.

16 On completion of the adjustments and checks, switch the engine off, disconnect the timing light and ensure that the distributor vacuum pipe is securely connected.

Distributor ignition systems (pre-September 1990 CVH engines with CFi fuel injection)

Note: *When an engine is timed in production it is set, using a microwave timing system, to an accuracy of within half a degree. Unless it is essential, do not remove the distributor or alter the ignition timing. If no distributor timing position punch marks are present on the cylinder head and distributor body flange,* *make your own before disturbing the setting (see illustration 8.2).*

17 The method of obtaining correct ignition timing, with both original punch marks present, is described in paragraph 3 above.

18 If (due to component renewal) one or both of the punch marks is missing, an approximate ignition timing setting can be obtained to enable starting of the engine by following the instruction given in Section 8, paragraph 16.

19 Accurate ignition timing adjustment can only be carried out using specialised equipment - this is a task for your Ford dealer or other suitably equipped specialist. The reason for this is that the EEC IV engine management module has to "lock" its internal ignition advance compensations and its idle speed control whilst the timing is set. The "locking" of the EEC IV module is performed in "self-test" mode when connected to the Ford STAR test (Self-Test Automatic Readout) equipment, which is also used to access fault codes stored in the module memory and analyse the performance of the system components. New punch marks should be made after accurate timing has been carried out, as necessary.

Chapter 6
Clutch

Contents

Clutch assembly - removal, inspection and refitting 4
Clutch cable - removal and refitting 2
Clutch pedal - removal and refitting 3
Clutch release bearing - removal, inspection and refitting 5
Clutch release shaft and bush - removal and refitting 6
General information 1

Degrees of difficulty

Easy, suitable for novice with little experience	**Fairly easy,** suitable for beginner with some experience	**Fairly difficult,** suitable for competent DIY mechanic	**Difficult,** suitable for experienced DIY mechanic	**Very difficult,** suitable for expert DIY or professional

Specifications

General

Type	Diaphragm spring, single dry plate, cable operation
Actuation	Self-adjusting cable
Disc diameter:	
1.0, 1.1, 1.3 and 1.4 litre engines	190 mm
1.6 and 1.8 litre engines	220 mm

Torque wrench settings

	Nm	lbf ft
Clutch cover (pressure plate) to flywheel	25 to 34	18 to 25
Clutch release lever to lever shaft	21 to 28	16 to 21

1 General information

All manual transmission models are equipped with a cable-operated single dry plate diaphragm spring clutch assembly. The unit consists of a clutch disc (or driven plate), a steel cover (doweled and bolted to the rear face of the flywheel, it contains the pressure plate and diaphragm spring) and a release mechanism.

The clutch disc is free to slide along the splines of the transmission input shaft, and is held in position between the flywheel and the pressure plate by the pressure of the diaphragm spring. Friction lining material is riveted to the clutch disc, which has a spring cushioned hub to absorb transmission shocks and help ensure a smooth take-up of the drive.

The clutch is actuated by a cable, controlled by the clutch pedal. The clutch release mechanism consists of a release arm and bearing, which is in permanent contact with the fingers of the diaphragm spring. Depressing the clutch pedal actuates the release arm by means of the cable. The arm pushes the release bearing against the diaphragm fingers, so moving the centre of the diaphragm spring inwards. As the centre of the spring is pushed in, the outside of the spring pivots out, so moving the pressure plate backwards and disengaging its grip on the clutch disc.

When the pedal is released, the diaphragm spring forces the pressure plate back into contact with the friction linings on the clutch disc. The disc is now firmly held between the pressure plate and the flywheel, thus transmitting engine power to the transmission.

Wear of the friction material on the clutch disc is automatically compensated for by a self-adjusting mechanism attached to the clutch pedal. The self-adjusting mechanism consists of a toothed segment, a notched pawl and a tension spring. One end of the clutch cable is attached to the segment which is free to pivot on the pedal, but is kept in tension by the spring. As the pedal is depressed, the pawl contacts the segment, thus locking it and allowing the pedal to pull the cable and operate the clutch. As the pedal is released, the tension spring causes the segment to move free of the pawl and rotate slightly, thus taking up any free play that may exist in the cable.

2 Clutch cable - removal and refitting

Removal

1 At the transmission end, disengage the clutch cable from the release lever by gripping the inner cable with pliers, pulling it forwards to disengage the cable nipple from the release lever. Take care not to damage the cable if it is to be re-used. Disengage the outer cable from the support lug on top of the bellhousing **(see illustrations)**.

2.1a Disengage the clutch cable from the lever . . .

2.1b . . . and withdraw the cable through the locating lug

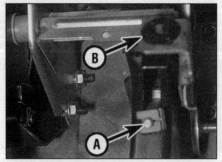

3.3 Brake servo operating link pushrod retaining clip (A) and stop light switch location (B)

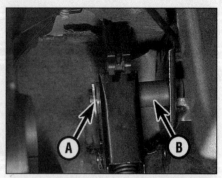

3.5 C-clip (A) and clutch pedal spacer (B)

2 Working from the driver's footwell, unhook the quadrant tension spring from its pedal location.

3 Release the cable from the pedal quadrant so that it may be withdrawn through the engine compartment.

4 Pull the cable through the aperture in the bulkhead, unhook the cable from its clip location and withdraw it from the engine compartment.

Refitting

5 To refit the cable, thread it through from the engine compartment and fit the inner cable over the quadrant, engaging the nipple to secure it. Reconnect the tension spring.

6 Reconnect the cable at the transmission end, passing it through the support lug on the top of the transmission and engaging it with the release lever.

7 On completion operate the clutch and check it for satisfactory operation.

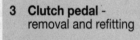

3 Clutch pedal - removal and refitting

Removal

1 Disconnect the battery negative (earth) lead (refer to Chapter 5A, Section 1).

2 Remove the clutch cable from its pedal location and pull it through into the engine compartment, as described in the previous Section.

3.7 Pedal box left-hand side retaining nuts in engine compartment (arrowed)

3 Remove the clip securing the brake servo operating link pushrod to the brake pedal, noting the bush fitted in the pedal, and disconnect the brake stop light switch wiring connector. Release the brake stop light switch in a clockwise direction, and extract it from the pedal bracket **(see illustration)**.

4 Remove the accelerator pedal by first disconnecting its cable from the cut-out in the top of the pedal moulding. Detach the clip securing the pedal onto its shaft, then slide the pedal off.

5 Detach the retaining C-clip from the left-hand side of the main pedal shaft **(see illustration)**.

6 Remove the two nuts securing the clutch end-bracket to the main pedal box.

7 Undo and remove the two nuts in the engine compartment that secure the left-hand side of the pedal box to the bulkhead **(see illustration)**.

8 Undo and remove the two nuts on the right-hand side of the pedal box that secure the

pedal box, and the right-hand brake servo operating link support bracket, to the bulkhead.

9 The pedal box can be pulled out to free the clutch end-bracket after slackening or removing the two bolts that secure the pedal box vertically to the bulkhead, as necessary.

10 Slide clutch end-bracket from its location, followed by the pedal and pedal spacer.

11 The pedal can now be dismantled as necessary, by prising out the bushes on either side, in order to renew the bushes, tension spring or adjustment mechanism **(see illustration)**.

12 If required, the main pedal shaft may be withdrawn at this stage by removing the C-clip retaining it, and sliding the shaft towards the centre of the vehicle. The C-clip is located next to the brake pedal. As the shaft is slid from its location, the brake pedal and its spacer must be removed. As clearance is tight, the pedal box will have to be manoeuvred to fully withdraw the shaft.

Refitting

13 To refit the main pedal shaft, reverse the removal procedure, locating the "D" section of the shaft into the pedal box right-hand support. Ensure that the brake pedal and spacer are correctly located.

14 Lubricate the pedal shaft using molybdenum disulphide grease.

15 Refit the pawl and its associated spring to the clutch pedal, then insert the quadrant, tension spring and bushes, so that the pawl bears on the smooth section of the quadrant **(see illustration)**. Do not hook the tension

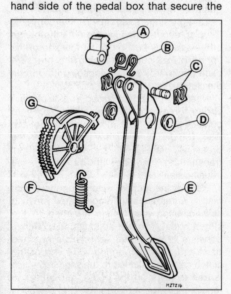

3.11 Clutch pedal and associated components

A Pawl
B Pawl tension spring
C Pedal connecting rod and clip
D Pedal/shaft bushes
E Clutch pedal
F Toothed quadrant tension spring
G Toothed quadrant

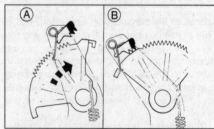

3.15 Positioning the clutch self-adjustment mechanism prior to refitting the pedal

A Lift pawl and turn the quadrant
B Pawl bearing on the smooth section of the quadrant

spring onto its lower pedal location at this stage.

16 Refit the pedal spacer, the clutch pedal assembly and the clutch end-bracket to the pedal shaft, then manipulate the pedal box assembly back into its correct location before refitting the two nuts to secure the end-bracket to the main pedal box.

17 The remainder of refitting is now a reversal of the removal procedure, fully tightening all the nuts once the individual components have been correctly assembled.

18 When refitting the stop light switch, insert the switch into its retainer, press it lightly against the brake pedal until all free play is just taken up, then turn the switch clockwise to secure. Reconnect the switch wiring connector.

19 On completion, operate the clutch pedal to ensure correct cable adjustment and check for correct functioning of the stop lights.

---

4 Clutch assembly - removal, inspection and refitting

> ⚠ **Warning: Dust created by clutch wear and deposited on the clutch components may contain asbestos, which is a health hazard. DO NOT blow it out with compressed air, or inhale any of it. DO NOT use petrol or petroleum-based solvents to clean off the dust. Brake system cleaner or methylated spirit should be used to flush the dust into a suitable receptacle. After the clutch components are wiped clean with rags, dispose of the contaminated rags and cleaner in a sealed, marked container.**

Removal

1 Access to the clutch may be gained in one of two ways. Depending on the engine fitted, either the engine or engine/transmission can be removed as described in Chapter 2D, and where applicable, the transmission separated from the engine, or the engine may be left in the car and the transmission removed independently, as described in Chapter 7A.

2 Having separated the transmission from the engine, check if there are any marks identifying the relation of the clutch cover to the flywheel. If not, make your own marks using a dab of paint or a scriber. These marks will be used if the original cover is refitted, and will help to maintain the balance of the unit. A new cover may be fitted in any position allowed by the locating dowels.

3 Unscrew and remove the clutch cover retaining bolts, working in a diagonal sequence and slackening the bolts only a few turns at a time. If necessary, the flywheel may be held stationary using a wide-bladed screwdriver, inserted in the teeth of the starter ring gear and resting against part of the cylinder block.

4 Ease the clutch cover off its locating dowels. Be prepared to catch the clutch disc, which will drop out as the cover is removed. Note which way round the disc is fitted **(see illustration)**.

Inspection

5 The most common problem which occurs in the clutch is wear of the clutch disc. However, all the clutch components should be inspected at this time, particularly if the vehicle has covered a high mileage. Unless the clutch components are known to be virtually new, it is worth renewing them all as a set (disc, pressure plate and release bearing). Renewing a worn clutch disc by itself is not always satisfactory, especially if the old disc was slipping and causing the pressure plate to overheat. Not renewing the release bearing is a false economy - it's bound to wear out eventually, and all the preliminary dismantling will have to be repeated if it's not renewed with the rest of the clutch.

6 Examine the linings of the clutch disc for wear and loose rivets, and the disc hub and rim for distortion, cracks, broken torsion springs, and worn splines. The surface of the friction linings may be highly glazed, but as long as the friction material pattern can be clearly seen, and the rivet heads are at least 1 mm below the lining surface, this is satisfactory. If there is any sign of oil contamination, indicated by shiny black discoloration, the disc must be renewed, and the source of the contamination traced and rectified. This will be a leaking crankshaft oil seal or transmission input shaft oil seal. The

renewal procedure for the former is given in the appropriate Part of Chapter 2; renewal of the transmission input shaft oil seal should be entrusted to a Ford dealer, as it involves major dismantling and the renewal of the clutch release bearing guide tube, using a press.

7 Check the machined faces of the flywheel and pressure plate. If either is grooved, or heavily scored, renewal is necessary. The pressure plate must also be renewed if any cracks are apparent, or if the diaphragm spring is damaged, or its pressure suspect. Pay particular attention to the tips of the spring fingers, where the release bearing acts upon them.

8 When obtaining new clutch components for 1.6 and 1.8 litre engine models, note that the clutch cover assemblies and clutch discs may be marked "Low-lift" **(see illustration)**. This is to identify them as being of a modified design which, by altering the pressure plate's internal ratio, increases the clutch's torque-handling capabilities without increasing pedal travel/effort; this results in reduced pressure plate lift, hence the designation.

9 Clutch cover assemblies and clutch discs marked in this way must never be mixed with unmarked components, or the clutch take-up may be faulty; it is possible that a mixture may even result in a clutch that cannot release. **Always** use only a cover assembly and driven pate that are correctly marked when renewing these components.

10 With the transmission removed, it is also advisable to check the condition of the release bearing, as described in Section 5. Having got this far, it is almost certainly worth renewing it.

Refitting

11 It is important that no oil or grease is allowed to come into contact with the friction material of the clutch disc or the pressure plate and flywheel faces. To ensure this, it is advisable to refit the clutch assembly with clean hands, and to wipe down the pressure plate and flywheel faces with a clean rag before assembly begins.

12 Begin reassembly by placing the clutch disc against the flywheel, ensuring that it is correctly orientated. It may be marked "flywheel side" **(see illustration)**, but if not,

4.4 Removing the clutch cover and disc from the flywheel

4.8 "Low-lift" markings (arrowed) on clutch components

4.12 Clutch disc orientation markings

4.18 Tightening the cover retaining bolts with the alignment tool in position

position it with the word "schwungradseite" stamped in the disc face towards the flywheel.

13 Place the clutch cover over the dowels, refit the retaining bolts, and tighten them finger-tight so that the clutch disc is gripped, but can still be moved.

14 The clutch disc must now be centralised so that, when the engine and transmission are mated, the splines of the input shaft will pass through the splines in the centre of the clutch disc hub.

15 Centralisation can be carried out by inserting a round bar through the hole in the centre of the clutch disc, so that the end of the bar rests in the innermost hole in the rear end of the crankshaft. Move the bar sideways or up and down to move the clutch disc in whichever direction is necessary to achieve centralisation.

16 Centralisation can then be checked by removing the bar and viewing the clutch disc hub in relation to the diaphragm spring fingers. When the disc hub appears exactly in the centre of the circle created by the diaphragm spring fingers, the position is correct.

17 An alternative and more accurate method of centralisation is to use a commercially-available clutch-aligning tool, obtainable from most accessory shops.

18 Once the clutch is centralised, progressively tighten the cover bolts in a diagonal sequence to the torque setting given in the Specifications **(see illustration)**.

19 Ensure that the input shaft splines, clutch disc splines and release bearing guide sleeve are clean. Apply a thin smear of high-melting-point grease to the input shaft splines and the release bearing guide sleeve. Only use a very small amount of grease, otherwise the excess will inevitably find its way onto the friction linings when the vehicle is in use.

20 The engine/transmission can now be refitted by referring to the relevant Chapters of this manual.

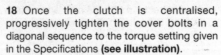

5 Clutch release bearing - removal, inspection and refitting

Note: *Refer to the warning at the beginning of Section 4 before proceeding.*

Removal

1 Separate the engine and transmission as described in the previous Section.

2 Withdraw the release bearing from its guide sleeve by turning the release arm **(see illustration)**.

Inspection

3 Check the bearing for smoothness of operation, and renew it if there is any sign of harshness or roughness as the bearing is spun. Do not attempt to dismantle, clean or lubricate the bearing.

4 As mentioned earlier, it is worth renewing the release bearing as a matter of course, unless it is known to be in perfect condition.

5 When obtaining new components, note that some transmissions have a steel sleeve fitted over the (aluminium alloy) guide sleeve. In such cases, only a modified release bearing with the necessary larger inside diameter can be fitted.

Refitting

6 Refitting of the clutch release bearing is a reversal of the removal procedure, making sure that it is correctly located on the release arm fork. It is helpful to slightly lift the release arm while locating the bearing on its guide sleeve. Keep the fork in contact with the plastic shoulders on the bearing (where fitted) as the bearing is being located.

6 Clutch release shaft and bush - removal and refitting

Removal

1 Remove the clutch release bearing as described in the previous Section.

2 Unscrew the clamp bolt securing the release arm to the shaft **(see illustration)**. Mark the relative position of the shaft to the arm, then withdraw the arm from the shaft. The shaft has a master spline, to ensure that the arm is fitted correctly.

3 Remove the protective cap from around the top of the release shaft splines to allow access to the bush.

4 Extract the bush by gently levering it from the housing using a pair of screwdrivers, then lift it out over the splines of the shaft.

5 With the bush removed, the release shaft can be withdrawn (if required) by lifting it from its lower bearing bore, manoeuvring it sideways and withdrawing it **(see illustration)**.

Refitting

6 Refit in the reverse order of removal. Slide the bush over the shaft, and locate it so that it is flush in the upper housing, then fit the protective cap.

7 Refit the release bearing as described in the previous Section.

5.2 Withdrawing the clutch release bearing

6.2 Clutch release arm-to-shaft connection with clamp bolt and nut (arrowed)

6.5 Removing the clutch release shaft

4 Speedometer drive pinion - removal and refitting

Removal

1 Disconnect the battery negative (earth) lead (refer to Chapter 5A, Section 1).

2 Undo the retaining nut, and withdraw the speedometer cable from the drive pinion or vehicle speed sensor in the top face of the transmission. If a vehicle speed sensor is fitted, use two spanners to loosen the nut - one to counterhold the sensor, and the other to unscrew the cable nut.

3 Where applicable, disconnect the wiring from the vehicle speed sensor, then unscrew the sensor from the top of the drive pinion.

4 Grip the drive pinion retaining pin with self-locking grips or pliers, and withdraw it from the drive pinion housing.

5 Pull the drive pinion and bearing out of the housing, but take care not to tilt it, because the pinion and bearing are not secured and can easily be separated if the pinion is snagged **(see illustration)**.

6 Using a small screwdriver, prise the O-ring from the groove in the bearing; obtain a new one for reassembly.

7 Wipe clean the drive pinion and bearing, also the seating bore in the transmission casing.

Refitting

8 Refitting is a reversal of the removal procedure, but lightly oil the new O-ring before inserting the assembly in the transmission casing. Drive in the retaining roll pin using a hammer **(see illustration)**.

5 Oil seals - renewal

1 Oil leaks frequently occur due to wear or deterioration of the differential side gear seals and/or the gearchange selector shaft oil seal and speedometer drive pinion O-ring. Renewal of these seals is relatively easy, since the repairs can be performed without removing the transmission from the vehicle.

Differential side gear oil seals

2 The differential side gear oil seals are located at the sides of the transmission, where the driveshafts enter the transmission. If leakage at the seal is suspected, raise the vehicle and support it securely on axle stands (see *"Jacking and vehicle support"*). If the seal is leaking, oil will be found on the side of the transmission below the driveshaft.

3 Refer to Chapter 8 and remove the appropriate driveshaft.

4 Wipe clean the old oil seal, note its orientation and measure its fitted depth below

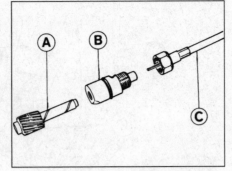

4.5 Speedometer drive pinion (A) pinion bearing (B) and drive cable (C)

the casing edge. This is necessary to determine the correct fitted position of the new oil seal.

5 Using a large screwdriver or lever, carefully prise the oil seal out of the transmission casing, taking care not to damage the casing **(see illustration)**. If the oil seal is reluctant to move, it is sometimes helpful to carefully drive it *into* the transmission a little way, applying the force at one point only. This will have the effect of swivelling the seal out of the casing, and it can then be pulled out. If the oil seal is particularly difficult to remove, an oil seal removal tool may be obtained from a garage or accessory shop.

6 Wipe clean the oil seal seating in the transmission casing.

7 Dip the new oil seal in clean oil, then press it a little way into the casing by hand, making sure that it is square to its seating.

8 Using suitable tubing or a large socket, carefully drive the oil seal fully into the casing up to its previously-noted fitted depth **(see illustration)**.

9 Refit the driveshaft with reference to Chapter 8.

Gearchange selector shaft oil seal

10 Working inside the car, first engage 2nd gear (4-speed transmission) or 4th gear (5-speed transmission). This will provide the correct re-engagement and adjustment for the gearchange mechanism during reassembly.

5.5 Levering out an old differential side gear oil seal

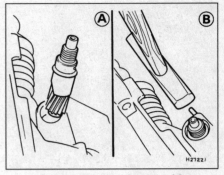

4.8 Insert the speedometer drive pinion/bearing (A) and secure with a new retaining pin (B)

11 Chock the rear wheels then jack up the front of the car and support it on axle stands (see *"Jacking and vehicle support"*). Remove the front roadwheels.

12 Unscrew the bolt securing the gearchange linkage to the shaft on the rear of the transmission. Pull off the linkage and remove the rubber boot.

13 Using a suitable tool or grips, pull the oil seal out of the transmission casing. Ford technicians use a slide hammer, with an end fitting which locates over the oil seal extension. In the absence of this tool, if the oil seal is particularly tight, drill one or two small holes in the oil seal, and screw in self-tapping screws. The oil seal can then be removed from the casing by pulling on the screws.

14 Wipe clean the oil seal seating in the transmission.

15 Dip the new oil seal in clean oil, then press it a little way into the casing by hand, making sure that it is square to its seating.

16 Using suitable tubing or a large socket, carefully drive the oil seal fully into the casing.

17 Locate the rubber boot over the selector shaft.

18 The gearchange linkage can now be reconnected and adjusted using the procedure described in Section 2.

Speedometer drive pinion oil seal

19 The procedure is covered in Section 4 of this Chapter.

5.8 Driving a new oil seal into position using a suitable socket

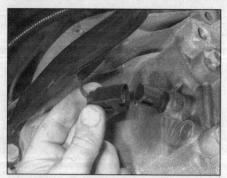

6.2 Disconnecting the reversing light switch lead

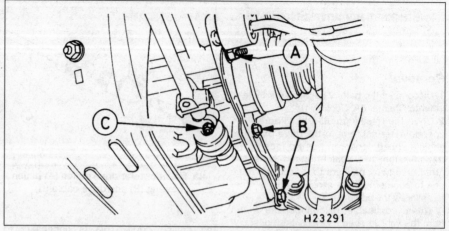

7.15 Exhaust forward mounting bracket retaining nut (A), lower engine adaptor plate bolts (B) and gearchange mechanism shift rod clamp bolt (C)

6 Reversing light switch - removal and refitting

Removal

1 Chock the rear wheels then jack up the front of the car and support it on axle stands (see "Jacking and vehicle support").

2 Disconnect the wiring from the reversing light switch **(see illustration)**.

3 Unscrew the switch from the side of the transmission, and remove the washer.

Refitting

4 Clean the location in the transmission, and the threads of the switch.

5 Insert the switch together with a new washer, and tighten it to the specified torque wrench setting.

6 Reconnect the wiring.

7 Check and top-up the transmission oil level if necessary, with reference to Chapter 1.

8 Lower the vehicle to the ground.

7 Manual transmission - removal and refitting

Note: *Read through this procedure before starting work to see what is involved, particularly in terms of lifting equipment. Depending on the facilities available and the engine fitted, it may be preferable to remove the engine and transmission together, then separate them on the bench, as described in Chapter 2D.*

Removal

1 The manual transmission is removed downwards from the engine compartment, after disconnecting it from the engine. Due to the weight of the unit, it will be necessary to have a suitable method of supporting the transmission as it is lowered during removal and subsequently raised during its refitting. A trolley jack fitted with a suitable saddle to support the transmission as it is removed will be ideal, but failing this, an engine lift hoist

and sling will suffice. The weight of the engine will also need to be supported whilst the transmission is detached from it - an engine support bar fitted in the front wing drain channel each side is ideal for this purpose, but care must be taken not to damage the wings or their paintwork. If this type of tool is not available (or cannot be fabricated), the engine can be supported by blocks or a second jack from underneath.

2 Disconnect the battery negative (earth) lead (refer to Chapter 5A, Section 1).

3 Refer to the applicable Part of Chapter 4 and remove the air cleaner and air inlet components as necessary for access to the transmission. Disconnect the clutch cable from the clutch release lever as described in Chapter 6.

4 Undo the retaining nut, and detach the speedometer drive cable from the transmission. Also where applicable, disconnect the speed sensor lead multi-plug. Position the cable (and where applicable, the sensor lead) out of the way.

5 Unbolt and disconnect the radio earth strap from the transmission.

6 Extract the transmission breather tube from the aperture in the chassis side member.

7 On 4-speed models, engage 2nd gear. On 5-speed models, engage 4th gear. This will ease realignment and adjustment of the gearchange linkage during the refitting procedures.

8 Unscrew and remove the upper transmission-to-engine flange bolts. Note that one bolt secures the main earth strap to the battery, and one bolt retains the coolant hose locating strap.

9 Apply the handbrake, then raise the vehicle at the front. Support it on axle stands at a sufficient height to allow the transmission to be withdrawn from under the front end (see "Jacking and vehicle support").

10 On XR2i models, the one-piece undertray (if fitted) should be removed, followed by the front suspension crossmember (see Chapter 10).

11 On models equipped with anti-lock brakes, refer to Chapter 9 and detach the left-hand modulator from its mounting bracket (without disconnecting the rigid brake pipes or return hose); tie the modulator securely to the bulkhead.

12 Fit the engine support bar, or failing this, position a jack under the engine. Whichever is used, raise the engine so that its weight is just taken from the mountings.

13 Disconnect the lead connector from the reversing light switch.

14 Detach the wiring, and then unbolt and withdraw the starter motor. Refer to Chapter 5A for full details.

15 Detach the exhaust forward mounting bracket (if fitted) by unscrewing its retaining nut and the clutch housing cover plate bolts **(see illustration)**. Remove the lower engine adapter plate.

16 Where fitted, undo the retaining bolts and remove the engine/transmission adapter plate.

17 Before disconnecting the gearshift rod, mark the relative fitted positions of the gearshift rod and the selector shaft, as a guide for refitting and adjustment.

18 Undo the gearshift rod stabiliser-to-transmission retaining bolt. Separate the stabiliser from the transmission (noting the washer fitted between the stabiliser and the transmission). Tie the gearshift rod and stabiliser up out of the way.

19 Referring to Chapter 10 for details, detach the track rod end balljoint from the steering arm on the left-hand side, and the suspension arm-to-spindle carrier balljoint on the left and right-hand sides. Where fitted, disconnect the anti-roll bar connecting links from both suspension struts.

20 On models equipped with anti-lock brakes, refer to Chapter 9 and detach the right-hand modulator from its mounting bracket (without disconnecting the rigid brake pipes or return hose); tie the modulator securely to the bulkhead. Additionally, undo the three bolts securing the modulator mounting bracket.

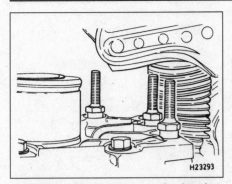

7.25 Rear transmission mounting bracket threaded studs in transmission housing

21 Insert a suitable lever between the driveshaft inner CV joint and the transmission, and carefully lever the driveshaft free from the transmission. Lever against the reinforcement rib or use a suitable protective block of wood to avoid damaging the transmission housing, and have an assistant pull the suspension strut outwards on the side being detached, to assist in the driveshaft withdrawal from the transmission. As the driveshaft is withdrawn, be prepared for escaping oil.

22 When the driveshaft is detached from the transmission, tie it up out of the way. Do not allow the inner CV joint or the driveshaft to be angled by more than 20°.

23 Repeat the above procedure and detach the driveshaft on the opposite side. After removal of both driveshafts, plug the apertures in the differential (or preferably and if available, insert old CV joints) to prevent further oil leakage, and to immobilise the differential gears.

24 With the engine/transmission supported, detach the transmission bearer from the transmission and the floorpan and remove it.

25 Lower the engine/transmission as far as the engine support bar allows, then unscrew the three nuts securing the rear transmission mounting bracket to the transmission and remove the bracket **(see illustration)**.

26 Unscrew the three threaded studs of the rear transmission mounting bracket from the transmission.

27 Make a final check to ensure that all of the transmission connections have been detached and are positioned out of the way.

The transmission is ready to be withdrawn after removing the four remaining engine/transmission flange bolts.

28 Check that the engine remains securely supported. The method of supporting the transmission during its removal is largely a matter of personal choice and/or the facilities available. It can be supported from above, and lowered (using a conventional hoist) onto a trolley for withdrawal from under the vehicle. Failing this, it can be supported underneath with a suitable trolley jack, and withdrawn from under the front end. Whichever method is employed, engage the aid of an assistant to help guide the transmission down and clear of the surrounding components in the engine compartment.

29 Withdraw the transmission from the engine, taking care not to allow the weight of the transmission to rest on the input shaft at any time. Once the input shaft is clear of the clutch unit, the transmission can be lowered and manoeuvred down through the engine compartment, and then withdrawn from underneath the vehicle.

Refitting

30 Refitting is a reversal of removal, but note the following additional points:

a) *Make sure that all mating faces are clean.*
b) *Apply a smear of high-melting-point grease to the splines of the transmission input shaft. Do not apply too much, otherwise there is the possibility of the grease contaminating the clutch friction disc.*
c) *Where applicable, ensure that the engine adapter plate is correctly seated on the locating dowels on the engine.*
d) *On vehicles fitted with anti-lock brakes, ensure that the belts are located over the driveshafts and that the right hand modulator mounting bracket is in position before reconnecting the driveshaft assemblies.*
e) *Fit new snap-rings to the grooves in the inner end of each driveshaft CV joint, and ensure that they are felt to snap fully into engagement as they are fitted into position in the transmission.*
f) *Refer to Chapter 10 for details on reconnecting the suspension arm/steering balljoint and track rod end balljoint.*

g) *Reconnect and adjust the gearchange linkage as described in Section 2.*
h) *Tighten all nuts and bolts to the specified torque settings.*
i) *Replenish the transmission oil, and check the level with reference to Chapter 1.*

9 Manual transmission overhaul - general

No work can be carried out to the transmission until the engine/transmission has been removed from the car and cleaned externally.

Overhauling a manual transmission is a difficult and involved job for the DIY home mechanic. In addition to dismantling and reassembling many small parts, clearances must be precisely measured and, if necessary, changed by selecting shims and spacers. Internal transmission components are also often difficult to obtain, and in many instances, are extremely expensive. Because of this, if the transmission develops a fault or becomes noisy, the best course of action is to have the unit overhauled by a specialist repairer, or to obtain an exchange reconditioned unit.

Nevertheless, it is not impossible for the more experienced mechanic to overhaul the transmission, provided the special tools are available, and that the job is done in a deliberate step-by-step manner so that nothing is overlooked.

The tools necessary for an overhaul may include internal and external circlip pliers, bearing pullers, a slide hammer, a set of pin punches, a dial test indicator, and possibly a hydraulic press. In addition, a large, sturdy workbench and a vice will be required.

During dismantling of the transmission, make careful notes of how each component is fitted, to make reassembly easier and accurate.

Before dismantling the transmission, it will help if you have some idea which area is malfunctioning. Certain problems can be closely related to specific areas in the transmission, which can make component examination and replacement easier.

7A

Notes

Chapter 7 Part B:
Automatic transmission

Contents

Automatic transmission fluid renewal . . . . .See Chapter 1
Automatic transmission fluid level check . . . . .See Chapter 1
Automatic transmission - removal and refitting 6
Automatic transmission overhaul - general 7
Fluid seals - renewal 5
Gear selector mechanism - removal and refitting 3
General information and precautions 1
Selector cable - removal, refitting and adjustment 2
Speedometer drive pinion - removal and refitting 4
Starter inhibitor switch - removal and refitting 8

Degrees of difficulty

Easy, suitable for novice with little experience		Fairly easy, suitable for beginner with some experience		Fairly difficult, suitable for competent DIY mechanic		Difficult, suitable for experienced DIY mechanic		Very difficult, suitable for expert DIY or professional	

Specifications

Torque wrench settings	Nm	lbf ft
Transmission fluid cooling pipes to oil cooler	18 to 22	13 to 16
Transmission fluid cooling pipe connectors to transmission housing . .	24 to 31	18 to 23
Transmission fluid cooling pipes to connectors	22 to 26	16 to 19
Starter inhibitor switch	9 to 14	7 to 10
Flange bolts - transmission to engine	27 to 50	20 to 37
Torsional vibration damper to flywheel	24 to 33	18 to 24
Lower engine adapter plate (clutch housing cover)	7.5 to 9	5 to 7
Selector lever housing to floor	8.5 to 11.5	6 to 8
Selector cable bracket to transmission housing	34 to 46	25 to 34
Selector lever rod to selector lever guide	20 to 25	15 to 18
Transmission bearer to body	52 to 64	38 to 47

1 General information and precautions

The CTX transmission is an automatic transmission providing continuously-variable drive over the entire speed range. Torque from the engine is transmitted to the transmission via an input shaft and a multi-plate wet clutch (rather than a conventional torque converter employed on most automatic transmissions).

A steel thrust-link drivebelt made of disc-shaped steel elements transmits the torque from the primary cone pulley (driven by the engine) to the secondary cone pulley. The secondary cone pulley is linked by a series of gears to the final drive gear which drives the differential unit and the driveshafts.

The continuous variation in ratio is produced by altering the diameter of the path followed by the drivebelt around the two cone pulleys. This alteration of the drivebelt path is produced by an hydraulic control system which moves one half of each cone pulley in

an axial direction. The secondary pulley cone is also spring-loaded, to keep the drivebelt at the required tension needed to transmit the torque. The hydraulic control system is governed by the position of the transmission selector lever, the accelerator and the load resistance encountered (such as up or down gradients), as well as road speed.

The selector lever is connected to the transmission selector shaft by a cable.

A gear-type pump delivers fluid (according to the input speed) to the hydraulic control system. A transmission fluid cooler is located in the side tank of the engine coolant radiator.

As with conventional automatic transmission systems, the CTX type has a parking mechanism. The parking pawl engages with the teeth on the outside of the secondary pulley. A starter inhibitor switch prevents the engine from being started in selector positions R, D or L.

When accelerating, the engine speed may sound higher than would normally be expected, similar to a slipping clutch on a manual transmission vehicle. The reverse is true when decelerating, with the engine speed dropping faster than the comparable drop in

road speed. These are normal characteristics of the CTX transmission.

Precautions

When the vehicle is parked and left with the engine running, or when any checks and/or adjustments are being carried out, the handbrake must be applied and the selector lever moved to the "P" position.

Do not allow the engine speed to rise above the normal idle speed when the vehicle is stationary with the selector lever in the R, D or L position.

The engine must not run at more than 3000 rpm with the selector lever in the R, D or L position when the driving (front) roadwheels are clear of the ground.

If the vehicle is to be towed with the front wheels on the road, move the selector lever to position N. If the distance that the vehicle is to be towed is no more than 30 miles (50 km), it can be towed up to a maximum towing speed of 30 mph (50 kph). Ideally, the vehicle should always be towed on a trailer or dolly with the front wheels clear of the road - where the towing distance exceeds 30 miles (50 km), this is essential.

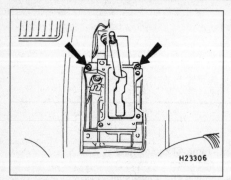

2.4 Transmission selector gate securing screws (arrowed)

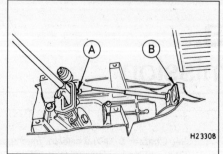

2.5 Selector cable fixture to selector lever (A) and selector cable abutment retaining clip arrangement (B)

2.7 Removing the clip that secures the selector cable yoke to the lever on the transmission selector shaft

2 Selector cable - removal, refitting and adjustment

Removal

1 Disconnect the battery negative (earth) lead (refer to Chapter 5A, Section 1).

2 Refer to Chapter 11 and remove the centre console, if fitted.

3 Move the selector lever to position "P" (the lever on the transmission selector shaft should also be in position "P" - the most forward position). This is important for correct subsequent adjustment of the selector cable.

4 Detach the selector gate from the selector lever housing by undoing its two securing screws **(see illustration)**. Slide it off over the selector lever, having unscrewed the selector lever knob (if not already removed).

5 Using a suitable screwdriver as a lever, prise free the plastic connecting eye of the selector lever from the cable, then prise free the cable retaining clip, and withdraw the cable from the selector housing. If necessary, cut the carpet at the front to allow extra access **(see illustration)**.

6 Chock the rear wheels then jack up the front of the car and support it on axle stands (see *"Jacking and Vehicle Support"*).

7 Working underneath the vehicle, release the retaining clip and pin, and detach the cable from the selector shaft lever and the transmission housing bracket **(see illustration)**.

8 Pull free the rubber gaiter from the floor, and then withdraw the selector cable from the vehicle.

Refitting

9 Feed the selector cable up through the floor, refit the rubber gaiter, then lower the vehicle to the ground.

10 Reconnect the selector cable to the lever and housing, ensuring that the annular bead of the cable eye faces the end of the pin. Use a suitable pair of pliers to press the pin in until it is heard to clip into engagement **(see illustration)**.

11 The selector lever must now be moved to the "P" position, and the vehicle then raised and supported at the front end again.

12 Reconnect the cable to the transmission, then adjust the cable as follows before refitting the centre console and selector gate assembly.

Adjustment

13 The vehicle must be raised and supported on axle stands at the front end to make the cable adjustment check (see *"Jacking and Vehicle Support"*).

14 With the selector lever set in the "P" position, the parking pawl engaged and the gears immobilised, check that the lever/selector shaft drilling and the cable yoke are in alignment, and that the connecting pin is an easy fit. If required, draw the gaiter back from the yoke, and screw the yoke in the appropriate direction to reposition it on the

cable so that the pin fits freely. Fit the pin and retaining clip, then relocate the bellows.

15 The vehicle can now be lowered to the ground.

3 Gear selector mechanism - removal and refitting

Removal

1 Refer to Section 2, paragraphs 1 to 5 inclusive, to disconnect the cable from the selector housing unit.

2 Pull free the quadrant illumination light bulbholder, then undo the four retaining bolts and remove the selector housing unit **(see illustration)**.

3 To remove the selector lever from the housing, release the clip and extract the lever pivot pin.

4 To remove the selector lever rod from the guide, detach the spring, unscrew the retaining pin nut, withdraw the pin, nut and washer, and withdraw the lever rod **(see illustration)**.

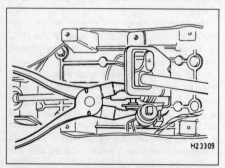

2.10 Securing the selector cable to the selector lever

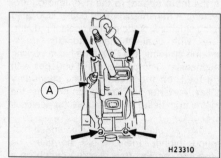

3.2 Selector lever housing retaining bolts (arrowed), and selector cover illumination bulbholder (A)

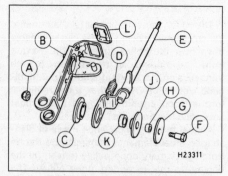

3.4 Exploded view of selector lever assembly

A Nut
B Selector lever guide
C Guide bush
D Spring
E Selector lever
F Retaining pin

G Steel washer
H Spacer bush
J Plastic spacer washer
K Bush
L Plastic guide

Refitting

5 Reassemble and refit in the reverse order of removal. When refitting the selector lever and bushes to the housing, ensure that the wide side of the bush guide faces up.

4 Speedometer drive pinion - removal and refitting

Removal

1 Disconnect the battery negative (earth) lead (refer to Chapter 5A, Section 1).
2 Undo the retaining nut, and withdraw the speedometer cable from the drive pinion or vehicle speed sensor in the top face of the transmission. If a vehicle speed sensor is fitted, use two spanners to loosen the nut - one to counterhold the sensor, and the other to unscrew the cable nut.
3 Where applicable, disconnect the wiring from the vehicle speed sensor, then unscrew the sensor from the top of the drive pinion.
4 Grip the drive pinion retaining roll pin with self-locking grips or pliers, and withdraw it from the drive pinion housing.
5 Pull the drive pinion and bearing out of the housing, but take care not to tilt it, because the pinion and bearing are not secured and can easily be separated if the pinion is snagged.
6 Using a small screwdriver, prise the O-ring from the groove in the bearing; obtain a new one for reassembly.
7 Wipe clean the drive pinion and bearing, also the seating bore in the transmission casing.

Refitting

8 Refitting is a reversal of the removal procedure, but lightly oil the new O-ring before inserting the assembly in the transmission. Drive in the retaining roll pin as far as the stop. When fitted, it should protrude by approximately 5.0 mm.

5 Fluid seals - renewal

Differential side gear fluid seals

1 The procedure is the same as described for the manual transmission (refer to Chapter 7A, Section 5).

Speedometer drive pinion fluid seal

2 The procedure is covered in Section 4 of this Chapter.

6 Automatic transmission - removal and refitting

Note: *This Section describes the removal of the automatic transmission, leaving the engine in position in the car. However, if an adequate hoist is available, it may be easier to remove both the engine and the transmission together as described in Chapter 2D, and then to separate the transmission from the engine on the bench.*

Removal

1 The automatic transmission is removed downwards from the engine compartment, after disconnecting it from the engine. Due to the weight of the unit, it will be necessary to have a suitable method of supporting the transmission as it is lowered during removal, and subsequently raised during its refitting. A trolley jack fitted with a suitable saddle to support the transmission as it is removed will be ideal, but failing this, an engine lift hoist and sling will suffice. The weight of the engine will also need to be supported whilst the transmission is detached from it. An engine support bar fitted in the front wing drain channel on each side is ideal for this purpose, but care must be taken not to damage the

wings or their paintwork. If this type of tool is not available (or cannot be fabricated), the engine can be supported by blocks or a second jack from underneath.
2 Disconnect the battery negative (earth) lead (refer to Chapter 5A, Section 1).
3 Remove the air cleaner and air inlet components.
4 If fitted, disconnect the lead from the vehicle speed sensor.
5 Detach the cable bracket assembly from the transmission by unscrewing its two securing nuts, then disconnect the throttle valve cable from the assembly. Tie the cable bracket assembly out of the way in a convenient location **(see illustration)**.
6 Unscrew the two upper transmission flange bolts and remove them. On certain models, these bolts also hold wiring loom securing brackets - the loom should be tied up out of the way.
7 Chock the rear wheels then jack up the front of the car and support it on axle stands (see *"Jacking and Vehicle Support"*).
8 Disconnect the selector cable at the transmission as described in Section 2.
9 Refer to Chapter 5A and remove the starter motor.
10 Detach the lower engine adapter plate (clutch housing cover).
11 Detach all earth leads from the transmission, as applicable.
12 Disconnect the automatic transmission fluid oil cooler pipes at the transmission, and move them aside. Fit blanking plugs to prevent excessive fluid loss, and to avoid dirt ingress.
13 Referring to Chapter 10 for details, detach the track rod end balljoints from the steering arms, and the suspension arm-to-spindle carrier balljoint on the left and right-hand sides. Where fitted, disconnect the anti-roll bar connecting links from both suspension struts.
14 Insert a suitable lever between the driveshaft inner CV joint and the transmission, and carefully lever the driveshaft free from the transmission. Lever against the reinforcement rib or use a suitable protective block of wood to avoid damaging the transmission housing, and have an assistant pull the suspension strut outwards on the side being detached, to assist in the driveshaft withdrawal from the transmission. As the driveshaft is withdrawn, be prepared for escaping oil.
15 When the driveshaft is detached from the transmission, tie it up out of the way. Do not allow the inner CV joint or the driveshaft to be angled by more than 20°.
16 Repeat the above procedure and detach the driveshaft on the opposite side. After removal of both driveshafts, plug the apertures in the differential (or preferably and if available, insert old CV joints) to prevent further oil leakage, and to immobilise the differential gears.
17 With the engine/transmission supported, detach the transmission bearer from the

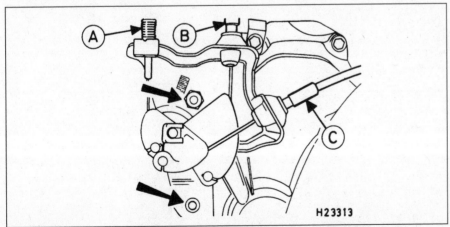

6.5 Automatic transmission cable bracket assembly. Note retaining nuts (arrowed)

A Accelerator pedal cable   *B Throttle valve cable*   *C Carburettor cable*

7B

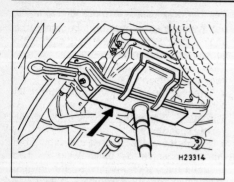

6.19 Supporting the transmission. Large support plate (arrowed) to spread the load

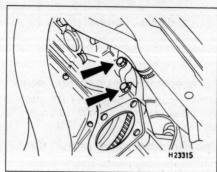

6.20 Transmission flange bolts (front shown)

vehicle body by undoing its four securing bolts. The transmission bearer is removed along with the transmission.

18 Lower the engine/transmission as far as the engine support bar allows.

19 Support the transmission from underneath using a jack, and resting it on a support plate to spread the weight. Support directly on the transmission beater, not the sump, and take great care not to dent or damage the sump **(see illustration)**.

20 At this stage it is advisable to have an assistant at the ready. Undo the four remaining transmission flange bolts (two at the front and two at the rear) and carefully withdraw the transmission from the engine **(see illustration)**.

21 Lower the jack and remove the transmission.

Refitting

22 When refitting the transmission do not lubricate the transmission input shaft, as this may contaminate and adversely affect the operation of the torsional vibration damper.

23 In a reversal of the removal technique, connect the transmission to the engine, with the transmission input shaft engaging centrally in the torsional vibration damper. Insert and tighten the transmission flange bolts to the specified torque. Do not draw the transmission onto the engine using the flange bolts.

24 Remove the jack and support plate, and raise the engine/transmission on the engine support bar to enable the refitting of the transmission bearer. Tighten the transmission bearer securing bolts to the specified torque.

25 Remove the engine support bar.

26 With a new snap-ring fitted to both inner CV joint splined shafts, lubricate the splined shafts with transmission fluid.

27 Remove the plug (or old inner CV joint) from the transmission casing and insert the right-hand driveshaft inner CV joint through the transmission casing into its splined differential location. Apply pressure at the roadwheel to ensure that the snap-ring fully locates in the differential.

28 Repeat the above procedure on the left-hand driveshaft assembly.

29 Refer to Chapter 10 and reconnect the lower suspension arm balljoints to the spindle carriers and the track rod end balljoints to the steering arms.

30 Remove the blanking plugs, and reconnect the automatic transmission fluid oil cooler pipes.

31 The remainder of refitting is now a reversal of the removal procedure. Refer to Section 2 when refitting the selector cable, and adjust as necessary.

32 On completion, check the transmission fluid level and top-up as necessary (see Chapter 1).

33 Note that the throttle valve cable adjustment, along with that of the other two cables attached to the cams on the cable bracket assembly, will need to be checked by a Ford dealer at the earliest opportunity.

7 Automatic transmission overhaul - general

In the event of a fault occurring on the transmission, it is first necessary to determine whether it is of an electrical, mechanical or hydraulic nature, and to do this, special test equipment is required. It is therefore essential to have the work carried out by a Ford dealer if a transmission fault is suspected.

Do not remove the transmission from the car for possible repair before professional fault diagnosis has been carried out, since most tests require the transmission to be in the vehicle.

8 Starter inhibitor switch - removal and refitting

Refer to Chapter 12, Section 4 for details.

Chapter 8
Driveshafts

Contents

Driveshaft inner CV joint gaiter - renewal 3
Driveshaft outer CV joint gaiter - renewal 4
Driveshaft rubber gaiter and constant velocity (CV)
   joint check ....See Chapter 1
Driveshafts - removal and refitting 2
Driveshafts - inspection and overhaul 5
General information 1

Degrees of difficulty

Easy, suitable for novice with little experience		**Fairly easy,** suitable for beginner with some experience		**Fairly difficult,** suitable for competent DIY mechanic		**Difficult,** suitable for experienced DIY mechanic		**Very difficult,** suitable for expert DIY or professional	

Specifications

Type .... Unequal length solid shafts splined to inner and outer constant velocity (CV) joints

Lubrication
Driveshaft CV joint grease type .... Grease to Ford specification SQM-1C-9004-A (Duckhams LBM 10)
Outer joint grease quantity:
  1.1 and 1.3 litre HCS engine models (except Van) .... 30 grams
  All other models .... 40 grams
Inner joint grease quantity:
  With ball and cage type CV joints:
    1.1 and 1.3 litre HCS engine models (except Van) .... 30 grams
    All other models .... 40 grams
  With tripod type inner CV joints:
    All models .... 95 grams

Torque wrench settings

	Nm	lbf ft
Hub/driveshaft retaining nut	205 to 235	151 to 173
Roadwheel nuts	70 to 110	52 to 74

8

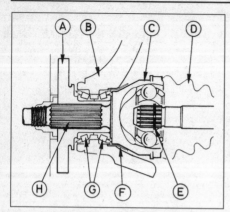

1.2a Sectional view of the driveshaft outer CV joint assembly

A Wheel hub
B Spindle carrier
C Outer CV joint
D Gaiter
E Snap-ring
    (driveshaft-to-
    outer CV joint)
F Dust shield
G Hub bearings
H Outer CV joint
    splined shaft
    section

1 General information

Drive is transmitted from the differential to the front wheels by means of two unequal-length steel driveshafts. On certain models, the right-hand driveshaft incorporates a vibration/harmonic damper, which is bolted in position on the shaft.

Each driveshaft consists of three main components - a ball and cage type outer CV joint, the main driveshaft (which is splined at each end) and either a ball and cage type (early models) or a sliding tripod type (later models) inner CV joint (see illustrations). The inner splined section of the ball and cage type or tripod type inner joint is secured in the differential by the engagement of a snap-ring, whilst the outer ball and cage type CV joint is secured in the front hub by the hub/driveshaft retaining nut. The nut has a shouldered outer section which is peened over to lock it in position.

On vehicles fitted with the anti-lock braking

2.3 Remove the hub/driveshaft retaining nut and washer

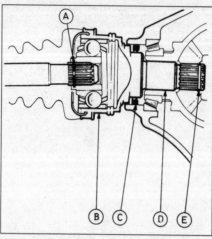

1.2b Sectional view of the driveshaft inner ball and cage type CV joint assembly

A Circlip (driveshaft-
    to-inner CV joint)
B Inner CV joint
    housing
C Oil seal
D Inner CV joint shaft
    section
E Snap-ring

system, the inner CV joints drive the modulators through a Kevlar reinforced rubber belt. The main distinguishing feature of these inner CV joints, over those fitted to vehicles with a conventional braking system, is the teeth machined into the outer housings.

2 Driveshafts - removal and refitting

Removal

1 Remove the wheel trim from the front roadwheel on the side concerned, then using a small pin punch, peen back the locking portion of the front hub/driveshaft nut. Loosen off the nut about half-a-turn.
2 Loosen off the front roadwheel retaining nuts on the side concerned.
3 Chock the rear wheels then jack up the front of the car and support it on axle stands (see "Jacking and Vehicle Support"). Remove the appropriate roadwheel, and unscrew and

2.11 Driveshaft separation from the front wheel hub using a conventional puller. Note the spacer location (arrowed)

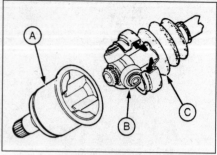

1.2c Sliding tripod type inner CV joint assembly

A Tripod housing
B Tripod
C Gaiter

remove the hub/driveshaft retaining nut and washer (see illustration).
4 Undo the two retaining bolts, and remove the brake caliper and anchor bracket from the spindle carrier. Support the caliper by suspending it from above, to prevent the hydraulic hose from being strained or distorted.
5 Where an anti-roll bar is fitted, undo the nut securing the connecting link to the suspension strut bracket, and separate the link from the strut bracket.
6 Where fitted, remove the undertray from beneath the engine and, additionally on XR2i models, remove the front suspension crossmember as described in Chapter 10.
7 Detach the track rod end balljoint from the steering arm on the side concerned as described in Chapter 10.
8 On pre-June 1990 models, fabricate a home-made bracket to secure the wheel hub and brake disc to the spindle carrier. Retain the bracket at one end with a wheel nut and at the other end with a brake caliper retaining bolt. This will prevent the hub and disc from becoming detached from the spindle carrier (with possible damage to the hub bearings) when the driveshaft is removed. On later models the hub is an interference fit in the bearing inner races and is unlikely to become detached.
9 On vehicles equipped with anti-lock brakes, remove the belt break switch and drivebelt cover, then slacken the modulator pivot and adjuster bolts to release drivebelt tension before slipping the drivebelt from its modulator pulley location (see Chapter 9).
10 Remove the Torx-head pinch-bolt and nut securing the lower suspension arm balljoint to the spindle carrier. Lever the suspension arm downwards to detach it from the spindle carrier unit.
11 Release the driveshaft from its location in the hub by pulling the spindle carrier outwards, away from the centre of the vehicle. Do not fully withdraw the shaft from the hub at this stage, but ensure that it is free to be withdrawn when required. If it is tight in the hub, lightly tap its outer end with a soft-faced hammer, or use a conventional puller and spacer (see illustration).

2.12 Levering the driveshaft free from the transmission

2.14 Prising free the snap-ring from the groove in the inner end of the driveshaft

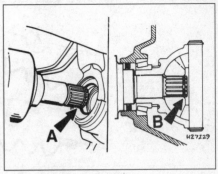

2.17 Snap-ring (A) must be renewed and fully engage in groove (B)

12 Insert a suitable lever between the inner driveshaft joint and the transmission case, adjacent to a reinforcing rib, then prise free the inner joint from the differential. If it proves reluctant to move, strike the lever firmly with the palm of the hand **(see illustration)**. Be careful not to damage the adjacent components, and be prepared for oil spillage from the transmission case through the vacated driveshaft aperture. If both driveshafts are to be removed, plug the aperture (or preferably, and if available, insert an old CV joint) to immobilise the differential gears. Do not allow the CV joints or the driveshaft to bend more than 20° from the horizontal.

13 Withdraw the driveshaft from the hub, and remove it as a unit from the vehicle.

14 Remove the snap-ring from the groove in the splines of the inner joint housing **(see illustration)**. *This snap-ring must be renewed each time the driveshaft is withdrawn from the differential. The hub/driveshaft retaining nut and the track rod end balljoint split pin must also be renewed when refitting the driveshaft.*

Refitting

15 Fit a new snap-ring to the groove in the splines of the inner joint housing.

16 Smear the splines at the wheel hub end of the shaft with grease, then insert it into the spindle carrier. Use the old nut and retaining washer to assist in drawing the shaft into position. Remove the bracket securing the hub to the spindle carrier (where applicable).

17 Having ensured that the modulator drivebelt is located over the driveshaft (ABS models), lubricate the inner CV joint splined shaft with transmission oil. Remove the temporary plug (fitted to immobilise the differential gears), then insert the joint, through the transmission casing, into its splined differential location **(see illustration)**. Apply pressure at the hub to ensure that the snap-ring fully locates in the differential.

18 Reconnect the suspension lower arm balljoint to the spindle carrier. Insert the pinch-bolt, ensure that the bolt is fully engaged in the groove of the ballstud, then fit and tighten the retaining nut to the specified torque wrench setting (see Chapter 10).

19 Reconnect the track rod end balljoint to the steering arm as described in Chapter 10.

20 Refit the brake caliper unit to the spindle carrier, and tighten the retaining bolts to the specified torque wrench setting (see Chapter 9).

21 Where an anti-roll bar is fitted, refit the connecting link to the suspension strut bracket.

22 Where applicable, refit the engine undertray and, on XR2i models, refit the front suspension crossmember (see Chapter 10).

23 Refit the roadwheel, and lightly tighten its retaining nuts.

24 Fit a new hub nut and washer, and tighten the nut as much possible at this stage. As the nut is being tightened, rotate the roadwheel to ensure that the wheel bearings seat correctly.

25 Lower the vehicle to the ground, then tighten the hub nut to the specified torque wrench setting. Using a pin punch, stake-lock the nut in the groove in the end of the axle stub.

26 Tighten the roadwheel nuts to the specified torque setting.

27 Check the level of the transmission oil, and top-up if necessary with the recommended lubricant (see Chapter 1).

---

3 Driveshaft inner CV joint gaiter - renewal

Note: *In addition to the new gaiter, new gaiter retaining clips and driveshaft retaining circlip or snap-ring will be required (some or all of these parts may be contained in the gaiter repair kit).*

1 The inner CV joint gaiter can only be renewed once the driveshaft has been detached from the CV joint at the transmission end. This can be done with the driveshaft fully removed (as described in Section 2), or by leaving it in situ in the wheel hub. The latter method is described below. If it is wished to fully remove the driveshaft, refer to Section 2 for details, then proceed as described in this Section in paragraphs 9

to 14 or 20 to 28 (according to CV joint type), to renew the gaiter.

2 Loosen off the front roadwheel nuts on the side concerned.

3 Chock the rear wheels then jack up the front of the car and support it on axle stands (see *"Jacking and Vehicle Support"*). Remove the appropriate roadwheel.

4 Detach the track rod end balljoint from the steering arm as described in Chapter 10.

5 Where an anti-roll bar is fitted, undo the nut securing the connecting link to the suspension strut bracket and separate the link from the strut bracket.

6 Where fitted, remove the undertray from beneath the engine and, additionally on XR2i models, remove the front suspension crossmember as described in Chapter 10.

7 Remove the Torx-head pinch-bolt and nut securing the lower suspension arm balljoint to the spindle carrier. Lever the suspension arm downwards to detach it from the spindle carrier.

8 Proceed as described in the following sub-headings according to the type of inner CV joint fitted.

Ball and cage type CV joint

9 Remove the gaiter retaining clips by prising open the looped section of the clamp with a screwdriver, then slide the gaiter along the shaft (away from the transmission) to expose the CV joint. Wipe as much of the surplus grease from the joint as possible.

10 Get an assistant to help pull the suspension strut outwards, then prise open the retaining circlip and pull the shaft from the joint. Take care not to allow the driveshaft to bend at an angle greater than 20°.

11 Withdraw the gaiter from the driveshaft, then remove the driveshaft retaining circlip.

12 Fit the new gaiter into position on the shaft and repack the CV joint with the specified type and quantity of grease. Fit the new circlip then insert the driveshaft back through the joint unit, pushing through until the circlip is felt to engage and secure it.

13 Locate the new gaiter into position over the joint. The gaiter positioning is important. Check that, when in position with the inner joint fully contracted and the driveshaft at an

8

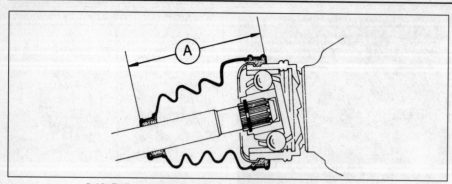

3.13 Ball and cage type inner CV joint gaiter fitting details

A (shaft angle 10° to 20°) = 80 to 90 mm

angle of 10° to 20°, the gaiter is positioned as shown **(see illustration)**.

14 Fit and fasten the gaiter clips by holding them round the gaiter tightly, then locate the peg into the next engagement hole. Crimp the looped section of the clip with pincers to secure it **(see illustration 3.28)**.

15 Reconnect the suspension lower arm balljoint to the spindle carrier. Insert the pinch-bolt, ensure that the bolt is fully engaged in the groove of the ballstud, then fit and tighten the retaining nut to the specified torque wrench setting (see Chapter 10).

16 Reconnect the track rod end balljoint to the steering arm as described in Chapter 10.

17 Where an anti-roll bar is fitted, refit the connecting link to the suspension strut bracket.

18 Where applicable, refit the engine undertray and, on XR2i models, refit the front suspension crossmember (see Chapter 10).

19 Refit the roadwheel and tighten its nuts, then lower the vehicle to the ground. Tighten the roadwheel nuts to the specified torque wrench setting.

Sliding tripod type CV joint

20 Remove the gaiter retaining clips by prising open the looped section of the clamp with a screwdriver, then slide the gaiter along the shaft (away from the transmission).

21 Get an assistant to help pull the suspension strut outwards, and separate the driveshaft and tripod from the tripod housing.

Take care not to allow the driveshaft to bend at an angle greater than 20°.

22 Wipe the grease from the tripod joint assembly.

23 Prise free the snap-ring retaining the tripod on the inner end of the driveshaft **(see illustration)**. Check if the inner end face of the driveshaft and the tripod are "match-marked" for position, then remove the tripod from the shaft, followed by the old gaiter.

24 Clean the driveshaft. Note that the joint retaining snap-ring, the track rod end balljoint split pin and the gaiter retaining clips must be renewed on reassembly.

25 Slide the new gaiter into position on the shaft to allow sufficient access for reassembly of the tripod joint.

26 Refit the tripod on the driveshaft. It must be fitted with the chamfered edge leading (towards the driveshaft), and with the match-marks aligned **(see illustration)**. Secure it in position using a new snap-ring. Ensure that the snap-ring is fully engaged in its groove.

27 Refit the driveshaft and tripod to the tripod housing, then pack the housing with the specified type and quantity of grease.

28 Move the gaiter along the driveshaft, and locate it over the joint and onto its inner and outer seatings. Ensure that it is correctly seated and not twisted or distorted. Fit and fasten the gaiter clips by holding them round the gaiter tightly, then locate the peg into the next engagement hole. Crimp the looped section of the clip with pincers to secure it **(see illustration)**.

29 Reconnect the suspension lower arm balljoint to the spindle carrier. Insert the pinch-bolt, ensure that the bolt is fully engaged in the groove of the ballstud, then fit and tighten the retaining nut to the specified torque wrench setting (see Chapter 10).

30 Reconnect the track rod end balljoint to the steering arm as described in Chapter 10.

31 Where an anti-roll bar is fitted, refit the connecting link to the suspension strut bracket.

32 Where applicable, refit the engine undertray and, on XR2i models, refit the front suspension crossmember (see Chapter 10).

33 Refit the roadwheel and tighten its nuts, then lower the vehicle to the ground. Tighten the roadwheel nuts to the specified torque wrench setting.

4 Driveshaft outer CV joint gaiter - renewal

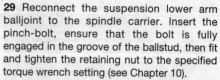

1 The outer CV joint gaiter can be renewed with the driveshaft fully removed or with it in situ in the wheel hub, but with the outer CV joint disconnected. If the driveshaft has already been removed, proceed as described in paragraphs 6 to 14 inclusive to renew the outer CV joint gaiter.

2 Loosen off the front roadwheel nuts on the side concerned.

3 Chock the rear wheels then jack up the front of the car and support it on axle stands (see *"Jacking and Vehicle Support"*). Remove the relevant roadwheel.

4 Detach the track rod end balljoint from the steering arm as described in Chapter 10.

5 Where an anti-roll bar is fitted, undo the nut securing the connecting link to the suspension strut bracket and separate the link from the strut bracket.

6 Remove the Torx-head pinch-bolt and nut securing the lower suspension arm balljoint to the spindle carrier. Lever the suspension arm downwards to detach it from the spindle carrier.

7 Remove the gaiter retaining clips by prising open the looped section of the clamp with a screwdriver, then slide the gaiter along the

3.23 Remove the snap-ring from the tripod end of the driveshaft

3.26 Tripod refitted onto the driveshaft with the match-marks aligned (arrowed)

3.28 Crimp the looped section of the clip with pincers

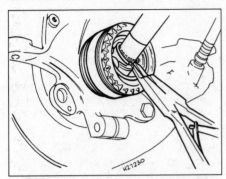

4.8 Expand the snap-ring to enable the driveshaft to be withdrawn from the outer CV joint

shaft (away from the transmission) to expose the CV joint.

8 To disconnect the driveshaft from the outer CV joint, first wipe away the grease from the joint. Using suitable circlip pliers, expand the snap-ring, and have an assistant simultaneously pull the CV joint outwards (or when *in situ,* pull the suspension strut outwards) to separate the driveshaft from the CV joint **(see illustration)**. Take care not to allow the driveshaft to bend at an angle greater than 20°.

9 Withdraw the gaiter from the driveshaft.

10 Clean the driveshaft. Note that the joint retaining snap-ring, the track rod end balljoint split pin and the gaiter retaining clips must be renewed on reassembly.

11 Slide the new gaiter along on the shaft to allow access for reassembly of the outer CV joint.

12 Locate a new snap-ring into position in the outer CV joint, then lubricate the joint with some of the specified grease **(see illustrations)**.

13 Engage the driveshaft with the CV joint, and push them together so that the circlip engages in the groove of the driveshaft **(see illustration)**. If the task is being carried out

with the spindle carrier attached, pull the suspension strut outwards, and guide the driveshaft into the CV joint. Progressively release the suspension until the shaft is fully engaged with the joint, and the snap-ring engages in the groove in the driveshaft.

14 Pack the joint with the remainder of the specified grease.

15 Move the gaiter along the driveshaft, and locate it over the joint and onto its inner and outer seatings. Check that it is correctly seated and not twisted or distorted. Fit and fasten the gaiter clips by holding them round the gaiter tightly, then locate the peg into the next engagement hole. Crimp the looped section of the clip with pincers to secure it.

16 Reconnect the suspension lower arm balljoint to the spindle carrier. Insert the pinch-bolt, ensure that the bolt is fully engaged in the groove of the ballstud, then fit and tighten the retaining nut to the specified torque wrench setting (see Chapter 10).

17 Reconnect the track rod end balljoint to the steering arm as described in Chapter 10.

18 Where an anti-roll bar is fitted, refit the connecting link to the suspension strut bracket.

19 Refit the roadwheel and tighten its nuts, then lower the vehicle to the ground. Tighten the roadwheel nuts to the specified torque wrench setting.

5 Driveshafts - inspection and overhaul

1 Remove the driveshaft as described in Section 2.

2 Clean away all external dirt and grease from the driveshaft and gaiters.

3 Note the direction of fitting of the inner and outer CV joint gaiter retaining clips, then release the clips from the gaiters, and slide the gaiters along the driveshaft towards the centre.

4 Wipe the grease from the inner and outer CV joints.

5 Using suitable circlip pliers, expand the snap-ring and have an assistant simultaneously pull the outboard joint outwards to separate the shaft from the joint.

6 If the driveshaft is fitted with a ball and cage type inner CV joint, this is removed in the same way as the outer joint described in the previous paragraph.

7 If the driveshaft is fitted with a sliding tripod type inner CV joint, withdraw the inner joint tripod housing from the driveshaft, then prise free the snap-ring retaining the tripod on the inboard end of the driveshaft. Check if the inner end face of the driveshaft and the tripod are "match-marked" for position, then remove the tripod from the shaft, followed by the large nylon washer and the gaiter.

8 If removing the vibration damper from the right-hand driveshaft, mark its relative position on the shaft before unbolting it.

9 Thoroughly clean the joint components, and examine them for wear or damage. A repair kit may resolve a minor problem, but extensive wear or damage will necessitate renewal of the component concerned or the complete driveshaft.

10 Where the joints and possibly even the gaiters, are found to be in a serviceable condition, it will still be necessary to renew the CV joint retaining snap-rings, the gaiter retaining clips, and also to obtain the recommended type and quantity of CV joint grease.

11 Reassembly of the joints is as described in Section 3 (paragraphs 12 to 14) for the ball and cage type inner CV joint, Section 3 (paragraphs 25 to 28) for the sliding tripod type inner CV joint, and Section 4 (paragraphs 11 to 15) for the outer CV joint. If the vibration damper unit was removed from the right-hand driveshaft, ensure that it is refitted in the same position as noted during removal.

12 Refit the driveshaft on completion as described in Section 2.

4.12a Locate the new snap-ring (arrowed) in the outer CV joint . . .

4.12b . . . partially lubricate the joint . . .

4.13 . . . and reassemble the shaft to the joint so that the circlip (A) engages in the groove in the shaft (B)

8

Notes

Chapter 9
Braking system

Contents

ABS modulator drivebelt check .See Chapter 1
Anti-lock braking system (ABS) - general information 23
Anti-lock braking system (ABS) components - removal and refitting . . 24
Brake check . . . . .See Chapter 1
Brake fluid level check .See "Weekly Checks"
Brake fluid renewal . . . . .See Chapter 1
Brake pedal - removal and refitting 10
Brake pedal-to-servo cross-link - removal and refitting 11
Brake pressure control valves - removal and refitting 20
Front brake caliper - removal, overhaul and refitting 3
Front brake disc - inspection, removal and refitting 4
Front brake pads - renewal 2
General information 1
Handbrake adjustment . . . . .See Chapter 1
Handbrake lever - removal and refitting 17
Handbrake primary cable - removal and refitting 18
Handbrake rear cable - removal and refitting 19
Hydraulic pipes and hoses - renewal 12
Hydraulic system - bleeding (anti-lock braking system) 14
Hydraulic system - bleeding (conventional braking system) 13
Light-laden valve (Courier models) - adjustment 22
Light-laden valve (Courier models) - removal and refitting 21
Load-apportioning valve (ABS models) - adjustment 25
Load-apportioning valve (ABS models) - removal and refitting 26
Master cylinder - removal, overhaul and refitting 9
Rear brake backplate - removal and refitting 8
Rear brake drum - removal, inspection and refitting 5
Rear brake shoes - renewal 6
Rear wheel cylinder - removal, overhaul and refitting 7
Vacuum servo unit - testing, removal and refitting 15
Vacuum servo unit vacuum hose and non-return valve - removal,
      testing and refitting 16

Degrees of difficulty

Easy, suitable for novice with little experience	Fairly easy, suitable for beginner with some experience	Fairly difficult, suitable for competent DIY mechanic	Difficult, suitable for experienced DIY mechanic	Very difficult, suitable for expert DIY or professional 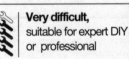

Specifications

Front brakes

Type	Solid or ventilated disc, with single-piston sliding calipers
Disc diameter	240.0 mm
Disc thickness:	
Solid disc	10.0 mm
Ventilated disc	20.0 mm
Minimum disc thickness:	
Solid disc	8.0 mm
Ventilated disc	18.0 mm
Maximum disc run-out (disc fitted)	0.1 mm
Minimum brake pad thickness	1.5 mm

Rear brakes

Type	Drum with leading and trailing shoes and automatic adjusters
Nominal drum diameter:	
All except XR2i and ABS equipped models	180 mm
XR2i and ABS equipped models	203 mm
Maximum drum diameter	1.0 mm above nominal diameter
Wheel cylinder bore diameter:	
All except XR2i and ABS equipped models	17.5 mm
XR2i models with conventional braking system	19.0 mm
All ABS equipped models	22.0 mm
Minimum brake shoe lining thickness	1.0 mm

9

Torque wrench settings

	Nm	lbf ft
Master cylinder to servo	20 to 25	15 to 18
Servo to mounting bracket	35 to 45	26 to 33
Pedal-to-servo cross-link brackets to bulkhead	20 to 25	15 to 18
Rear drum/hub to axle flange bolts*	56 to 76	41 to 56
Caliper-to-spindle carrier (anchor bracket) bolts	50 to 66	37 to 49
Caliper piston housing retaining bolts	20 to 25	15 to 18
Load-apportioning valves to bracket	20 to 25	15 to 18
Load-apportioning valve bracket to vehicle	21 to 28	15 to 21
Load-apportioning valve adjustment screw	12 to 16	9 to 12
Load-apportioning valve-to-axle beam link rod nut	21 to 28	15 to 21
Modulator pivot and adjusting clamp bolts	22 to 28	16 to 21
Modulator drivebelt cover	8 to 12	6 to 9
Roadwheel nuts	70 to 110	52 to 74

Applies to all models except Courier. No figures are quoted by the manufacturers for Courier models.

1 General information

The braking system is of the diagonally split, dual-circuit hydraulic type, with servo assistance to the front disc brakes and rear drum brakes. The dual-circuit hydraulic system is a safety feature - in the event of a malfunction somewhere in one of the hydraulic circuits, the other circuit continues to operate, providing at least some braking effort. Under normal circumstances, both brake circuits operate in unison, to provide efficient braking.

The master cylinder (and the vacuum servo unit to which it is bolted) is located on the left-hand side of the bulkhead in the engine compartment. On all right-hand drive variants, they are jointly operated via a transverse cross-link from the brake pedal.

Brake pressure control valves are fitted in-line to each rear brake circuit, their function being to regulate the braking force available at each rear wheel, reducing the possibility of the rear wheels locking up under heavy braking. Courier models also have a "light-laden" valve incorporated into the rear braking circuits for the same reason.

The front brake discs are of the ventilated type on XR2i and ABS-equipped models, with solid discs fitted on all other models. The front brake calipers are of single sliding piston type mounted on the front spindle carriers each side.

Each rear brake shoe assembly is operated by a twin-piston wheel cylinder. The leading brake shoe in each brake unit has a thicker lining than the trailing shoe, so that they wear proportionally. To take up the brake adjustment as the linings wear, each rear brake assembly incorporates an automatic adjuster mechanism.

The cable-operated handbrake acts on both rear brakes, to provide an independent means of brake operation.

An anti-lock braking system (ABS) is available on some models, and has many of the components in common with the conventional braking system. Further details on ABS can be found later in this Chapter.

Note: *When servicing any part of the system, work carefully and methodically; also observe scrupulous cleanliness when overhauling any part of the hydraulic system. Always renew components (in axle sets, where applicable) if in doubt about their condition, and use only genuine Ford replacement parts, or at least those of known good quality. Note the warnings given in "Safety first" and at relevant points in this Chapter concerning the dangers of asbestos dust and hydraulic fluid.*

2 Front brake pads - renewal

⚠ *Warning: Disc brake pads MUST be renewed on both front wheels at the same time - NEVER renew the pads on only one wheel, as uneven braking may result. The front brake calipers will be of Bendix or Teves manufacture, and if they or their component parts require renewal, ensure that the correct type is fitted. Dust created by wear of the pads may contain asbestos, which is a health hazard. Never blow it out with compressed air, and do not inhale any of it. DO NOT use petroleum-based solvents to clean brake parts - use brake cleaner or methylated spirit only. DO NOT allow any brake fluid, oil or grease to contact the brake pads or disc. Also refer to the warning in Section 13 concerning the dangers of hydraulic fluid.*

1 Chock the rear wheels then jack up the front of the car and support it on axle stands (see "Jacking and Vehicle Support"). Remove the front roadwheels.

2 Hold the caliper support spring with a pair of pliers, and prise it out of its location in the caliper housing using a screwdriver **(see illustration)**.

3 Prise free the blanking plugs from the caliper upper and lower mounting bolts. Unscrew the bolts, then withdraw the caliper from the anchor bracket **(see illustrations)**. Suitably support the caliper to avoid straining the brake hose.

2.2 Prise out the caliper support spring with a screwdriver

2.3a Remove the rubber blanking plugs for access to the caliper mounting bolts . . .

2.3b . . . unscrew the bolts then withdraw the caliper from the anchor bracket

4 Withdraw the pads from the caliper piston housing or anchor bracket. The outer pad will normally remain in position in the anchor bracket, but the inner pad will stay attached to the piston in the caliper, and may need to be carefully prised free. If the old pads are to be refitted, ensure that they are identified so that they can be returned to their original positions.

5 Brush the dust and dirt from the caliper and piston, but *do not inhale it, as it is a health hazard*. Inspect the dust cover around the piston for damage and for evidence of fluid leaks, which if found will necessitate caliper overhaul as described in Section 3.

6 If new brake pads are to be fitted, the caliper piston will need to be pushed back into its housing, to allow for the extra pad thickness - use a C-clamp to do this. Note that, as the piston is pressed back into the bore, it will displace the fluid in the system, causing the fluid level in the brake master cylinder reservoir to rise and possibly overflow. To avoid this possibility, a small quantity of fluid should be removed from the reservoir. If any brake fluid is spilt onto the bodywork, hoses or adjacent components in the engine compartment, wipe it clean without delay.

 An ideal way to remove fluid from the master cylinder reservoir is to use a clean syringe or an old poultry baster.

7 Prior to refitting, check that the pads and the disc are clean. Where new pads are to be installed, peel the protective backing paper from them. If the old pads are to be refitted, ensure that they are correctly located as noted during their removal.

8 Locate the inner and outer brake pad into position in the caliper. Relocate the caliper into position on the anchor bracket, and insert the mounting bolts.

9 Tighten the mounting bolts to the specified torque, and refit the blanking plugs. Relocate the caliper support spring.

10 Repeat the procedure on the opposite front brake.

11 Before lowering the vehicle, check that the fluid level in the brake master cylinder reservoir is up to the "Maximum level" mark, and top-up with the specified fluid type if required (see "Weekly Checks"). Depress the brake pedal a few times to position the pads against the disc, then recheck the fluid level in the reservoir and further top-up if necessary.

12 Refit the roadwheels, then lower the vehicle to the ground. Tighten the roadwheel retaining nuts to the specified torque.

13 To allow the new brake pads to bed-in and reach full efficiency, a running-in period of approximately 100 miles or so should be observed before hard use and heavy braking.

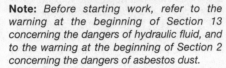
3 Front brake caliper - removal, overhaul and refitting

Note: *Before starting work, refer to the warning at the beginning of Section 13 concerning the dangers of hydraulic fluid, and to the warning at the beginning of Section 2 concerning the dangers of asbestos dust.*

Removal

1 Chock the rear wheels then jack up the front of the car and support it on axle stands (see "Jacking and Vehicle Support"). Remove the front roadwheels.

2 Fit a brake hose clamp to the flexible brake hose leading to the front brake caliper. This will minimise brake fluid loss during subsequent operations.

3 Loosen by half a turn, the union on the caliper end of the flexible brake hose.

4 Remove the front brake pads as described in Section 2.

5 Support the caliper in one hand, and prevent the brake hose from turning with a spanner in the other hand. Unscrew the caliper from the hose, making sure that the hose is not twisted unduly or strained **(see illustration)**. Once the caliper is detached, cover or plug the open hydraulic unions to keep them clean.

6 If required, the caliper anchor bracket can be unbolted and removed from the spindle carrier **(see illustration)**.

Overhaul

7 With the caliper on the bench, wipe away all traces of dust and dirt, but *avoid inhaling the dust, as it is a health hazard*.

8 Remove the piston from its bore by applying low air pressure (from a foot pump, for example) into the caliper hydraulic fluid hose port. In the event of a high-pressure air hose being used, keep the pressure as low as possible, to enable the piston to be extracted, but to avoid the piston being ejected too quickly and being damaged. Position a suitable piece of wood between the caliper frame and the piston to prevent this possibility. Any fluid remaining in the caliper will probably be ejected with the piston.

9 Using a suitable hooked tool, carefully extract the dust cover from its groove in the piston and the seal from its groove in the caliper bore, but take care not to scratch or damage the piston and/or the bore in the caliper.

10 Clean all the parts in methylated spirit or clean brake fluid, and wipe dry using a clean lint-free cloth **(see illustration)**. Inspect the piston and caliper bore for signs of damage, scuffing or corrosion. If these conditions are evident, renew the caliper body assembly.

11 If the components are in satisfactory condition, a repair kit which includes a new seal and dust cover must be obtained.

12 Lubricate the piston bore in the caliper and the seal with clean brake fluid. Carefully fit the seal in the caliper bore, using fingers only (no tools) to manipulate it into position in its groove. When in position, check that it is not distorted or twisted.

13 Locate the dust cover over the piston so that its inner diameter is engaged in the piston groove. Smear the area behind the piston groove with the special lubricating grease supplied in the repair kit, then insert the piston into the caliper. Push the piston into position in the bore, and simultaneously press the dust cover into the piston housing so that it is seated correctly. Take particular care not to distort or damage the seal or cover as they are fitted.

Refitting

14 If the anchor bracket was removed, fit it into position on the spindle carrier, and tighten the retaining bolts to the specified torque.

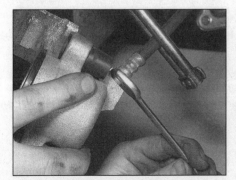
3.5 Hold the brake hose with a spanner and unscrew the caliper from the hose

3.6 Undoing a brake caliper anchor bracket bolt

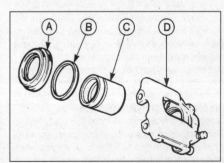
3.10 Brake caliper and piston components

A *Dust cover* C *Piston*
B *Piston seal* D *Brake caliper*

9

4.4 Checking brake disc run-out using a dial gauge

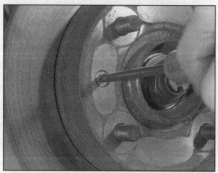

4.8a Extract the brake disc securing screw . . .

4.8b . . . and remove the disc from the hub

15 Unplug the hydraulic hose, and check that the unions are clean. Reconnect the caliper to the hose so that the hose is not twisted or strained. The hose union connection can be fully tightened when the caliper is refitted.

16 Refit the brake pads as described in Section 2.

17 The brake hydraulic hose can now be fully tightened. When secured, turn the steering from lock-to-lock to ensure that the hose does not foul on the wheel housing or suspension components.

18 Bleed the brake hydraulic system as described in Section 13 or 14 according to type. Providing suitable precautions were taken to minimise loss of fluid, it should only be necessary to bleed the relevant front brake.

19 Refit the roadwheel, lower the vehicle to the ground, then tighten the wheel nuts to the specified torque.

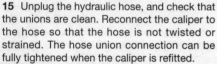

4 Front brake disc - inspection, removal and refitting

Note: *Before starting work, refer to the warning at the beginning of Section 2 concerning the dangers of asbestos dust.*

Inspection

Note: *If a disc requires renewal, BOTH front discs should be renewed or reground at the same time to ensure even and consistent braking. New brake pads should also be fitted.*

1 Chock the rear wheels then jack up the front of the car and support it on axle stands (see *"Jacking and Vehicle Support"*). Remove the appropriate front roadwheel.

2 Temporarily refit two of the wheel nuts to diagonally-opposite studs, with the flat sides of the nuts against the disc. Tighten the nuts progressively, to hold the disc firmly.

3 Scrape any corrosion from the disc. Rotate the disc, and examine it for deep scoring, grooving or cracks. Using a micrometer, measure the thickness of the disc in several places. Light wear and scoring is normal, but if excessive, the disc should be removed, and either reground by a specialist, or renewed. If

regrinding is undertaken, at least the minimum thickness must be maintained. Obviously, if the disc is cracked, it must be renewed.

4 Using a dial gauge, check that the disc run-out, measured at a point 10.0 mm from the outer edge of the disc, does not exceed the limit given in the Specifications. To do this, fix the measuring equipment, and rotate the disc, noting the variation in measurement as the disc is rotated **(see illustration)**. The difference between the minimum and maximum measurements recorded is the disc run-out.

> **HAYNES HiNT**
> *If a dial gauge is not available, check the run-out by positioning a fixed pointer near the outer edge, in contact with the disc face. Rotate the disc and measure the maximum displacement of the pointer with feeler blades.*

5 If the run-out is greater than the specified amount, check for variations of the disc thickness as follows. Mark the disc at eight positions 45° apart, then using a micrometer, measure the disc thickness at the eight positions, 15.0 mm in from the outer edge. If the variation between the minimum and maximum readings is greater than the specified amount, the disc should be renewed.

Removal

6 Remove the caliper and its anchor bracket with reference to Section 3, but do not disconnect the hydraulic brake hose. Suspend the caliper assembly from the front suspension coil spring, taking care to avoid straining the brake hose.

7 Remove the wheel nuts which were temporarily refitted in paragraph 2.

8 Unscrew the screw securing the disc to the hub, and withdraw the disc **(see illustrations)**. If it is tight, lightly tap its rear face with a hide or plastic mallet.

Refitting

9 Refit the disc in a reversal of the removal sequence. If new discs are being fitted, first

remove their protective coating. Ensure complete cleanliness of the hub and disc mating faces and tighten the screw securely.

10 Refit the caliper/anchor bracket with reference to Section 3.

11 Refit the roadwheel, lower the vehicle to the ground, and tighten the wheel nuts to the specified torque.

5 Rear brake drum - removal, inspection and refitting

Note: *Before starting work, refer to the warning at the beginning of Section 6 concerning the dangers of asbestos dust.*

Removal

1 Chock the front wheels then jack up the rear of the car and support it on axle stands (see *"Jacking and Vehicle Support"*). Remove the appropriate rear roadwheel, and release the handbrake.

2 Undo the four bolts securing the drum/hub and stub axle assembly to the rear axle flange, then withdraw the drum/hub from the axle. If the brake drum is stuck on the shoes, remove the rubber access plug from the rear of the brake backplate, and release the automatic brake adjuster by levering the release catch on the adjuster pawl through the backplate **(see illustration)**.

3 With the brake drum removed, brush or wipe the dust from the drum, brake shoes,

5.2 Removing the rubber access plug from the rear of the brake backplate

6.3 Depress and turn the cups securing the brake shoes

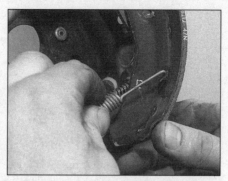

6.4a Detach the lower pull-off spring

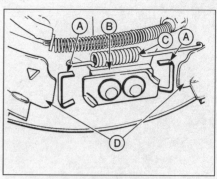

6.4b Arrangement of brake shoe anti-rattle shims - where fitted

A Shims   C Lower pull-off spring
B Lower pivot   D Brake shoes

wheel cylinder and backplate. *Take great care not to inhale the dust, as it may contain asbestos.*

4 If required, remove the hub from the drum as described in Chapter 10.

Inspection

Note: *If a brake drum requires renewal, BOTH rear drums should be renewed at the same time to ensure even and consistent braking. New brake shoes should also be fitted.*

5 Clean the inside surfaces of the brake drum and hub, then examine the internal surface of the brake drum for signs of scoring or cracks. If any deterioration of the friction surface is evident, renewal of the drum is necessary. To detach the hub from the drum, refer to Chapter 10.

Refitting

6 Check that the automatic brake adjuster is fully retracted, then refit the drum/hub to the axle. Tighten the retaining bolts to the specified torque.

7 With the brake drum refitted, refit the roadwheel. Fully depress the brake pedal several times, to actuate the rear brake adjuster and take up the adjustment. Check that the rear wheels spin freely when the brakes are released, then apply the handbrake, lower the vehicle and tighten the wheel nuts to the specified torque.

6 Rear brake shoes - renewal

Warning: Drum brake shoes MUST be renewed on both rear wheels at the same time - NEVER renew the shoes on only one wheel, as uneven braking may result. Also, the dust created by wear of the shoes may contain asbestos, which is a health hazard. Never blow it out with compressed air, and don't inhale any of it. An approved filtering mask should be worn when working on the brakes. DO NOT use petroleum-based solvents to clean brake parts - use brake cleaner or methylated spirit only.

1 Remove the rear brake drum with reference to Section 5.

2 Note the fitted positions of the springs and the adjuster strut.

3 Depress the cups holding the brake shoes in position and rotate them through 90° to release them from the locking pins **(see illustration)**. Carefully remove the cups and springs, then withdraw the locking pins from the rear of the brake backplate.

4 Lift the shoes from their lower pivot and remove the lower pull-off spring **(see illustration)**. Note that on some models anti-rattle shims may be fitted between the brake shoe and the lower pivot **(see illustration)**. If

fitted, remove the shims and store them safely.

5 With the shoe assembly pulled away from the wheel cylinder, disengage the handbrake cable from its operating lever on the trailing shoe **(see illustration)**.

6 Remove the upper pull-off spring, noting the method of location.

7 Release the automatic brake adjuster cam and pawl, then remove the adjuster strut which is held in position by spring tension **(see illustrations)**.

8 Using a screwdriver, lever off the spring clip securing the handbrake operating lever to the trailing shoe and separate the assembly **(see illustration)**.

6.5 Disengage the handbrake cable from its operating lever on the trailing shoe

6.7a Release the automatic brake adjuster cam and pawl

6.7b Detach the adjuster strut

6.8 Lever off the spring clip securing the handbrake operating lever to the trailing shoe

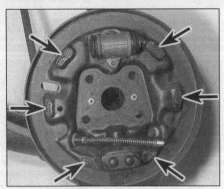

6.11 Brake shoe contact points on brake backplate (arrowed)

9 Detach the automatic brake adjuster cam in a similar manner to that described in the previous paragraph, noting its orientation.

10 Clean the adjuster strut and its associated components.

11 Clean the backplate, then apply a little high-melting-point grease to the shoe contact points on the backplate and the lower anchor plate **(see illustration)**. On models so equipped, refit the anti-rattle shims to the brake shoe lower pivot on the backplate ensuring that they are securely located.

12 Fit the handbrake operating lever to the trailing shoe, using a new spring clip.

13 Fit the automatic brake adjuster cam to the leading shoe, using a new spring clip.

14 Apply a small amount of high-melting-point grease to the automatic brake adjuster cam and pawl contact faces, and where the cam and handbrake operating lever sweep across their respective brake shoes. Do not over-apply, as this may result in lining contamination in use - a thin smear will suffice. Take care not to allow any grease to contact the brake linings.

15 Fit the adjuster strut to the trailing shoe, securing with its spring, then connect the free end of the strut to the automatic brake adjuster cam. Fit the upper pull-off spring between the tops of the two brake shoes.

16 Reconnect the handbrake cable to its operating lever.

17 Position the brake shoes onto the backplate so that their upper leading edges rest against the wheel cylinder pistons, and their lower leading edges engage either side of the lower pivot. Fit the lower pull-off spring into its locating slots at the bottom end of each brake shoe.

18 Insert the brake shoe locking pins through the rear of the backplate, then relocate the springs and cups. Depress and turn the cups through 90° to secure.

19 Check that the brake shoes and their associated components are correctly refitted, then refit the brake drum with reference to Section 5.

20 Repeat the procedure on the remaining rear brake.

7 Rear wheel cylinder - removal, overhaul and refitting

Note: *Before starting work, refer to the warning at the beginning of Section 13 concerning the dangers of hydraulic fluid.*

Removal

1 Remove the brake drum as described in Section 5.

2 Using a suitable hose clamp, isolate the relevant rear brake unit by clamping its flexible brake hose.

3 Disconnect the brake pipe at the wheel cylinder union, and fit a blanking plug to the brake pipe to prevent dirt ingress.

4 On all models except Courier, drill out the pop-rivets securing the brake backplate to the axle flange, and withdraw the backplate assembly with the brake shoes in situ. Note that it is not possible to remove the backplate completely as the handbrake cable will still be attached to the brake shoes.

5 Expand the brake shoes by pulling their tops away from the wheel cylinder. The automatic brake adjuster will hold the shoes clear of the wheel cylinder for ease of removal.

6 Remove the single bolt securing the wheel cylinder to the brake backplate, and withdraw the wheel cylinder **(see illustration)**.

Overhaul

7 Clean any heavy dirt or grease deposits from the external surfaces of the wheel cylinder, then pull off the dust-excluding covers **(see illustration)**.

8 The pistons and seals will probably shake out. If they do not, apply air pressure from a foot-operated tyre pump to the brake pipe connection to eject them.

9 Examine the surfaces of the pistons and the cylinder bores for scoring or signs of metal-to-metal rubbing. If evident, renew the complete cylinder assembly.

10 If the cylinder is to be renewed, note that

three sizes are used across the Fiesta range, dependent on specification. Ensure that the new cylinder obtained is of the correct size to maintain the rear braking balance.

11 Where the pistons and cylinder bores are in good condition, discard the rubber seals and dust excluders and obtain a repair kit.

12 Any cleaning of the components should be done using clean hydraulic fluid or methylated spirit - nothing else.

13 Reassemble by dipping the first piston in clean hydraulic fluid, then manipulate its seal into position using fingers only. Ensure that the seal is fitted correctly with its raised lip facing away from the brake shoe bearing face of the piston.

14 Insert the first piston into the wheel cylinder from the opposite end of the cylinder body. With it located in position, fit a dust-excluding cover to it.

15 Fit the seal to the second piston, as described in paragraph 13, then insert the spring to the wheel cylinder, followed by the second piston. Take care not to damage the lip of the seal when fitting to the wheel cylinder - additional lubrication with clean hydraulic fluid and a slight twisting action may help. Once again, only fingers should be used.

16 Fit the dust excluding cover to the second piston.

Refitting

17 Refitting is the reverse sequence to removal. When refitting the backplate, locate it in position and temporarily insert the hub/drum retaining bolts to ensure correct alignment. Now secure the brake backplate using new pop rivets. Release the automatic brake adjuster so that the brake shoes are brought into contact with the wheel cylinder, before refitting the hub/drum assembly as described in Section 5.

18 On completion, bleed the brake hydraulic system as described in Section 13 or 14 (as applicable).

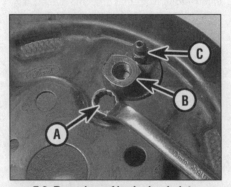

7.6 Rear view of brake backplate

A *Wheel cylinder-to-brake backplate retaining bolt*
B *Wheel cylinder brake pipe connection*
C *Bleed screw*

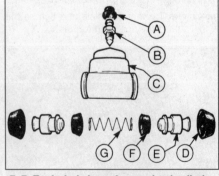

7.7 Exploded view of rear wheel cylinder components

A Dust cap
B Bleed screw
C Wheel cylinder
D Dust-excluding cover
E Piston
F Seal
G Spring

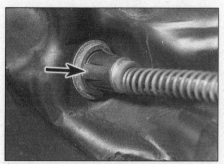

8.3 Compress the retaining lugs (arrowed), and release the handbrake cable from the backplate

8.6 Drilling out a pop-rivet securing the brake backplate to the axle flange

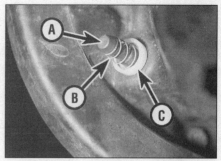

8.8 Handbrake adjustment plunger

A Plunger   B Spring   C Collar

8 Rear brake backplate - removal and refitting

Removal

1 Remove the brake drum/hub assembly as described in Section 5.
2 Remove the rear brake shoes as described in Section 6.
3 Compress the three retaining lugs, and release the handbrake cable from the backplate by pushing it back through the plate **(see illustration)**.
4 Using a suitable hose clamp, isolate the relevant rear brake unit by clamping its flexible brake hose.
5 Disconnect the brake pipe at the wheel cylinder union, and fit blanking plugs to prevent dirt ingress.
6 Drill out the pop-rivets securing the backplate to the rear axle, and remove the backplate **(see illustration)**.
7 Remove the single bolt securing the wheel cylinder to the brake carrier plate, and withdraw the wheel cylinder.
8 If required, remove the handbrake adjustment plunger from the backplate by gently prising the spring off, over the plunger abutment, then withdraw the plunger from the brake shoe side **(see illustration)**. Remove the plunger collar from the rear of the backplate.

Refitting

9 Locate the wheel cylinder in position and securely tighten the retaining bolt.

10 If removed, refit the handbrake adjustment plunger to the backplate.
11 Place the backplate in position and temporarily insert the hub/drum retaining bolts to ensure correct alignment. Now secure the brake backplate using new pop rivets
12 Refit the handbrake cable, and ensure that the retaining lugs are secure.
13 Connect the brake pipe to the wheel cylinder and remove the brake hose clamp.
14 Refit the rear brake shoes as described in Section 6.
15 Refit the brake drum/hub as described in Section 5.
16 On completion, bleed the brake hydraulic system as described in Section 13 or 14 (as applicable).

9 Master cylinder - removal, overhaul and refitting

Note: *Before starting work, refer to the warning at the beginning of Section 13 concerning the dangers of hydraulic fluid.*

Removal

1 Disconnect the wiring multi-plug from the fluid level warning indicator in the reservoir filler cap, then remove the filler cap from the reservoir. Note that the filler cap must not be inverted. The brake fluid should now be removed from the reservoir.
2 Identify each brake pipe and its connection to the master cylinder. Unscrew the fluid pipe

 HAYNES HiNT *An ideal way to remove fluid from the master cylinder reservoir is to use a clean syringe or an old poultry baster.*

to master cylinder union nuts and disconnect the pipes. On models equipped with anti-lock brakes, disconnect the modulator return hoses from the brake fluid reservoir, collecting fluid spillage from the hoses in a suitable tray **(see illustration)**. The modulator return hose unions should be disconnected by first pushing the hose into the reservoir, then retaining the collar against the reservoir body whilst withdrawing the hose. Note that the modulator return hoses are colour coded - the left-hand modulator has a black return hose and connector, and should be fitted to the forward section of the reservoir, whilst the right-hand modulator has a grey return hose and connector, and should be fitted to the rear section of the reservoir.
3 Unscrew the mounting nuts and withdraw the master cylinder from the servo unit.

Overhaul

4 With the master cylinder removed, empty any remaining fluid from it, and clean it externally.
5 Withdraw the brake fluid reservoir from the top of the master cylinder by pulling and rocking it free from its retaining seals **(see illustration)**.
6 Extract the reservoir seals from the top face of the master cylinder **(see illustration)**.

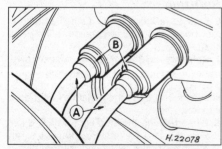

9.2 Modulator return hose connections at the brake fluid reservoir

A Return hoses   B Collars

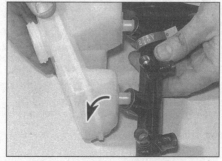

9.5 Removing the brake fluid reservoir from its seals in the master cylinder

9.6 Brake fluid reservoir seal

9

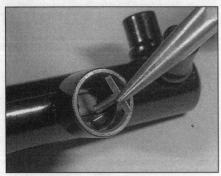

9.7 Removing the secondary piston retaining pin

9.8a Removing the primary piston assembly from the master cylinder . . .

9.8b . . . followed by the secondary piston assembly

7 Using a suitable socket, firmly press the primary piston into the master cylinder until the secondary piston retaining pin becomes visible through the secondary piston reservoir opening. Remove the retaining pin using needle-nosed pliers or similar tool **(see illustration)**.

8 Remove the primary and secondary pistons by shaking or gently tapping the master cylinder **(see illustrations)**.

9 Examine the piston and cylinder bore surfaces for scoring or signs of metal-to-metal rubbing. If evident, renew the master cylinder assembly as a complete unit.

10 Cleaning of components should be done using clean brake hydraulic fluid or methylated spirit - nothing else.

11 Obtain a master cylinder repair kit, and brake fluid reservoir seals.

12 Having dipped the secondary piston assembly in clean hydraulic fluid, insert it into the master cylinder. Note that the seals on the secondary piston have raised lips which face away from each other, towards the extremities of the piston **(see illustration)**. A slight twisting action will assist insertion.

13 Using a suitable socket bar extension, or similar tool, press the secondary piston into the master cylinder to enable fitting of the secondary piston retaining pin.

14 Dip the primary piston assembly in clean hydraulic fluid and, using a similar twisting action to that used for the secondary piston, insert it into the master cylinder. Note that both the seals fitted to the primary piston have raised lips that face the same way - towards its captive spring.

15 Insert new brake fluid reservoir seals to the master cylinder then, using a similar rolling action to that used to remove it, fit the reservoir to the master cylinder.

16 It is recommended that a small quantity of fluid is now poured into the reservoir and the pistons depressed several times to prime the unit.

Refitting

17 Locate the master cylinder to the servo unit, having fitted a new dust cover as applicable. Refit the two spring washers and nuts, then tighten to the specified torque.

18 Remove the blanking plugs fitted on removal of the unit, then reconnect the brake pipes, tightening the unions securely. Additionally, on vehicles equipped with anti-lock brakes, reconnect the modulator return hoses to the brake fluid reservoir in accordance with their colour coding (see paragraph 2), pushing the hoses firmly into the reservoir body then levering out the collars to retain.

19 Refill the brake fluid reservoir with fresh fluid of the specified type, then bleed the braking system in accordance with Section 13 or 14, as applicable.

20 On completion, ensure that the brake fluid level is up to the MAX mark on the reservoir before refitting the reservoir cap and the warning indicator wiring multi-plug.

10 Brake pedal - removal and refitting

Removal

1 Disconnect the battery negative (earth) lead (refer to Chapter 5A, Section 1).

2 Remove the clip securing the brake servo operating link pushrod to the brake pedal, noting the bush fitted in the pedal, and disconnect the brake stop light switch wiring connector. Release the brake stop light switch in a clockwise direction, and extract it from the pedal bracket.

3 Remove the C-clip from its pedal shaft location, at the right-hand side of the brake pedal, to allow the shaft to be withdrawn towards the centre of the vehicle.

4 As the pedal shaft is withdrawn, remove the brake pedal from the servo operating link pushrod. The brake pedal spacer can now be slid off the shaft if required, and the brake rod bush removed.

5 Prise the bushes out from both sides of the brake pedal, and renew as necessary.

Refitting

6 Prior to refitting, apply a small amount of molybdenum disulphide grease to the pedal shaft.

7 Refitting is the reverse sequence to removal, ensuring that the brake rod bush is located correctly, and that the pedal shaft "D" section locates into the pedal box right-hand support.

8 When refitting the stop light switch, insert the switch into its retainer, press it lightly against the brake pedal until all free play is just taken up, then turn the switch clockwise to secure. Reconnect the switch wiring connector.

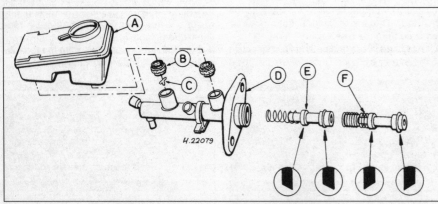

H.22079

9.12 Exploded view of master cylinder components

A Brake fluid reservoir
B Reservoir seals
C Secondary piston retaining pin
D Master cylinder
E Secondary piston
F Primary piston

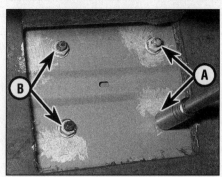

11.6 Servo mounting bracket retaining nuts

A Inner section retaining nuts
B Outer section retaining nuts

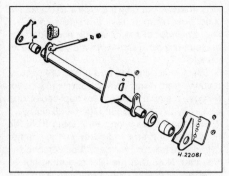

11.10 Exploded view of brake pedal-to-servo cross link and its retaining brackets

12.2 Prising out a spring retaining clip from a rigid pipe/flexible hose support bracket

11 Brake pedal-to-servo cross-link - removal and refitting

Removal

1 Disconnect the battery negative (earth) lead (refer to Chapter 5A, Section 1).

2 Disconnect the cross link pushrod from its brake pedal location by removing the retaining clip on the brake pedal, noting the bush fitted in the pedal.

3 Disconnect the wiring multi-plug from the fluid level warning indicator in the master cylinder reservoir filler cap, then remove the filler cap. Note that the filler cap must not be inverted. The brake fluid should now be removed from the reservoir.

> **HAYNES HINT** *An ideal way to remove fluid from the master cylinder reservoir is to use a clean syringe or an old poultry baster.*

4 Identify each brake pipe and its connection to the master cylinder. Unscrew the fluid pipe to master cylinder union nuts and disconnect the pipes. On models equipped with anti-lock brakes, disconnect the modulator return hoses from the brake fluid reservoir, collecting fluid spillage from the hoses in a suitable tray. The modulator return hose unions should be disconnected by first pushing the hose into the reservoir, then retaining the collar against the reservoir body whilst withdrawing the hose. Note that the modulator return hoses are colour coded - the left-hand modulator has a black return hose and connector, and should be fitted to the forward section of the reservoir, whilst the right-hand modulator has a grey return hose and connector, and should be fitted to the rear section of the reservoir.

5 Disconnect the vacuum hose from the servo unit by carefully levering between the hose connector and the servo housing collar with a screwdriver.

6 Lift up the flap of sound insulation on the

bulkhead, in the passenger side footwell, to expose the servo mounting bracket retaining nuts, and remove them **(see illustration)**.

7 Remove the four nuts securing the servo unit to its mounting bracket assembly.

8 Pull the servo/master cylinder assembly forward and remove the inner servo support bracket.

9 Remove the spring clip and clevis pin securing the servo actuating rod to the cross link, then lift out the servo/master cylinder assembly.

10 Remove the two nuts on the right-hand side of the pedal box assembly to free the cross link right-hand support bracket, then withdraw the link from the vehicle **(see illustration)**.

Refitting

11 Refitting is the reverse procedure to removal, ensuring that the brake pedal pushrod grommet is seated correctly in the bulkhead and that the pushrod itself locates through the brake pedal before securing the servo operating link support brackets. Ensure correct location of the pushrod bush in the brake pedal.

12 Bleed the complete brake hydraulic system in accordance with Section 13 or 14 (as applicable).

12 Hydraulic pipes and hoses - renewal

Note: *Before starting work, refer to the warning at the beginning of Section 13 concerning the dangers of hydraulic fluid.*

1 If any pipe or hose is to be renewed, minimise hydraulic fluid loss by disconnecting the wiring multi-plug from the fluid level warning indicator in the master cylinder reservoir filler cap, then remove the filler cap. Note that the filler cap must not be inverted. Place a piece of plastic film over the reservoir and seal it with an elastic band. Alternatively, flexible hoses can be sealed, if required, using a proprietary brake hose clamp; metal brake

pipe unions can be plugged (if care is taken not to allow dirt into the system) or capped immediately they are disconnected. Place a wad of rag under any union that is to be disconnected, to catch any spilt fluid.

2 If a flexible hose is to be disconnected, unscrew the brake pipe union nut before removing the spring clip which secures the hose to its mounting **(see illustration)**. Where the other end of the hose is connected directly to the brake caliper, disconnect it by unscrewing it from its tapped hole.

3 To unscrew the union nuts, it is preferable to obtain a brake pipe spanner of the correct size; these are available from most large motor accessory shops. Failing this, a close-fitting open-ended spanner will be required, though if the nuts are tight or corroded, their flats may be rounded-off if the spanner slips. In such a case, a self-locking wrench is often the only way to unscrew a stubborn union, but it follows that the pipe and the damaged nuts must be renewed on reassembly. Always clean a union and surrounding area before disconnecting it. If disconnecting a component with more than one union, make a careful note of the connections before disturbing any of them.

4 If a brake pipe is to be renewed, it can be obtained, cut to length and with the union nuts and end flares in place, from Ford dealers. All that is then necessary is to bend it to shape, following the line of the original, before fitting it to the car. Alternatively, most motor accessory shops can make up brake pipes from kits, but this requires very careful measurement of the original, to ensure that the replacement is of the correct length. The safest answer is usually to take the original to the shop as a pattern.

5 Before refitting, blow through the new pipe or hose with dry compressed air. Do not overtighten the union nuts. It is not necessary to exercise brute force to obtain a sound joint.

6 If flexible rubber hoses are renewed, ensure that the pipes and hoses are correctly routed, with no kinks or twists, and that they are secured in the clips or brackets provided.

7 After fitting, bleed the hydraulic system as described in Section 13 or 14 (as applicable), wash off any spilt fluid, and check carefully for fluid leaks.

9

13 Hydraulic system - bleeding (conventional braking system)

Note: *For vehicles equipped with an anti-lock braking system, refer to Section 14.*

 Warning: Hydraulic fluid is poisonous; wash off immediately and thoroughly in the case of skin contact, and seek immediate medical advice if any fluid is swallowed or gets into the eyes. Certain types of hydraulic fluid are inflammable, and may ignite when allowed into contact with hot components; when servicing any hydraulic system, it is safest to assume that the fluid IS inflammable, and to take precautions against the risk of fire as though it is petrol that is being handled. Hydraulic fluid is also an effective paint stripper, and will attack plastics; if any is spilt, it should be washed off immediately, using copious quantities of clean water. Finally, it is hygroscopic (it absorbs moisture from the air). The more moisture is absorbed by the fluid, the lower its boiling point becomes, leading to a dangerous loss of braking under hard use. Old fluid may be contaminated and unfit for further use. When topping-up or renewing the fluid, always use the recommended type, and ensure that it comes from a freshly-opened sealed container.

1 The correct operation of any hydraulic system is only possible after removing all air from the components and circuit; and this is achieved by bleeding the system.

2 During the bleeding procedure, add only clean, unused hydraulic fluid of the recommended type; never re-use fluid that has already been bled from the system. Ensure that sufficient fluid is available before starting work.

3 If there is any possibility of incorrect fluid being already in the system, the brake components and circuit must be flushed completely with uncontaminated, correct fluid, and new seals should be fitted throughout the system.

4 If hydraulic fluid has been lost from the system, or air has entered because of a leak, ensure that the fault is cured before proceeding further.

5 Park the vehicle on level ground, and apply the handbrake. Switch off the engine, then (where applicable) depress the brake pedal several times to dissipate the vacuum from the servo unit. **Note:** *When bleeding the system, the vehicle must maintain a level attitude, ie not tilted in any manner, to ensure that air is not trapped within the pressure control valves. During certain operations in this manual, instructions are given to bleed the brake hydraulic system with the front or the rear of the vehicle raised. In such cases raise the rest of the vehicle so that it maintains a*

level attitude, but only if it is safe to do so. If it is not possible to achieve this safely, complete the remainder of the operation and bleed the brake hydraulic system with the vehicle on its wheels.

6 Check that all pipes and hoses are secure, unions tight and bleed screws closed. Remove the dust caps (where applicable), and clean any dirt from around the bleed screws.

7 Disconnect the wiring multi-plug from the fluid level warning indicator in the master cylinder reservoir filler cap, then remove the filler cap. Note that the filler cap must not be inverted. Top-up the reservoir with the specified fluid to the "Maximum" level (see *"Weekly Checks"*). *Remember to maintain the fluid level at least above the "Minimum" level line throughout the procedure, otherwise there is a risk of further air entering the system.*

8 There are a number of one-man, do-it-yourself brake bleeding kits currently available from motor accessory shops. It is recommended that one of these kits is used whenever possible, as they greatly simplify the bleeding operation, and also reduce the risk of expelled air and fluid being drawn back into the system. If such a kit is not available, the basic (two-man) method must be used, which is described in detail below.

9 If a kit is to be used, prepare the vehicle as described previously, and follow the kit manufacturer's instructions, as the procedure may vary slightly according to the type being used; generally, they are as outlined below in the relevant sub-section.

10 Whichever method is used, the same sequence must be followed (paragraphs 11 and 12) to ensure the removal of all air from the system.

Bleeding sequence

11 If the system has been only partially disconnected, and suitable precautions were taken to minimise fluid loss, it should be necessary to bleed only that part of the system (ie the primary or secondary circuit).

12 If the complete system is to be bled, then it is suggested that you work in the following sequence:

   a) *Right-hand front wheel.*
   b) *Left-hand rear wheel.*
   c) *Left-hand front wheel.*
   d) *Right-hand rear wheel.*

Bleeding - basic (two-man) method

13 Collect a clean glass jar, a suitable length of plastic or rubber tubing which is a tight fit over the bleed screw, and a ring spanner to fit the screw. The help of an assistant will also be required.

14 Remove the dust cap from the first screw in the sequence (if not already done). Fit a suitable spanner and tube to the screw, place the other end of the tube in the jar, and pour in sufficient fluid to cover the end of the tube.

15 Ensure that the master cylinder reservoir

fluid level is maintained at least above the "Minimum" level throughout the procedure.

16 Have the assistant fully depress the brake pedal several times to build up pressure, then maintain it down on the final downstroke.

17 While pedal pressure is maintained, unscrew the bleed screw (approximately one turn) and allow the compressed fluid and air to flow into the jar. The assistant should maintain pedal pressure, following the pedal down to the floor if necessary, and should not release the pedal until instructed to do so. When the flow stops, tighten the bleed screw again. Have the assistant release the pedal slowly, and recheck the reservoir fluid level.

18 Repeat the steps given in paragraphs 16 and 17 until the fluid emerging from the bleed screw is free from air bubbles. If the master cylinder has been drained and refilled, and air is being bled from the first screw in the sequence, allow at least five seconds between cycles for the master cylinder passages to refill.

19 When no more air bubbles appear, tighten the bleed screw securely, remove the tube and spanner, and refit the dust cap (where applicable). Do not overtighten the bleed screw.

20 Repeat the procedure on the remaining screws in the sequence, until all air is removed from the system and the brake pedal feels firm again.

Bleeding - using a one-way valve kit

21 As their name implies, these kits consist of a length of tubing with a one-way valve fitted, to prevent expelled air and fluid being drawn back into the system; some kits include a translucent container, which can be positioned so that the air bubbles can be more easily seen flowing from the end of the tube.

22 The kit is connected to the bleed screw, which is then opened **(see illustration)**. The user returns to the driver's seat, depresses the brake pedal with a smooth, steady stroke, and slowly releases it; this is repeated until the expelled fluid is clear of air bubbles.

23 Note that these kits simplify work so much that it is easy to forget the master cylinder reservoir fluid level; ensure that this is maintained at least above the "Minimum" level at all times.

13.22 Bleeding the hydraulic system using a one-way valve kit

Bleeding - using a pressure-bleeding kit

24 These kits are usually operated by the reservoir of pressurised air contained in the spare tyre. However, note that it will probably be necessary to reduce the pressure to a lower level than normal; refer to the instructions supplied with the kit.

25 By connecting a pressurised, fluid-filled container to the master cylinder reservoir, bleeding can be carried out simply by opening each screw in turn (in the specified sequence), and allowing the fluid to flow out until no more air bubbles can be seen in the expelled fluid.

26 This method has the advantage that the large reservoir of fluid provides an additional safeguard against air being drawn into the system during bleeding.

27 Pressure-bleeding is particularly effective when bleeding "difficult" systems, or when bleeding the complete system at the time of routine fluid renewal.

All methods

28 When bleeding is complete, and firm pedal feel is restored, wash off any spilt fluid, tighten the bleed screws securely, and refit their dust caps.

29 Check the hydraulic fluid level in the master cylinder reservoir, and top-up if necessary.

30 Discard any hydraulic fluid that has been bled from the system; it will not be fit for re-use.

31 Check the feel of the brake pedal. If it feels at all spongy, air must still be present in the system, and further bleeding is required. Failure to bleed satisfactorily after a reasonable repetition of the bleeding procedure may be due to worn master cylinder seals.

14 Hydraulic system - bleeding (anti-lock braking system)

Note: *Before starting work, refer to the warning at the beginning of Section 13 concerning the dangers of hydraulic fluid.*

1 On vehicles equipped with the anti-lock braking system there are two bleed procedures possible, depending on which part of the brake hydraulic system has been disturbed.

2 If any one of the following conditions are present, bleed procedure A should be adopted:
  a) *A modulator has been removed.*
  b) *A modulator return hose (between modulator and brake fluid reservoir) has been drained.*
  c) *The rigid brake pipes have been disconnected from a modulator.*

3 If any one of the following conditions are present, bleed procedure B should be adopted:
  a) *Any condition where the master cylinder has been removed or drained, providing that the modulator return hoses have not lost their head of fluid.*
  b) *Removal or disconnection of any of the basic braking system components ie, brake caliper, flexible hose or rigid pipe, wheel cylinder, or load-apportioning valve.*

Bleed procedure A

4 Raise the vehicle on ramps, or drive it over an inspection pit, so that working clearance may be obtained with the full weight of the vehicle on its roadwheels. Remove the one-piece undertray, as applicable, by turning its bayonet-type fasteners and, on XR2i models, remove the front suspension crossmember (see Chapter 10).

5 Disconnect the wiring multi-plug from the fluid level warning indicator in the master cylinder reservoir filler cap, then remove the filler cap. Note that the filler cap must not be inverted. Top-up the brake fluid reservoir to the MAX mark using fresh fluid of the specified type (see *"Weekly Checks"*), and keep it topped up throughout the bleeding procedure.

6 Slacken the modulator bypass valve Torx screw, located between the two rigid brake pipe connections on the modulator body, and unscrew it two full turns **(see illustration)**.

7 Fully depress the auto-bleed plunger on the modulator and hold it down so that the plunger circlip contacts the modulator body **(see illustration)**. With the plunger

depressed, have an assistant steadily pump the brake pedal at least twenty times whilst you observe the fluid returning to the brake fluid reservoir. Continue this operation until the returning fluid is free from air bubbles.

8 Release the auto-bleed plunger, ensuring that it returns to its normal operational position - pull it out by hand if necessary.

9 Tighten the modulator bypass valve Torx screw.

10 Repeat the operation on the other modulator, if applicable, then refit the one-piece undertray and the front suspension crossmember if removed.

11 Now carry out bleed procedure B.

Bleed procedure B

12 This procedure is the same as for conventional braking systems, and reference should be made to Section 13. Note, however, that all the weight of the vehicle must be on the roadwheels, otherwise the load-apportioning valves will not bleed. If problems are encountered whereby the rear brakes will not bleed satisfactorily, ensure that the load-apportioning valves are correctly adjusted (see Section 25). As with the conventional braking system, the brake fluid level must be kept topped up during bleeding.

15 Vacuum servo unit - testing, removal and refitting

Testing

1 To test the operation of the servo, depress the footbrake four or five times to exhaust the vacuum, then start the engine while keeping the footbrake depressed. As the engine starts, there should be a noticeable "give" in the brake pedal as vacuum builds up. Allow the engine to run for at least two minutes, and then switch it off. If the brake pedal is depressed again, it should be possible to detect a hiss from the servo when the pedal is depressed. After about four or five applications, no further hissing will be heard, and the pedal will feel considerably firmer.

2 Before assuming that a problem exists in the servo itself, check the non-return valve as described in the next Section.

Removal

3 Refer to Section 9 and remove the master cylinder.

4 Disconnect the vacuum hose at the servo non-return valve by pulling it free. If it is reluctant to move, assist it by prising it free using a screwdriver with its blade inserted under the elbow flange.

5 Lift up the flap of sound insulation on the bulkhead, in the passenger side footwell, to expose the servo mounting bracket retaining nuts **(see illustration 11.6)**. Remove the two innermost nuts to free the inner section of the servo mounting bracket from its bulkhead

9

14.6 Modulator bypass valve Torx screw (arrowed)

14.7 Modulator auto-bleed plunger (arrowed)

15.6 Nuts securing servo unit to its mounting bracket assembly (arrowed)

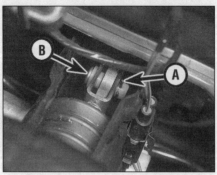

15.7 Spring clip (A) and clevis pin (B) securing servo pushrod to the cross link

location. Slacken the other two nuts or remove them, as necessary.

6 Remove the four nuts securing the servo unit to its mounting bracket assembly, then pull the servo forward to remove the inner servo support bracket **(see illustration)**.

7 Remove the spring clip and clevis pin securing the servo pushrod to the cross link, then lift out the servo unit **(see illustration)**.

8 Note that the servo unit cannot be dismantled for repair or overhaul and, if faulty, must be renewed.

Refitting

9 Refitting is a reversal of removal. Refer to Section 9 for details of refitting the master cylinder.

---

16 Vacuum servo unit vacuum hose and non-return valve - removal, testing and refitting

Removal

1 Depress the brake pedal three or four times to exhaust any remaining vacuum from the servo unit.

2 Carefully pull free and detach the servo vacuum hose from the servo unit. If the hose is reluctant to move, prise it free with the aid of a screwdriver, inserting its blade under the flange of the elbow.

3 Detach the vacuum hose from its inlet manifold connection. Depending on the fixing, undo the union nut and withdraw the hose, or press the hose and its retaining collar inwards, then holding the collar in, withdraw the hose.

4 If the hose or the fixings are damaged or in poor condition, they must be renewed.

Non-return valve testing

5 Examine the non-return valve for damage and signs of deterioration, and renew it if necessary. The valve may be tested by blowing through its connecting hoses in both directions. It should only be possible to blow from the servo end to the manifold end.

Refitting

6 Refitting is a reversal of removal. If fitting a new non-return valve, ensure that it is fitted the correct way round.

---

17 Handbrake lever - removal and refitting

Removal

1 Disconnect the battery negative (earth) lead (refer to Chapter 5A, Section 1), then chock the wheels to secure the vehicle.

2 Undo the bolts securing the front seats to the floorpan, and remove both seats from the vehicle (see Chapter 11). Move the seats on their slide mechanisms to expose the mounting bolts, as necessary.

3 Remove the screws securing the rear seat cushion, then raise the cushion to obtain access to the carpet retaining screws. Remove the carpet retaining screws.

4 Undo the bolt securing the seat belt clips to the centre of the floorpan, then remove the clip assembly.

5 Remove the seat belt lower anchor bracket bolt from its location at the base of the B-pillar behind the driver's seat.

6 Remove the screws securing the sill scuff plate to the driver's side of the vehicle, then carefully pull the sill scuff plate away from its location so that the carpet is released.

7 Fold the carpet forwards, at the same time carefully easing it out from under the sill scuff plate. Lift the carpet over the handbrake lever.

8 Lift out the noise insulation for access to the lever mounting bolts and the primary cable fixing.

9 Fully release the handbrake lever, then remove the handbrake primary cable clevis pin securing clip **(see illustration)**. Remove the clevis pin and withdraw the primary cable from the handbrake lever assembly.

10 Remove the cover **(see illustration)**, then disconnect the handbrake warning light switch wiring connection, and undo the two screws securing the switch to the handbrake lever assembly.

11 Undo the handbrake lever mounting bolts, then withdraw the handbrake lever assembly from the vehicle.

Refitting

12 Refitting is the reverse procedure to removal, ensuring that the handbrake warning light wiring is routed away from the lever ratchet. The loom should be secured to the floorpan with tape.

13 Check the handbrake adjustment as described in Chapter 1 to complete.

---

18 Handbrake primary cable - removal and refitting

Removal

1 Release the primary cable from the handbrake lever, as described in the previous Section.

2 Chock the front wheels then jack up the rear of the car and support it on axle stands (see "Jacking and Vehicle Support").

3 Where applicable, detach the exhaust system and remove the heat shields from the underside floorpan to allow access to the primary cable connections underneath the vehicle (see Chapter 4E).

4 Release the spring clip securing the pin, and extract the equaliser/cable pin. Detach

17.9 Removing the handbrake primary cable clevis pin securing clip

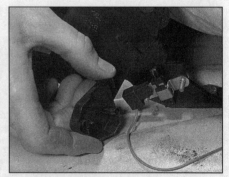

17.10 Removing the cover from the handbrake warning light switch

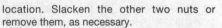

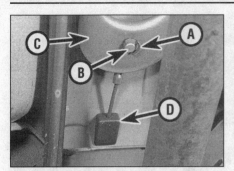

18.4 Handbrake equaliser yoke arrangement

A *Clevis pin securing clip*
B *Clevis pin*
C *Equaliser yoke*
D *Primary cable guide*

the equaliser from the primary cable **(see illustration)**.

5 Remove the primary cable guide by drifting it out rearwards, through the floorpan, from the inside of the vehicle.

Refitting

6 Refit in the reverse order of removal. Ensure that the cable guide is secured in the floorpan, and lubricate the pivot pin with a liberal amount of high-melting-point grease.
7 Refit the exhaust system and heat shields with reference to Chapter 4E (where applicable).
8 Refer to Chapter 1 for details, and adjust the handbrake as required before lowering the vehicle to the ground.

19 Handbrake rear cable - removal and refitting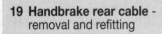

Removal

1 Chock the front wheels then jack up the rear of the car and support it on axle stands (see *"Jacking and Vehicle Support"*). Fully release the handbrake lever and remove the rear roadwheels.
2 Refer to the previous Section for details, and disconnect the handbrake primary cable from the equaliser.
3 Disconnect the handbrake cable from its adjuster body location and its fixed body

20.1a Pressure control valves located on left-hand inner wing panel

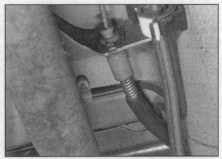

19.3 Handbrake rear cable fixed body location

location **(see illustration)**, then remove it from its retaining clips.
4 Remove the rear brake drum(s) and brake shoes as described in Sections 5 and 6 respectively.
5 Compress the handbrake cable retainer lugs and release the cable from the backplate, then pull the cable through. Release the cable from the underbody fixings, and remove it from the vehicle.

Refitting

6 Refitting is a reversal of the removal procedure. Refer to Sections 6 and 5 respectively for details on the refitting of the brake shoes and drums.
7 When the cable is fully refitted (but before lowering the vehicle rear wheels to the ground) check and adjust the handbrake as described in Chapter 1.

20 Brake pressure control valves - removal and refitting

Note: *Before starting work, refer to the warning at the beginning of Section 13 concerning the dangers of hydraulic fluid.*

Removal

1 The pressure control valves are located in the engine compartment, fixed to the left-hand inner wing panel or screwed directly into the master cylinder fluid outlet ports **(see illustrations)**.
2 Minimise hydraulic fluid loss by disconnecting the wiring multi-plug from the

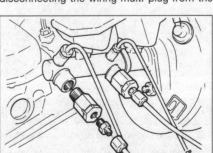

20.1b Pressure control valves and pipe connections at the master cylinder - later models

fluid level warning indicator in the master cylinder reservoir filler cap, then remove the filler cap. Note that the filler cap must not be inverted. Place a piece of plastic film over the reservoir and seal it with an elastic band. Detach the rigid brake pipes from the valves. As the pipes are disconnected, tape over the exposed ends, or fit plugs, to prevent the ingress of dirt and excessive fluid loss.
3 To remove the inner wing panel mounted assembly, remove the two screws securing the valve assembly mounting bracket to the inner wing panel, and withdraw the valve assembly from the vehicle. To remove the valves from the bracket, slide free the retaining clips and detach the valve(s).
4 To remove the master cylinder mounted valves, unscrew them from the master cylinder body.

Refitting

5 Refitting is a reversal of the removal procedure.
6 On completion, bleed the complete hydraulic system as described in Section 13.

21 Light-laden valve (Courier models) - removal and refitting

Note: *Before starting work, refer to the warning at the beginning of Section 13 concerning the dangers of hydraulic fluid.*

Removal

1 For this operation, the vehicle must be raised for access underneath at the rear, but must still be resting on its wheels. Suitable ramps (or an inspection pit) will therefore be required. If positioning the vehicle on a pair of ramps, chock the front roadwheels.
2 Minimise hydraulic fluid loss by disconnecting the wiring multi-plug from the fluid level warning indicator in the master cylinder reservoir filler cap, then remove the filler cap. Note that the filler cap must not be inverted. Place a piece of plastic film over the reservoir and seal it with an elastic band.
3 Disconnect the four brake pipes from the valve, and drain any escaping fluid into a suitable container for disposal **(see illustration)**. Due to its location, care will be

21.3 Hydraulic pipe and linkage attachments at the light-laden valve

9

needed not to spill the fluid onto the hands - wear suitable protective gloves. Plug or cap the disconnected pipes and valve openings, to prevent dirt ingress and further fluid loss.

4 Unbolt the valve from its mounting bracket, unhook the linkage from the rear axle, then withdraw the valve **(see illustration)**. The intermediate bracket may be unbolted if required.

Refitting

5 Refitting is the reverse of the removal procedure; adjust the valve as described in Section 22, then bleed the complete hydraulic system as described in Section 13. Check the operation of the brakes before taking the vehicle out on the road.

22 Light-laden valve (Courier models) - adjustment

Note: *To adjust the valve accurately, the vehicle must be at a known rear axle loading - owners who cannot determine the loading with sufficient accuracy must have this check made by a Ford dealer or similar expert.*

1 For this operation, the vehicle must be raised for access underneath at the rear, but must be standing on its wheels. Suitable ramps (or an inspection pit) will therefore be required. If positioning the vehicle on a pair of ramps, chock the front roadwheels.

2 Measure the distance between the inner radius of the linkage's hooked end and the first shoulder **(see illustration)**. If the dimension is not as specified for the axle loading, adjustment is required.

3 To adjust the setting, slacken the locknut on the valve linkage, move the rod until the setting is correct, then tighten the locknut securely **(see illustration)**. Check the operation of the brakes before taking the vehicle out on the road.

23 Anti-lock braking system (ABS) - general information

A mechanically-driven, two-channel anti-lock braking system is available as a factory-fitted option on certain model variants within the Fiesta range.

The system comprises four main components; two modulators, one for each brake circuit, and two rear axle load-apportioning valves, again, one for each brake circuit. Apart from the additional hydraulic piping, the remainder of the braking system is the same as for conventional models.

The modulators are located in the engine compartment with one mounted on each side of the transmission, directly above the driveshaft inner constant velocity joints. Each modulator contains a shaft which actuates a flywheel by means of a ball and ramp clutch.

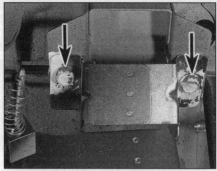

21.4 Light-laden valve mounting bolts (arrowed)

A rubber toothed belt is used to drive the modulator shaft from the driveshaft inner constant velocity joint.

During driving and under normal braking the modulator shaft and the flywheel rotate together and at the same speed through the engagement of a ball and ramp clutch. In this condition hydraulic pressure from the master cylinder passes to the modulators and then to each brake in the conventional way. In the event of a front wheel locking the modulator shaft rotation will be less than that of the flywheel and the flywheel will overrun the ball and ramp clutch. This causes the flywheel to slide on the modulator shaft, move inward and operate a lever which in turn opens a dump valve. Hydraulic pressure to the locked brake is released via a de-boost piston allowing the wheel to once again revolve. Fluid passed through the dump valve is returned to the master cylinder reservoir via the modulator return hoses. At the same time hydraulic pressure from the master cylinder causes a pump piston to contact an eccentric cam on the modulator shaft. The flywheel is then decelerated at a controlled rate by the flywheel friction clutch. When the speed of the modulator shaft and flywheel are once again equal the dump valve closes and the cycle repeats. This complete operation takes place many times a second until the vehicle stops or the brakes are released.

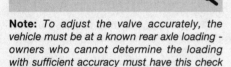

22.2 Light-laden valve adjustment details

With rear axle load at 400 kg,
        "X" should be 147 mm
With rear axle load at 850 kg,
        "X" should be 166 mm

The load-apportioning valves are mounted on a common bracket attached to the rear body, just above the rear axle twist beam location, and are actuated by linkages attached to the axle beam. The valves regulate hydraulic pressure to the rear brakes, in accordance with vehicle load and attitude, so that the braking force available at the rear brakes will always be lower than that available at the front.

A belt-break warning switch is fitted to the cover which surrounds each modulator drivebelt. The switch contains an arm which is in contact with the drivebelt at all times. If the belt should break, or if the adjustment of the belt is too slack, the arm will move out closing the switch contacts and informing the driver via an instrument panel warning light.

24 Anti-lock braking system (ABS) components - removal and refitting

Modulator

Note: *Before starting work, refer to the warning at the beginning of Section 13 concerning the dangers of hydraulic fluid.*

1 Disconnect the battery negative (earth) lead (refer to Chapter 5A, Section 1).

2 Minimise hydraulic fluid loss by disconnecting the wiring multi-plug from the fluid level warning indicator in the master cylinder reservoir filler cap, then remove the filler cap. Note that the filler cap must not be inverted. Place a piece of plastic film over the reservoir and seal it with an elastic band.

3 Disconnect the modulator return hoses from the master cylinder reservoir, collecting any fluid spillage from the hoses in a suitable tray. The modulator return hose unions should be disconnected by first pushing the hose into the reservoir, then retaining the collar against the reservoir body whilst withdrawing the hose. Note that the hoses are colour coded - the left-hand modulator has a black return hose and connector, and should be fitted to the forward section of the reservoir, whilst the right-hand modulator has a grey return hose and connector, and should be fitted to the rear section of the reservoir.

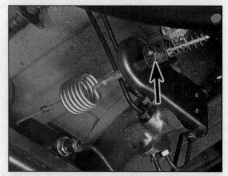

22.3 Light-laden valve linkage adjustment locknut (arrowed)

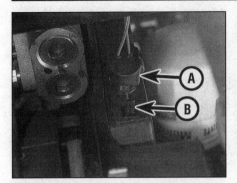

24.6 Belt-break switch in drivebelt cover

A Main switch body   B Release lever

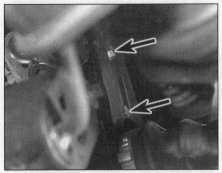

24.7 Modulator drivebelt cover to mounting bracket securing bolts (arrowed)

24.9 Modulator pivot bolt (A) and adjuster bolt (B)

Right-hand side

4 Chock the rear wheels then jack up the front of the car and support it on axle stands (see *"Jacking and Vehicle Support"*).

5 Remove the one-piece undertray where fitted, by turning the bayonet type fasteners, and on XR2i models, remove the front suspension crossmember (see Chapter 10).

6 From underneath, remove the belt-break switch from the right-hand drivebelt cover by squeezing its release lever towards the main body of the switch **(see illustration)**, then carefully withdraw, ensuring that the belt contact arm does not catch on the drivebelt cover.

7 Remove the two bolts securing the modulator drivebelt cover to the modulator mounting bracket, and withdraw the cover **(see illustration)**.

8 Disconnect the rigid brake pipes from the modulator, fitting blanking plugs to prevent excessive fluid loss and dirt ingress.

9 Remove the modulator pivot bolt and adjuster bolt **(see illustration)**, then slip the drivebelt from its pulley, and withdraw the modulator unit from the vehicle. Ensure that the modulator return hose does not become kinked as the modulator unit is withdrawn.

10 Disconnect the modulator return hose from the modulator unit, and fit a blanking plug to prevent dirt ingress. Allow for residual fluid spillage as the hose is disconnected.

11 If a new modulator is to be fitted, note that these units are not interchangeable from side to side, and the correct replacement must be obtained. The modulator units are colour-coded, and must be fitted with the arrows on top of the casings pointing towards the front of the vehicle.

12 To refit, first connect the modulator return hose to the return outlet on the modulator unit.

13 Locate the modulator unit to its bracket and fit the pivot bolt, having applied a thin smear of anti-seize compound to the bolt, but do not fully tighten at this stage. Take care not to damage the modulator return hose as it is manoeuvred into position.

14 Fit the drivebelt to its modulator pulley location, ensuring that it sits correctly over the driveshaft pulley, then refit the adjuster bolt but do not fully tighten at this stage.

15 Adjust the tension of the drivebelt by moving the modulator unit, until a belt deflection of 5.0 mm is obtained under firm finger pressure. Check this using a ruler at a point midway between the two pulleys.

16 With the drivebelt tensioned correctly, tighten the pivot and adjuster bolts to the specified torque. Re-check the tension of the drivebelt after tightening the bolts.

17 Reconnect the rigid brake pipes to the modulator, tightening the unions securely.

18 Refit the modulator drivebelt cover to the modulator mounting bracket, and secure with its two retaining bolts.

19 Refit the belt-break switch to the modulator drivebelt cover, taking care not to damage the belt contact arm as it passes through the cover.

20 Reconnect the modulator return hose by pushing the hose firmly into its brake fluid reservoir location, then lever out the collar to retain it.

21 Refit the front suspension crossmember and the one-piece undertray, as applicable.

22 Lower the vehicle to the ground.

23 Top-up the brake fluid reservoir using fresh fluid of the specified type (see *"Weekly checks"*), then bleed the brake hydraulic system in accordance with Section 14. Refit the reservoir filler cap and warning indicator wiring multi-plug on completion.

24 Reconnect the battery negative lead.

Left-hand side

25 Repeat the procedures given in paragraphs 1 to 3.

26 Chock the rear wheels then jack up the front of the car and support it on axle stands (see *"Jacking and Vehicle Support"*). Remove the front roadwheels.

27 Remove the one-piece undertray where fitted, by turning the bayonet type fasteners, and on XR2i models, remove the front suspension crossmember (see Chapter 10).

28 Remove the belt-break switch from the left-hand drivebelt cover in a similar manner to that described in paragraph 6, this time from the engine compartment.

29 Remove the two bolts securing the modulator drivebelt cover to the modulator mounting bracket, then ease the lower portion of the cover over the driveshaft taking care not to damage the driveshaft CV joint gaiter. Withdraw the cover through the engine compartment, manoeuvring it to clear obstructions.

30 Disconnect the rigid brake pipes from the modulator, fitting blanking plugs to prevent excessive fluid loss and dirt ingress.

31 Slacken the modulator pivot and adjuster bolts, then swing the modulator downwards to release the drivebelt tension before slipping the drivebelt from its modulator pulley location.

32 Remove the modulator pivot and adjuster bolts, withdraw the modulator upwards through the engine compartment. Ensure that the modulator return hose does not become kinked as the modulator unit is withdrawn.

33 Disconnect the modulator return hose from the modulator unit, and fit a blanking plug to prevent dirt ingress. Allow for residual fluid spillage as the hose is disconnected.

34 If a new modulator is to be fitted, note that these units are not interchangeable from side to side, and the correct replacement must be obtained. The modulator units are colour-coded, and must be fitted with the arrows on top of the casings pointing towards the front of the vehicle.

35 To refit, first connect the modulator return hose to the return outlet on the modulator unit.

36 Locate the modulator unit to its mounting bracket and fit the pivot bolt, having applied a thin smear of anti-seize compound to the bolt, but do not fully tighten at this stage. Take care not to damage the modulator return hose as it is manoeuvred into position.

37 Fit the drivebelt to its modulator pulley location, ensuring that it sits correctly over the driveshaft pulley, then refit the adjuster bolt but do not fully tighten at this stage.

38 Adjust the tension of the drivebelt by moving the modulator unit, until a belt deflection of 5.0 mm is obtained under firm finger pressure. Check this using a ruler at a point midway between the two pulleys.

9

39 With the drivebelt tensioned correctly, tighten the pivot and adjuster bolts to the specified torque. Re-check the tension of the drivebelt after tightening the bolts.

40 Reconnect the rigid brake pipes to the modulator, tightening the unions to seal the system.

41 Refit the modulator drivebelt cover and secure with its two retaining bolts. Take care not to damage the driveshaft CV joint gaiter as the cover is eased into position.

42 Refit the belt-break switch to the modulator drivebelt cover, taking care not to damage the belt contact arm as it passes through the cover.

43 Reconnect the modulator return hose by pushing the hose firmly into its brake fluid reservoir location, then lever out the collar to retain it.

44 Refit the front suspension crossmember and the one-piece undertray, as applicable.

45 Refit the roadwheels, then remove the axle stands and lower the vehicle to the ground. Tighten the wheel nuts to the specified torque.

46 Top-up the brake fluid reservoir using fresh fluid of the specified type (see "*Weekly checks*"), then bleed the brake hydraulic system in accordance with Section 14. Refit the reservoir filler cap and the warning indicator wiring multi-plug on completion.

47 Reconnect the battery negative lead.

Modulator drivebelt

48 Disconnect the battery negative (earth) lead (refer to Chapter 5A, Section 1).

49 Chock the rear wheels then jack up the front of the car and support it on axle stands (see "*Jacking and Vehicle Support*"). Remove the relevant front roadwheel.

50 Remove the one-piece undertray where fitted, by turning its bayonet-type fasteners, and on XR2i models, remove the front suspension crossmember (see Chapter 10).

51 Remove the belt-break switch from the relevant drivebelt cover, then remove the drivebelt cover, as described in the previous sub-Section.

52 Slacken the modulator pivot and adjuster bolts to release drivebelt tension, then slip the drivebelt from the modulator.

53 Remove the track rod end balljoint from the steering arm on the spindle carrier (see Chapter 10).

54 Disconnect the anti-roll bar connecting link (where applicable) and release the brake hose from their locations on the suspension strut.

55 Remove the pinch bolt and nut securing the lower suspension arm balljoint to the spindle carrier, and separate the balljoint from the spindle carrier assembly.

56 To release the driveshaft inner CV joint from the differential, have an assistant pull the spindle carrier away from the centre of the vehicle whilst you insert a lever between the inner CV joint and the transmission casing, then firmly strike the lever with the flat of the

hand, but be careful not to damage adjacent components. Make provision for escaping transmission oil, if possible plugging the opening to prevent excessive loss. Do not allow the CV joints to bend more than 20° from the horizontal or internal damage may occur. If both driveshafts are to be removed, immobilise the differential by inserting an old joint or suitable shaft, before the other driveshaft is removed.

57 Slide the drivebelt off the driveshaft.

58 Remove the snap-ring from the groove in the splines of the inner CV joint. *This snap-ring must be renewed every time the driveshaft is withdrawn from the differential.*

59 With the drivebelt removed, closely examine the condition of the belt over its entire length. Renew the belt if any cracks are noticed in the fabric at the roots of the teeth, if there is any abrasion of the fabric facing material, or if there are any tears starting from the edge of the belt.

60 If, since the drivebelts were last renewed, a vehicle has covered more than 30 000 miles (48 000 km) or a period of more than two years has elapsed, the drivebelts should be renewed as a matter of course.

61 Prior to refitting the drivebelt, thoroughly clean its CV joint pulley location.

62 Fit the drivebelt over the driveshaft then, with a new snap-ring fitted to the inner CV joint splines, lubricate the splines with transmission oil. Remove the temporary plug and insert the inner CV joint to its transmission casing location. Press against the spindle carrier so that the snap-ring engages fully to hold the CV joint splines in the differential.

63 Refitting is now a reversal of the removal procedure, tensioning the drivebelt as described in the previous sub-Section. Ensure that the pinch-bolt securing the lower suspension arm balljoint to the spindle carrier locates in the annular groove on the balljoint spindle. Secure the track rod and balljoint, using a new split pin. Tighten the suspension components to their specified torque (see Chapter 10).

64 Check the level of the transmission oil, and top-up as required (see Chapter 1).

Modulator belt-break switch

65 Modulator belt-break switches are fitted to each of the two drivebelt covers, and clip into position. To remove, gently squeeze the protruding lever on the switch towards the main switch body and lift out, ensuring that the belt contact arm does not catch on the drivebelt cover.

25 Load-apportioning valve (ABS models) - adjustment

1 Before attempting to adjust the load-apportioning valves, the vehicle must be at its kerb weight, ie with approximately half a tank of fuel and carrying no load. Note that a special setting tool will be required to adjust the valves - this can be fabricated, to the dimensions shown **(see illustration)**.

2 Raise the vehicle on ramps or drive it over an inspection pit, so that working clearance is obtained with the full weight of the vehicle resting on its roadwheels. Remove the spare wheel and its carrier.

3 To check adjustment, insert the load-apportioning valve setting tool into the nylon sleeve without pre-loading the valve. If unable to insert the tool, carry out the following adjustment procedure.

4 Slacken the operating link adjustment fixing screw then insert the setting tool into the nylon sleeve, applying light pressure to the operating link upper arm, so that the setting tool fully locates. With the setting tool just resting up against the adjustment post, tighten the operating link adjustment fixing screw to the specified torque **(see illustration)**.

5 Repeat the procedure on the other valve.

6 Refit the spare wheel on completion.

26 Load-apportioning valve (ABS models) - removal and refitting

1 Minimise hydraulic fluid loss by disconnecting the wiring multi-plug from the fluid level warning indicator in the master

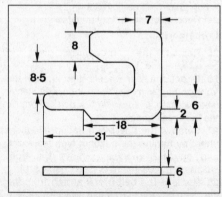

25.1 Load-apportioning valve adjustment tool (dimensions given in mm)

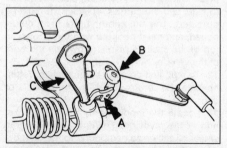

25.4 Load-apportioning valve adjustment

A Setting tool
B Operating link adjustment fixing screw
C Adjustment post

cylinder reservoir filler cap, then remove the filler cap. Note that the filler cap must not be inverted. Place a piece of plastic film over the reservoir and seal it with an elastic band.

2 Raise the vehicle on ramps, or drive it over an inspection pit, so that working clearance may be obtained with the full weight of the vehicle on its roadwheels.

3 Remove the spare wheel and its carrier for access to the load-apportioning valves **(see illustration)**.

4 Disconnect the load-apportioning valve operating links from the rear axle twist beam, by undoing the nuts securing them.

5 Disconnect the rigid brake pipes from the load-apportioning valves, and fit blanking plugs to prevent dirt ingress. Make provision for escaping fluid as the pipes are disconnected.

6 Remove the bolts securing the valve assembly mounting bracket to the vehicle body, then carefully lower from the vehicle.

7 The valves can now be individually removed from the mounting bracket, as required, by undoing the fixings securing them from the other side of the bracket.

8 Refitting is the reverse sequence to removal, adjusting the load-apportioning valves, as described in the previous Section, before refitting the spare wheel. When fitting a new valve, the plastic tie must be cut off before attempting any adjustment, and the setting tool must be used as described in the previous Section.

9 Bleed the brake hydraulic system in accordance with Section 14.

26.3 General view of load-apportioning valve arrangement (spare wheel and carrier removed for access)

9

Notes

Chapter 10
Suspension and steering

Contents

Auxiliary drivebelt check and renewal . . . . .See Chapter 1
Front hub bearings - renewal 3
Front spindle carrier - removal and refitting 2
Front suspension anti-roll bar - removal and refitting 6
Front suspension crossmember - removal and refitting 7
Front suspension lower arm - removal and refitting 8
Front suspension strut - dismantling, examination and reassembly . . 5
Front suspension strut - removal and refitting 4
General information 1
Power steering fluid cooler - removal and refitting 26
Power steering fluid level check . . . . .See "Weekly Checks"
Power steering hydraulic system - bleeding 27
Power steering pump - removal and refitting 25
Rear axle (all models except Courier) - removal and refitting 12
Rear axle pivot bushes (all models except Courier) - renewal 13
Rear hub bearings - renewal 9
Rear shock absorber (Courier models) - removal, examination
and refitting 16
Rear strut (all models except Courier) - dismantling, examination
and reassembly 11
Rear strut (all models except Courier) - removal and refitting 10
Rear suspension anti-roll bar (all models except Courier) -
removal and refitting 14
Rear suspension assembly (Courier models) - removal and refitting . . 17
Rear suspension components (Courier models) - general 15
Rear suspension ride height (Courier models) - adjustment 18
Steering column (manual steering) - removal and refitting 20
Steering column (power steering) - removal and refitting 21
Steering gear (manual steering) - removal and refitting 23
Steering gear (power steering) - removal and refitting 24
Steering gear rubber gaiters - renewal 22
Steering wheel - removal and refitting 19
Suspension and steering check . . . . .See Chapter 1
Track rod end balljoint - removal and refitting 28
Tyre condition and pressure checks . . . . .See "Weekly Checks"
Wheel alignment and steering angles - general information 29

Degrees of difficulty

Easy, suitable for novice with little experience	**Fairly easy,** suitable for beginner with some experience 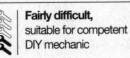	**Fairly difficult,** suitable for competent DIY mechanic
Difficult, suitable for experienced DIY mechanic	**Very difficult,** suitable for expert DIY or professional	

Specifications

Wheel alignment and steering angles

Front wheel toe setting:

Pre-1990 models:

Tolerance allowed before resetting required	3.0 mm toe-out to 3.0 mm toe-in (0°30' toe-out to 0°30' toe-in)
Adjustment setting (if required)	Parallel ± 1.0 mm (0° ± 0°10')

1990 models onward:

All models except Turbo:

Tolerance allowed before resetting required	4.5 mm toe-out to 0.5 mm toe-in (0°45' toe-out to 0°05' toe-in)
Adjustment setting (if required)	2.0 mm toe-out ± 1.0 mm (0°20' toe-out ± 0°10')

Turbo models:

Tolerance allowed before resetting required	4.0 mm toe-out to parallel (0°40' toe-out to 0°0')
Adjustment setting (if required)	2.0 mm toe-out ± 1.0 mm (0°20' toe-out ± 0°10')

Roadwheels

Wheel types and sizes (dependent on model):
Steel . . . . 13 x 4.5, 13 x 5, 13 x 5.5
Alloy . . . . 13 x 5.5, 14 x 5.5

Tyres

Tyre sizes (dependent on model) . . . . 135 R 13, 145 R 13, 155/70 R 13, 165/55 R 13, 165/65 R 13, 175/60 R 13, 185/55 R 14 or 185/60 R 13
Tyre pressures . . . . See *"Weekly Checks"*

Torque wrench settings

	Nm	lbf ft
Front suspension		
Hub/driveshaft retaining nut	205 to 235	151 to 173
Lower arm balljoint-to-spindle carrier pinch bolt	48 to 60	35 to 44
Front suspension strut to spindle carrier pinch-bolt	80 to 90	59 to 66
Anti-roll bar link to front suspension strut nut	41 to 58	30 to 43
Anti-roll bar link to anti-roll bar nut	41 to 58	30 to 43
Anti-roll bar retaining clamp bolts to lower arm	20 to 28	15 to 21
Front suspension strut top-mount retaining nut	40 to 52	30 to 38
Front suspension strut spring retaining nut	52 to 65	38 to 48
Front suspension crossmember bolts (XR2i only)	80 to 90	59 to 66
Lower arm to lower arm mounting bracket bolts (using torque-to-yield method with vehicle standing on its wheels):		
Stage 1	50	37
Stage 2	Slacken completely	
Stage 3	50	37
Stage 4	Tighten through a further 90°	
Rear suspension (all models except Courier)		
Rear hub bearing retaining nut	250 to 290	184 to 214
Rear drum/hub to axle flange bolts	56 to 76	41 to 56
Rear axle to body mounting bracket bolts	41 to 58	30 to 43
Rear axle trailing arm bush bolt*	58 to 79	43 to 58
Rear strut top-mount retaining nuts	28 to 40	20 to 30
Rear strut-to-axle mounting bolt	102 to 138	75 to 102
Rear strut spring retaining through-bolt	41 to 58	30 to 42
Anti-roll bar front mounting bolts	41 to 58	30 to 42
Anti-roll bar rear mounting bolts	88 to 113	65 to 83
Load-apportioning valve operating link to axle beam	21 to 28	15 to 21
Torque to be measured from the bolt head (not the nut)		
Rear suspension (Courier models)		
Rear hub bearing retaining nut	250 to 290	184 to 214
Shock absorber upper mounting	102 to 138	75 to 102
Shock absorber lower mounting	70 to 97	52 to 72
Rear suspension mounting bracket bolts	70 to 97	52 to 72
Manual steering		
Steering gear to bulkhead	70 to 97	57 to 72
Track rod end balljoint to spindle carrier steering arm	25 to 30	18 to 22
Track rod locknut to track rod end balljoint	57 to 68	42 to 50
Steering wheel to column shaft bolt	45 to 55	33 to 40
Steering column mounting nuts	10 to 14	7 to 10
Steering column universal joint pinch-bolt	45 to 56	33 to 41
Power steering		
Steering wheel to column shaft bolt	50	37
Steering gear to bulkhead	84	62
Steering gear fluid pipe unions	31	23
Steering gear flexible coupling pinch-bolt	51	38
Track rod end balljoint to spindle carrier steering arm	26	19
Track rod locknut to track rod end balljoint	63	46
Steering pump mounting bolts	25	18
Steering pump pulley bolts	25	18
High pressure fluid pipe to pump union	65	48
High pressure fluid pipe coupling joint	17	13
Steering column mounting nuts	12	9
Roadwheel nuts		
All models	70 to 110	52 to 74

1 General information

The front suspension is of independent type, achieved by the use of MacPherson struts **(see illustration)**. The struts, which incorporate coil springs and integral shock absorbers, are located at their upper mountings by rubber insulators and secured to the inner wing panels by cup seat mountings and locknuts. The lower end of each strut is bolted to the top of a cast spindle carrier. The spindle carriers house non-adjustable hub bearings as a variation of a proven design. The lower mountings of the spindle carriers are attached, via balljoints, to a pressed-steel lower arm assembly. The lower arm assembly consists of two sections. The lower arm mounting bracket is bolted securely to the underside of the vehicle, and has a locating peg and unique outer fixing bolt to ensure correct location. The A-shaped lower arm is attached to its mounting bracket by double vertical bushes and controls both lateral and fore and aft movement of the front wheels. The balljoints connecting the lower mountings of the spindle carriers to the lower arms are riveted to the lower arms, and are not available as separate service items. An anti-roll bar is fitted to high specification models and, additionally on the XR2i, a front suspension crossmember is fitted.

On all models except Courier, the rear suspension is semi-independent, with an inverted V-section beam welded between tubular trailing arms **(see illustration)**. This inverted V-section beam allows a limited torsional flexibility, giving each rear wheel a certain degree of independent movement, whilst maintaining optimum track and wheel camber control. This type of arrangement is called a "twist beam" rear axle. The axle is attached to the body by rubber void bushes, through brackets bolted to the underside of the vehicle. Each bracket has a conical locating peg to ensure accurate alignment of the axle assembly. The rear suspension struts, which are similar to the MacPherson struts used at the front, are mounted at their upper ends by nut and captive bolt fixings through the suspension turrets in the luggage compartment. At their lower ends, the struts are attached, close to the wheels, by bolts passed through the trailing arms and lower strut integral bushes. The rear wheel hub/brake drum unit and spindle on each side form an assembly which can be unbolted from the axle without disturbing the hub bearings. An anti-roll bar is fitted to the rear suspension on certain later models.

Courier models are fitted with a modified version of the twist beam rear axle, using linked torsion bars as springs and to provide anti-roll stabilisation **(see illustration)**. Separate shock absorbers are fitted to control suspension movement.

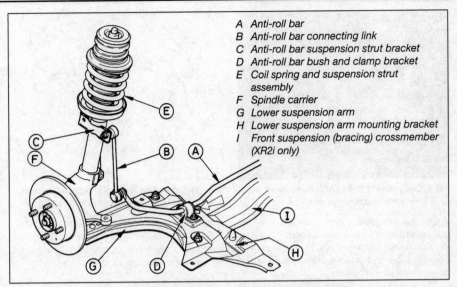

A Anti-roll bar
B Anti-roll bar connecting link
C Anti-roll bar suspension strut bracket
D Anti-roll bar bush and clamp bracket
E Coil spring and suspension strut assembly
F Spindle carrier
G Lower suspension arm
H Lower suspension arm mounting bracket
I Front suspension (bracing) crossmember (XR2i only)

1.1 General view of front suspension components

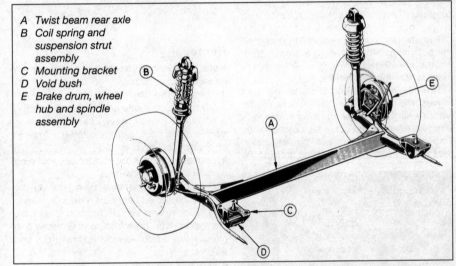

A Twist beam rear axle
B Coil spring and suspension strut assembly
C Mounting bracket
D Void bush
E Brake drum, wheel hub and spindle assembly

1.2 General view of rear suspension components (all models except Courier)

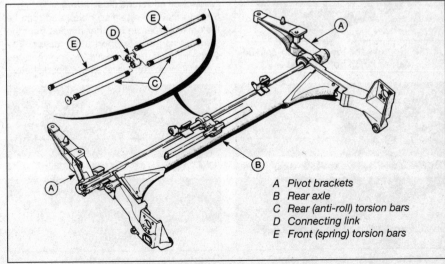

A Pivot brackets
B Rear axle
C Rear (anti-roll) torsion bars
D Connecting link
E Front (spring) torsion bars

1.3 General view of rear suspension components (Courier models)

10

2.4 Disconnect the brake hose from the front suspension strut

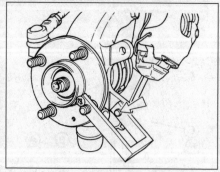

2.7 Securing the hub to the spindle carrier using a home-made bracket

2.10 Remove the suspension strut-to-spindle carrier pinch bolt

On all models, the steering is of conventional rack-and-pinion type, incorporating a safety system of convoluted column tube and double universally-jointed lower steering shaft links.

The steering column tube is supported at its upper end by bracketry, and at its lower end by a nylon support bush. The steering shaft is supported within the column tube by two support bearings, one at either end of the tube.

The steering rack assembly is located on the bulkhead. Steering input is transmitted, via the steering shaft, to the pinion which meshes with the teeth on the rack.

The pinion transferring the steering input moves the rack within its housing tube, withdrawing and extending the track rods attached to either end of the rack by balljoints. This movement is transferred, by balljoints in the track rod ends, to the steering arms on the

spindle carriers which direct the roadwheels.

From the 1994 model year onwards, power steering is available as standard or optional equipment on certain models.

2 Front spindle carrier - removal and refitting

Removal

Note: *A new hub/driveshaft retaining nut will be required for refitting.*

1 Remove the wheel trim from the front roadwheel on the side concerned, then using a small pin punch, peen back the locking portion of the front hub/driveshaft nut. Loosen off the nut about half-a-turn.

2 Loosen off the front roadwheel retaining nuts on the side concerned.

3 Chock the rear wheels then jack up the front of the car and support it on axle stands (see *"Jacking and Vehicle Support"*). Remove the appropriate roadwheel, and unscrew and remove the hub/driveshaft retaining nut and washer.

4 Unscrew the retaining bolt and detach the brake hose and its locating bracket from the suspension strut **(see illustration)**.

5 Undo the two retaining bolts, and remove the brake caliper and anchor bracket from the spindle carrier. Support the caliper by suspending it from above, to prevent the hydraulic hose from being strained or distorted.

6 Remove the single screw securing the brake disc to the hub, and slide the disc off the wheel studs.

7 On pre-June 1990 models, fabricate a home-made bracket to secure the wheel hub and brake disc to the spindle carrier **(see illustration)**. Retain the bracket at one end with a wheel nut and at the other end with a brake caliper retaining bolt. This will prevent the hub and disc from becoming detached from the spindle carrier (with possible damage to the hub bearings) when the driveshaft is removed. On later models the hub is an interference fit in the bearing inner races and is unlikely to become detached.

8 Where an anti-roll bar is fitted, undo the nut securing the connecting link to the suspension strut bracket, and separate the link from the strut bracket.

9 Detach the track rod end balljoint from the steering arm on the side concerned as described in Section 28.

10 Remove the pinch-bolt securing the spindle carrier to the suspension strut **(see illustration)**.

11 Remove the Torx-head pinch-bolt and nut securing the lower suspension arm balljoint to the spindle carrier. Prise open the joint using a large screwdriver and detach the balljoint from the spindle carrier unit **(see illustrations)**.

12 Using a small crowbar with a thin tip, or a stout screwdriver as an alternative, lever the spindle carrier slot to separate the spindle carrier from the suspension strut **(see illustration)**. Lower the spindle carrier slightly

2.11a Remove the lower arm-to-spindle carrier pinch bolt and nut . . .

2.11b . . . prise open the joint . . .

2.11c . . . and detach the lower arm balljoint from the spindle carrier

2.12 Separate the spindle carrier from the strut

2.17 Lower suspension arm balljoint showing annular groove (arrowed)

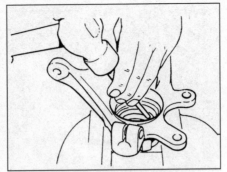

3.4 Using a punch to remove the hub bearing outer race from the spindle carrier

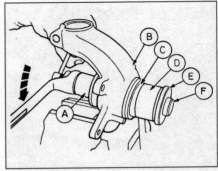

3.7 Using home-made tools to fit the outer bearing assembly to the spindle carrier

A Steel tube   D Steel tube
B Spindle carrier   E Flat washer
C Bearing   F Threaded bolt

(tapping it down with a soft-faced mallet if necessary) and carefully pull it off the driveshaft, having supported the driveshaft to prevent damage to the CV joints - the driveshaft must not be bent at an angle greater than 20° from the horizontal. If the driveshaft is tight in the hub, lightly tap its outer end with a soft-faced hammer, or use a conventional puller and spacer to free it. Remove the dust sleeve from the inner rim groove of the spindle carrier.

Refitting

13 Fit the dust sleeve to its groove, then locate the spindle carrier over the driveshaft. Draw the driveshaft CV joint through the hub using the old retaining nut and washer.
14 Lever the spindle carrier slot open and refit the spindle carrier to the suspension strut. Remove the lever, refit the pinch-bolt and tighten it to the specified torque.
15 Fit a new hub/driveshaft nut and washer, and tighten the nut as much possible at this stage. As the nut is being tightened, rotate the hub to ensure that the bearings seat correctly.
16 Refit the track rod end balljoint to the steering arm on the spindle carrier, tighten the nut to the specified torque and insert a new split-pin to secure.
17 Reconnect the lower suspension arm balljoint to the spindle carrier, refit the pinch-bolt and nut, and tighten to the specified torque. Note that the bolt must locate in the annular groove on the ballstud **(see illustration)**.
18 Remove the bracket securing the hub to the spindle carrier (where applicable), refit the brake disc and tighten the single screw securing the disc to the hub.
19 Refit the brake caliper and anchor bracket to the spindle carrier, tightening the bolts to the specified torque (see Chapter 9).
20 Refit the bolt securing the brake hose bracket to the front suspension strut.
21 Where an anti-roll bar is fitted, refit the connecting link to the suspension strut bracket.
22 Refit the roadwheel, lower the vehicle to the ground, then tighten the hub nut to the specified torque. Using a pin punch, stake-

lock the nut in the groove in the end of the axle stub.
23 Tighten the roadwheel nuts to the specified torque setting.

3 Front hub bearings - renewal

Note: *The front hub bearings should only be removed from the spindle carrier if they are to be renewed. The removal procedure renders the bearings unserviceable, and they must not be re-used. Prior to dismantling, it should be noted that a hub/bearing puller and an assortment of metal tubes of various diameters (and preferably, a press) will be required. Unless these tools are available, the renewal of the hub bearings will have to be entrusted to a Ford garage. Under no circumstances attempt to tap the hub bearings into position, as this will render them unserviceable.*

Pre-June 1990 models

1 Remove the spindle carrier from the vehicle as described in Section 2.
2 Remove the home-made bracket used to retain the hub in place and slide the hub out of the spindle carrier assembly.
3 Securely support the spindle carrier in a vice with its inner face uppermost.
4 Using a suitable punch, tap the outer bearing outer race at diametrically-opposed points and remove the bearing assembly from the spindle carrier **(see illustration)**. Do not allow the bearing to tilt during its withdrawal from the housing, or it will jam and possibly damage the surface of the bore. Any burrs left in a bearing bore will prevent the new bearing from seating correctly.
5 Turn the spindle carrier over and remove the inner bearing assembly in the same way.
6 Thoroughly clean the bearing bore and hub, then secure the spindle carrier in the vice in an upright position.
7 Press the new outer bearing assembly into the spindle carrier using a length of metal tube of diameter slightly less than the outer race.

Do not apply any pressure to the inner race. Alternatively, a long threaded rod or bolt, a nut and large flat washers may be used to draw the bearing into position **(see illustration)**. Once the bearing has been installed, take care not to dislodge the inner race and seal.
8 Using the same method as for the outer bearing, draw in the new inner bearing assembly from the other side of the spindle carrier. Again, take care not to dislodge the inner race and seal once the bearing is in position.
9 Support the inner bearing inner race on a length of metal tube, and draw the hub fully into the bearings using the same tooling arrangement as before. It may even be possible to insert the hub using firm hand pressure only, but make sure that the inner bearing inner race is well supported.
10 Fit the home-made bracket to secure the hub into the spindle carrier, dismantling the service tools or equivalent as necessary. Ensure that the hub and spindle carrier do not become separated at any time, as this will displace the bearings seals and lead to premature bearing failure.
11 The assembly can now be refitted to the vehicle, as described in the previous Section.

June 1990 models onward

Note: *On these later models, the bearing's inner races are an interference fit on the hub. During removal of the hub from the spindle carrier, the outer bearing inner race will remain in position on the hub and a knife-edged bearing puller will be required to remove it.*
12 Remove the spindle carrier from the vehicle as described in Section 2.
13 The hub must now be removed from the bearing inner races. It is preferable to use a press to do this, but it is possible to drive out the hub using a length of metal tube of suitable diameter.
14 Part of the inner race will remain on the hub, and this should be removed using a knife-edged puller.
15 Securely support the spindle carrier in a vice with its inner face uppermost.

10

4.2a Removing cap from front suspension strut top-mount retaining nut

4.2b Slackening the front suspension strut top-mount retaining nut whilst preventing the piston rod from turning

16 Using a suitable punch, tap the outer bearing outer race at diametrically-opposed points and remove the bearing assembly from the spindle carrier. Do not allow the bearing to tilt during its withdrawal from the housing, or it will jam and possibly damage the surface of the bore. Any burrs left in a bearing bore will prevent the new bearing from seating correctly.

17 Turn the spindle carrier over and remove the inner bearing assembly in the same way.

18 Thoroughly clean the bearing bore and hub, then secure the spindle carrier in the vice in an upright position.

19 Draw the new outer bearing assembly into the spindle carrier using a length of metal tube of diameter slightly less than the outer race. Do not apply any pressure to the inner race. Alternatively, a long threaded rod or bolt, a nut and large flat washers may be used to draw the bearing into position **(see illustration 3.7)**. Once the bearing has been installed, take care not to dislodge the inner race and seal.

20 Using the same method as for the outer bearing, draw in the new inner bearing assembly from the other side of the spindle carrier. Again, take care not to dislodge the inner race and seal once the bearing is in position.

21 Using the same tooling arrangement as before, and with the metal tube or washers contacting the inner bearing inner race, draw the hub fully into the bearings. Alternatively, if a press is available, support the hub face down on the press bed and using a metal tube in contact with the inner bearing inner race, press the spindle carrier onto the hub.

22 Check that the hub spins freely in the bearings, then refit the spindle carrier as described in Section 2.

4 Front suspension strut - removal and refitting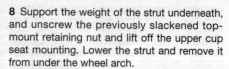

Removal

1 Chock the rear wheels then jack up the front of the car and support it on axle stands (see "*Jacking and Vehicle Support*"). Remove the appropriate front roadwheel.

2 Open and support the bonnet. Prise free the protective cap from the suspension strut top-mount retaining nut, then slacken the nut, but do not remove it at this stage **(see illustrations)**. Hold the strut piston rod with an Allen key to prevent the rod from turning as the nut is slackened.

3 Detach the front brake hose from the support bracket on the strut.

4 Where applicable, unbolt and detach the anti-roll bar connecting link from the strut bracket.

5 Undo the two bolts securing the front brake caliper anchor bracket to the spindle carrier. Slide the caliper assembly, complete with brake pads off the disc and spindle carrier and suspend the caliper within the wheelarch with a length of strong wire, to prevent the flexible brake hose from straining.

6 Unscrew and remove the strut-to-spindle carrier pinch-bolt.

7 Prise open the spindle carrier-to-strut joint using a stout screwdriver, and separate the carrier from the strut. Tap the carrier downwards using a soft-faced hammer to release it from the strut if necessary. Once the two components are separated, support the lower suspension arm to avoid straining the CV joints.

8 Support the weight of the strut underneath, and unscrew the previously slackened top-mount retaining nut and lift off the upper cup seat mounting. Lower the strut and remove it from under the wheel arch.

Refitting

9 Locate the strut through the wheel arch and refit the upper cup seat mounting and top-mount retaining nut. Do not tighten the nut at this stage.

10 Apply leverage to the spindle carrier slot so that the spindle carrier can be refitted to the base of the suspension strut. Refit the suspension strut to spindle carrier pinch-bolt and tighten to the specified torque.

11 Tighten the suspension strut top-mount retaining nut to the specified torque, using an Allen key to prevent the piston rod from rotating. The final torque will have to be applied without the use of the Allen key unless a suitable open-ended torque wrench adapter is available. Refit the cap over the nut.

12 Refit the brake caliper assembly to the spindle carrier, and tighten the caliper anchor bracket bolts to the specified torque (see Chapter 9).

13 Refit the bolt to secure the brake hose bracket to the suspension strut, and fully tighten.

14 Remove the support from under the lower suspension arm.

15 Reconnect the anti-roll bar connecting link to the strut bracket, where applicable, tightening the nut to the specified torque.

16 Refit the roadwheel, remove the axle stands and lower the vehicle to the ground.

17 Tighten the roadwheel nuts according to the specified torque.

5 Front suspension strut - dismantling, examination and reassembly

⚠️ *Warning: Before attempting to dismantle the suspension strut, a suitable tool to hold the coil spring in compression must be obtained. Adjustable coil spring compressors which can be positively secured to the spring coils are readily available, and are recommended for this operation. Any attempt to dismantle the strut without such a tool is likely to result in damage or personal injury.*

Dismantling

1 With the strut removed from the vehicle, clean away all external dirt, then mount it upright in a vice.

2 Fit the spring compressor tool (ensuring that it is fully engaged) and compress the coil spring until all tension is relieved from the upper mounting **(see illustration)**.

3 Remove the spring retaining nut, then withdraw the lower cup seat mounting, thrust

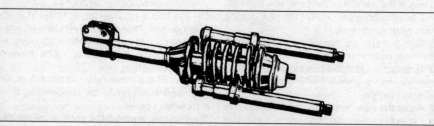

5.2 Typical pair of coil spring compressors in use

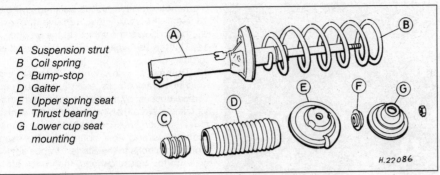

A Suspension strut
B Coil spring
C Bump-stop
D Gaiter
E Upper spring seat
F Thrust bearing
G Lower cup seat mounting

H.22086

5.3 Exploded view of front suspension strut assembly

5.9 Correct spring location in its lower seat

bearing, upper spring seat, gaiter and bump-stop from the piston rod **(see illustration)**.

4 The suspension strut and coil spring may now be separated. If a new suspension strut is to be fitted there is no need to release the coil spring from compression, but if a new coil spring is to be fitted, release the compressors gently until the spring is in its released state, then remove it.

Examination

5 With the strut assembly now completely dismantled, examine the mounting components for wear, damage or deformation. Renew any of the components as necessary.

6 Examine the strut for signs of fluid leakage. Check the strut piston for signs of pitting along its entire length, and check the strut body for signs of damage or corrosion. Test the operation of the strut, holding it in an upright position, by moving the piston through a full stroke, and then through short strokes of 50 to 100 mm. In both cases, the resistance felt should be smooth and continuous. If the resistance is jerky, or uneven, or if there is any visible sign of wear or damage to the strut, renewal is necessary.

Reassembly

7 If a new spring is to be fitted, engage the

compressors as during removal, and compress the spring sufficiently to enable suspension strut reassembly.

8 Reunite the spring and suspension strut, and refit the bump-stop gaiter, spring seat, thrust bearing and lower cup seat mounting, renewing components as necessary. Refit the spring retaining nut and tighten to the specified torque.

9 Carefully release the spring tension, ensuring that the spring locates correctly into its upper and lower spring seats **(see illustration)**.

10 Remove the spring compressors.

11 The rubber insulator fitted to the top of the inner wing is a simple push fit, and is easily replaceable. Ensure when replacing this, that the lip sits evenly around the locating hole.

---

6   Front suspension anti-roll bar - removal and refitting

Removal

1 Chock the rear wheels then jack up the front of the car and support it on axle stands (see *"Jacking and Vehicle Support"*). Remove the front roadwheels.

2 Remove the one-piece undertray where fitted, by turning its bayonet-type fasteners, and on XR2i models, remove the front

suspension crossmember as described in Section 7.

3 Undo the nut securing the upper end of the anti-roll bar connecting link to the suspension strut bracket, and disconnect the link **(see illustration)**.

4 Undo the nut securing the lower end of the connecting link to the anti-roll bar, and remove the link.

5 Remove the two bolts securing the anti-roll bar brackets to each lower suspension arm mounting bracket **(see illustration)**, remove the anti-roll bar brackets and withdraw the anti-roll bar from the vehicle.

6 The rubber bushes locating the anti-roll bar can be removed by sliding them off over the link connections.

Refitting

7 Refitting is a reversal of the removal procedure, tightening the retaining nuts to the specified torque settings.

---

7   Front suspension crossmember - removal and refitting

Note: *The front suspension crossmember is only fitted to XR2i models,*

Removal

1 Chock the rear wheels then jack up the front of the car and support it on axle stands (see *"Jacking and Vehicle Support"*). Remove the front roadwheels.

2 Remove the one-piece undertray where fitted, by turning its bayonet-type fasteners.

3 The crossmember, which serves as an additional bracing component, is located between the lower suspension arm mounting brackets, and is secured to these brackets by four bolts. To remove it, simply undo the four bolts and lower it from the vehicle.

Refitting

4 Refitting is the reverse sequence to removal, ensuring that the bolts are tightened to the specified torque.

6.3 Anti-roll bar connecting link-to-strut connection

6.5 Anti-roll bar bracket and mounting bolts

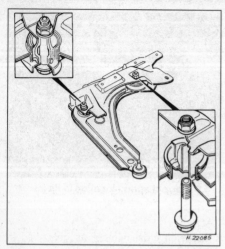

8.6 Lower suspension arm arrangement in its mounting bracket

8.10 Lower suspension arm and mounting bracket arrangement

A Arm-to-mounting bracket bolts
B Special "shouldered" locating bolt
C Mounting bracket retaining bolts

8 Front suspension lower arm - removal and refitting

Removal

1 Chock the rear wheels then jack up the front of the car and support it on axle stands (see *"Jacking and Vehicle Support"*). Remove the appropriate front roadwheel.

2 Remove the one-piece undertray (where fitted), by turning its bayonet-type fasteners.

3 If lower arm mounting brackets are to be removed on XR2i models, remove the front suspension crossmember as described in the previous Section.

4 Unscrew and remove the lower arm balljoint-to-spindle carrier pinch-bolt. Prise the joint open using a large flat-bladed tool, and detach the balljoint from the spindle carrier. Take care not to damage the balljoint seal during the separation procedures.

5 Where an anti-roll bar is fitted, undo the two bolts and remove the clamp bracket.

6 To remove the lower arm from its mounting bracket, undo the two bolts that pass through the vertical bushes, remove the bolts and pull the arm clear (see illustration). Note that new bolts will be required for refitting.

7 The lower arm mounting brackets are each

retained by five bolts. To remove a mounting bracket, undo the five bolts and lower it from the vehicle.

8 If the balljoint and/or the inboard mounting bushes are found to be in poor condition, the complete suspension arm must be renewed. The suspension arm must also be renewed if it has suffered structural damage.

Refitting

9 Insert the lower arm into its mounting bracket and fit the two bolts that pass through the vertical bushes finger tight only at this stage.

10 Fit the lower arm mounting bracket to the vehicle, ensuring that the locating dowel is correctly located in its recess. One of the five bolts securing the mounting bracket has a locating shoulder and a larger thread diameter, and this should be fitted first to ensure correct alignment of the mounting bracket to the vehicle (see illustration). Refit the other four bolts and tighten all five to the specified torque.

11 Refit the anti-roll bar bracket and front suspension crossmember, as applicable, in accordance with the relevant Sections of this Chapter.

12 Locate the lower suspension arm balljoint into the spindle carrier assembly then fit and tighten the pinch-bolt and nut to the specified torque. Note that the bolt must locate to

the annular groove on the balljoint spindle.

13 Refit the roadwheel, remove the axle stands and lower the vehicle to the ground.

14 Tighten the wheel nuts to the specified torque.

15 Tighten the lower arm-to-lower arm mounting bracket bolts, that pass through the vertical bushes, by the torque-to-yield method as follows. Note that the weight of the vehicle must be on the roadwheels for these procedures and new bolts must be used. Tighten the bolts to the Stage 1 torque setting given in the Specifications, then back off to zero torque (Stage 2). Retighten to the Stage 3 torque setting, then tighten further through the angle specified for Stage 4, using an angle-tightening gauge. It is vitally important that these procedures are followed and that the bolts are not subjected to further rotation which could result in them failing. The torque-to-yield method must be followed every time that these bolts are disturbed.

16 Raise the front of the vehicle again and support it securely on axle stands to refit the one-piece undertray (where applicable).

9 Rear hub bearings - renewal

1 Chock the front wheels then jack up the rear of the car and support it on axle stands (see *"Jacking and Vehicle Support"*). Remove the appropriate rear roadwheel.

2 Check that the handbrake is released, then remove the rubber blanking plug from the inside face of the brake backplate, reach through with a suitable screwdriver, and release the automatic brake adjuster by levering the catch from the pawl.

3 Prise free the outer grease cap from the centre of the hub (see illustration). The cap will be deformed during its removal, and will need to be renewed when the hub is refitted.

4 Unscrew and remove the hub nut, but note that the hub nut threads are "handed" according to side - right-hand to right, left-hand to left (see illustration). A left-hand thread unscrews in a clockwise direction.

5 Withdraw the brake drum/hub from the spindle of the rear stub axle (see illustration).

9.3 Removing the outer grease cap from the hub centre

9.4 Undoing the hub bearing retaining nut

9.5 Slide off the wheel hub/brake drum unit

9.6 Prise the grease retainer from the hub bore

9.7 Removing a bearing cone from the hub bore

9.8 Removing bearing cups

6 Use a screwdriver or suitable lever to prise free the grease retainer (seal) from the hub bore, but take care not to damage the bore surface **(see illustration)**.

7 Remove the inner and outer bearing cones from the bore of the hub **(see illustration)**.

8 To remove the bearing cups from the hub, drive them out using a suitable punch. Drive each cup from its respective end by tapping it alternately at diametrically-opposed points **(see illustration)**. Do not allow the cups to tilt in the bore, or the surfaces may become burred and prevent the new bearings from seating correctly as they are fitted.

9 Clean the bore and spindle thoroughly before reassembly.

10 To reassemble, tap the new bearing cups into position in the hub, using a piece of tubing slightly smaller in its outside diameter than that of the bearing cup. Ensure that the cups are squarely inserted and abut their respective shoulders in the hub.

11 Pack the inner bearing cone with the specified grease, and insert it into its cup in the hub.

12 To fit the grease retainer (seal), first lubricate its inner lip to ease installation, then lightly tap the seal into position using a block of wood. Ensure that the seal is correctly orientated.

13 Pack the outer bearing cone with the specified grease, and fit it into position in its cup.

14 The brake drum/hub can now be refitted to the axle spindle. Before fitting into position, first check that the brake surface area in the drum is free of grease and oil. Locate the drum/hub into position, then fit the retaining nut. Tighten it to the specified torque setting whilst simultaneously rotating the assembly to ensure that the bearings are correctly seated.

15 Carefully tap the new hub grease cap into position in a progressive manner around its outer edge until it is fully fitted.

16 Refit the rubber blanking plug to the brake backplate, and firmly apply the footbrake a few times to take up the brake adjustment. Check that the rear brakes do not bind when the brakes are released. Refit the roadwheel, lower the vehicle and then tighten the retaining nuts to the specified torque setting.

10 Rear strut (all models except Courier) - removal and refitting

Removal

1 Chock the front wheels then jack up the rear of the car and support it on axle stands (see *"Jacking and Vehicle Support"*).

2 On ABS-equipped models, unscrew the retaining nuts and detach the load-apportioning valve connecting links from the axle beam.

3 Support the relevant trailing arm of the axle assembly and unscrew and remove the securing bolt from the strut-to-axle mounting **(see illustration)**.

4 Prise free the protective cap from the top of the strut mounting, located in the luggage compartment **(see illustration)**.

5 Unscrew and remove the two retaining nuts to detach the strut from its upper mounting. Do not unscrew the central upper mounting bolt.

6 Lower the trailing arm slightly to allow the lower suspension strut mounting to clear its axle location, and withdraw the suspension strut from the vehicle.

Refitting

7 Refitting is a reversal of the removal procedure, but note the following special points:

10.3 Lower suspension strut-to-axle mounting bolt

a) With the suspension strut located to its upper mounting, tighten the retaining nuts to the specified torque.

b) When reconnecting the suspension strut to the lower mounting, hand-tighten the retaining bolt, then lower the vehicle so that it is standing on its wheels before fully tightening the bolt to its specified torque.

11 Rear strut (all models except Courier) - dismantling, examination and reassembly

Warning: Before attempting to dismantle the suspension strut, a suitable tool to hold the coil spring in compression must be obtained. Adjustable coil spring compressors which can be positively secured to the spring coils are readily available, and are recommended for this operation. Any attempt to dismantle the strut without such a tool is likely to result in damage or personal injury.

Dismantling

1 With the strut removed from the vehicle, clean away all external dirt, then secure it in a vice.

2 Fit the spring compressor tool (ensuring that it is fully engaged) and compress the coil spring until all tension is relieved from the upper mounting.

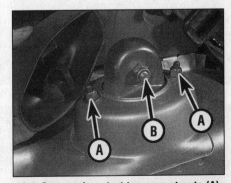

10.4 Suspension strut top-mount nuts (A), and spring retaining through-bolt fixing (B)

10

3 Unscrew and remove the upper mounting through-bolt and nut.

4 Withdraw the upper mounting cup and the spring seat.

5 The suspension strut and coil spring can now be separated. If the coil spring or strut is to be renewed, the original coil spring must be released from the compressor. If it is to be re-used, the coil spring can be left in compression.

Examination

6 With the strut assembly now completely dismantled, examine the mounting components for wear, damage or deformation. Renew any of the components as necessary.

7 Examine the strut for signs of fluid leakage. Check the strut piston for signs of pitting along its entire length, and check the strut body for signs of damage or deterioration of the mountings. Test the operation of the strut, holding it in an upright position, by moving the piston through a full stroke, and then through short strokes of 50 to 100 mm. In both cases, the resistance felt should be smooth and continuous. If the resistance is jerky, or uneven, or if there is any visible sign of wear or damage to the strut, renewal is necessary.

Reassembly

8 Reassembly is a reversal of the dismantling procedure but note the following points:

a) When the spring is located over the suspension strut, the spring seat, cup and through-bolt fitted, tighten the retaining bolt to the specified torque.

b) When reassembled, check that the upper and lower spring tails are correctly engaged with their spring seats before removing the spring compressor.

12 Rear axle (all models except Courier) - removal and refitting

Removal

1 Chock the front wheels then jack up the rear of the car and support it on axle stands (see "Jacking and Vehicle Support"). Remove the rear roadwheels.

2 Refer to Chapter 9 for details, and disconnect the handbrake cable equaliser from the primary cable. Remove the handbrake rear cable from its adjuster and its fixed body locations.

3 Disconnect the rear brake flexible hydraulic brake hoses from their rigid line connections. Clamp the hoses before disconnecting them, to minimise the fluid loss and air entry into the hydraulic system (see Chapter 9 for details).

4 On ABS-equipped models, undo the retaining nuts and detach the ABS load-apportioning valve operating links from the axle beam. Do not remove the load-apportioning valve (see Chapter 9).

5 Locate suitable jacks or axle stands under the axle beam to support its weight (not to lift it), then unscrew the four mounting bracket bolts each side.

6 Unscrew and remove the strut-to-axle mounting bolt each side.

7 Check that all associated fittings are clear, then lower the axle and remove it from under the vehicle.

8 If the twist beam axle has been damaged, it must be renewed. Refer to Chapter 9 for details on removing the rear brakes from the axle. To remove the front mounting/pivot brackets from the axle, unscrew the pivot bolt.

Refitting

9 Refitting is a reversal of the removal procedure, but note the following:

a) Reconnect the axle at the front floor mountings first, and tighten the retaining bolts to the specified torque.

b) Reconnect the axle to the suspension struts, but do not fully retighten the securing bolts until after the vehicle is lowered to the ground and is standing on its wheels.

c) Ensure that all brake fluid line connections are clean before reconnecting them. Refer to the appropriate Sections in Chapter 9 for specific details on reconnecting the brake lines, bleeding the brake hydraulic system, and for reconnecting the handbrake cable and its adjustment.

d) When the vehicle is lowered and is standing on its wheels, tighten the suspension fastenings to their specified torque settings.

13 Rear axle pivot bushes (all models except Courier) - renewal

Note: *Two different types of pivot bushes have been fitted during the course of Fiesta production. It is understood that once stocks of the early type are exhausted, only the latter type will be supplied by Ford parts dealers. If renewing pivot bushes on a pre-April 1990 model, and only the later type bushes are available, fit the new bushes as described from paragraph 15 onward.*

Pre-April 1990 models

1 Chock the front wheels then jack up the rear of the car and support it on axle stands (see "Jacking and Vehicle Support").

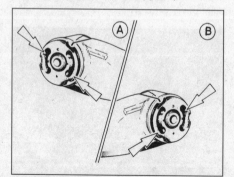

13.8a Correct pivot bush positioning in trailing arm

A Left-hand side   B Right-hand side

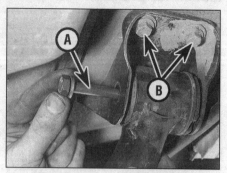

13.4 Pivot bush bolt (A) and body mounting bracket bolts (B)

2 Position a suitable support (preferably adjustable) under the axle twist beam so that it is capable of carrying the weight of the axle (not the weight of the vehicle).

3 On ABS-equipped models, undo the retaining nuts and detach the ABS load-apportioning valve operating links from the axle beam. Do not remove the load-apportioning valve (see Chapter 9).

4 Unscrew the nuts, withdraw the pivot bolts, then lower the rear axle so that the bushes are clear of their mounting brackets **(see illustration)**. Take care not to allow the brake pipes to become distorted and stretched - if necessary, disconnect the hydraulic lines (see Chapter 9 for details).

5 Undo the four body mounting bracket bolts and remove the brackets.

6 Using a soft-faced hammer and a suitable punch or drift, drive the bushes from their locations, taking care not to raise any burrs on the trailing arm eyes.

7 To fit the new bushes, obtain a steel tube of a diameter slightly less than that of the bush location in the axle, various flat washers and a long bolt and nut.

8 Place the new bush in position in its axle location with the bush collar nearest to the outer edge of the vehicle. The bush must be installed with its voids positioned as shown **(see illustration)**. Using the steel tube, washers, long bolt and nut, draw the bush inwards towards the centre of the vehicle **(see illustration)**. Care should be taken to avoid damage to the bush and to obtain correct

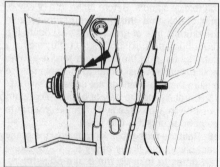

13.8b Fitting pivot bush with its collar (arrowed) towards the outer edge of the vehicle

positioning of the voids. Install the bush on the other side in the same way.

9 With the new bushes in position, refit the body mounting brackets loosely to the trailing arms - do not fully tighten the pivot bolts at this stage. Final tightening is carried out with the vehicle standing on its roadwheels.

10 Raise the axle assembly so that the conical locating pegs on the body mounting brackets engage in their body locations. Refit the body mounting bracket bolts and tighten to the specified torque.

11 On ABS equipped models, reconnect the load-apportioning valve operating links to the rear axle beam

12 If the flexible brake hoses were disconnected during this operation, reconnect them and bleed the brake hydraulic system (see Chapter 9).

13 Lower the vehicle to the ground.

14 Fully tighten the bush pivot bolt nuts to the specified torque.

April 1990 models onward

15 As mentioned in the note at the start of this Section, all later models are fitted with revised bushes which use 12 mm (thread size) pivot bolts. If the later type bushes are to be fitted to a pre-April 1990 model, two corresponding bolts and nuts must be obtained at the same time, and either the body mounting brackets must be replaced by the corresponding modified items, or the holes in the original brackets must be opened out (to 12.5 mm) to suit the new bolts.

16 Carry out the operations described in paragraphs 1 to 4 above.

17 Using a steel tube of suitable diameter, various flat washers and a long bolt and nut, draw the bush out of its location in the axle trailing arm.

18 Clean the bush eye in the trailing arm; lubricate it, and the new bush, with a soapy solution (washing-up liquid, for example) prior to installation.

19 Locate the new bush in position, together with the steel tube, washers, bolt and nut as used for removal. Ensure that the bush flange is positioned on the outside, then draw the bush fully into position so that its lip is engaged **(see illustration)**.

20 Raise the axle to reposition the bush pin

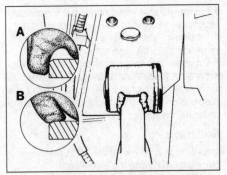

13.19 Pivot bush renewal (April 1990 models onwards) - correct engagement of bush lip on rear axle

A New bush, installed correctly
B New bush, installed incorrectly

bores in line with the bolt holes in the mounting brackets, then insert the pivot bolts. Screw the retaining nuts into position on the pivot bolts, but do not fully tighten them at this stage.

21 Carry out the operations described in paragraphs 11 to 14 above.

14 Rear suspension anti-roll bar (all models except Courier) - removal and refitting

Removal

1 Chock the front wheels then jack up the rear of the car and support it on axle stands (see *"Jacking and Vehicle Support"*).

2 Undo the front clamp bolt from each end of the bar, then support the bar and undo the rear bolt at each end; withdraw the bar **(see illustration)**.

3 Prise open the clamps to release the rubber bushes, if required. Fit the new bushes using soapy water as a lubricant.

Refitting

4 On refitting, offer up the bar and align first the front clamp on each side, refitting the bolts loosely.

5 Align and refit the rear clamp on each side; again, tighten the bolts only loosely.

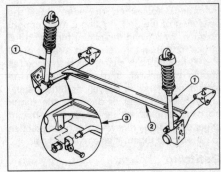

14.2 Rear suspension anti-roll bar

1 Rear suspension strut
2 Anti-roll bar
3 Inset showing (front) mounting clamp

6 Lower the vehicle to the ground, rock it to settle the suspension, then tighten the clamp bolts to the specified torque settings.

15 Rear suspension components (Courier models) - general

Although it is possible to remove the rear suspension torsion bars and stabiliser bar independently of the complete rear axle assembly, it is essential to have certain special tools available to complete the work successfully.

Due to the complexity of the tasks, and the requirement for special tools to accurately set the suspension geometry and vehicle ride height on refitting, the removal and refitting of individual rear suspension components is considered to be beyond the scope of DIY work and should be entrusted to a Ford dealer.

Procedures for removal and refitting of the rear shock absorbers, and the complete rear suspension assembly are given in Sections 16 and 17 respectively.

16 Rear shock absorber (Courier models) - removal, examination and refitting

Removal

1 Chock the front wheels then jack up the rear of the car and support it on axle stands (see *"Jacking and Vehicle Support"*).

2 Support the relevant trailing arm of the suspension assembly and unscrew the upper mounting bolt and nut, followed by the lower bolt. Withdraw the shock absorber from under the vehicle **(see illustrations)**.

Examination

3 Examine the shock absorber body for signs of fluid leakage or damage and check the

16.2a Removing a shock absorber upper mounting . . .

16.2b . . . and lower mounting on Courier models

mountings for signs of wear. Test the operation of the unit, holding it in an upright position, by moving the piston through a full stroke, and then through short strokes of 50 to 100 mm. In both cases, the resistance felt should be smooth and continuous. If the resistance is jerky, or uneven, or if there is any visible sign of wear or damage, the shock absorber should be renewed. Note that if either unit is to be renewed, it is good practice to renew both together as a matched pair.

Refitting

4 Locate the unit in position and refit the mounting bolts and nut. Do not fully tighten the mountings at this stage.

5 Lower the vehicle to the ground and rock it to settle the suspension. Raise the vehicle again, as necessary, until the shock absorber is at an angle of 50° ± 5° to the horizontal. With the shock absorber in this position, tighten the upper and lower mountings to the specified torque.

17 Rear suspension assembly (Courier models) - removal and refitting

Removal

1 Chock the front wheels then jack up the rear of the car and support it on axle stands (see "Jacking and Vehicle Support"). Remove the rear roadwheels.

2 Refer to Chapter 9 for details, and disconnect the handbrake cable equaliser from the primary cable. Remove the handbrake rear cable from its adjuster and its fixed body locations. Release the exhaust system mountings as necessary to allow the handbrake cable to be withdrawn over the rear of the exhaust.

3 Disconnect the rear brake flexible hydraulic brake hoses from their rigid line connections **(see illustration)**. Clamp the hoses before disconnecting them, to minimise the fluid loss and air entry into the hydraulic system (see Chapter 9 for details).

4 Detach the light-laden valve linkage from the bracket on the suspension assembly.

5 Locate suitable jacks under the suspension assembly to support its weight (not to lift it).

6 Unscrew the shock absorber lower mounting bolts on each side.

7 Unscrew the two mounting bracket bolts each side **(see illustration)**, check that all associated fittings are clear, then lower the suspension assembly and remove it from under the vehicle.

Refitting

8 Refitting is a reversal of the removal procedure, but note the following:

a) Refit the front mounting brackets first, and tighten the retaining bolts to the specified torque.

b) Reconnect the shock absorber lower mountings, but do not fully retighten the securing bolts until after the vehicle is lowered to the ground and is standing on its wheels.

c) Ensure that all brake fluid line connections are clean before reconnecting them. Refer to the appropriate Sections in Chapter 9 for specific details on reconnecting the brake lines, bleeding the brake hydraulic system, adjusting the light laden valve, and reconnecting and adjusting the handbrake cable.

d) Once the vehicle is standing on its wheels, raise it again, as necessary, until the shock absorbers are at an angle of 50° ± 5° to the horizontal. With the shock absorbers in this position, tighten the lower mountings to the specified torque.

18 Rear suspension ride height (Courier models) - adjustment

Checking of the ride height requires the use of Ford special tools to accurately compress the suspension to a pre-determined value. Further special tools are then required to reposition the torsion bars to the new setting.

This operation should be entrusted to a Ford dealer, as it is not possible to carry out the procedure accurately without the use of the appropriate tools.

19 Steering wheel - removal and refitting

Removal

Models without air bag

1 Drive the vehicle in a straight line onto a level surface, so that the roadwheels are pointing straight ahead.

2 Carefully prise the motif from the centre of the steering wheel **(see illustration)**.

3 Mark the relative positions of the steering wheel and steering column shaft.

4 Unscrew the retaining bolt from the centre of the steering wheel, then insert the ignition key and turn it to position "I". Grip the wheel each side, then pull and withdraw it from the column shaft.

> **HAYNES HINT** *If the wheel is tight, tap it up near the centre, using the palm of your hand, or twist it from side to side, whilst pulling upwards to release it from the shaft splines.*

Models with air bag

⚠ **Warning: Handle the air bag with extreme care as a precaution against personal injury, and always hold it with the cover facing away from your body. If in doubt concerning any proposed work involving the air bag or its control circuitry, consult a Ford dealer or other qualified specialist.**

5 Disconnect the battery negative (earth) lead (refer to Chapter 5A, Section 1).

⚠ **Warning: Before proceeding, wait a minimum of 15 minutes, as a precaution against accidental firing of the air bag. This period ensures that any stored energy in the back-up capacitor is dissipated.**

6 Undo the screws, and remove the steering column lower shroud.

7 Undo the two external screws and the two internal screws and remove the steering column upper shroud.

17.3 Brake hose and rigid pipe connection on Courier rear suspension assembly

17.7 Courier rear suspension pivot brackets locate on dowels in underbody

19.2 Removing the motif from the steering wheel

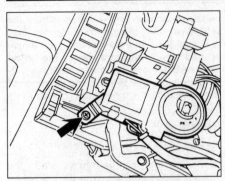

19.12 Undo the screw (arrowed) and withdraw the Passive Anti-Theft System (PATS) transceiver from the ignition switch/steering lock barrel

20.2 Manual choke control knob and its locating lug (arrowed)

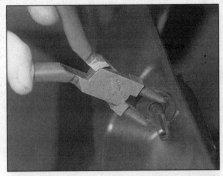

20.3 Removing the manual choke control assembly retaining collar

8 Turn the steering wheel as necessary so that one of the air bag module retaining bolts becomes accessible from the rear of the steering wheel. Undo the bolt, then turn the steering wheel again until the second bolt is accessible. Undo this bolt also.

9 Withdraw the air bag module from the steering wheel far enough to access the wiring multi-plug. Some force may be needed to free the module from the additional steering wheel spoke retainers.

10 Disconnect the multi-plug from the rear of the module, and remove the module from the vehicle.

 Warning: Position the air bag module in a safe place, with the mechanism facing downwards as a precaution against accidental operation.

11 Release the wiring harness from the side of the steering column and disconnect the air bag module wiring multi-plug (yellow lead).

12 Where applicable, undo the single screw and withdraw the Passive Anti-Theft System (PATS) transceiver from the ignition switch/steering lock barrel **(see illustration)**.

13 Turn the steering wheel so that the roadwheels are in the straight-ahead position, then remove the ignition key to lock the steering.

14 Unscrew the retaining bolt from the centre of the steering wheel, then insert the ignition

key and turn it to position "I". Grip the steering wheel each side, then pull and withdraw it from the column shaft.

Refitting

All models

15 Refit in the reverse order of removal. Make sure that the wheel is centralised, as noted on removal and turn the ignition key so that it is in position "I" (steering unlocked). Tighten the retaining bolt to the specified torque setting.

20 Steering column (manual steering) - removal and refitting

Removal

Models without air bag

1 Disconnect the battery negative (earth) lead (refer to Chapter 5A, Section 1).

2 Remove the manual choke control knob, where fitted, by depressing the lug securing it, and pulling it from its shaft **(see illustration)**. The lug is found on the side of the control knob shank.

3 Remove the lower steering column shroud by undoing its four retaining screws, then detach the choke warning light switch/pull control assembly from the lower shroud by unscrewing its retaining collar (bayonet-type

fixing), using a suitable tool to locate in the collar recesses **(see illustration)**.

4 Remove the two screws securing the upper steering column shroud from above, and the two screws securing it from below, the latter accessible only with the lower shroud removed.

5 Disconnect the wiring multi-plugs from the steering column multi-function switch assembly, then remove the single screw securing the multi-function switch assembly to the steering column lock housing. This retaining screw is located directly forward of the hazard warning light switch **(see illustration)**. Remove the multi-function switch assembly.

6 Disconnect the ignition switch wiring multi-plug connector and remove the loom plate from its location on the left-hand side of the steering column **(see illustration)**.

7 Unclip the bonnet release cable abutment from its location in the steering column lock housing, then detach the cable from the bonnet release lever by aligning the cable core with the slot on the release lever and withdrawing it through that slot. Detach the spring from the release lever arms, then disengage the arms from the steering column lock housing and remove the bonnet release lever **(see illustration)**.

20.5 Steering column multi-function switch retaining screw (arrowed) (steering wheel removed for clarity)

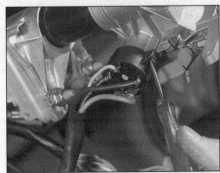

20.6 Removing ignition loom plate from steering column lock housing (steering wheel removed for clarity)

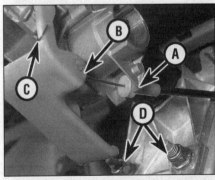

20.7 Bonnet release lever and cable

A Bonnet release cable abutment
B Bonnet release cable slot on release lever
C Bonnet release lever return spring
D Steering column to mounting bracket retaining nuts

10

20.9 Pinch-bolt securing lower steering shaft universal joint to pinion splined shaft (arrowed)

8 Remove the nuts securing the steering column mounting bracket.

9 Remove the pinch-bolt securing the lower steering shaft universal joint to the steering rack pinion splined shaft, located at the rear of the engine compartment **(see illustration)**, and separate the two as far as possible.

10 Pull the steering column assembly from its bulkhead location and withdraw it from the vehicle, ensuring that the lower steering shaft universal joint and the steering rack pinion splined shaft separate fully. The effort required to remove the column assembly may be quite high, due to the close tolerance of the lower column tube support bush in its location.

Models with air bag

 Warning: Handle the air bag with extreme care as a precaution against personal injury, and always hold it with the cover facing away from your body. If in doubt concerning any proposed work involving the air bag or its control circuitry, consult a Ford dealer or other qualified specialist.

11 Disconnect the battery negative (earth) lead (refer to Chapter 5A, Section 1).

 Warning: Before proceeding, wait a minimum of 15 minutes, as a precaution against accidental firing of the air bag. This period ensures that any stored energy in the back-up capacitor is dissipated.

12 Undo the screws, and remove the steering column lower shroud.

13 Undo the two external screws and the two internal screws and remove the steering column upper shroud.

14 Turn the steering wheel as necessary so that one of the air bag module retaining bolts becomes accessible from the rear of the steering wheel. Undo the bolt, then turn the steering wheel again until the second bolt is accessible. Undo this bolt also.

15 Withdraw the air bag module from the steering wheel far enough to access the wiring multi-plug. Some force may be needed to free the module from the additional steering wheel spoke retainers.

16 Disconnect the multi-plug from the rear of the module, and remove the module from the vehicle.

 Warning: Position the air bag module in a safe place, with the mechanism facing downwards as a precaution against accidental operation.

17 Turn the steering wheel so that the roadwheels are in the straight-ahead position, then remove the ignition key to lock the steering.

18 Release the wiring harness from the side of the steering column and disconnect the air bag module wiring multi-plug (yellow lead).

19 Disconnect the wiring multi-plugs from the steering column multi-function switch assembly.

20 Disconnect the ignition switch wiring multi-plug connector and remove the loom plate from its location on the left-hand side of the steering column.

21 Where applicable, undo the single screw and withdraw the Passive Anti-Theft System (PATS) transceiver from the ignition switch/steering lock barrel **(see illustration 19.12)**.

22 Unclip the bonnet release cable abutment from its location in the steering column lock housing, then detach the cable from the bonnet release lever by aligning the cable core with the slot on the release lever and withdrawing it through that slot. Detach the spring from the release lever arms, then disengage the arms from the steering column lock housing and remove the bonnet release lever.

23 Remove the nuts securing the steering column mounting bracket.

24 Remove the pinch-bolt securing the lower steering shaft universal joint to the steering rack pinion splined shaft, located at the rear of the engine compartment, and separate the two as far as possible.

25 Pull the steering column assembly from its

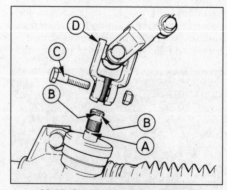

20.29 Steering rack-to-column engagement

A Steering rack pinion splined shaft
B Annular groove to ensure correct location of pinch-bolt
C Pinch-bolt
D Lower steering shaft universal joint

bulkhead location and withdraw it from the vehicle, ensuring that the lower steering shaft universal joint and the steering rack pinion splined shaft separate fully. The effort required to remove the column assembly may be quite high, due to the close tolerance of the lower column tube support bush in its location.

Refitting

All models

26 Ensure that the roadwheels are in the straight-ahead position. With the help of an assistant, insert the steering column assembly into the vehicle so that the lower steering shaft universal joint and the pinion splined shaft on the steering rack locate correctly, with the steering wheel centralized. Loosely refit the pinch-bolt to secure. Ensure that the steering shaft bulkhead seal seats correctly in its location.

27 With the column assembly located loosely in position, refit the nuts securing it to its mounting bracket, taking care to ensure that the lower column tube support bush seats correctly as the nuts are tightened to the specified torque.

28 Refit the steering column ancillary components, reversing the removal procedure given in paragraphs 2 to 7 (for models without air bag) or 12 to 22 (for models with air bag).

29 Tighten the pinch-bolt securing the lower steering shaft universal joint to the pinion splined shaft to the specified torque. Ensure that the pinch-bolt sits in the annular groove on the pinion splined shaft **(see illustration)**.

30 Reconnect the battery negative lead.

---

21 Steering column (power steering) - removal and refitting

Removal

 Warning: Handle the air bag with extreme care as a precaution against personal injury, and always hold it with the cover facing away from your body. If in doubt concerning any proposed work involving the air bag or its control circuitry, consult a Ford dealer or other qualified specialist.

1 Disconnect the battery negative (earth) lead (refer to Chapter 5A, Section 1).

Warning: Before proceeding, wait a minimum of 15 minutes, as a precaution against accidental firing of the air bag. This period ensures that any stored energy in the back-up capacitor is dissipated.

2 Undo the screws, and remove the steering column lower shroud.

3 Undo the two external screws and the two internal screws and remove the steering column upper shroud.

4 Turn the steering wheel as necessary so

that one of the air bag module retaining bolts becomes accessible from the rear of the steering wheel. Undo the bolt, then turn the steering wheel again until the second bolt is accessible. Undo this bolt also.

5 Withdraw the air bag module from the steering wheel far enough to access the wiring multi-plug. Some force may be needed to free the module from the additional steering wheel spoke retainers.

6 Disconnect the multi-plug from the rear of the module, and remove the module from the vehicle.

Warning: Position the air bag module in a safe place, with the mechanism facing downwards as a precaution against accidental operation.

7 Turn the steering wheel so that the roadwheels are in the straight-ahead position, then remove the ignition key to lock the steering.

8 Release the wiring harness from the side of the steering column and disconnect the air bag module wiring multi-plug (yellow lead).

9 Disconnect the wiring multi-plugs from the steering column multi-function switch assembly.

10 Disconnect the ignition switch wiring multi-plug connector and remove the loom plate from its location on the left-hand side of the steering column.

11 Undo the single screw and withdraw the Passive Anti-Theft System (PATS) transceiver from the ignition switch/steering lock barrel **(see illustration 19.12)**.

12 Unclip the bonnet release cable abutment from its location in the steering column lock housing, then detach the cable from the bonnet release lever by aligning the cable core with the slot on the release lever and withdrawing it through that slot. Detach the spring from the release lever arms, then disengage the arms from the steering column lock housing and remove the bonnet release lever.

13 Remove the C-clip at the base of the steering column shaft, below the universal joint.

14 Remove the nuts securing the steering column mounting bracket.

15 Pull the steering column assembly from its bulkhead location and withdraw it from the vehicle, ensuring that the steering column shaft and flexible coupling separate fully.

Refitting

16 Ensure that the roadwheels are in the straight-ahead position and the steering column is locked. With the help of an assistant, insert the steering column assembly into the vehicle so that the steering column shaft engages with the flexible coupling.

17 Refit the steering column shaft C-clip.

18 With the column assembly located loosely in position, refit and tighten the nuts securing it to its mounting bracket.

19 Refit the steering column ancillary

components, reversing the removal procedure given in paragraphs 2 to 12.

20 Reconnect the battery negative lead.

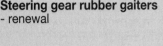

22 Steering gear rubber gaiters - renewal

1 Remove the track rod end balljoint as described in Section 28.

2 Remove the one-piece undertray where fitted, by turning its bayonet-type fasteners, and on XR2i models, remove the front suspension crossmember as described in Section 7.

3 Count the number of exposed threads visible, from the end of the track rod to the track rod end balljoint locknut, and record this figure. Now unscrew the locknut from the track rod.

4 Release the clip(s), and slide the gaiter off the rack-and-pinion housing and track rod.

5 Scrape off all grease from the old gaiter, and apply to the track rod inner joint. Wipe clean the seating areas on the rack-and-pinion housing and track rod.

6 Slide the new gaiter onto the housing and track rod, and secure with the retaining clips. Ensure that the narrow neck locates correctly in the track rod groove.

7 Screw the track rod end balljoint locknut back onto the track rod until the same number of threads, as counted on removal, are visible.

8 Refit the track rod end balljoint as described in Section 28.

9 Refit the front suspension crossmember and one-piece undertray, as applicable.

23 Steering gear (manual steering) - removal and refitting

Removal

1 Disconnect the battery negative (earth) lead (refer to Chapter 5A, Section 1).

2 Chock the rear wheels then jack up the front of the car and support it on axle stands (see *"Jacking and Vehicle Support"*). Remove the front roadwheels.

3 Remove the one-piece undertray where fitted, by turning its bayonet-type fasteners, and on XR2i models, remove the front suspension crossmember as described in Section 7.

4 Remove the pinch-bolt securing the pinion splined shaft to the lower steering shaft universal joints, located at the rear of the engine compartment.

5 Separate the track rod end balljoints from the steering arms, as described in Section 28.

6 Remove the lower brake servo support bracket bolt.

7 Remove the other bolt securing the steering rack assembly to the bulkhead, then withdraw it from the right-hand side of the vehicle,

taking care to disengage the pinion splined shaft from the lower steering shaft universal joint as the assembly is moved.

Refitting

8 Centralize the rack and steering wheel, then engage the pinion splined shaft to the lower steering shaft universal joint.

9 Refit the steering rack assembly mounting bolts to the bulkhead and tighten to the specified torque, ensuring that the servo support bracket is correctly held.

10 Refit the pinion splined shaft-to-lower steering shaft universal joint pinch-bolt and nut and tighten to the specified torque, ensuring that the pinch-bolt locates to the annular groove as the pinion splined shaft.

11 Refit the track rod end balljoints to the steering arms, as detailed in Section 28. As long as the track rod end-to-track rod relative positions have not been disturbed, it will not be necessary to reset the front wheel alignment.

12 Refit the front suspension crossmember and one-piece undertray, as applicable.

13 Refit the roadwheels, then lower the vehicle to the ground. Tighten the roadwheel nuts to the specified torque with the vehicle on its wheels.

24 Steering gear (power steering) - removal and refitting

Removal

1 Disconnect the battery negative (earth) lead (refer to Chapter 5A, Section 1).

2 Chock the rear wheels then jack up the front of the car and support it on axle stands (see *"Jacking and Vehicle Support"*). Remove the front roadwheels.

3 Remove the one-piece undertray where fitted, by turning its bayonet-type fasteners, and on XR2i models, remove the front suspension crossmember as described in Section 7.

4 Remove the pinch-bolt securing the pinion splined shaft to the lower steering shaft flexible coupling, located at the rear of the engine compartment.

5 Undo the retaining screws, and detach the clips securing the power steering hydraulic pressure pipes to the steering gear.

6 Position a suitable container under the hydraulic pipe connections to the steering gear. Unscrew the pipe unions, then detach the pipes from the valve body. Withdraw the pipes from the steering gear, and drain the hydraulic fluid into the container.

7 Plug the exposed ends of the hydraulic line connections, to prevent the ingress of dirt and further fluid loss. Note that new O-ring seals will be needed for the pressure and return hose connections when reconnecting.

8 Slacken the upper bolts securing the steering gear support brackets. On left-hand

10

drive models, remove the brace from the stud on the left-hand side of the steering gear.

9 Undo the two bolts securing the support brackets to the steering gear and move the brackets and swing the brackets clear.

10 Unhook the steering gear from the apertures in the bulkhead and remove the assembly from the right-hand wheel arch. Ensure that the pressure check valve does not fall out of the pressure port in the valve body as the steering gear is removed.

Refitting

11 Centralize the steering gear and steering wheel, then engage the pinion splined shaft to the lower steering shaft flexible coupling.

12 Hook the steering gear into the apertures in the bulkhead then align the support brackets and refit the two bolts. Tighten the support bracket upper bolts and support bracket-to-steering gear bolts to the specified torque.

13 On left-hand drive models, refit the brace to the stud on the left-hand side of the steering gear.

14 Fit new O-ring seals to the pressure and return hoses, then reconnect the hydraulic lines to the steering gear. Secure the pipes with the retaining clips.

15 Refit the pinion splined shaft-to-lower steering shaft flexible coupling pinch-bolt and nut and tighten to the specified torque.

16 Refit the track rod end balljoints to the steering arms, as detailed in Section 28. As long as the track rod end-to-track rod relative positions have not been disturbed, it will not be necessary to reset the front wheel alignment.

17 Refit the front suspension crossmember and one-piece undertray, as applicable.

18 Refit the roadwheels, then lower the vehicle to the ground. Tighten the roadwheel nuts with the vehicle on its wheels to the specified torque.

19 On completion, bleed the power steering hydraulic system as described in Section 27. Check for any signs of fluid leakage from the system hoses and connections.

25 Power steering pump - removal and refitting

Removal

HCS engine models

1 Disconnect the battery negative (earth) lead (refer to Chapter 5A, Section 1).

2 Chock the rear wheels then jack up the front of the car and support it on axle stands (see *"Jacking and Vehicle Support"*). Remove the front roadwheel.

3 Remove the auxiliary drivebelt as described in Chapter 1.

4 Insert a 9 mm Allen key into the centre of the pump drive spindle to prevent it from

turning, then unscrew and remove the three pump pulley retaining bolts. Withdraw the pulley from the pump.

5 Position a suitable container beneath the power steering pump, then unscrew and detach the fluid high pressure pipe and fluid return hose from the pump. As they are detached from the pump, allow the fluid to drain from the pipe and hose (and the pump) into the container. Plug the exposed ends of the pipe, hose and the pump connections, to prevent the ingress of dirt and excessive fluid loss.

6 Unscrew the four retaining bolts (three from the front and one from the rear) and withdraw the pump from the vehicle.

PTE engine models

7 Disconnect the battery negative (earth) lead (refer to Chapter 5A, Section 1).

8 Refer to the relevant Part of Chapter 4 and remove the air cleaner assembly and air inlet components as necessary for access to the pump.

9 Chock the rear wheels then jack up the front of the car and support it on axle stands (see *"Jacking and Vehicle Support"*). Remove the front roadwheel.

10 Refer to Chapter 1 and drain the cooling system.

11 Refer to Chapter 1 and remove the auxiliary drivebelt.

12 Insert a 9 mm Allen key into the centre of the pump drive spindle to prevent it from turning, then unscrew and remove the three pump pulley retaining bolts. Refit the roadwheel, lower the vehicle and withdraw the pump pulley from above.

13 Disconnect the cooling system hoses as necessary to gain access to the power steering pump.

14 Disconnect the pressure switch multi-plug from the pressure switch located in the fluid high pressure pipe.

15 Position a suitable container beneath the power steering pump, then disconnect the high pressure pipe at the union located part way along the pipe. Allow the fluid to drain from the pipe into the container.

16 Disconnect the high pressure pipe clamp bracket and the fluid return hose from the pump. Allow the fluid to drain into the container then plug the exposed ends of the pipe, hose and the pump connections, to prevent the ingress of dirt and excessive fluid loss.

17 Unscrew the pump mounting bolt located at the rear of the pump and remove the pipe clamp bracket.

18 Unscrew the three pump mounting bolts located at the front of the pump and remove the pump, complete with high pressure pipe, from the vehicle.

19 If required, the high pressure pipe can be removed from the pump after unscrewing the union nut.

Zetec engine models

Note: *For this operation, the engine will need to be supported from above to allow removal*

of the right-hand engine mounting, and also to allow the vehicle to be raised for work underneath, and lowered for work from above. A proprietary engine support bar (or home-made alternative) fitted in the front wing drain channel each side is ideal for this purpose, but care must be taken not to damage the wings or their paintwork.

20 Disconnect the battery negative (earth) lead (refer to Chapter 5A, Section 1).

21 Suitably support the right-hand side of the engine (see the note at the beginning of this sub-Section) so that all the load is removed from the engine mounting.

22 Remove the right-hand engine mounting as described in Chapter 2C.

23 Refer to Chapter 1 and drain the cooling system.

24 Chock the rear wheels then jack up the front of the car and support it on axle stands (see *"Jacking and Vehicle Support"*). Remove the front roadwheel.

25 Undo the retaining screws, and remove the drivebelt lower guard from the underbody.

26 Refer to Chapter 11 and remove the wheel arch liner.

27 Refer to Chapter 1 and remove the auxiliary drivebelt.

28 Insert a 9 mm Allen key into the centre of the pump drive spindle to prevent it from turning, then unscrew and remove the three pump pulley retaining bolts. Refit the roadwheel, lower the vehicle and withdraw the pump pulley from above.

29 Refer to Chapter 12 and remove the right-hand headlight unit.

30 Refit the roadwheel and lower the vehicle to the ground.

31 Position a suitable container beneath the power steering fluid reservoir, then disconnect the fluid return hose from the reservoir. Allow the fluid to drain from the hose and reservoir into the container.

32 Plug the exposed ends of the hose and the reservoir, to prevent the ingress of dirt and excessive fluid loss.

33 Remove the high pressure pipe clamp brackets from the engine then disconnect the high pressure pipe at the union located over the camshaft cover. Place absorbent rags under the union as it is disconnected to collect any escaping fluid. Plug the disconnected pipe ends to prevent the ingress of dirt and excessive fluid loss.

34 Disconnect the cooling system hoses as necessary to gain access to the power steering pump.

35 Unscrew the two pump mounting bolts located at the rear of the pump.

36 Unscrew the two pump mounting bolts located at the front of the pump and remove the pump, complete with high pressure pipe and fluid return hose, upwards and out of the engine compartment.

37 If required, the high pressure pipe and fluid return hose can be removed from the pump after unscrewing the union nut or slackening the hose clip as applicable.

Refitting

All models

38 Refitting is a reversal of removal, bearing in mind the following points:

a) *Tighten all nuts and bolts to the specified torque. Remove the plugs from the disconnected pipes, hoses and unions and ensure that the pipes are located correctly so that they do not foul any surrounding components.*

b) *Refit the auxiliary drivebelt as described in Chapter 1.*

c) *Where drained, refill the cooling system as described in Chapter 1.*

d) *Refit or reconnect any additional components removed for access as described in the relevant Sections and Chapters of this manual.*

e) *On completion, bleed the power steering hydraulic system as described in Section 27. Check for any signs of fluid leakage from the system hoses and connections.*

26 Power steering fluid cooler - removal and refitting

Removal

1 Disconnect the battery negative (earth) lead (refer to Chapter 5A, Section 1).

2 Position a suitable container beneath the power steering fluid cooler hose connections, then disconnect the hoses at the quick-fit couplings on the fluid cooler. Allow the fluid to drain from the hose and reservoir into the container.

3 Plug the exposed ends of the hose and the reservoir, to prevent the ingress of dirt and excessive fluid loss.

4 Refer to Chapter 11 and remove the bonnet lock assembly and the front bumper.

5 Undo the bolts securing the cooler side support bracket and the bonnet lock stay, and remove the fluid cooler and bonnet lock stay as an assembly.

6 Undo the two bolts and remove the stay from the fluid cooler.

Refitting

7 Refitting is a reversal of removal. On completion, bleed the power steering hydraulic system as described in Section 27.

27 Power steering hydraulic system - bleeding

1 Following any operation in which the power steering fluid lines have been disconnected, the power steering system must be bled to remove any trapped air.

2 With the front wheel in the straight-ahead position, check the power steering fluid level in the reservoir and, if low, top-up with fresh

fluid to the "MAX" or "MAX COLD" level mark. Pour the fluid slowly to prevent air bubbles forming, and use only the specified fluid (refer to *"Lubricants, fluids and tyre pressures"*).

3 Start the engine and allow it to idle. Check the hoses and connections for leaks.

4 Stop the engine and recheck the fluid level. Add more, if necessary, up to the "MAX" or "MAX COLD" level mark.

5 Start the engine again, allow it to idle, then bleed the system by slowly moving the steering from lock-to-lock several times. This should purge the system of all internal air. However, if air remains in the system (indicated by the steering operation being very noisy), leave the vehicle overnight and repeat the procedure again the next day.

6 If air still remains in the system, it may be necessary to resort to the Ford method of bleeding, which uses a vacuum pump and a modified reservoir filler cap to which the pump can be connected. Turn the steering to the right until it is near the stop, then fit the vacuum pump to the fluid reservoir, and apply 0.51 bars of vacuum. Maintain the vacuum for a minimum of 5 minutes, then repeat the procedure with the steering turned to the left.

7 Keep the fluid level topped-up throughout the bleeding procedure; note that the fluid temperature increases, the level will rise.

8 On completion, switch the engine off, and return the wheels to the straight-ahead position.

28 Track rod end balljoint - removal and refitting

Removal

1 Chock the rear wheels then jack up the front of the car and support it on axle stands (see *"Jacking and Vehicle Support"*). Remove the appropriate front roadwheel.

2 Using a suitable spanner, slacken the track rod end balljoint locknut on the track rod by a quarter of a turn only **(see illustration)**. Hold

28.2 Track rod end balljoint showing the locknut (A) retaining flats (B) and the balljoint-to-spindle carrier arm retaining nut and split pin (C)

the balljoint stationary with another spanner engaged with the flats at its inner end to prevent it from turning.

3 Extract the split pin, then loosen off the retaining nut. If the balljoint is to be renewed, the nut can be fully removed. If the existing balljoint is to be reconnected, the nut should be slackened off a couple of turns only at first, and left in position to protect the joint threads as the joint is separated from the spindle carrier. To release the tapered shank of the joint from the spindle carrier, use a balljoint separator tool as shown **(see illustration)**. If the joint is to be re-used, take care not to damage the rubber dust cover when using a separator tool.

4 Unscrew the balljoint from the track rod, counting the number of turns necessary to remove it.

Refitting

5 Screw the balljoint into the track rod the number of turns noted during removal until the balljoint just contacts the locknut. Now tighten the locknut while holding the balljoint.

6 Engage the shank of the balljoint with the spindle carrier arm, and refit the retaining nut. Tighten the nut to the specified torque and secure with a new split pin.

7 Refit the roadwheel, and lower the vehicle to the ground.

8 Finally, have the front wheel toe setting checked (see Section 29).

29 Wheel alignment and steering angles - general information

General

1 A car's steering and suspension geometry is defined in four basic settings - all angles are expressed in degrees (toe settings are also expressed as a measurement); the relevant settings are camber, castor, steering axis inclination, and toe-setting. With the exception of front wheel toe-setting, none of these settings are adjustable.

28.3 Balljoint separator tool in position. Note that the nut should be left loosely in position to protect the thread for re-use

Front wheel toe setting - checking and adjustment

2 Due to the special measuring equipment necessary to accurately check the wheel alignment, and the skill required to use it properly, checking and adjustment is best left to a Ford dealer or similar expert. Note that most tyre-fitting shops now possess sophisticated checking equipment. The following is provided as a guide, should the owner decide to carry out a DIY check.

3 The front wheel toe setting is checked by measuring the distance between the front and rear inside edges of the roadwheel rims. Proprietary toe measurement gauges are available from motor accessory shops. Adjustment is made by screwing the track rods in or out of their track rod end balljoints, to alter the effective length of the track rod assemblies.

4 For **accurate** checking, the vehicle **must** be at the kerb weight, ie unladen and with a full tank of fuel.

5 Before starting work, check the tyre pressures and tread wear, the condition of the hub bearings, the steering wheel free play, and the condition of the front suspension components (see Chapter 1). Correct any faults found.

6 Park the vehicle on level ground, check that the front roadwheels are in the straight-ahead position, then rock the rear and front ends to settle the suspension. Release the handbrake, and roll the vehicle backwards 1 metre, then forwards again, to relieve any stresses in the steering and suspension components.

7 Measure the distance between the front edges of the wheel rims and the rear edges of the rims. Subtract the smallest measurement from the largest, and check that the result is within the specified range.

8 If adjustment is necessary, apply the handbrake, then jack up the front of the vehicle and support it securely on axle stands (see *"Jacking and Vehicle Support"*). Turn the steering wheel onto full-left lock, and record the number of exposed threads on the right-hand track rod. Now turn the steering onto full-right lock, and record the number of threads on the left-hand side. If there are the same number of threads visible on both sides, then subsequent adjustment should be made equally on both sides. If there are more threads visible on one side than the other, it will be necessary to compensate for this during adjustment. **Note:** *It is most important that after adjustment, the same number of threads are visible on each track rod.*

9 First clean the track rod end; if they are corroded, apply penetrating fluid before starting adjustment. Release the rubber gaiter outboard clips (where necessary), and peel back the gaiter; apply a smear of grease to the inside of the gaiter, so that both are free, and will not be twisted or strained as their respective track rods are rotated.

10 Use a straight-edge and a scriber or similar to mark the relationship of each track rod to its track rod end balljoint, then, holding each track rod in turn, unscrew its locknut fully.

11 Alter the length of the track rods, bearing in mind the note made in paragraph 8. Screw them into or out of the track rod end balljoints, rotating the track rods using a self-grip wrench. Shortening the track rods (screwing them into their track rod end balljoints) will reduce toe-in/increase toe-out.

12 When the setting is correct, hold the track rods and securely tighten the track rod end balljoint locknuts. Count the exposed threads to check the length of both track rods. If they are not the same, then the adjustment has not been made equally, and problems will be encountered with tyre scrubbing in turns; also, the steering wheel spokes will no longer be horizontal when the wheels are in the straight-ahead position.

13 If the track rod lengths are the same, lower the vehicle to the ground and re-check the toe setting; re-adjust if necessary. When the setting is correct, securely tighten the track rod end balljoint locknuts. Ensure that the rubber gaiters are seated correctly, and are not twisted or strained, and secure them in position with new retaining clips (where necessary).

Chapter 11
Bodywork and fittings

Contents

Body adhesive emblems - renewal 9
Body trim mouldings - removal and refitting 10
Bodywork, paint and exterior trim check ....See Chapter 1
Bonnet - removal, refitting and adjustment 6
Bonnet latch - adjustment 8
Bonnet release mechanism - removal and refitting 7
Bumper and rear quarter mouldings - renewal 17
Bumpers - removal and refitting 16
Centre console - removal and refitting 45
Door aperture weatherstrip - removal and refitting 11
Door window glass - removal and refitting 32
Door window regulator - removal and refitting 31
Door, tailgate and bonnet check and lubrication .....See Chapter 1
Exterior mirror and glass - removal and refitting 18
Facia - removal and refitting 46
Front seat and slide assembly - removal and refitting 39
Full-length sunroof - general information 38
General information 1
Interior mirror - removal and refitting 19
Interior trim panels - removal and refitting 42
Maintenance - bodywork and underframe 2
Maintenance - upholstery and carpets 3
Major body damage - repair 5
Minor body damage - repair 4
Parcel shelf support/loudspeaker housing - removal and refitting .. 43

Passenger grab handle - removal and refitting 44
Rear door inner trim panels (Courier models) - removal and refitting .. 29
Rear door lock, catches and handles (Courier models) -
    removal and refitting 30
Rear doors (Courier models) - removal and refitting 28
Rear seat - removal and refitting 40
Seat belt check ....See Chapter 1
Seat belts - removal and refitting 41
Side door inner trim panel - removal and refitting 21
Side door lock, lock cylinder and handles - removal and refitting .. 22
Side doors - removal and refitting 20
Side window glass - removal and refitting 33
Sill extension moulding - removal and refitting 12
Sunroof panel - removal and refitting 35
Sunroof panel seal - renewal 36
Sunroof weatherseal - removal and refitting 37
Tailgate - removal and refitting 24
Tailgate inner trim panel - removal and refitting 26
Tailgate lock components - removal and refitting 27
Tailgate spoiler - removal and refitting 25
Tailgate support strut - removal and refitting 23
Wheelarch liners - removal and refitting 13
Wheelarch mouldings - removal and refitting 14
Wind deflector/radiator grille slat - removal and refitting 15
Windscreen and tailgate window glass - removal and refitting 34

Degrees of difficulty

Easy, suitable for novice with little experience	Fairly easy, suitable for beginner with some experience	Fairly difficult, suitable for competent DIY mechanic	Difficult, suitable for experienced DIY mechanic	Very difficult, suitable for expert DIY or professional

Specifications

Torque wrench settings	Nm	lbf ft
Front seat slide mechanism-to-floor mounting bolts	25 to 32	18 to 24
Rear seat backrest hinge to backrest	3.7 to 4.6	2.7 to 3.4
Rear seat backrest hinge to body	21 to 25	15 to 18
Rear seat belt anchors and stalks to body	25 to 45	18 to 34
Rear seat belt retractor assembly to body	25 to 45	18 to 34
Front seat belt stalks to floorpan	25 to 45	18 to 34
Front seat belt lower anchor bolt to body	25 to 45	18 to 34
Front seat belt lower anchor slide bar bolt to body	25 to 45	18 to 34
Front seat belt retractor to B-pillar bolt	25 to 45	18 to 34
Front seat belt upper anchor bolt to B-pillar (non-adjustable type)	25 to 45	18 to 34
Front seat belt upper anchor adjuster plate-to-B-pillar bolts	19 to 28	14 to 22
Front seat belt upper anchor bolt to adjuster slide	25 to 45	18 to 34
Bonnet hinge-to-bonnet bolts	8.5 to 12	6.5 to 9
Bonnet latch retaining bolts	8 to 12	6 to 9
Tailgate hinge-to-tailgate bolts	8.5 to 12	6.5 to 9
Tailgate latch retaining bolts	8 to 12	6 to 9
Rear door lower hinge cap bolts	8.5 to 12	6.5 to 9
Rear door latch retaining bolts	8.5 to 12	6.5 to 9
Front and rear bumper retaining nuts	8 to 12	6 to 9

11

1 General information

The bodyshell and underframe on all models is of all-steel welded construction, incorporating progressive crumple zones at the front and rear, and a rigid centre safety cell. The body styles available include three-door, five-door, Van and Courier configurations.

A multi-stage anti-corrosion process is applied to all new vehicles. This includes zinc phosphating on some panels, the injection of wax into boxed sections, and a wax and PVC coating applied to the underbody for its protection.

Inertia reel seat belts are fitted to all models, and from the 1994 model year onwards, the front seat belt stalks are mounted on automatic mechanical tensioners (also known as "grabbers"). In the event of a serious front impact, a spring mass sensor releases a coil spring which pulls the stalk buckle downwards and tensions the seat belt. It is not possible to reset the tensioner once fired, and it must therefore be renewed.

Central locking is a standard or optional fitment on all models. Where double-locking is also fitted, the lock mechanism is disconnected (when the system is in use) from the interior door handles, making it impossible to open any of the doors or the tailgate from inside the vehicle. This means that, even if a thief should break a side window, it will not be possible to open the door using the interior handle.

2 Maintenance - bodywork and underframe

The general condition of a vehicle's bodywork is the one thing that significantly affects its value. Maintenance is easy, but needs to be regular. Neglect, particularly after minor damage, can lead quickly to further deterioration and costly repair bills. It is important also to keep watch on those parts of the vehicle not immediately visible, for instance the underside, inside all the wheel arches, and the lower part of the engine compartment.

The basic maintenance routine for the bodywork is washing - preferably with a lot of water, from a hose. This will remove all the loose solids which may have stuck to the vehicle. It is important to flush these off in such a way as to prevent grit from scratching the finish. The wheel arches and underframe need washing in the same way, to remove any accumulated mud, which will retain moisture and tend to encourage rust. Oddly enough, the best time to clean the underframe and wheel arches is in wet weather, when the mud is thoroughly wet and soft. In very wet weather, the underframe is usually cleaned of large accumulations automatically, and this is a good time for inspection.

Periodically, except on vehicles with a wax-based underbody protective coating, it is a good idea to have the whole of the underframe of the vehicle steam-cleaned, engine compartment included, so that a thorough inspection can be carried out to see what minor repairs and renovations are necessary. Steam-cleaning is available at many garages, and is necessary for the removal of the accumulation of oily grime, which sometimes is allowed to become thick in certain areas. If steam-cleaning facilities are not available, there are some excellent grease solvents available which can be brush-applied; the dirt can then be simply hosed off. Note that these methods should not be used on vehicles with wax-based underbody protective coating, or the coating will be removed. Such vehicles should be inspected annually, preferably just prior to Winter, when the underbody should be washed down, and any damage to the wax coating repaired. Ideally, a completely fresh coat should be applied. It would also be worth considering the use of such wax-based protection for injection into door panels, sills, box sections, etc, as an additional safeguard against rust damage, where such protection is not provided by the vehicle manufacturer.

After washing paintwork, wipe off with a chamois leather to give an unspotted clear finish. A coat of clear protective wax polish will give added protection against chemical pollutants in the air. If the paintwork sheen has dulled or oxidised, use a cleaner/polisher combination to restore the brilliance of the shine. This requires a little effort, but such dulling is usually caused because regular washing has been neglected. Care needs to be taken with metallic paintwork, as special non-abrasive cleaner/polisher is required to avoid damage to the finish. Always check that the door and ventilator opening drain holes and pipes are completely clear, so that water can be drained out. Brightwork should be treated in the same way as paintwork. Windscreens and windows can be kept clear of the smeary film which often appears, by the use of proprietary glass cleaner. Never use any form of wax or other body or chromium polish on glass.

3 Maintenance - upholstery and carpets

Mats and carpets should be brushed or vacuum-cleaned regularly, to keep them free of grit. If they are badly stained, remove them from the vehicle for scrubbing or sponging, and make quite sure they are dry before refitting. Seats and interior trim panels can be kept clean by wiping with a damp cloth. If they do become stained (which can be more apparent on light-coloured upholstery), use a little liquid detergent and a soft nail brush to scour the grime out of the grain of the material. Do not forget to keep the headlining clean in the same way as the upholstery. When using liquid cleaners inside the vehicle, do not over-wet the surfaces being cleaned. Excessive damp could get into the seams and padded interior, causing stains, offensive odours or even rot.

Note: *If the inside of the vehicle gets wet accidentally, it is worthwhile taking some trouble to dry it out properly, particularly where carpets are involved.*

> ⚠ **Warning: Do not leave oil or electric heaters inside the vehicle for this purpose.**

4 Minor body damage - repair

Repairs of minor scratches in bodywork

If the scratch is very superficial, and does not penetrate to the metal of the bodywork, repair is very simple. Lightly rub the area of the scratch with a paintwork renovator, or a very fine cutting paste, to remove loose paint from the scratch, and to clear the surrounding bodywork of wax polish. Rinse the area with clean water.

Apply touch-up paint to the scratch using a fine paint brush; continue to apply fine layers of paint until the surface of the paint in the scratch is level with the surrounding paintwork. Allow the new paint at least two weeks to harden, then blend it into the surrounding paintwork by rubbing the scratch area with a paintwork renovator or a very fine cutting paste. Finally, apply wax polish.

Where the scratch has penetrated right through to the metal of the bodywork, causing the metal to rust, a different repair technique is required. Remove any loose rust from the bottom of the scratch with a penknife, then apply rust-inhibiting paint to prevent the formation of rust in the future. Using a rubber or nylon applicator, fill the scratch with bodystopper paste. If required, this paste can be mixed with cellulose thinners to provide a very thin paste which is ideal for filling narrow scratches. Before the stopper-paste in the scratch hardens, wrap a piece of smooth cotton rag around the top of a finger. Dip the finger in cellulose thinners, and quickly sweep it across the surface of the stopper-paste in the scratch; this will ensure that the surface of the stopper-paste is slightly hollowed. The scratch can now be painted over as described earlier in this Section.

Repairs of dents in bodywork

When deep denting of the vehicle's bodywork has taken place, the first task is to pull the dent out, until the affected bodywork almost attains its original shape. There is little point in trying to restore the original shape completely, as the metal in the damaged area will have stretched on impact, and cannot be reshaped fully to its original contour. It is better to bring the level of the dent up to a point which is about 3 mm below the level of the surrounding bodywork. In cases where the dent is very shallow anyway, it is not worth trying to pull it out at all. If the underside of the dent is accessible, it can be hammered out gently from behind, using a mallet with a wooden or plastic head. Whilst doing this, hold a suitable block of wood firmly against the outside of the panel, to absorb the impact from the hammer blows and thus prevent a large area of the bodywork from being "belled-out".

Should the dent be in a section of the bodywork which has a double skin, or some other factor making it inaccessible from behind, a different technique is called for. Drill several small holes through the metal inside the area - particularly in the deeper section. Then screw long self-tapping screws into the holes, just sufficiently for them to gain a good purchase in the metal. Now the dent can be pulled out by pulling on the protruding heads of the screws with a pair of pliers.

The next stage of the repair is the removal of the paint from the damaged area, and from an inch or so of the surrounding "sound" bodywork. This is accomplished most easily by using a wire brush or abrasive pad on a power drill, although it can be done just as effectively by hand, using sheets of abrasive paper. To complete the preparation for filling, score the surface of the bare metal with a screwdriver or the tang of a file, or alternatively, drill small holes in the affected area. This will provide a really good "key" for the filler paste.

To complete the repair, see the Section on filling and respraying.

Repairs of rust holes or gashes in bodywork

Remove all paint from the affected area, and from an inch or so of the surrounding "sound" bodywork, using an abrasive pad or a wire brush on a power drill. If these are not available, a few sheets of abrasive paper will do the job most effectively. With the paint removed, you will be able to judge the severity of the corrosion, and therefore decide whether to renew the whole panel (if this is possible) or to repair the affected area. New body panels are not as expensive as most people think, and it is often quicker and more satisfactory to fit a new panel than to attempt to repair large areas of corrosion.

Remove all fittings from the affected area, except those which will act as a guide to the original shape of the damaged bodywork (eg headlight shells etc). Then, using tin snips or a hacksaw blade, remove all loose metal and any other metal badly affected by corrosion. Hammer the edges of the hole inwards, in

order to create a slight depression for the filler paste.

Wire-brush the affected area to remove the powdery rust from the surface of the remaining metal. Paint the affected area with rust-inhibiting paint, if the back of the rusted area is accessible, treat this also.

Before filling can take place, it will be necessary to block the hole in some way. This can be achieved by the use of aluminium or plastic mesh, or aluminium tape.

Aluminium or plastic mesh, or glass-fibre matting, is probably the best material to use for a large hole. Cut a piece to the approximate size and shape of the hole to be filled, then position it in the hole so that its edges are below the level of the surrounding bodywork. It can be retained in position by several blobs of filler paste around its periphery.

Aluminium tape should be used for small or very narrow holes. Pull a piece off the roll, trim it to the approximate size and shape required, then pull off the backing paper (if used) and stick the tape over the hole; it can be overlapped if the thickness of one piece is insufficient. Burnish down the edges of the tape with the handle of a screwdriver or similar, to ensure that the tape is securely attached to the metal underneath.

Bodywork repairs - filling and respraying

Before using this Section, see the Sections on dent, deep scratch, rust holes and gash repairs.

Many types of bodyfiller are available, but generally speaking, those proprietary kits which contain a tin of filler paste and a tube of resin hardener are best for this type of repair. A wide, flexible plastic or nylon applicator will be found invaluable for imparting a smooth and well-contoured finish to the surface of the filler.

Mix up a little filler on a clean piece of card or board - measure the hardener carefully (follow the maker's instructions on the pack), otherwise the filler will set too rapidly or too slowly. Using the applicator, apply the filler paste to the prepared area; draw the applicator across the surface of the filler to achieve the correct contour and to level the surface. As soon as a contour that approximates to the correct one is achieved, stop working the paste - if you carry on too long, the paste will become sticky and begin to "pick-up" on the applicator. Continue to add thin layers of filler paste at 20-minute intervals, until the level of the filler is just proud of the surrounding bodywork.

Once the filler has hardened, the excess can be removed using a metal plane or file. From then on, progressively-finer grades of abrasive paper should be used, starting with a 40-grade production paper, and finishing with a 400-grade wet-and-dry paper. Always wrap the abrasive paper around a flat rubber, cork, or wooden block - otherwise the surface of

the filler will not be completely flat. During the smoothing of the filler surface, the wet-and-dry paper should be periodically rinsed in water. This will ensure that a very smooth finish is imparted to the filler at the final stage.

At this stage, the "dent" should be surrounded by a ring of bare metal, which in turn should be encircled by the finely "feathered" edge of the good paintwork. Rinse the repair area with clean water, until all of the dust produced by the rubbing-down operation has gone.

Spray the whole area with a light coat of primer - this will show up any imperfections in the surface of the filler. Repair these imperfections with fresh filler paste or bodystopper, and once more smooth the surface with abrasive paper. Repeat this spray-and-repair procedure until you are satisfied that the surface of the filler, and the feathered edge of the paintwork, are perfect. Clean the repair area with clean water, and allow to dry fully.

HAYNES HiNT *If bodystopper is used, it can be mixed with cellulose thinners to form a really thin paste which is ideal for filling small holes.*

The repair area is now ready for final spraying. Paint spraying must be carried out in a warm, dry, windless and dust-free atmosphere. This condition can be created artificially if you have access to a large indoor working area, but if you are forced to work in the open, you will have to pick your day very carefully. If you are working indoors, dousing the floor in the work area with water will help to settle the dust which would otherwise be in the atmosphere. If the repair area is confined to one body panel, mask off the surrounding panels; this will help to minimise the effects of a slight mis-match in paint colours. Bodywork fittings (eg chrome strips, door handles etc) will also need to be masked off. Use genuine masking tape, and several thicknesses of newspaper, for the masking operations.

Before commencing to spray, agitate the aerosol can thoroughly, then spray a test area (an old tin, or similar) until the technique is mastered. Cover the repair area with a thick coat of primer; the thickness should be built up using several thin layers of paint, rather than one thick one. Using 400-grade wet-and-dry paper, rub down the surface of the primer until it is really smooth. While doing this, the work area should be thoroughly doused with water, and the wet-and-dry paper periodically rinsed in water. Allow to dry before spraying on more paint.

Spray on the top coat, again building up the thickness by using several thin layers of paint. Start spraying at one edge of the repair area, and then, using a side-to-side motion, work until the whole repair area and about 2 inches of the surrounding original paintwork is covered. Remove all masking material 10 to

11

15 minutes after spraying on the final coat of paint.

Allow the new paint at least two weeks to harden, then, using a paintwork renovator, or a very fine cutting paste, blend the edges of the paint into the existing paintwork. Finally, apply wax polish.

Plastic components

With the use of more and more plastic body components by the vehicle manufacturers (eg bumpers. spoilers, and in some cases major body panels), rectification of more serious damage to such items has become a matter of either entrusting repair work to a specialist in this field, or renewing complete components. Repair of such damage by the DIY owner is not really feasible, owing to the cost of the equipment and materials required for effecting such repairs. The basic technique involves making a groove along the line of the crack in the plastic, using a rotary burr in a power drill. The damaged part is then welded back together, using a hot-air gun to heat up and fuse a plastic filler rod into the groove. Any excess plastic is then removed, and the area rubbed down to a smooth finish. It is important that a filler rod of the correct plastic is used, as body components can be made of a variety of different types (eg polycarbonate, ABS, polypropylene).

Damage of a less serious nature (abrasions, minor cracks etc) can be repaired by the DIY owner using a two-part epoxy filler repair material. Once mixed in equal proportions, this is used in similar fashion to the bodywork filler used on metal panels. The filler is usually cured in twenty to thirty minutes, ready for sanding and painting.

If the owner is renewing a complete component himself, or if he has repaired it with epoxy filler, he will be left with the problem of finding a suitable paint for finishing which is compatible with the type of plastic used. At one time, the use of a universal paint was not possible, owing to the complex range of plastics encountered in body component applications. Standard paints, generally speaking, will not bond to plastic or rubber satisfactorily. However, it is now possible to obtain a plastic body parts finishing kit which consists of a pre-primer treatment, a primer and coloured top coat. Full instructions are normally supplied with a kit, but basically, the method of use is to first apply the pre-primer to the component concerned, and allow it to dry for up to 30 minutes. Then the primer is applied, and left to dry for about an hour before finally applying the special-coloured top coat. The result is a correctly-coloured component, where the paint will flex with the plastic or rubber, a property that standard paint does not normally possess.

5 Major body damage - repair

Where serious damage has occurred, or large areas need renewal due to neglect, it means that complete new panels will need welding-in, and this is best left to professionals. If the damage is due to impact, it will also be necessary to check completely the alignment of the bodyshell, and this can only be carried out accurately by a Ford dealer, using special jigs. If the body is left misaligned, it is primarily dangerous, as the car will not handle properly; secondly, uneven stresses will be imposed on the steering, suspension and possibly transmission, causing abnormal wear, or complete failure, particularly to such items as the tyres.

6 Bonnet - removal, refitting and adjustment

Removal

1 Raise the bonnet and support it on its stay.
2 Using a felt tip marker pen or similar, mark around the hinge positions on the bonnet.
3 Cut the windscreen washer jet hose in the engine compartment, or release it from its one-way valve (if already fitted), then release the hose from the bonnet hinge clip (see illustration).
4 With the aid of an assistant, support the bonnet assembly and remove the four bolts securing it to its hinges. Remove the bonnet assembly, taking care to disengage the stay before the bonnet is moved.

Refitting and adjustment

5 To refit, first align the marks made on the bonnet with the hinges, then refit and fully tighten the four securing bolts. Support the bonnet on its stay.
6 Refit the windscreen washer jet hose into the bonnet hinge clip, and join it up using a one-way (non-return) valve, having ensured correct routing. Ensure that the valve is installed the correct way round, allowing flow to the jets but resisting return flow back to the reservoir.
7 Close the bonnet and ensure that there is an equal gap at each side, between the bonnet and the wings, and that it sits flush in relation to its surrounding panels.
8 The bonnet should close smoothly and positively with no excessive pressure being applied. If this is not the case, adjustment will be necessary.
9 To adjust the bonnet closure, adjustable bump stops are fitted to the closure panel (see illustration). These may be raised or lowered by screwing in or out, as necessary. The bonnet latch may also be adjusted, as required, and this is covered in Section 8 of this Chapter.

7 Bonnet release mechanism - removal and refitting

Removal

1 Remove the screws securing the lower steering column shroud to its location and, where applicable, detach the choke warning light switch/pull control assembly, from it.
2 Operate the bonnet release lever then raise and support the bonnet. If the release cable is broken, it will be necessary to detach the latch from its body location by undoing the three latch retaining screws through the gap between the leading edge of the bonnet and the radiator grille slot.
3 With the bonnet open, remove the three screws securing the latch to the body. Disengage the release cable from the latch (see illustrations).

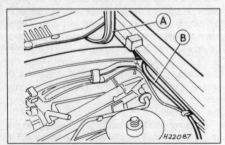

6.3 Windscreen washer jet hose in engine compartment

A Hose located to bonnet hinge clip
B Position of cut

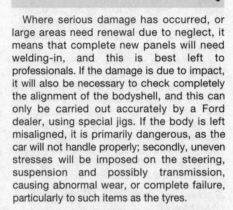

6.9 Altering the setting of a bonnet closure bump stop

7.3a Removing the bonnet release latch

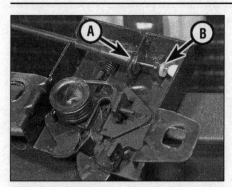

7.3b Bonnet release cable attachments at the latch

A Outer cable attachment
B Inner cable attachment

4 Pull the latch end of the cable into the engine compartment, noting cable routing and clips fitted. Remove the cable from its clips.
5 Detach the cable from its release lever on the steering column, by aligning the cable core with the slot on the release lever and withdrawing the end fixing. Detach the cable from its outer core abutment on the steering column lock housing.
6 Unclip the cable from its pedal box location, then detach the bulkhead grommet and pass the cable through into the engine compartment. Withdraw the cable from the vehicle.
7 The release lever on the steering column may be removed, if required, by unhooking the spring from its retaining arms, then disengaging its retaining arms from the steering column lock housing.

Refitting

8 Refit the release lever, if removed, by reversing the method of removal.
9 To install the release cable, first pass the latch end of the cable down the right-hand side of the steering column, through its bulkhead location, and out into the engine compartment.
10 Fit the cable to its clip on the pedal box assembly, then reconnect the cable to the release lever and the steering column lock housing abutment by reversing the method of removal.
11 Where applicable, refit the choke warning light switch/pull control assembly, to the lower

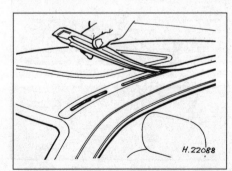

10.1 Removing a roof drip rail moulding

steering column shroud, by reversing the method of removal. Refit the shroud.
12 Seat the release cable grommet into the bulkhead.
13 Route and secure the release cable in the engine compartment.
14 Reconnect the release cable to the latch, then refit the latch to the body, setting the latch at its maximum height position, and tightening only the bottom retaining screw.
15 Adjust the latch for flush bonnet closure in accordance with Section 8.

8 Bonnet latch - adjustment

1 To adjust the bonnet latch, remove the two upper latch retaining screws, then with the latch raised to its maximum height position and secured with the lower retaining screw, close the bonnet.
2 Slacken the lower latch retaining screw, through the gap between the leading edge of the bonnet and the radiator grille slot, then set the bonnet so it sits flush with its surrounding panels - it may be necessary to adjust the height of the bump stops (see Section 6) if they have been moved in any way, or if fitting a new bonnet.
3 With the desired bonnet closure obtained, fully tighten the lower latch retaining screw, then open the bonnet and refit the two upper latch retaining screws, tightening to the specified torque.

9 Body adhesive emblems - renewal

1 Using a length of strong thin diameter cord (fishing line is ideal), break the adhesive bond between the emblem and the panel.
2 Thoroughly clean all traces of the old adhesive from the emblem location, using methylated spirit, taking all normal safety precautions. Allow the emblem location to dry.
3 Gently heat the new emblem until it is warm to the touch.

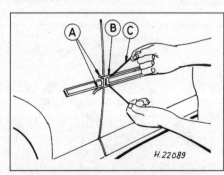

10.7 Removing a door side moulding

A Masking tape   C Nylon cord (fishing line)
B Moulding

4 Peel the protective backing paper from the emblem then, taking care not to touch the adhesive, position the emblem on the panel. Maintain hand pressure evenly for at least thirty seconds to ensure a good bond.

10 Body trim mouldings - removal and refitting

Roof drip rail moulding (all models except Courier)

Removal

1 Remove the drip rail moulding by gently raising the forward end from its retaining flange, taking care not to bend or kink it, then carefully pull it off the retaining flange **(see illustration)**.

Refitting

2 To refit the drip rail moulding, first align the rear of the moulding to the roof panel edge by the tailgate, then, using the flat palm of the hand, gently tap the moulding down.
3 If fitting the Ford roof rack, the drip rail mouldings on both sides must be removed and replaced by a ten-piece moulding kit, available from Ford dealerships.

Roof drip rail moulding (Courier models)

Removal

4 These are released by lifting and gripping the moulding's inboard edge, then by rotating the whole length of the moulding towards the outside of the vehicle to release it from its outboard lip.

Refitting

5 Refitting is the reverse of the removal procedure; ensure that the moulding's outboard edge is seated securely in its lip before pressing the inboard edge firmly into place.

Door side moulding

Removal

6 Apply masking tape, as an alignment guide and to protect the paintwork, just above and just below the moulding to be renewed.
7 Using a length of strong thin diameter cord (fishing line is ideal), break the bond between the moulding and the panel, and remove the moulding **(see illustration)**.

Refitting

8 Thoroughly clean the moulding location of any trace of old adhesive, using methylated spirit, taking all normal safety precautions. Allow the moulding location to dry.
9 Continue to proceed using a similar technique to that described in Section 9 taking care to align the moulding correctly.
10 To improve the adhesive bond, apply pressure over the whole length of the moulding using a roller.
11 Remove the masking tape carefully.

11

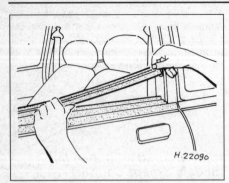

10.12 Removing a door belt weatherseal moulding

Door belt weatherseal moulding

Removal

12 Remove the exterior mirror, as described in Section 18 then, using a screwdriver, carefully prise up the moulding and remove it **(see illustration)**. Do not bend or kink the moulding, as this will permanently deform it.

Refitting

13 To refit, align the moulding to its rearward location (latch end of the door), then carefully tap it into position by hand.

14 Refit the mirror as described in Section 18.

11 Door aperture weatherstrip - removal and refitting

Removal

1 To remove, pull the weatherstrip off the door aperture flange, starting with one end of the joint and working around to the other end.

Refitting

2 To refit, roughly align the weatherstrip joint so that it lies in the centre of the bottom (sill panel) flange.

3 Loop the weatherstrip into the corners of the door aperture **(see illustration)**.

4 With all the corners roughly in position, work around the aperture from one end of the weatherstrip, pressing the seal fully home.

Ensure that it follows the contours of the corners without wrinkling, and that it sits over any interior trim edgings.

5 Seal the weatherstrip joint with a little caulking compound applied to the body flange, to prevent water entering by capillary action.

6 Check that the door closes properly, without excessive effort being required. If the door requires excessive effort to close, the door striker plate may be adjusted as necessary.

12 Sill extension moulding - removal and refitting

Removal

1 Open the door and prise out the four retaining studs from the upper surface of the moulding.

2 From underneath, drill out the five securing rivets then remove the moulding from the vehicle.

Refitting

3 To refit, first align the moulding to its location, centring it between the two wheelarch mouldings, then refit the four retaining studs to secure.

4 Insert the rivets to secure the moulding from underneath.

13 Wheelarch liners - removal and refitting

Removal

1 Chock the rear wheels then jack up the front of the car and support it on axle stands (see *"Jacking and vehicle support"*). Remove the relevant front roadwheel.

2 Release the fasteners securing the wheelarch liner in position **(see illustration)**, then remove the liner from the vehicle, manoeuvring it to clear obstructions as necessary.

Refitting

3 Refitting is a reversal of the removal procedure, tightening the roadwheel nuts to the specified torque (see Chapter 10).

14 Wheelarch mouldings - removal and refitting

Front

Removal

1 Remove the wheelarch liner, as described in Section 13.

2 From underneath the wheelarch, remove the four fixing nuts securing the upper part of the moulding.

3 Remove the plastic stud from the lower edge of the wheelarch flange.

4 Remove the forward jacking position cover from the sill extension moulding, by pulling the lower section of the cover, then using a suitably-sized drill, remove the rivet securing the rear edge of the wheelarch moulding.

5 Carefully detach the wheelarch moulding from the vehicle, sliding its rear out from under the sill extension moulding.

Refitting

6 Refitting is a reversal of the removal procedure, adjusting alignment as necessary before riveting the rear of the moulding.

Rear

Removal

7 Remove the sill extension moulding, as described in Section 12.

8 Drill out the rivet securing the forward end of the wheelarch moulding **(see illustration)**.

9 Remove the plastic stud from the lower edge of the wheelarch flange.

10 From underneath the wheelarch, remove the four fixing nuts securing the upper part of the moulding.

11 Carefully pull the wheelarch moulding away from the body, disengage it from the clamp, and remove.

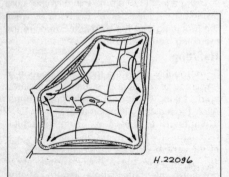

11.3 Loop the weatherstrip into the door aperture

13.2 Front wheelarch liner fixings

A Locating lug at top of wheelarch

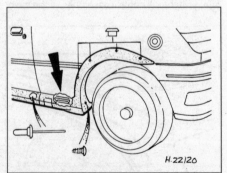

14.8 Rear wheelarch moulding fixings (clamp cutaway arrowed)

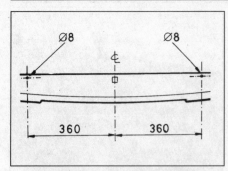

15.2 Radiator grille slot fixing holes required on service replacement bumpers (dimensions given in mm - see text)

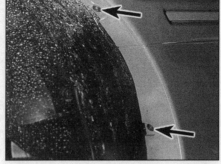

16.2 Front bumper-to-wheelarch retaining screws (arrowed)

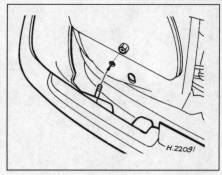

16.3 Front bumper retaining nut location

Refitting

12 To refit, engage the wheelarch moulding into the clamp, align the moulding studs with their wheelarch locations, then position the moulding onto the wheelarch. Refit the four fixing nuts to secure the upper part of the moulding, but do not fully tighten.
13 Refit the plastic stud, but do not fully tighten.
14 Offer the sill extension moulding to its location, centring it between the front and rear wheelarches to check the rear wheelarch moulding alignment. Adjust the alignment as necessary.
15 With the rear wheelarch moulding alignment correct, fully tighten the fixing nuts and the plastic stud.
16 Insert the rivet to secure the forward end of the moulding.
17 Refit the sill extension moulding, as described in Section 12.

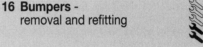

15 Wind deflector/radiator grille slat - removal and refitting

Removal

1 The radiator grille slat is secured to the front bumper by three clips. To remove it, simply slide the clips rearwards to release them, then withdraw the grille slat from its bumper locating holes.
2 If fitting a radiator grille slat to a service

replacement bumper, two 8.0 mm diameter holes will need to be drilled to accommodate the grille slat end fixings and, in addition, a 12.0 mm square central hole must also be made **(see illustration)**.

Refitting

3 Refitting is a reversal of the removal procedure.

16 Bumpers - removal and refitting

Front bumper

Removal

1 Open the bonnet and disconnect the auxiliary light multi-plugs, as applicable.
2 Remove the bumper retaining screws from the leading edge of the wheelarch flanges, then ease the bumper away from its wheelarch location **(see illustration)**.
3 Remove the bumper retaining nuts from the reverse side of the body panel beneath the headlights **(see illustration)** then, with the help of an assistant, remove the bumper assembly from the vehicle.

Refitting

4 To refit, (again with assistance) position the bumper onto its panel, ensuring that the retaining studs pass through their body

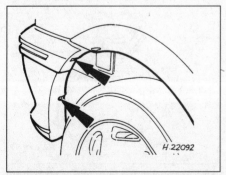

16.11 Rear bumper-to-wheelarch retaining screws (arrowed)

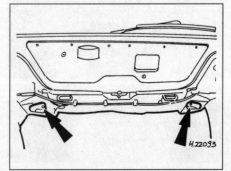

16.12 Rear bumper retaining nut locations (arrowed)

locations, and that its ends align to the wheelarches.
5 Loosely refit the bumper retaining nuts and the bumper-to-wheelarch retaining screws.
6 Ensuring that the bumper is level, and that an even gap is maintained between it and surrounding body panels, tighten the retaining nuts to the specified torque.
7 Tighten the bumper to wheelarch retaining screws.
8 Refit the auxiliary light multi-plugs, as applicable.
9 The alignment of light units requires the use of optical beam setting equipment so, where applicable, entrust this task to a Ford dealer.

Rear bumper (all models except Courier)

Removal

10 Using a screwdriver or similar tool, prise up the number plate light unit from the rear bumper, being careful not to damage the bumper. Disconnect the bulbholder and remove from the bumper.
11 Remove the bumper-to-wheelarch retaining screws as necessary **(see illustration)**.
12 Open the tailgate then, using a suitably-sized socket, remove the bumper retaining nuts located inside the luggage compartment **(see illustration)**.
13 Carefully remove the bumper from its location.

Refitting

14 To refit, first align the bumper to the vehicle body, ensuring that the ends engage correctly at the wheelarches and the securing studs enter through the body panel.
15 Refit the bumper-to-wheelarch inner rim retaining screws, as applicable.
16 Refit the bumper retaining nuts, tightening to the specified torque.
17 Reconnect the number plate light bulbholder, then refit the light unit to the bumper.

Rear bumper (Courier models)

Removal

18 Unscrew the two screws securing each bumper end moulding to its respective wheel

11

16.18 Courier rear bumper mounting screws (arrowed) at wheel arch - note also bumper mounting bracket bolts (arrowed) visible under rear of vehicle

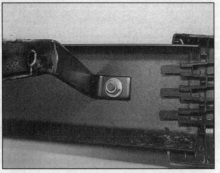

16.19a Courier rear bumper removed, showing mounting bracket retaining nut and end moulding clips . . .

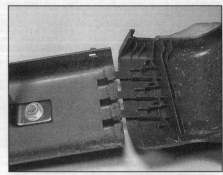

16.19b . . . Courier rear bumper end moulding unclipped

arch, then remove the two bolts securing each bumper mounting bracket to the rear underside of the vehicle (see illustration). Withdraw the bumper.

19 The mounting brackets can be unbolted, if required, from the bumper. The end mouldings can be unclipped for renewal separately (see illustrations).

Refitting

20 Refitting is the reverse of the removal procedure.

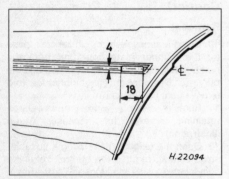

17.4 Bumper moulding slot required on service replacement bumpers (dimensions given in mm)

17 Bumper and rear quarter mouldings - renewal

Bumper mouldings

1 With the bumper removed as described in Section 16, place it on a clean flat surface, then remove the clips from the moulding ends.

2 Prise up and remove the old moulding from its bumper recess.

3 Remove all trace of old adhesive from the bumper recess, using methylated spirit, taking all normal safety precautions. Allow the recess to dry.

4 If fitting a new moulding to a service replacement bumper, slots must be cut into the bumper to accommodate the moulding end fixings (see illustration).

5 Apply adhesive primer (available from Ford dealers) to the recess, and allow it to dry.

6 Gently heat the moulding until it is warm to the touch, then insert the first moulding end clip into the bumper and press the moulding to its recess, secured with its moulding end, peeling the protective backing paper off as it is applied.

7 Apply the moulding smoothly and carefully across the bumper, rolling into its recess

using a plastic roller or similar tool, then, when the other end is reached, secure with the other moulding end and clip.

Rear quarter mouldings (Courier models)

8 Remove the rear bumper as described in Section 16.

9 Each moulding is secured by two screws at its forward edge, in the wheel arch, and by a single screw at the rear (see illustrations). Remove the screws and withdraw the moulding, unclipping it at its front end.

10 Refitting is the reverse of the removal procedure.

18 Exterior mirror and glass - removal and refitting

Mirror glass

Removal

1 Insert a thin flat-headed screwdriver behind the mirror glass, at the upper outermost corner, then carefully lever the glass assembly forward to disconnect the outer pivot (see illustration).

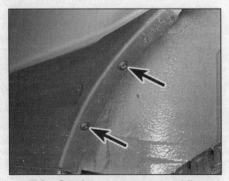

17.9a Courier rear quarter moulding mounting screws (arrowed) in wheel arch . . .

17.9b . . . and at rear of vehicle

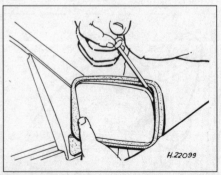

18.1 Removing the door mirror glass from the mirror housing

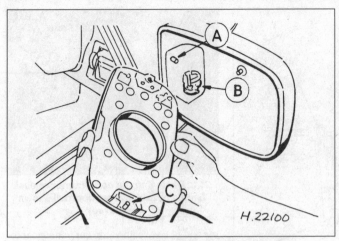

18.2 Mirror glass connections within mirror housing

A Inner pivot   *B Operating link*   *C Outer pivot*

18.6 Lift the retaining clip, then pull the door mirror operating knob from its shaft

2 Disengage the inner pivot then, using a screwdriver, disconnect the operating link to allow the glass assembly to be withdrawn **(see illustration)**.

Refitting

3 To refit, first reconnect the operating link and engage the inner pivot.
4 Align the outer pivot in the mirror housing, then push the glass assembly carefully into position so that the outer pivot engages fully.

Mirror assembly

Removal

5 Remove the door inner trim panel as described in Section 21.
6 Remove the door mirror operating knob by lifting its retaining clip, using a small screwdriver, then pulling it from its shaft **(see illustration)**.
7 Remove the mirror trim retaining screw, then ease the mirror trim out from its forward lug location and slide it out towards the rear of the vehicle, to clear its rearward fixings **(see illustration)**.
8 Remove the three mirror retaining screws, and manoeuvre the mirror from the door **(see illustration)**.

Refitting

9 Refitting is the reverse sequence to removal.

19 Interior mirror -
removal and refitting

Removal

1 Using a length of strong thin cord or fishing line, break the adhesive bond between the mirror base and the windscreen, then remove the mirror from the vehicle.
2 During installation, it is important to note that the mirror base, windscreen black patch and the adhesive patch should not be touched, other than for cleaning, or the adhesive bond may be adversely affected.
3 Remove all traces of old adhesive from the mirror base, using a lint-free cloth and methylated spirit, taking all normal safety precautions. Allow the mirror base to dry.
4 Clean the windscreen black patch in a similar manner.

Refitting

5 Note that, before installing the mirror, the vehicle should have been in an ambient temperature of approximately 20°C for at least an hour.
6 With the contact surfaces scrupulously clean, remove the protective tape from one side of the adhesive patch and press firmly into contact with the mirror base.
7 Note that when fitting a mirror to a new windscreen, the protective tape must be removed from the windscreen black patch.
8 Warm the mirror base and adhesive patch for about thirty seconds, to a temperature of 50 to 70°C.
9 Remove the protective tape from the other side of the adhesive patch on the mirror base, then align the mirror base and windscreen black patch accurately, and firmly press the mirror base into position. Hold the mirror base firmly in position for at least two minutes.
10 Wait at least thirty minutes before adjusting the mirror.

20 Side doors -
removal and refitting

Removal

1 Open the door and detach the door aperture weatherseal from around the hinge area.
2 Remove the screw securing the door check arm to the body.
3 Squeeze the ears together on the electrical multi-plug and withdraw it from its body location on the A-pillar, as applicable. Disconnect the multi-plug.
4 Using a screwdriver, remove the door hinge pin retaining clips from the top of both hinges, by levering them off.
5 Ford dealers use a special tool for removing door hinge pins. If this is not available, it is possible to fabricate an alternative. Engage

11

18.7 Removing the mirror trim retaining screw

18.8 Removing the three mirror retaining screws (arrowed)

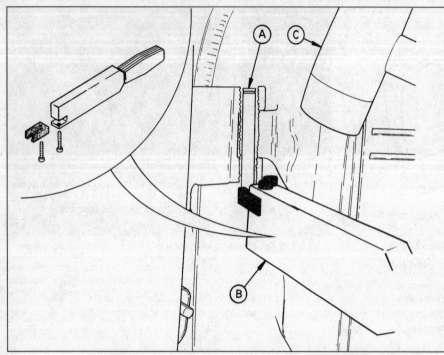

20.5 Door hinge pin removal using Ford special tools

A Hinge pin   B Removal tool   C Soft-faced hammer

21.2 Removing the door interior release handle bezel (armrest/doorpull shown removed)

the special tool **(see illustration)**, then strike the main body of the tool with a soft-faced hammer to extract the lower hinge pin from its location.

6 With the help of an assistant to support the door, remove the upper hinge pin from its location, in a similar manner to that used for the lower hinge pin, and then remove the door assembly.

Refitting

7 To refit, align the door hinge sections to the hinge sections on the body, and insert both hinge pins as far as possible, by hand. Ensuring that the hinge pins have entered all three sections of hinge, tap them gently through, with a soft-faced hammer, until their retaining clips can be fitted. New retaining clips should be used.

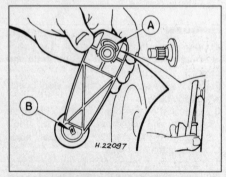

21.3 Window regulator handle. Inset shows removal

A Spring clip
B Rotate the tag to remove the knob

8 Reconnect the multi-plug and insert it to its body location on the A- pillar, ensuring that it seats correctly.

9 Refit the door check arm to its body location. Press the door aperture weatherseal back into position on its flange.

10 There should be no need to adjust the door striker, or check door alignment.

21 Side door inner trim panel - removal and refitting

Removal

1 Using a screwdriver with a broad flat blade, carefully prise up and remove the interior weatherstrip from its location at the top of the door trim panel. Be careful not to kink or bend it as it is being removed. On front doors, pull

the end of the weatherstrip out from under the door mirror trim.

2 Detach the door interior release handle bezel by removing its retaining screw **(see illustration)**.

3 Using a small thin screwdriver, release the window regulator handle (where fitted) by releasing its spring clip from behind and pulling it from the regulator shaft **(see illustration)**. Remove its bezel also. On models with electric front window switches in the door trim panel, disconnect the switch wiring multi-plugs as the trim panel is withdrawn.

4 Detach the armrest/doorpull assembly from the door. Some models are fitted with an armrest/doorpull secured by three screws, two of which are concealed behind a removable panel. Certain lower specification vehicles have the door pull secured with only two screws. **(see illustrations)**

5 On front doors, remove the three screws securing the door stowage pocket/speaker grille moulding, then pull the moulding upper edge away from the door, and disengage the hook fixings on its base from their locations **(see illustration)**.

6 Using a trim clip tool, release the retaining clips around the base and the sides of the panel, then raise it to free it from the door. If a trim clip tool is unavailable, two thin flat-bladed screwdrivers carefully inserted between the trim panel and the door may suffice. Place the screwdrivers on each side of the clips and then apply gentle leverage.

21.4a Detaching armrest/doorpull removable panel

21.4b Undoing armrest/doorpull retaining screws

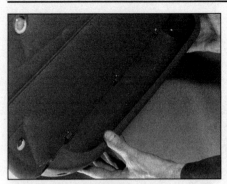

21.5 Disengaging the hook fixings on the base of the door stowage pocket/speaker grille moulding

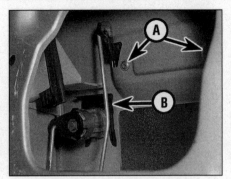

22.4a Door exterior handle and lock barrel securing arrangements (front door)

A   Handle screw locations
B   Lock barrel retaining clip

22.4b Removing the door exterior handle, guiding its operating rod out through the door skin (front door)

Refitting

7 To refit, first align the trim panel to the door, secure its upper edge into its hook fastenings, then press into position to engage the trim clips. Where electric window switches are fitted, reconnect the switch wiring multi-plugs before fitting the panel.

8 If necessary, refit the clip to the window regulator handle, then refit the handle to the regulator shaft by pushing it on. The clip should engage positively, in the annular groove on the shaft.

9 Refit the door stowage pocket/speaker grille moulding, armrest/doorpull and door interior release handle bezel, as applicable, by reversing the method of removal.

10 Refit the interior weatherstrip to its location, tapping it down into position, being careful not to bend or kink it. On front doors, it will be necessary to slide its forward edge under the door mirror trim before tapping into position.

---

22 Side door lock, lock cylinder and handles - removal and refitting

Exterior handle

Removal

1 Remove the door inner trim panel, as described in Section 21.

2 Locally detach the PVC sheet from the door to allow access into the door cavity. Do not tear the sheet; cut closely around the clips, as required.

3 Disconnect the handle operating rod from the latch assembly, by twisting the clip and withdrawing the rod, as applicable.

4 Remove the two screws securing the handle then, from the outside, withdraw the handle and rod, guiding the rod out through the door skin as necessary **(see illustrations)**. The handle and rod may be disconnected as required.

Refitting

5 Refitting is a reversal of the removal procedure. On completion, re-secure the PVC sheet then refit the inner trim panel as described in Section 21.

Door lock barrel

Removal

6 Remove the door inner trim panel, as described in Section 21.

7 Locally detach the PVC sheet from the door to allow access into the door cavity. Do not tear the sheet; cut closely around the clips, as required.

8 Drill out the rivets securing the door glass guide above the lock barrel, and remove it.

9 Disconnect the lock barrel operating rod from the latch assembly, by twisting the clip and withdrawing the rod.

10 Release the lock barrel retaining clip by withdrawing it upwards, then from the outside, withdraw the lock barrel and rod, guiding the rod out through the door skin. The lock barrel and rod may be disconnected as required.

Refitting

11 Refitting is a reversal of the removal procedure. Ensure that the lock barrel gasket is located correctly between the lock barrel outer surround and the door skin, and that the

door glass guide is riveted securely. Check that the window operates smoothly and correctly, by temporarily refitting the regulator handle or operating the electric window motor.

12 On completion, re-secure the PVC sheet then refit the inner trim panel as described in Section 21.

Door latch and interior release handle

Removal

13 Remove the door inner trim panel, as described in Section 21.

14 Locally detach the PVC sheet from the door to allow access into the door cavity. Do not tear the sheet; cut closely around the clips, as required.

15 On rear doors fitted with central locking, undo the two screws securing the rod guard and remove it **(see illustration)**.

16 Disconnect the operating rods from the latch assembly as necessary. On rear doors with central locking, disconnect and release the motor loom multi-plug assembly, and withdraw the motor side of the loom back into the door cavity. Undo the three screws securing the motor assembly, disengage its operating rod and remove it from the vehicle **(see illustration)**.

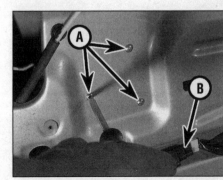

22.15 Rod guard securing screws (arrowed) on rear doors with central locking only

22.16 Central locking motor retaining screws (A), and loom multi-plug assembly (B) on rear door

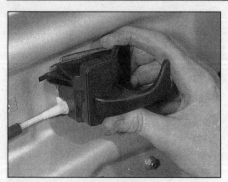

22.18 Detaching the interior door release handle

22.20 Removing the latch securing screws (arrowed)

17 On front doors, vehicles fitted with central locking have a latch with an integral motor. If central locking is fitted, prise up and twist the rearward clips securing the motor loom to the door, to free the loom, disconnect the multi-plugs and withdraw the loom (motor side) back into the door cavity.
18 Remove the interior release handle surround, then prise up the forward end of the handle unit. Release the handle from its rearward location by sliding it forward to disengage the hooks **(see illustration)**.
19 Detach the door interior release cable from its retaining clips on the door panel.
20 Remove the latch securing screws from the upper rear edge of the door, and withdraw the latch and interior release mechanism from the vehicle **(see illustration)**.
21 Remove the cable cover from the latch assembly, then detach the cable from the latch.
22 Peel the sponge pad from the reverse side of the interior release handle, and remove the outer cable from its abutment in the body of the handle. Remove the inner cable core by aligning the core with the slot by its end fixing, then slide the end fixing out.

Refitting

23 Refitting is a reversal of the removal procedure. On completion, re-secure the PVC sheet then refit the inner trim panel as described in Section 21.

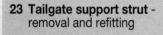

23 Tailgate support strut - removal and refitting

Removal

1 Open the tailgate and support it securely, using a length of timber, or have an assistant hold it open.
2 Detach the support strut by raising the retaining clip and pulling the strut away from its ball stud fixing on the tailgate. Do not raise the clip more than 4.0 mm, or the support strut will be damaged.
3 Repeat the operation on the other end of the support strut.

Refitting

4 To refit, align the thicker (cylinder) end of the support strut to the ball stud fixing on the tailgate, then push until it snaps into engagement.
5 Repeat the operation with the thinner (piston) end of the support strut to the ball stud fixing on the body.

24 Tailgate - removal and refitting

Removal

1 Open the tailgate and mark around the hinge positions on the tailgate panel itself.
2 Remove the central blanking plug from the upper portion of the tailgate to expose the washer jet, and disconnect the washer hose from the jet base, as applicable. Free the washer hose grommet and withdraw the hose from the tailgate.
3 Disconnect the support strut from the tailgate, as described in Section 23.
4 With the aid of an assistant, undo the four bolts securing the tailgate to the vehicle body and remove the tailgate.

Refitting

5 To refit, align the hinges on the body with the marks made on the tailgate panel, then refit and tighten the four bolts to secure. Refit the support strut as described in Section 23.
6 The remainder of the refitting operation is a reversal of the removal procedure.
7 Close the tailgate and check the alignment. Adjust as necessary to obtain an even gap between the tailgate and all adjacent panels.

25 Tailgate spoiler - removal and refitting

Removal

1 Drill out the rivets securing the outer edges of the spoiler to the tailgate.

2 Open the tailgate and remove the four blanking plugs covering the spoiler retaining nuts. Undo the nuts and remove the spoiler.

Refitting

3 To refit, first align the spoiler mounting studs to their tailgate fixing holes, then rivet the outer edges of the spoiler to the tailgate.
4 Refit the four retaining nuts and tighten to the specified torque.
5 Refit the blanking plugs.

26 Tailgate inner trim panel - removal and refitting

Removal

1 Open the tailgate then, using a screwdriver, remove the seven plastic retaining screws from the trim panel.
2 Remove the square plastic clip from the trim panel.
3 Disengage the clips from the panel edge nearest the window, and manoeuvre the panel to release the hooks on the other panel edge. Withdraw the trim panel from the vehicle.

Refitting

4 Refitting is a reversal of removal.

27 Tailgate lock components - removal and refitting

Note: *For vehicles equipped with remote tailgate release, removal and refitting procedures for the tailgate remote release motor are contained in Chapter 12.*

Removal

1 Remove the tailgate inner trim panel as described in Section 26.
2 Remove the two Torx screws securing the tailgate latch, then pull it down, disconnect its operating rod and remove the latch from the vehicle **(see illustration)**.
3 Remove the bolt securing the lock barrel

27.2 Tailgate latch and its Torx securing screws (arrowed)

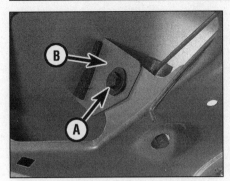

27.3 Tailgate lock retention arrangement

A Lock barrel retainer securing bolt
B Lock barrel retainer

retainer to the tailgate, then withdraw the retainer (see illustration).
4 Remove the lock assembly from the tailgate by partially withdrawing the lock, twisting it so that the lock rod can be removed, then fully withdrawing.

Refitting

5 To refit, first ensure that the lock gasket is in position, then partially insert the lock into the tailgate and reconnect the lock rod. Fully insert the lock and refit its retainer and securing bolt.
6 Using an electrician's thin screwdriver, prise up the lever on the latch and fit the lock rod to it, ensuring that it fully engages.
7 Align the latch with its location and refit its two securing screws.
8 Check for correct lock operation before refitting the tailgate interior trim panel as described in Section 26.

28 Rear doors (Courier models) - removal and refitting

Removal

1 Open the door and disconnect the wiring leading to it; all connectors are accessible from the openings inside the door frame.

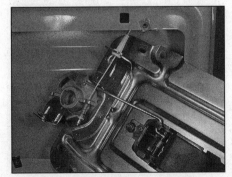

30.2b Latch assembly released - disconnect cables to withdraw

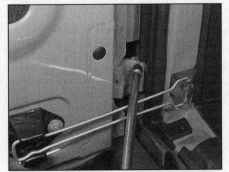

28.2 Unscrewing the bottom hinge's cap securing bolt on Courier rear door

2 Unclip the door check arm, and unscrew the bottom hinge's cap securing bolt (see illustration).
3 Lift the door off its hinges and withdraw it.

Refitting

4 Refitting is the reverse of the removal procedure; apply grease to the hinge pins, and tighten the cap bolt securely.
5 The door hinges can be unbolted from the door and frame; either remove the door first, or support it carefully and remove the hinge with it in place.

29 Rear door inner trim panels (Courier models) - removal and refitting

Removal

1 Remove the interior handle bezel by pushing it away from the door's hinges until it can be withdrawn.
2 Using either a trim clip releasing tool or a screwdriver with a broad flat blade, and protecting the paintwork and trim with a layer of rag, extract the clips securing the panel and withdraw it.

Refitting

3 Refitting is the reverse of the removal procedure.

30.7a Release locking ring and withdraw gaskets . . .

30.2a Courier rear door latch assembly retaining screws (arrowed)

30 Rear door lock, catches and handles (Courier models) - removal and refitting

Interior handle

Removal

1 Remove the inner trim panel, as described in Section 29.
2 Remove its four retaining screws, and withdraw the complete latch assembly (see illustrations).
3 Disconnect the link rod and remove the single retaining screw to withdraw the interior handle.

Refitting

4 Refitting is the reverse of the removal procedure.

Exterior handle and lock assembly

Removal

5 Remove the inner trim panel, as described in Section 29.
6 Remove its four retaining screws, and withdraw the complete latch assembly.
7 Using pliers, rotate the exterior handle locking ring anti-clockwise to release it, then withdraw the handle with the inner and outer gaskets (see illustrations).
8 The lock assembly is secured by a circlip to the handle.

30.7b . . . to release Courier rear door exterior handle

11

30.12 Courier rear door lower catch removal

Refitting

9 Refitting is the reverse of the removal procedure.

Upper and lower door catches

Removal

10 Remove the inner trim panel, as described in Section 29.
11 Remove its four retaining screws, and withdraw the complete latch assembly. Disconnect the upper and lower catch cables

from the latch assembly operating mechanism.
12 Unbolt the catch and withdraw it from the door **(see illustration)**. If the cables are available separately (seek the advice of a Ford dealer) they can be disconnected from each catch by releasing the retaining clip.

Refitting

13 Refitting is the reverse of the removal procedure; check the adjustment of the catch before finally tightening the bolts.
14 The striker plates can be adjusted on their slotted mounting bolt locations, if required.

---

31 Door window regulator - removal and refitting

Manual front regulator

Removal

1 Remove the door inner trim panel, as described in Section 21.
2 Locally detach the PVC sheet from the door to allow access into the door cavity. Do not

tear the sheet; cut closely around the clips, as required.
3 Remove the door window glass, as described in Section 32.
4 Drill the heads off the regulator securing rivets and manoeuvre the regulator assembly from the door **(see illustration)**. Lay the regulator body in the bottom of the door, then withdraw the gear mechanism and cable followed by the rigid "pillar".

Refitting

5 Refit the regulator by reversing the method of removal, ensuring that it is securely riveted to the door.
6 Refit the door window glass, as described in Section 32.
7 Re-secure the PVC sheet then refit the door inner trim panel as described in Section 21.

Electric front regulator

Removal

Note: *For motor removal and refitting procedure, refer to Chapter 12.*
8 Remove the door inner trim panel, as described in Section 21.
9 Locally detach the PVC sheet from the door to allow access into the door cavity. Do not tear the sheet; cut closely around the clips, as required.
10 Remove the door window glass, as described in Section 32.
11 Disconnect the multi-plug on the regulator motor body, and remove the three nuts securing the motor/winding mechanism section of the assembly to the door.
12 Drill the heads off the regulator securing rivets and manoeuvre the regulator assembly from the door. Lay the regulator body in the bottom of the door, then withdraw the gear mechanism and cable followed by the rigid "pillar".

Refitting

13 To refit, first position the regulator assembly in the door, and refit the three nuts securing the motor/winding mechanism section.
14 Re-rivet the pillar section of the regulator assembly securely to door.
15 Reconnect the multi-plug to the regulator motor body.
16 Refit the door window glass, as described in Section 32.
17 Re-secure the PVC sheet then refit the door inner trim panel as described in Section 21.

Rear regulator

Removal

18 Remove the door inner trim panel, as described in Section 21.
19 Locally detach the PVC sheet from the door to allow access into the door cavity. Do not tear the sheet; cut closely around the clips, as required.
20 Drill the heads off the four regulator securing rivets, and remove the two lower

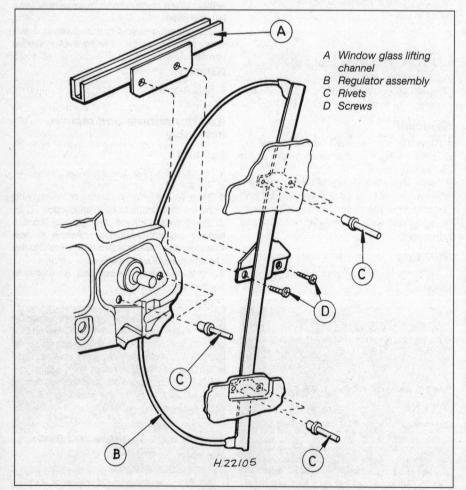

A *Window glass lifting channel*
B *Regulator assembly*
C *Rivets*
D *Screws*

H.22105

31.4 Window regulator assembly (manual, front)

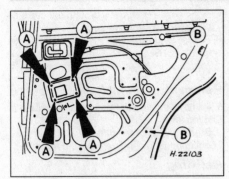

31.20 Regulator retaining rivets (A) and lower window glass guide securing screws (B) on rear door

window glass guide securing screws **(see illustration)**.

21 Support the window glass then, having pushed the regulator into the door cavity, disconnect the regulator arm from it. Remove the regulator assembly.

Refitting

22 Refitting is a reversal of the removal procedure, ensuring that the window regulator is securely riveted to the door. Check the operation of the window regulator, by temporarily refitting the regulator handle and, if necessary, adjust the window glass guide to ensure that the window glass does not stick or judder.

23 Re-secure the PVC sheet then refit the door inner trim panel as described in Section 21.

32 Door window glass - removal and refitting

Front side door glass

Removal

1 Remove the door inner trim panel, as described in Section 21.

2 Locally detach the PVC sheet from the door to allow access into the door cavity. Do not tear the sheet; cut closely around the clips, as required.

3 Remove the door belt weatherseal moulding as described in Section 10.

4 Remove the two screws securing the window glass lifting channel to the regulator assembly, through either their upper or lower access holes. Support the glass as the screws are removed.

5 Remove the window glass by tilting it forwards towards the hinge end of the door, then withdraw it towards the latch end.

Refitting

6 To refit, position the window glass into the door by reversing the method of removal.

7 Loosely refit the two screws to hold the window glass lifting channel to the regulator

assembly, but do not tighten them at this stage.

8 Raise the window glass fully, then tighten the retaining screws through their upper access holes. This ensures correct positioning of the window glass in its aperture.

9 Refit the door belt weatherseal moulding as described in Section 10.

10 Re-secure the PVC sheet then refit the door inner trim panel as described in Section 21.

Rear side door sliding glass

Removal

11 Remove the door window regulator, as described in Section 31, then fully lower the window glass into the door.

12 Remove the door belt weatherseal mouldings in a similar manner to that described in Section 10.

13 Remove the remaining two window glass guide securing screws from their location at the top of the door, and disengage the top of the guide.

14 Manoeuvre the fixed rear quarter window glass forwards and out from its location, along with the window glass guide. Lift out the plastic strip.

15 Manoeuvre the door window glass up and out of the door, from the exterior side of the door.

Refitting

16 Refitting is a reversal of the removal procedure, ensuring that the fixed rear quarter window seats correctly in its location, and that the window glass guide holds the window glass correctly (refer to Section 31).

Rear side door fixed quarter glass

17 The fixed rear quarter window glass is removed and refitted in conjunction with the rear side door sliding glass described previously in this Section.

Rear door glass (Courier models)

18 The rear door window glass on Courier models is removed and refitted using the same technique as for the fixed side window glass described in Section 33.

33 Side window glass - removal and refitting

Fixed side window glass

Removal

1 The lip of the weatherseal surrounding the window glass must be released from the top and sides of the body aperture flange, using a suitable tool, before exerting pressure from the inside of the vehicle to remove the glass. Any surrounding interior trim should be removed. It is important that an assistant

helps and holds the glass from the outside as it is pressed out from the inside.

2 With the assembly removed from the vehicle, detach the weatherseal from the window glass.

3 If the weatherseal is to be re-used it should be cleaned. Do not use petrol, white spirit or other similar substances, as they may cause rapid rubber deterioration. Ensure that the glass groove in the weatherseal is free from any sealant or glass fragments.

4 Ensure that the body aperture flange is free from any sealant also.

Refitting

5 Commence refitting by attaching the weatherseal to the window glass, ensuring that it is seated correctly.

6 Insert a length of nylon or terylene cord into the body aperture flange groove of the weatherseal, so that the cord ends emerge at the top centre of the window, and overlap by approximately 150.0 mm.

7 Offer the assembly to the body aperture, and engage the lower lips of the weatherseal over the body aperture flange. Ensure that the engagement of the weatherseal lips is not hampered in any way, and that the cord ends are protruding inside the vehicle.

8 With an assistant applying a gentle even pressure on the window glass from the outside, pull one end of the cord at right-angles to the glass. This will pull the inner lip of the weatherseal over the body aperture flange.

9 When the cord has been pulled halfway around the aperture, repeat the procedure with the other end of the cord. The cord should release when the window glass is fully fitted.

10 Refit any disturbed interior trim as necessary.

Hinged side window glass

Removal

11 With an assistant standing outside ready to take the window, unscrew the single screw securing each hinge, then open the window and unscrew the two screws securing the catch to the body. Withdraw the window.

12 The weatherstrip can now be removed and refitted, if required.

Refitting

13 To refit the window, have your assistant stand outside and offer up the window so that both hinge leaves enter their sockets, then loosely refit the catch securing screws. Refit the hinge securing screws, then adjust the catch position to ensure that the window is clamped evenly on to the weatherstrip over the whole mating surface when the catch is fastened. Tighten all screws securely.

Sliding side window and glass

Removal

14 To remove the complete sliding window assembly on Courier Kombi models requires special cutting equipment and supplies of

11

suitable adhesive; it is recommended that this task be left to a Ford dealer or similar expert.

15 To remove the window glass, remove their retaining screws and withdraw the lock assemblies, slide the front glass as far to the rear as possible, then prise up and withdraw the front glass guide; it will be necessary to pull the last part of the guide from under the glass.

16 Withdraw the vertical seal and two support blocks from between the two glasses, slide the seal to the front of the frame, and withdraw it. Slide each glass in turn to the front of the frame and withdraw it, then prise up and withdraw the rear glass guide.

Refitting

17 On refitting, check that the glass guides are undamaged; renew them if necessary. Ensure that the lock assemblies are removed from both glasses.

18 Press the rear glass guide into place. Refit first the rear glass, fitting it to the front of the frame and sliding it to the rear, then the front glass, in the same way.

19 To refit the vertical seal, sandwich it between two strips of thin sheet metal and install it, with its support blocks, first in the front part of the frame, then push it into place. This will require some effort as the glass is reached, due to the distortion caused by the location notch on the block. When the seal is fully in place, withdraw the metal strips, and check that the seal's lips have not folded back on themselves.

20 When refitting the front glass guide, locate it first around the frame's detent catch, then slide it under the glass using soapy water as a lubricant.

21 Refit the lock assemblies, clean the glasses, and check the operation of the windows and locks.

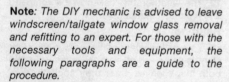

34 Windscreen and tailgate window glass - removal and refitting

Note: *The DIY mechanic is advised to leave windscreen/tailgate window glass removal and refitting to an expert. For those with the necessary tools and equipment, the following paragraphs are a guide to the procedure.*

Removal

1 Remove the windscreen/tailgate wiper arms as described in Chapter 12.

2 If removing the windscreen, remove both A-pillar trims, and release the front of the headlining by removing the sun visors and courtesy light. If a heated windscreen is fitted, disconnect its electrical contacts at the windscreen. If removing the tailgate window glass, disconnect the wiring to the heating element.

3 As a precautionary measure to prevent damage to the paintwork, cover the surrounding bodywork with an old blanket or similar.

4 Using a suitable tool, release the weatherseal from the top and sides of the body aperture flange before exerting pressure from the inside of the vehicle to remove the assembly. It is strongly advised that an assistant outside the vehicle is ready to receive the glass as it is pushed out.

5 With the assembly removed from the vehicle, detach the weatherseal from the windscreen/tailgate glass.

Refitting

6 With reference to the procedures described for the fixed side window glass in Section 33, clean the weatherseal, then refit in accordance with the rest of that Section.

7 Any trim and equipment removed during preparation should now be refitted.

35 Sunroof panel - removal and refitting

Removal

1 Open the sunroof fully using the handwheel.

2 Detach the sunroof from its rearward mounting point by pressing in the red locking bar on the handwheel, then raise it and remove.

Refitting

3 To refit, engage the hinges in their locations, in the forward edge of the sunroof opening, then lower the sunroof. Allow the handwheel to click into its safety lock.

4 Check that the safety lock mechanism retains the panel securely.

5 Close the sunroof fully using the handwheel.

36 Sunroof panel seal - renewal

1 Remove the sunroof panel, as described in Section 35, then lay the panel on a soft cloth.

2 Remove the two hinge plate assemblies from the panel by undoing the hinge plate retaining screws.

3 Pull the seal from the panel edge, noting the position of its join.

4 Starting from the position of the original join, press the seal into position, ensuring that it sits evenly right around. Adjust as necessary so that the ends butt tightly together.

5 Refit the two hinge plate assemblies to the panel.

6 Refit the sunroof panel, as described in Section 35.

37 Sunroof weatherseal - removal and refitting

Removal

1 Remove the sunroof panel, as described in Section 35.

2 Starting from the joint on the rearward opening edge, pull the seal up and remove.

Refitting

3 Refitting is a reversal of the removal procedure, ensuring that the weatherseal does not deform at the corners, or split at the joint.

38 Full-length sunroof - general information

1 The full-length sunroof is electrically-operated, the operating system consisting of the motor and the roof-mounted switch. The circuit is fed via fuses 18 and 28 from the ignition switch; switch illumination is via fuse 6.

2 All components are mounted in the roof of the passenger compartment, above the headlining at the front of the vehicle.

3 To open the sunroof, press the switch lightly on the upper side; to close it, check first that the opening is completely unobstructed, and press the switch on the lower side.

4 Maintenance is confined to checking for freedom of action and a snug fit when shut. Check that the seals are in good clean condition and not scratched or damaged.

5 Owners must note the following to ensure that the maximum trouble-free life from this feature:

a) *It is normal for the motor to slow down as the sunroof approaches full opening.*

b) *If the sunroof stops before it is fully opened in cold weather, this may be due to the material being too hard to fold correctly; do not force the sunroof open if this is suspected.*

c) *If the material does not fold correctly on opening at any time, close the sunroof again, correct the folds by hand, and try again.*

d) *Never open or close the sunroof with the vehicle travelling at more than 70 mph (120 km/h), and never allow passengers to travel standing up or with any part of their bodies in the opening.*

e) *Ensure that any collected water, snow or ice is removed from the sunroof before opening it. Check that the deflector is clear of water, particularly after washing the vehicle; sponge it dry if necessary.*

f) *Never place heavy objects on the sunroof or its surrounds.*

g) *The sunroof should be cleaned frequently*

to avoid the material being stained by dirt. Use a sponge, soft brush or soft cloth and a neutral detergent, rinsing with a gentle flow of clean water from directly above until all traces of dirt and detergent are removed. **Never** use a high-pressure jet, pressure washer or similar, and do not aim the jet from a hose at the joints of the sunroof with the body (or water will enter the passenger compartment). **Never** use alcohol, petrol, thinners or similar products to clean the material.

h) If the vehicle is parked in heavy rain, or if it is parked outside for long periods, a proprietary car cover or tarpaulin should be used to protect the roof and body. **Do not** leave the sunroof open for long periods; the material will stiffen in its folds, with a consequent risk of tearing when the sunroof is eventually operated again.

6 If the system fails with the sunroof open, it can be closed in emergency by switching off the ignition, prising out the access plug in front of the switch, and using the crank provided to rotate the motor shaft clockwise until the roof is closed.

7 If the switch is thought to be at fault, it can be removed after first disconnecting the battery negative (earth) lead (refer to Chapter 5, Section 1) ; the switch can then be eased from its housing until the wires can be disconnected. Refitting is the reverse of the removal procedure.

8 If any other failure or problem is encountered, the general inaccessibility of the system's components means that servicing and fault-finding is beyond the capabilities of most owners; the vehicle should be taken to a Ford dealer for attention.

39 Front seat and slide assembly - removal and refitting

Removal

 Warning: On vehicles fitted with mechanical seat belt pre-tensioning stalks, be careful when handling the seat, as the tensioning device ("grabber") contains a powerful spring, which could cause injury if released in an uncontrolled fashion. The tensioning mechanism should be immobilised by inserting a safety "transit clip" available from Ford parts stockists. You are strongly advised to seek the advice of a Ford dealer as to the correct use of the "transit clip" and the safety implications before proceeding.

1 On pre-1994 models, slide the seat fully rearwards to expose the two front slide assembly to floorpan bolts. Remove all four bolts securing the slides to the floorpan, and remove the seat from the vehicle.

2 On later models, pull off the trim cover from the outer slide.

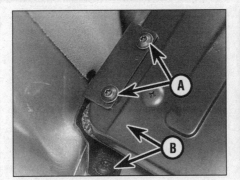

40.2 Rear seat hinge arrangement

A Hinge-to-backrest screw locations
B Hinge-to-body screw locations (removed after backrest detached)

3 On vehicles fitted with mechanical seat belt pre-tensioning stalks, fit the safety "transit clip".

4 Slide the seat fully rearwards, remove the inner slide trim cover then unscrew and remove the front slide assembly to floorpan bolts.

5 Now slide the seat fully forward, and unscrew the rear slide securing bolts each side. Lift the seat and remove it from the vehicle.

Refitting

6 Position the seat in the vehicle, and align the slide assemblies with their mounting bolt locations in the floorpan. Refit the front securing bolts first, followed by the rear securing bolts, to ensure that the seat runs smoothly in its slide mechanism. Tighten the bolts to the specified torque. On later models, remove the "transit clip" (where applicable) and refit the trim covers.

40 Rear seat - removal and refitting

Backrest and catch

Removal

1 To remove the backrest, release the backrest catch/catches, then fold the backrest forwards.

2 Remove the hinge-to-backrest securing screws, then remove the backrest **(see illustration)**.

3 The hinges may be removed at this stage if required, by undoing the hinge-to-body securing screws.

4 If desired, the rear seat backrest catch may be removed by removing the catch retaining bolts **(see illustration)**.

Refitting

5 If removed, refit the backrest catch and secure with the retaining bolts.

6 To install the backrest, align the hinges to the body and backrest, then loosely refit the securing screws.

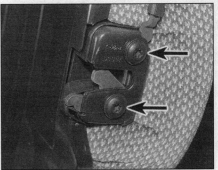

40.4 Rear seat backrest catch retaining bolts (arrowed)

7 Fold the backrest into its upright position and engage the backrest catch/catches. Adjust the alignment of the components then, when correct, tighten the securing screws to their specified torques.

8 Check for correct catch engagement.

Cushion

Removal

9 To remove the cushion, remove the three screws securing the forward edge of the seat cushion to the raised floorpan section.

10 Push down and back on the cushion, to disengage the hook and catch on the rear underside of the seat.

11 Remove the seat from the vehicle after guiding the seat belt clips through the slits in the seat cushion.

Refitting

12 Refitting the cushion is a reversal of the removal procedure.

Seat assembly (Courier Kombi models)

Removal

13 The seats are secured by two bolts at each forward hinge, visible once the seat has been folded forwards. Unbolt the hinges and withdraw the seat assembly.

Refitting

14 Refitting is the reverse of the removal procedure.

41 Seat belts - removal and refitting

Removal

Front seat belt (five-door models)

1 Remove the cover from the upper anchor position and remove the anchor bolt.

2 Remove the lower anchor bolt from its location on the floor by the base of the B-pillar. Prevent the retractor unit from reeling in too great a quantity of seat belt by attaching a clothes peg, or similar item, to the seat belt.

11

41.4 Seat belt retractor unit location in base of B-pillar (five-door models)

A Retractor unit locating tag
B Retractor unit securing bolt

3 Remove the B-pillar trim and sill scuff plate as described in Section 42.
4 Remove the bolt (two bolts on later models) securing the seat belt retractor unit to its location in the base of the B-pillar (see illustration), then remove the retractor unit and the seat belt from the vehicle.

Front seat belt (three-door models)

5 Remove the rear quarter trim panel, as described in Section 42.
6 Undo the bolt securing the seat belt retractor unit to its location, then remove the retractor unit and seat belt from the vehicle.

Front seat belt (Van models)

7 Remove the cover from the upper anchor position and remove the anchor bolt.
8 Undo the bolt securing the retractor unit and integral lower anchor position, then remove the retractor unit and seat belt from the vehicle.

Front seat belt stalk

 Warning: On vehicles fitted with mechanical seat belt pre-tensioners, any work on the seat belt stalk should be entrusted to a Ford dealer. The following procedure is therefore only applicable to models with

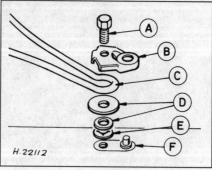

41.9 Front seat belt stalk assembly

A Bolt
B Anti-rotation plate
C Stalk
D Metal washers
E Paper washer
F Floorpin

conventional seat belt stalks which DO NOT incorporate any form of pre-tensioning device.

9 Remove the bolt securing the seat belt stalk assembly to the floor, between the two front seats, noting the arrangement of washers and spacers (see illustration). Remove the stalk assembly from the vehicle.

Front seat belt height adjuster

Note: If a height adjuster mechanism is not fitted, it is possible to lower the upper anchor position from its production setting, by removing the plug from the lower adjuster plate hole and bolting the anchor into this (see illustration 41.13). The plug can then be fitted to the production setting hole.
10 Remove the height adjuster knob by carefully inserting a small screwdriver into the aperture on the underside of the knob, and gently levering it off.
11 Remove the anchor cover, again using a screwdriver, then remove the anchor bolt and anchor (see illustration).
12 Remove the door aperture weatherseal(s) around the B-pillar location, then remove the B-pillar trim, as described in Section 42.
13 Remove the bolts securing the adjuster plate to the B-pillar, noting washer fitment,

41.11 Removing a seat belt upper anchor cover

then remove the adjuster plate from the vehicle (see illustration).

Rear seat belts

14 Remove the rear seat cushion, as described in Section 40, then also remove the parcel shelf.
15 Undo the bolt securing each seat belt buckle assembly to its body location (see illustration), and remove the buckle assemblies from the vehicle, as required.
16 Prevent the retractor units from reeling in too much seat belt by attaching a clothes peg or similar item to the belt, close to the retractor unit.
17 Detach the seat belt lower anchor by removing its retaining bolt.
18 Remove the upper anchor bolt cover and undo the bolt securing the anchor to its location. Detach the anchor, noting any spacer fitment.
19 On vehicles fitted with a parcel shelf, remove the seat belt guide from the parcel shelf support/rear loudspeaker housing, then pass the seat belt through it.
20 On vehicles without a parcel shelf as standard, remove the trim panel covering the seat belt retractor unit, where fitted, by undoing its retaining screws. Remove the seat belt guide from the trim panel, then pass the seat belt through it.
21 Remove the bolt securing the seat belt retractor unit to its body location, then withdraw the retractor unit and the seat belt from the vehicle.

Refitting

22 Refitting is a reversal of the removal procedure, noting the following points. Ensure that the tag on the retractor unit engages in its body location and, in the case of the rear seat belts, that it does not trap the wiring loom between itself and the body. Having fitted the upper anchor to its location, ensure that it can rotate freely. The stalk assembly anchor(s) must engage to the anti-rotation floorpin(s) and, when refitting a rear centre lap belt/buckle assembly, the lap belt must be fitted to lie on the right-hand side of the vehicle. Tighten all bolts to their specified torque.

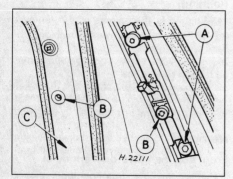

41.13 Seat belt upper anchor position (fixed and adjustable)

A Adjuster plate securing bolt
B Anchor bolt position (production setting)
C Lower setting for fixed type (if required)

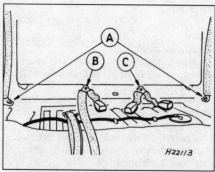

41.15 Rear seat belt and buckle securing arrangements (rear seat cushion removed)

A Seat belt lower anchor retaining bolts
B Centre lap belt/single buckle assembly securing bolt
C Dual buckle assembly securing bolt

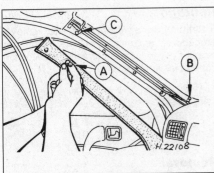

42.1 A-pillar trim retaining screw (A), heated windscreen live wire (B) and heated windscreen earth wire (C)

42 Interior trim panels - removal and refitting

A-pillar trim

Removal

1 Remove the securing screw from the trim panel, located near to the windscreen top corner **(see illustration)**.
2 Detach the door aperture weatherseal from around the trim panel, then pull the trim panel from the pillar.

Refitting

3 To refit, align the trim fixing lugs to the pillar and press into position. Refit the securing screw then push the door aperture weatherseal back onto its flange.

B-pillar trim

Removal

4 Remove the front seat belt height adjuster knob, as applicable, by inserting a small screwdriver into the aperture on the underside of the knob and levering it off.
5 Remove the upper seat belt anchor bolt cover, and remove the bolt, as required.
6 Open the doors and detach the door aperture weatherstrip from the area around the B-pillar trim.

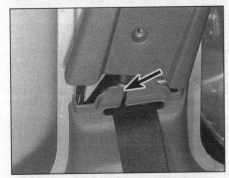

42.23 B-pillar trim being removed to expose seat belt removal/refitting slot in sill scuff plate (arrowed)

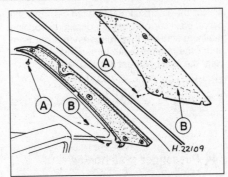

42.11 C-pillar trim fixings

A Screw locations
B Parcel shelf support/rear loudspeaker housing location

7 Remove the securing screws and detach the trim.

Refitting

8 Refitting is the reverse sequence to removal, tightening the seat belt anchor bolt to the specified torque. Ensure that the anchor is free to rotate.

C-pillar trim

Removal

9 Open the tailgate, then detach the loudspeaker from its location by disconnecting its multi-plug connection, removing its two retaining screws and unhinging it.
10 Detach the tailgate weatherstrip from its flange, around the trim panel.
11 Remove the parcel shelf, then slacken the parcel shelf support/rear loudspeaker housing retaining screws, and remove the single screw from the base of the C-pillar trim **(see illustration)**.
12 Remove the upper seat belt anchor bolt cover, and remove the bolt and anchor, noting any spacer fitment.
13 Remove the screw(s) from the top of the C-pillar trim, then remove the trim from the vehicle.

Refitting

14 To refit, position the base of the trim

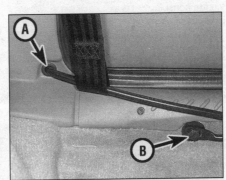

42.29 Seat belt lower slide bar anchor arrangement (three-door models)

A Bush location   B Anchor bolt

behind the parcel shelf support/rear loudspeaker housing, then loosely refit the upper and lower securing screws.
15 Refit the seat belt anchor, bolt, and spacer, as applicable, tightening the bolt to the specified torque. Refit the anchor bolt cover, and ensure that the anchor is free to rotate.
16 Tighten the trim and parcel shelf support/rear loudspeaker housing screws, then refit the parcel shelf.
17 Refit the loudspeaker by reversing the method of removal, then press the tailgate weatherstrip back into place.

Sill scuff plate

Removal

18 Remove the front seat adjacent to the scuff plate to be removed (see Section 39).
19 Detach the door aperture weatherstrip(s) from around the scuff plate location.
20 Remove the B-pillar trim, as applicable.
21 Remove the lower seat belt anchor bolt on five-door models, and detach the anchor from its location.
22 On three-door models, remove the bolt securing the forward end of the seat belt slide bar, then manoeuvre the slide bar to free it from its rear location.
23 Remove the plastic screws securing the sill scuff plate, then slip the seat belt through its slot on five-door models, and remove the sill scuff plate from the vehicle **(see illustration)**. Should the soft plastic screws round off during attempts to remove them, force an electrician's thin screwdriver into the body of the screw and try again, fitting a new screw upon reassembly.

Refitting

24 Refitting is a reversal of the removal procedure, tightening the seat belt anchor bolts to the specified torque.

Rear quarter trim panel

Removal

25 Detach the door aperture weatherstrip from around the trim location.
26 Remove the rear seat cushion, as described in Section 40.
27 Remove the screw from the upper rear corner of the trim panel.
28 Remove the plastic stud from the lower rear corner of the trim panel.
29 Detach the seat belt slide bar by removing the bolt from its forward end then manoeuvring it to free it from its rear location **(see illustration)**. Remove the seat belt from the slide bar.
30 Release the trim clips from the front and top edges of the panel using a trim clip tool. This may be achieved by carefully inserting two thin flat-bladed screwdrivers between the panel and the body - one each side of the clip being released, and applying gentle leverage, if a trim clip tool is not available.

11

31 Remove the seat belt upper anchor bolt cover and undo the bolt.

32 Carefully prise up the seat belt guide from its trim panel location, and remove it from the seat belt. Allow the seat belt to retract through the trim panel, clamping a clothes peg, or similar item, onto its end to prevent it being fully wound into the retractor.

33 Manoeuvre the trim panel out from under the scuff plate, slackening or removing the rearward scuff plate retaining screws if necessary.

Refitting

34 Engage the trim panel under the scuff plate, and refit and tighten the scuff plate retaining screws as necessary.

35 Pull the seat belt through the trim panel, refit the guide and press the panel onto the body to re-engage the trim clips.

36 Refit the upper seat belt anchor, tightening the bolt to the specified torque, and refit its cover. Ensure that the anchor is free to rotate.

37 Refit the plastic stud and the screw to the lower and upper rear corners of the trim, respectively.

38 Refit the seat belt to the slide bar, then refit the slide bar by reversing the method of removal. Ensure that the seat belt is not twisted as it is located on the slide bar, and that the bolt is tightened to the specified torque.

39 Refit the rear seat cushion by reversing the method of removal.

40 Press the door aperture weatherstrip back into position.

Load compartment trim panels (Courier models)

Removal

41 Using either a trim clip releasing tool or a screwdriver with a broad flat blade, and protecting the paintwork and trim with a layer of rag, extract the clips securing the panel and withdraw it.

Refitting

42 Refitting is the reverse of the removal procedure.

43 Parcel shelf support/ loudspeaker housing - removal and refitting

Removal

1 Remove the rear seat belt and retractor unit from the appropriate side of the vehicle, as described in Section 41.

2 Disconnect the luggage compartment (courtesy) light, where fitted, by prising the light assembly from its location using a thin flat-bladed screwdriver, then twist the bulbholder anti-clockwise to remove.

3 Detach the loudspeaker, where fitted, by removing its retaining screws, disengaging its locating tags and disconnecting its multi-plug.

4 Fold the seat backrest forward. Remove the parcel shelf support/rear loudspeaker housing retaining screws, then manoeuvre it out from under the quarter panel trim as necessary, to clear the seat backrest catch striker pin.

Refitting

5 Refitting is a reversal of the removal procedure.

44 Passenger grab handle - removal and refitting

Removal

1 Carefully prise up the trim flaps on either end of the handle to expose the two mounting screws.

2 Undo the mounting screws and remove the grab handle.

Refitting

3 Refitting is the reverse procedure to removal.

45 Centre console - removal and refitting

Removal

1 Disconnect the battery negative (earth) lead (refer to Chapter 5A, Section 1).

2 Carefully prise up the console switches, as necessary, using a flat-bladed screwdriver, then disconnect their multi-plugs.

3 Unscrew the gear lever knob, then raise the gaiter from its location and lift it off over the gear lever **(see illustration)**. A similar method is also used to remove the selector cover on automatic transmission equipped vehicles.

4 Undo the four screws securing the centre console to the floor pan **(see illustration)**. On automatic transmission equipped models, ensure that the bulb assembly does not restrict centre console removal. Remove the centre console.

45.3 Removing the gear lever gaiter from the centre console

Refitting

5 Refitting is a reversal of the removal procedure, ensuring that the gaiter (or selector cover) locates correctly to the centre console (as applicable).

46 Facia - removal and refitting

Removal

> ⚠ **Warning: On vehicles fitted with a passenger's air bag, seek the advice of a Ford dealer concerning safety implications when removing the facia assembly.**

1 Disconnect the battery negative (earth) lead (refer to Chapter 5A, Section 1).

2 Remove the upper and lower steering column shrouds, and the steering wheel as described in Chapter 10.

3 Remove the two screws securing the instrument cluster bezel from its underside, and carefully detach the bezel (see Chapter 12).

4 Disconnect the steering column multi-function switch assembly and remove its single retaining screw. Remove the assembly.

5 Disconnect the ignition loom multi-plug on the steering column.

6 Disconnect the brake pedal stop-light switch loom connection.

7 Disconnect the speedometer cable at the transmission casing, to allow easier removal of the instrument cluster.

8 Remove the four screws securing the instrument cluster to its location, then carefully pull it out to allow access to the speedometer cable and multi-plug connections. Disconnect the speedometer cable and multi-plug, then remove the instrument cluster from the vehicle (see Chapter 12).

9 Remove the radio assembly and loudspeaker balance control, where fitted (see Chapter 12).

10 Remove the centre console, where fitted, as described in Section 45.

11 Pull the heater fan motor control knob off,

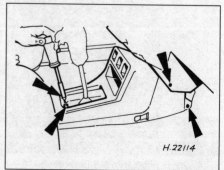
45.4 Centre console securing screws (arrowed)

H.22114

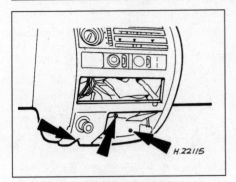

46.12 Facia centre panel retaining screws (arrowed)

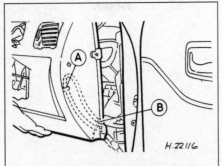

46.23 Wiring loom loop securing arrangements on reverse side of facia

A Retaining clip   B Cable tie

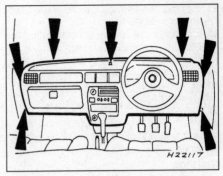

46.24 Facia retaining screw locations (arrowed)

then move the air distribution and temperature controls fully to the right. Unclip and remove the heater slide facia towards the left-hand side of the vehicle, removing the slide control knobs only as necessary, and disconnecting its bulbholder (bayonet type) as it is withdrawn.

12 Remove the ashtray, then undo the three screws from the base of the centre panel **(see illustration)**. Detach the centre panel, disconnecting the cigarette lighter connections as it is withdrawn.

13 Squeeze the two release tabs together on the heater fan motor control switch, and remove it, disconnecting its multi-plug as it is withdrawn. Remove the three heater control panel securing screws (see Chapter 3).

14 Remove the switches from the centre panel and disconnect their multi-plugs.

15 Using a thin flat-bladed screwdriver, prise the clock from its location and disconnect its multi-plug, as applicable.

16 Remove the fusebox lid, then remove the two retaining screws and detach the fusebox from the facia.

17 Disconnect the earth strap on the right-hand side of the steering column mounting bracket, by removing its securing bolt, and remove any cable-ties fitted.

18 Open both front doors and disconnect the multi-plugs in the A-pillars, where fitted, by squeezing their ears and withdrawing.

19 Detach the door aperture weatherstrips from the A-pillar and along the base of the door aperture, on both front doors.

20 Remove both front door courtesy light switches, disconnecting their loom connections as they are withdrawn.

21 Remove the sill scuff plate retaining screws on both sides of the vehicle.

22 Release the wiring loom from its securing clips, under the sill scuff plates.

23 Remove the right-hand adjustable side vent from the facia by carefully prising it out, using a thin flat-bladed screwdriver, then release the wiring loom loop from its facia retaining clip through the resultant opening **(see illustration)**.

24 Prise up the cover obscuring the central facia retaining screw, using a thin flat-bladed

screwdriver then remove the seven facia retaining screws **(see illustration)**.

25 Gently ease the facia from its location, having ensured that all wires are clear to move, then remove the cable-ties securing the loom to the facia. Ensure that the loom is free, then remove the facia from the vehicle. The aid of an assistant, at this stage, is recommended.

Refitting

26 Refitting is a reversal of the removal procedure, noting the following points. Secure the wiring loom loop to its clip and cable-tie before refitting the facia retaining screws, tightening its cable-tie, along with the rest, when the viewing loom connections have been pulled out through their relevant facia openings. New cable-ties should be used. Ensure that the multi-plugs seat correctly in their A-pillar locations. When refitting the instrument cluster, ensure that the tape mark on the speedometer cable is positioned at the bulkhead grommet (as applicable).

11

Notes

Chapter 12
Body electrical systems

Contents

Air bag (driver's side) - removal and refitting 28
Air bag (passenger's side) - removal and refitting 29
Air bag clock spring - removal and refitting 31
Air bag control module - removal and refitting 30
Anti-theft systems - general information 27
Battery, bulbs and fuses ....See "Weekly checks"
Bulbs (exterior lights) - renewal 5
Bulbs (interior lights) - renewal 6
Cigarette lighter - removal and refitting 12
Clock - removal and refitting 13
Electric window regulator motor - removal and refitting 20
Electrical fault-finding - general information 2
Exterior light units - removal and refitting 7
Fuses and relays - general information 3
General information and precautions 1
Headlight and auxiliary light beam alignment - checking and
    adjustment 8
Horn - removal and refitting 14

Instrument panel - removal and refitting 9
Instrument panel components - removal and refitting 10
"Lights-on" warning module - removal and refitting 26
Radio aerial - removal and refitting 25
Radio/cassette player - removal and refitting 22
Screen washer fluid level check ....See "Weekly checks"
Speaker balance control joystick - removal and refitting 24
Speakers - removal and refitting 23
Speedometer cable - removal and refitting 11
Switches - removal and refitting 4
Tailgate remote release motor - removal and refitting 21
Tailgate wiper motor assembly - removal and refitting 18
Windscreen wiper motor and linkage - removal and refitting 16
Windscreen wiper pivot shaft - removal and refitting 17
Windscreen/tailgate washer system components - removal and
    refitting 19
Wiper arms - removal and refitting 15
Wiper blade check ....See "Weekly checks"

Degrees of difficulty

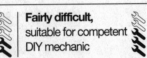

Easy, suitable for novice with little experience	Fairly easy, suitable for beginner with some experience	Fairly difficult, suitable for competent DIY mechanic	Difficult, suitable for experienced DIY mechanic	Very difficult, suitable for expert DIY or professional

Specifications

Fuses - pre-1992 models

Main fuse board:

No	Rating (amps)	Circuit(s) protected
1	3	Electronic engine control system
2	15	Interior light, cigarette lighter, clock and radio memory
3	20	Central locking system
4	30	Heated rear window element
5	10	Dim-dip lighting
6	10	Left-hand side lights and rear fog light
7	10	Right-hand side lights
8	10	Left-hand dipped beam
9	10	Right-hand dipped beam
10	15	Left-hand main beam and right-hand auxiliary driving light
11	15	Right-hand main beam and left-hand auxiliary driving light
12	20	Heater fan motor and reversing light
13	30	Radiator cooling fan motor
14	15	Front foglights (XR2i only)
15	15	Horn
16	20	Wiper motor and windscreen/tailgate washer pump
17	10	Brake stop lights, instrument illumination and instrument warning
18	30	Electrically operated windows
19	20	Electric fuel pump
20	10	Oxygen sensor (vehicles with catalytic converter)
21	10	Left-hand direction indicators
22	10	Right-hand direction indicators

Additional fuses behind main fuse board:

No	Rating (amps)	Circuit(s) protected
23	-	Unused
24/25	10	Rear fog lights
26	15	Tailgate remote release
27/28	30	Heated windscreen

Fuses - 1992 models onward

Main fuse board:

Fuses 1 to 22	Unchanged from pre-1992 models

Additional fuses behind main fuse board:

No	Rating (amps)	Circuit(s) protected
23*	-	Unused
23**	10	Rear fog lights
24*	-	Unused
24**	10	Rear fog lights
25	15	Tailgate remote release, anti-theft warning system
26	30	Heated windscreen
27	30	Heated windscreen
28*	20	Full-length sunroof
28**	30	Automatic transmission starter inhibitor
29	10	Air bag

* Pre-1994 models
** 1994 models onward

Relays (pre-1992 models)

Note: *Relay locations and circuits controlled are liable to change from year to year. Consult a Ford dealer, for specific information.*

No	Circuit(s) controlled
I	Heated rear window
II	Windscreen wiper delay
III	CFi (fuel injection) delay relay
IV	Not used on UK models
V	Ignition switch
VI	Automatic transmission starter inhibitor/electric fuel pump (bridge fitted to carburettor engines without automatic transmission)
VII	Headlight main beam
VIII	Dim-dip lighting
IX	Not used on UK models
X	Not used on UK models
XI	Heated windscreen
XII	Anti-lock braking system
A	Idle speed control (automatic transmission) two-tone horn (where fitted)
B	Not used on UK models
C	Front foglights (XR2i)
D	Headlight dipped beam
E	Dim-dip lighting

Relays (1992 models onward)

Note: *Relay locations and circuits controlled are liable to change from year to year. Consult a Ford dealer, for specific information.*

No	Circuit(s) controlled
I	Heated rear window
II	Windscreen wiper delay
III	CFi delay relay or EFi supply relay (fuel injection)
IV	Not used on UK models
V	Ignition switch
VI	Automatic transmission starter inhibitor, anti-theft warning system
VII	Headlight main beam
VIII	Anti-lock braking system and/or dim-dip lighting
IX	Not used on UK models
X	Not used on UK models
XI	Heated windscreen
XII	Anti-lock braking system
A	Idle speed control (automatic transmission) or two-tone horn (where fitted)
B	Fuel pump
C	Front foglights (XR2i, RS Turbo and RS 1800)
D	Headlight dipped beam
E	Dim-dip lighting
F	Not used on UK models

Bulbs

	Wattage
Headlight (halogen)	H4, 60/55
Sidelight (front)	5
Direction indicators (main)	21
Side direction indicator repeaters	5
Auxiliary driving and foglights (S and XR2i)	H3, 55
Stop/tail light	21/5
Rear foglight	21
Reversing light	21
Number plate light	10
Interior light	10
Luggage compartment light	5
Instrument warning lights	1.3 or 2.6
Panel illumination	1.3 or 2.6
Cigarette lighter illumination	1.4
Automatic transmission selector illumination	2

Lubricants

Grease for windscreen wiper linkage and pivots	To Ford specification SAM-1C-911-A

Torque wrench settings

	Nm	lbf ft
Wiper motor to bracket	8 to 9	6 to 7
Wiper motor bracket to bulkhead/tailgate	6 to 8	4 to 6
Windscreen wiper crank to driving shaft nut	22 to 24	16 to 18
Windscreen/tailgate wiper arm retaining nut	17 to 18	12 to 13
Windscreen wiper pivot shaft nut	9 to 12	7 to 9
Windscreen/tailgate washer reservoir securing bolts	2.5 to 3.5	2 to 3
Headlight retaining bolt	5.4 to 7.0	4 to 5
Tail light securing nuts	1.5 to 2.5	1 to 2
Auxiliary light retaining nut (S models)	6.8 to 9.2	5 to 7
Horn bracket retaining bolt	24 to 33	18 to 24
Starter inhibitor switch	9 to 14	7 to 10

1 General information and precautions

General information

The electrical system is of 12-volt negative earth type. Power for the lights and all electrical accessories is supplied by a lead/acid battery, which is charged by the engine-driven alternator.

This Chapter covers repair and service procedures for the various electrical components not associated with the engine. Information on the battery, ignition system, alternator, and starter motor can be found in Chapter 5A and B.

All models from 1994 onwards are fitted with a driver's air bag, which is designed to prevent serious chest and head injuries to the driver during an accident. A similar bag for the front seat passenger is also available. The combined sensor and electronics for the air bag is located next to the steering column inside the vehicle, and contains a back-up capacitor, crash sensor, decelerometer, safety sensor, integrated circuit and microprocessor. The air bag is inflated by a gas generator, which forces the bag out of the module cover in the centre of the steering wheel. A "clock spring" ensures that a good electrical connection is maintained with the air bag at all times - as the steering wheel is turned in each direction, the spring winds and unwinds.

An anti-theft alarm system is available on later models, and is triggered if the vehicle is broken into through the doors, bonnet, or tailgate. The alarm will also be triggered if the ignition or audio equipment is tampered with. Additionally, from the 1994 model year onwards, a Passive Anti-Theft System (PATS) is fitted. This system, (which works independently of the standard alarm) prevents the engine from being started unless a specific code, programmed into the ignition key, is recognised by the PATS transceiver.

Precautions

Warning: Before carrying out any work on the electrical system, read through the precautions given in "Safety first!" at the beginning of this manual and in Chapter 5A, Section 1.
Caution: Prior to working on any component in the electrical system, the battery negative lead should first be disconnected, to prevent the possibility of electrical short-circuits and/or fires. If a radio/cassette player with anti-theft security code is fitted, refer to the information given in the reference sections of this manual before disconnecting the battery.

2 Electrical fault-finding - general information

Note: *Refer to the precautions given in "Safety first!" and in Section 1 of this Chapter before starting work. The following tests relate to testing of the main electrical circuits, and should not be used to test delicate electronic circuits (such as engine management systems), particularly where an electronic control unit is used. Also refer to the precautions given in Chapter 5A, Section 1.*

General

1 A typical electrical circuit consists of an electrical component, any switches, relays, motors, fuses, fusible links or circuit breakers related to that component, and the wiring and connectors which link the component to both the battery and the chassis. To help to pinpoint a problem in an electrical circuit,

12

wiring diagrams are included at the end of this manual.

2 Before attempting to diagnose an electrical fault, first study the appropriate wiring diagram, to obtain a complete understanding of the components included in the particular circuit concerned. The possible sources of a fault can be narrowed down by noting if other components related to the circuit are operating properly. If several components or circuits fail at one time, the problem is likely to be related to a shared fuse or earth connection.

3 Electrical problems usually stem from simple causes, such as loose or corroded connections, a faulty earth connection, a blown fuse, a melted fusible link, or a faulty relay (refer to Section 3 for details of testing relays). Visually inspect the condition of all fuses, wires and connections in a problem circuit before testing the components. Use the wiring diagrams to determine which terminal connections will need to be checked in order to pinpoint the trouble-spot.

4 The basic tools required for electrical fault-finding include a circuit tester or voltmeter (a 12-volt bulb with a set of test leads can also be used for certain tests); an ohmmeter (to measure resistance and check for continuity); a battery and set of test leads; and a jumper wire, preferably with a circuit breaker or fuse incorporated, which can be used to bypass suspect wires or electrical components. Before attempting to locate a problem with test instruments, use the wiring diagram to determine where to make the connections.

 Warning: Under no circumstances may live measuring instruments such as ohmmeters, voltmeters or a bulb and test leads be used to test any of the air bag circuitry or components. Any testing in these areas must be left to a Ford dealer as there is a danger of activating the system if the correct procedures are not followed.

5 To find the source of an intermittent wiring fault (usually due to a poor or dirty connection, or damaged wiring insulation), a "wiggle" test can be performed on the wiring. This involves wiggling the wiring by hand to see if the fault occurs as the wiring is moved. It should be possible to narrow down the source of the fault to a particular section of wiring. This method of testing can be used in conjunction with any of the tests described in the following sub-Sections.

6 Apart from problems due to poor connections, two basic types of fault can occur in an electrical circuit - open-circuit, or short-circuit.

7 Open-circuit faults are caused by a break somewhere in the circuit, which prevents current from flowing. An open-circuit fault will prevent a component from working.

8 Short-circuit faults are caused by a "short" somewhere in the circuit, which allows the current flowing in the circuit to "escape" along an alternative route, usually to earth. Short-circuit faults are normally caused by a breakdown in wiring insulation, which allows a feed wire to touch either another wire, or an earthed component such as the bodyshell. A short-circuit fault will normally cause the relevant circuit fuse to blow.

Finding an open-circuit

9 To check for an open-circuit, connect one lead of a circuit tester or the negative lead of a voltmeter either to the battery negative terminal or to a known good earth.

10 Connect the other lead to a connector in the circuit being tested, preferably nearest to the battery or fuse. At this point, battery voltage should be present, unless the lead from the battery or the fuse itself is faulty (bearing in mind that some circuits are live only when the ignition switch is moved to a particular position).

11 Switch on the circuit, then connect the tester lead to the connector nearest the circuit switch on the component side.

12 If voltage is present (indicated either by the tester bulb lighting or a voltmeter reading, as applicable), this means that the section of the circuit between the relevant connector and the switch is problem-free.

13 Continue to check the remainder of the circuit in the same fashion.

14 When a point is reached at which no voltage is present, the problem must lie between that point and the previous test point with voltage. Most problems can be traced to a broken, corroded or loose connection.

Finding a short-circuit

15 To check for a short-circuit, first disconnect the load(s) from the circuit (loads are the components which draw current from a circuit, such as bulbs, motors, heating elements, etc).

16 Remove the relevant fuse from the circuit, and connect a circuit tester or voltmeter to the fuse connections.

17 Switch on the circuit, bearing in mind that some circuits are live only when the ignition switch is moved to a particular position.

18 If voltage is present (indicated either by the tester bulb lighting or a voltmeter reading, as applicable), this means that there is a short-circuit.

19 If no voltage is present during this test, but the fuse still blows with the load(s) reconnected, this indicates an internal fault in the load(s).

Finding an earth fault

20 The battery negative terminal is connected to "earth" - the metal of the engine/transmission and the vehicle body - and many systems are wired so that they only receive a positive feed, the current returning via the metal of the car body. This means that the component mounting and the body form part of that circuit. Loose or corroded mountings can therefore cause a range of electrical faults, ranging from total failure of a circuit, to a puzzling partial failure. In particular, lights may shine dimly (especially when another circuit sharing the same earth point is in operation), motors (eg wiper motors or the radiator cooling fan motor) may run slowly, and the operation of one circuit may have an apparently-unrelated effect on another. Note that on many vehicles, earth straps are used between certain components, such as the engine/transmission and the body, usually where there is no metal-to-metal contact between components, due to flexible rubber mountings, etc.

21 To check whether a component is properly earthed, disconnect the battery (refer to Chapter 5A, Section 1) and connect one lead of an ohmmeter to a known good earth point. Connect the other lead to the wire or earth connection being tested. The resistance reading should be zero; if not, check the connection as follows.

22 If an earth connection is thought to be faulty, dismantle the connection, and clean both the bodyshell and the wire terminal (or the component earth connection mating surface) back to bare metal. Be careful to remove all traces of dirt and corrosion, then use a knife to trim away any paint, so that a clean metal-to-metal joint is made. On reassembly, tighten the joint fasteners securely; if a wire terminal is being refitted, use serrated washers between the terminal and the bodyshell, to ensure a clean and secure connection. When the connection is remade, prevent the onset of corrosion in the future by applying a coat of petroleum jelly or silicone-based grease, or by spraying on (at regular intervals) a proprietary ignition sealer or a water-dispersant lubricant.

3 Fuses and relays - general information

Note: *It is important to note that the ignition switch and the appropriate electrical circuit must always be switched off before any of the fuses (or relays) are removed and renewed.*

1 The main fuse and relay board is located below the facia panel to the right of the steering wheel. The fuses can be inspected and if necessary renewed, by removing the hinged access cover. The remaining additional fuses and relays (depending on model) may be accessed by removing the two fuse board retaining screws, releasing the retaining lugs on either side of the main fuse plate and withdrawing the fuse/relay board downwards into the driver's footwell. Each fuse location is numbered - refer to the fuse chart in the *Specifications* at the start of this Chapter to check which circuits are protected by each fuse. Plastic tweezers are attached to

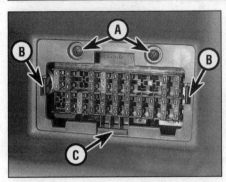

3.1a Method of fuse/relay board retention

A *Retaining screws*   C *Support*
B *Retaining lugs*

3.1b Withdrawing the fuse/relay board downwards into the driver's footwell

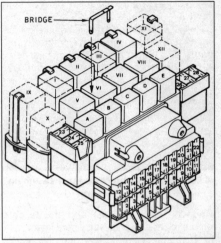

3.1c Component layout on the fuse/relay board. See *Specifications* for relay identification

the inside face of the cover to remove and fit the fuses **(see illustrations)**.

2 To remove a fuse, use the tweezers provided to pull it out of the holder. Slide the fuse sideways from the tweezers. The wire within the fuse is clearly visible, and it will be broken if the fuse is blown.

3 Always renew a fuse with one of an identical rating. Never renew a fuse more than once without tracing the source of the trouble. The fuse rating is stamped on top of the fuse.

4 With the exception of the indicator flasher relay, the remainder of the relays are fitted to the reverse side of the main fuse/relay board. Access is as described in paragraph 1.

5 The various relays can be removed from their respective locations on the fuse board by carefully pulling them from the sockets.

6 The direction indicator flasher relay is attached to the multi-function switch unit on the steering column. Access to the relay is made by undoing the retaining screws and removing the steering column shrouds. The relay can then be withdrawn from the switch.

7 If a system controlled by a relay becomes inoperative and the relay is suspect, listen to the relay as the circuit is operated. If the relay is functioning, it should be possible to hear it click as it is energised. If the relay proves satisfactory, the fault lies with the components or wiring of the system. If the relay is not being energised, then it is not receiving a main supply voltage or a switching voltage, or the relay is faulty.

4 Switches - removal and refitting

Ignition switch (loom plate and lock barrel)

1 Disconnect the battery negative (earth) lead (refer to Chapter 5A, Section 1).

2 Remove the manual choke control knob, where fitted, by depressing the lug securing it, and pulling it from its shaft. The lug is found on the side of the control knob shank.

3 Remove the lower steering column shroud by undoing its four retaining screws, then detach the choke warning light switch/pull control assembly from the lower shroud by unscrewing its retaining collar (bayonet-type fixing), using a suitable tool to locate in the collar recesses.

4 Remove the two screws securing the upper steering column shroud from above, and the two screws securing it from below, the latter accessible only with the lower shroud removed.

5 Disconnect the ignition switch wiring multi-plug connector. Insert a thin-bladed screwdriver into the lock tab aperture, release the locking tab and remove the loom plate from its location on the left-hand side of the steering column.

6 Where applicable, undo the single screw and withdraw the Passive Anti-Theft System (PATS) transceiver from the ignition switch/steering lock barrel.

7 Insert the key and turn the ignition switch to position "I". Depress the lock barrel plunger through the steering column lock housing. As the lock barrel plunger is depressed, pull on the ignition key to remove the lock barrel **(see illustration)**.

8 Refitting is a reversal of the removal procedure. When relocating the switch to the steering lock, the barrel driveshaft must align

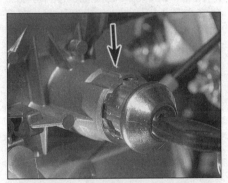

4.7 Withdraw the lock barrel after depressing its plunger through the aperture in the steering column lock housing (arrowed)

with the switch shaft as it is pushed into position. Check the switch for satisfactory operation on completion.

Steering column multi-function switch

9 Carry out the operations described in paragraphs 1 to 4 above.

10 Disconnect the wiring multi-plugs from the multi-function switch assembly, then remove the single screw securing the switch assembly to the steering column lock housing. This retaining screw is located directly forward of the hazard warning light switch. Remove the switch assembly.

11 Refitting is a reversal of the removal procedure.

Facia centre panel switches (below heater controls)

12 These switches individually control the front and rear foglights, heated windscreen and heated rear window element. Where these features are not fitted to the vehicle, blanking plates are installed instead of switches.

13 Disconnect the battery negative (earth) lead (refer to Chapter 5A, Section 1).

14 Remove the radio/cassette player as described in Section 22.

15 Remove the ashtray, then undo the three screws from the base of the centre panel. Withdraw the centre panel, disconnecting the cigarette lighter connections as it is withdrawn.

16 Push the required switch/switches out from behind, disconnect the multi-plug and remove the switch.

17 Refitting is a reversal of the removal procedure.

Centre console switches

18 The switches mounted on the centre console control the electrically operated

12

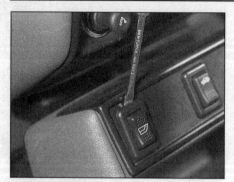

4.20a Prise the centre console switch up from its location . . .

4.20b . . . then disconnect its multiplug and remove the switch

4.23 Heater fan motor control switch removal

windows (early models) and the tailgate remote release mechanism, where fitted.

19 Disconnect the battery negative (earth) lead (refer to Chapter 5A, Section 1).

20 To remove a switch, carefully prise it from its location using a thin flat-bladed screwdriver, then disconnect the multi-plug **(see illustrations)**.

21 To refit, connect the multi-plug then push home to secure.

Heater fan motor control switch

22 Disconnect the battery negative (earth) lead (refer to Chapter 5A, Section 1).

23 Pull the heater fan motor control knob off, then move the air distribution and temperature controls fully to the right. Unclip and remove the heater slide facia towards the left-hand side of the vehicle, removing the slide control knobs only as necessary, and disconnecting its bulbholder (bayonet type) as it is withdrawn **(see illustration)**.

24 Squeeze the two release tabs together on the heater fan motor control switch, and remove it, disconnecting its multi-plug as it is withdrawn.

25 Refit by reversing the removal procedure.

Brake stop-light switch

26 The brake stop-light switch is attached to the brake pedal mounting bracket.

27 Detach the wiring multi-plug from the switch, then twist the switch through a quarter of a turn (90°) anticlockwise and withdraw it from the bracket.

28 Insert the switch into its retainer, press it lightly against the brake pedal until all free play is just taken up, then turn the switch clockwise to secure. Reconnect the switch wiring connector and the battery.

Handbrake warning light switch

29 Push the carpet mounding down as necessary to gain access to the switch, located on the handbrake lever.

30 Remove the cover, then disconnect the warning light switch wiring multi-plug **(see illustration)**. Undo the two screws securing the switch to the handbrake lever assembly and remove the switch.

31 Refit by reversing the removal procedure.

Low brake fluid level warning light switch

32 This is incorporated into the brake fluid reservoir cap, and senses fluid level in the reservoir. It cannot be renewed separately from the cap.

33 To remove, disconnect the warning indicator loom multi-plug and unscrew the reservoir cap.

34 Refit by reversing the removal procedure.

Courtesy light switches

35 Disconnect the battery negative (earth) lead (refer to Chapter 5A, Section 1).

36 With the door open, undo the retaining screw and withdraw the switch from the door pillar. Pull out the wiring slightly, and tie a

piece of string to it, so that it can be retrieved if it drops down into the door pillar.

37 Disconnect the wiring from the switch.

38 Refitting is a reversal of removal.

Reversing light switch

39 Refer to Chapter 7A, Section 6.

Starter inhibitor switch (automatic transmission)

40 Disconnect the battery negative (earth) lead (refer to Chapter 5A, Section 1).

41 The starter inhibitor switch is located on the transmission housing, and prevents the engine from being started with the selector lever in any position except "P" or "N". Access to the switch is gained after raising and supporting the vehicle at the front end on axle stands (see "Jacking and vehicle support").

42 Detach the switch multi-plug, then unscrew and remove the switch from the transmission, together with its O-ring. As the switch is removed, catch any fluid spillage in a suitable container, and plug the switch aperture in the transmission to prevent any further loss.

43 Refitting is a reversal of the removal procedure. Use a new O-ring, and tighten the switch securely. Ensure that the wiring connection is securely made. On completion, check and if necessary top-up the automatic transmission fluid (see Chapter 1) then check that the engine only starts when the selector is in the "P" or "N" position.

Luggage area contact plate

44 Disconnect the battery negative (earth) lead (refer to Chapter 5A, Section 1).

45 Open the tailgate and release the contact plate side retaining clips using a thin-bladed screwdriver. Push the contact plate from its location in the body.

46 Disconnect the wiring multi-plug and remove the plate **(see illustration)**.

47 Refit in the reverse order of removal.

Luggage area contact switch

48 Disconnect the battery negative (earth) lead (refer to Chapter 5A, Section 1).

49 Open the tailgate and remove its inner trim panel (see Chapter 11).

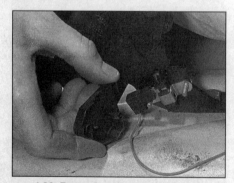

4.30 Removing the cover from the handbrake warning light switch

4.46 Withdrawing the luggage area contact plate for access to disconnect the multi-plug

50 Undo the two screws securing the contact switch and withdraw it from its tailgate location.

51 Unclip and disconnect the switch multi-plug, and disconnect the earth wiring. Remove the switch.

52 Refit in the reverse order of removal. Make sure that the pins and their contacts are clean. On completion, check the operation of the rear wipers, courtesy light, heated rear window and the tailgate release/central locking system.

Electric window switches (1992 models onward)

53 On later models the electric window switches are located in the upper surfaces of the door stowage pockets. Removal and refitting is the same as for the earlier centre console mounted switches described previously in this Section.

5 Bulbs (exterior lights) - renewal

Note: *Ensure that all exterior lights are switched off before disconnecting the wiring connectors to any exterior light bulbs. Note that if a bulb fails, and has just been in use, it will still be extremely hot, particularly in the case of a headlight bulb.*

Headlight

1 From within the engine compartment, disconnect the multi-plug from the back of the headlight.

2 Remove the rubber bulb protective cap, then unlock the bulb retaining spring clip or retaining ring (according to type) and withdraw the bulb **(see illustrations)**.

Caution: Take care not to touch the bulb glass with your fingers - if accidentally touched, clean the bulb with methylated spirit.

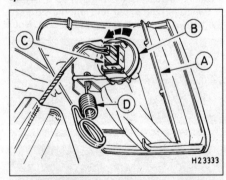

5.8 Remove the front direction indicator light bulbholder by turning it anti-clockwise

A Light unit
B Bulbholder
C Multi-plug
D Retaining spring

5.2a Remove the protective cap . . .

3 Refitting is a reversal of the removal procedure.

Front sidelight

4 The bulbholder is located on the side of the headlight unit, and is removed by twisting anti-clockwise and withdrawing from within the engine compartment.

5 Withdraw the push-fit bulb from its holder.

6 Refitting is a reversal of the removal procedure.

Front direction indicator

7 Remove the direction indicator light unit by releasing the retaining spring from its body location, then pulling the light assembly forwards. Disconnect its multi-plug as it is withdrawn.

8 Turn the bulbholder anti-clockwise and remove it **(see illustration)**. The bulb is a bayonet type fitting in its holder.

9 Refitting is a reversal of the removal procedure.

Front direction indicator side repeater

10 Remove the appropriate front wheel arch liner as described in Chapter 11.

11 Remove the appropriate sill scuff plate as described in Chapter 11, and release the clip securing the insulation to the panel forward of the lower A-pillar.

12 Disconnect the supply lead connector and

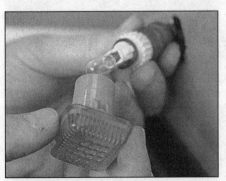

5.13 Removing the direction indicator side repeater bulbholder assembly

5.2b . . . then unlock the headlight bulb retaining spring and withdraw the bulb

the earth lead, then release their grommet from its panel location.

13 From outside the vehicle, twist the light assembly to release it, then withdraw it and its leads **(see illustration)**.

14 Refitting is a reversal of the removal procedure, ensuring that the grommet is seated correctly in its panel location.

Auxiliary lights

S models

15 Undo the screw at the base of the light, then withdraw the lens and reflector assembly from the light housing.

16 Disconnect the wiring then release the bulb retainer and remove the bulb.

17 Refitting is a reversal of the removal procedure.

XR2i models

18 Remove the auxiliary light assembly from its bumper location, as described in Section 7.

19 Release the bulb retainer, then remove the bulb **(see illustration)**.

20 Refitting is a reversal of the removal procedure.

Rear light cluster (all models except Courier)

21 Access to the rear light cluster bulbholder is gained from the luggage compartment. Disconnect the multi-plug from the bulbholder, then press the retaining lugs on

5.19 Releasing the auxiliary light bulb retainer (XR2i models)

12

5.21a Disconnect the ear light cluster multi-plug from the bulbholder . . .

5.21b . . . then having pressed its retaining lugs, withdraw the bulbholder for access to the bulbs

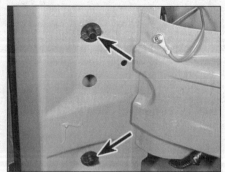

5.24a On Courier models, unscrew the two black plastic nuts securing the rear light cluster assembly . . .

5.24b . . . then withdraw the assembly to the outside of the vehicle

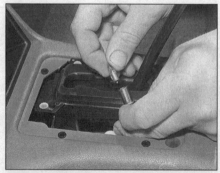

5.29 Release the number plate light securing tab (arrowed) and separate the bulbholder and light cover

the bulbholder together and remove it **(see illustrations)**.

22 All bulbs are of bayonet type fitting.

23 Refitting is a reversal of the removal procedure.

Rear light cluster (Courier models)

24 Working inside the load compartment, unscrew the two black plastic nuts securing the light cluster assembly. Withdraw the assembly to the outside of the vehicle, disconnecting the wiring from the bulbholder **(see illustrations)**.

25 All bulbs are of bayonet type fitting.

26 Refitting is a reversal of the removal procedure.

Number plate lights

27 Insert a thin flat-bladed screwdriver between the light assembly and the bumper, and carefully prise the light out. Use a rag, or a piece of card, between the screwdriver and the bumper, to prevent damage to the bumper.

28 Detach the connections on the underside of the light assembly.

29 Release the tab securing the light cover to the bulbholder, and remove the cover **(see illustration)**.

30 The bulb is a bayonet type fitting in its holder.

31 Refitting is a reversal of the removal procedure.

6 Bulbs (interior lights) - renewal

Instrument panel illumination and warning lights

1 Refer to Section 10.

Automatic transmission selector illumination

2 Using a thin flat-bladed screwdriver, prise up the selector cover and remove it.

3 Pull the bulb assembly to release it from the selector lever, then remove its cover. The bulb is a bayonet fit in its holder **(see illustrations)**.

4 Refitting is a reversal of the removal procedure.

Hazard warning switch

5 The hazard warning light switch, an integral part of the steering column multi-function switch assembly, has a bulb cover which pulls off. The bulb is removed by pulling it from its location.

6 Refitting is a reversal of the removal procedure.

Clock illumination

7 Carefully prise the clock out of its facia location, as described in Section 13.

8 Twist the bulbholder and withdraw it from the rear of the clock **(see illustration)**. Note

6.3a Remove the selector illumination bulb cover . . .

6.3b . . . followed by the (bayonet fitting) bulb

6.8 Withdrawing the clock illumination bulb and its integral holder from the rear of the clock

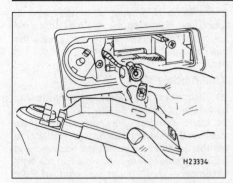

6.13 Heater fan illumination arrangement

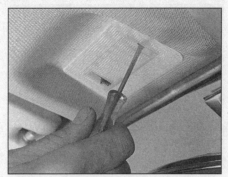

6.16a Releasing the interior (courtesy) light from its location

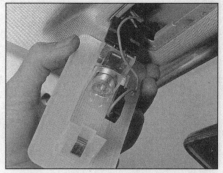

6.16b Interior (courtesy) light pivoted for access to the bulb

that the bulb and bulbholder cannot be separated - they are replaced as an assembly.
9 Refitting is a reversal of the removal procedure.

Cigarette lighter illumination

10 Remove the cigarette lighter, as described in Section 12.
11 Pull the bulbholder from its location in the illuminated surround, then pull the bulb out of the bulbholder.
12 Refitting is a reversal of the removal procedure.

Heater facia illumination

13 Pull the heater fan motor control knob off, then move the air distribution and temperature controls fully to the right. Unclip and remove the heater slide facia towards the left-hand side of the vehicle, removing the slide control knobs only as necessary, and disconnecting its bulbholder (bayonet type) as it is withdrawn **(see illustration)**.
14 The bulb is removed by pulling it from its bulbholder.
15 Refitting is a reversal of the removal procedure.

Interior (courtesy) light

16 Insert a thin flat-bladed screwdriver into the slot in the light assembly, and carefully lever it out of its aperture. The bulb is a bayonet fit **(see illustrations)**.
17 Refit the bulb by reversing the method of

removal, then insert the switch end of the light to the aperture, pivot the light upwards and push home to secure.

Luggage compartment (courtesy) light

18 Carefully prise the luggage compartment (courtesy) light assembly out of its location, using a thin flat-bladed screwdriver. Twist the bulbholder anti-clockwise to remove.
19 The bulb is removed by pulling it from its bulbholder.
20 Refitting is a reversal of the removal procedure.

---

7 Exterior light units -
removal and refitting

1 Disconnect the battery negative (earth) lead (refer to Chapter 5A, Section 1), before removing any of the light units.

Headlight

2 Disconnect the multi-plug from the back of the headlights **(see illustration)**.
3 Twist the sidelight bulb holder to release, then withdraw it.
4 Remove the headlight securing bolt and depress the headlight retaining spring, to allow the headlight assembly to be hinged

7.2 Disconnecting the multi-plug from the back of the headlight

forwards and out of its location **(see illustration)**.
5 Refitting is a reversal of the removal procedure, ensuring that the lower headlight mounting guide is inserted correctly, and that the retaining spring engages fully **(see illustration)**.
6 On completion, check the headlight beam alignment as described in Section 8.

Front direction indicator

7 To remove, release the indicator light retaining spring from its body location, then pull the light assembly forwards and disconnect its multi-plug as it is withdrawn **(see illustrations)**.

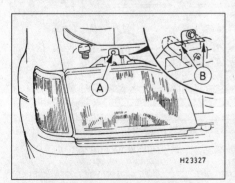

7.4 Headlight retaining bolt (A), and retaining spring arrangement (B)

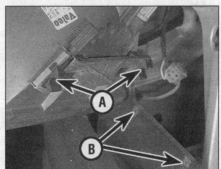

7.5 Refitting the headlight. Mounting guides (A) to fit to panel (B)

7.7a Release the front direction indicator light retaining spring from its body location . . .

12

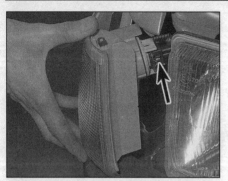

7.7b . . . then pull the light unit out to enable the multi-plug (arrowed) to be disconnected

8 Refitting is a reversal of the removal procedure.

Front direction indicator side repeater

9 Remove the appropriate front wheel arch liner as described in Chapter 11.

10 Remove the appropriate sill scuff plate as described in Chapter 11, and release the clip securing the insulation to the panel forward of the lower A-pillar.

11 Disconnect the supply lead connector and the earth lead, then release their grommet from its panel location.

12 From outside the vehicle, twist the light assembly to release it, then withdraw it and its leads.

13 Refitting is a reversal of the removal procedure, ensuring that the grommet is seated correctly in its panel location.

Rear light cluster

14 Disconnect the multi-plug from the bulbholder, then press the retaining lugs on the bulbholder together and remove it **(see illustration)**.

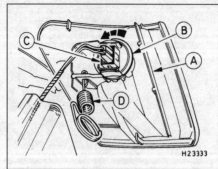

7.14 Press the retaining lugs on the rear light cluster bulbholder together (broken arrows) to release the bulbholder

15 Unscrew the four nuts securing the light unit, then remove the unit and its seal.

16 Refitting is a reversal of the removal procedure. Tighten the light unit securing nuts to their specified torque.

Number plate light

17 Insert a thin flat-bladed screwdriver between the light assembly and the bumper, and carefully prise the light out. Use a rag, or a piece of card, between the screwdriver and the bumper, to prevent damage to the bumper.

18 Detach the connections on the underside of the light assembly.

19 Refitting is a reversal of the removal procedure.

Auxiliary lights

S models

20 Disconnect the battery negative (earth) lead (refer to Chapter 5A, Section 1).

21 Disconnect the light wiring multi-plug then unscrew its retaining nut, withdraw the bolt and remove the light unit **(see illustration)**.

22 Refitting is a reversal of the removal procedure, tightening the retaining nut to the specified torque. On completion, check the auxiliary light beam alignment as described in Section 8.

XR2i models

23 Disconnect the battery negative (earth) lead (refer to Chapter 5A, Section 1).

24 Undo the four Torx retaining screws securing the relevant dual light assembly to its bumper location. Note that the retaining and adjusting screws are captive within the light assembly - they cannot be removed from the assembly **(see illustration)**.

25 Withdraw the light assembly from its location, then remove the caps protecting the bulbs and disconnect the wiring.

26 If required, the lights may be removed individually from their housing at this stage. Each light is secured to its housing unit by a combination of two types of clips - foglight retention differs from driving light retention.

27 The adjusting/retaining clips are removed by undoing the adjustment screws on the front of the housing unit, then turning the clips using pliers or similar tool, before withdrawing. To remove a retaining-only clip, lift the lug on the side of the clip using a screwdriver, then turn the clip using pliers or similar tool, before withdrawing.

28 Refitting is a reversal of the removal procedure. On completion, check the auxiliary light beam alignment as described in Section 8.

---

8 Headlight and auxiliary light beam alignment - checking and adjustment

1 Accurate adjustment of the headlight and auxiliary light beams is only possible using optical beam-setting equipment, and this

---

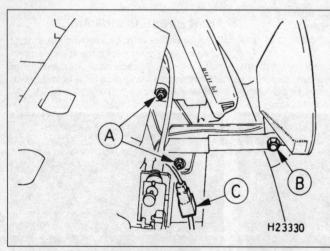

7.21 Auxiliary light fixture (S models)

A Bracket retaining nuts
B Auxiliary light retaining nut
C Auxiliary light multi-plug

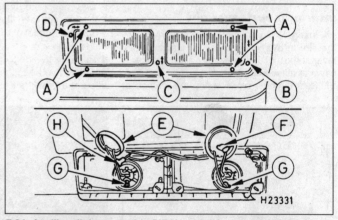

7.24 Auxiliary light assembly (XR2i models) - left-hand unit shown

A Light assembly retaining screws
B Fog light vertical adjustment screw
C Driving light vertical adjustment screw
D Driving light horizontal adjustment screw
E Bulb protective caps
F Fog light bulb connector
G Bulb earth leads
H Driving light bulb connector

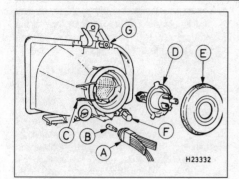

8.2 Exploded view of the headlight unit

A   *Sidelight bulb holder*
B   *Sidelight bulb*
C   *Headlight bulb retainer*
D   *Headlight bulb*
E   *Bulb protective cap*
F   *Horizontal adjustment screw*
G   *Vertical adjustment screw*

work should therefore be carried out by a Ford dealer or service station with the necessary facilities.

2 Temporary adjustment can be made when the headlight has been removed and refitted, or to compensate for normal adjustment whenever a heavy load is being carried. Turn the adjustment screws at the rear of the headlight unit to make the adjustment **(see illustration)**.

3 Before making any adjustments to the headlight settings, it is important that the tyre pressures are correct, and that the vehicle is standing on level ground. Bounce the front of the vehicle a few times to settle the suspension. Ideally, somebody of normal size should sit in the driver's seat during the adjustment, and the vehicle should have a full tank of fuel.

4 S model auxiliary lights are adjusted by slackening the light retaining nuts and swivelling the light assemblies **(see illustration 7.21)**. Tighten the nuts upon completion.

5 XR2i model auxiliary lights are individually adjustable within their housings, provision being made for both vertical and horizontal adjustment of the driving lights, and vertical

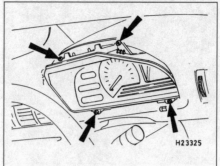

9.4a Instrument cluster securing screws (arrowed)

adjustment only of the foglights. Adjustment is made via Torx-head captive screws on the front of the housings **(see illustration 7.24)**.

6 Whenever temporary adjustments are made, the settings must be reset as soon as possible once the vehicle is in normal use.

9 Instrument panel - removal and refitting

Removal

1 Disconnect the battery negative (earth) lead (refer to Chapter 5A, Section 1).
2 Disconnect the speedometer cable at the transmission casing (see Section 11).
3 Remove the two screws securing the instrument panel bezel from its underside. Remove the bezel.
4 Remove the four screws securing the instrument panel to its location, then carefully pull it out to allow access to the speedometer cable and multi-plug connections. Disconnect the speedometer cable and multi-plug, then remove the instrument panel from the vehicle **(see illustrations)**.

Refitting

5 Refitting is a reversal of removal. On completion check the function of all electrical components.

9.4b Disconnect the speedometer cable from the rear of the instrument cluster . . .

10 Instrument panel components - removal and refitting

Removal

1 Remove the instrument panel as described in Section 9.

Panel illumination and warning light bulbs

2 All bulbholders are a bayonet fit, requiring a "twist and withdraw" removal technique **(see illustration)**. Bulbs cannot be removed from their holders -they are renewed complete.

Printed circuit

3 Insert a thin flat-bladed screwdriver into the multi-plug retainer and carefully unclip it, having noted its orientation **(see illustration)**.
4 Remove all panel illumination and warning light bulbholders.
5 Using a suitable tool (a trim clip removal tool is ideal), carefully prise the printed circuit off its instrument terminals, and release it from its retainers before removing.

Speedometer

6 Remove the two bulbholders on the top of the panel assembly, and release their strip of printed circuit from its retainers, so that the instrument panel halves may be separated.
7 Separate the panel halves by releasing the

9.4c . . . then disconnect the multi-plug

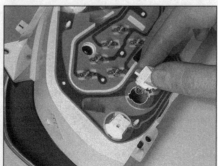

10.2 Removing a bulbholder from the rear of the instrument cluster (bayonet type fitting)

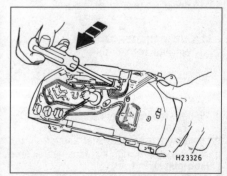

10.3 Unclipping the multi-plug retainer from the rear of the instrument cluster

12

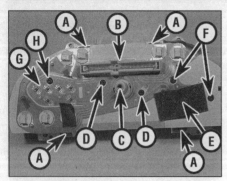

10.7 Rear view of instrument cluster

A *Retaining tags*
B *Multi-plug retainer*
C *Speedometer cable connection*
D *Speedometer gauge retaining screws*
E *Tachometer terminals (obscured by protective pad)*
F *Tachometer gauge retaining screws*
G *Fuel and temperature gauge assembly terminals*
H *Fuel and temperature gauge assembly retaining screw*

retaining tags, taking care to avoid damaging or losing the warning light graphic strips **(see illustration)**.

8 Remove its two Torx-head retaining screws, then detach and withdraw the speedometer from the front of the assembly.

Tachometer

9 Carry out the procedure given in paragraphs 6 and 7.
10 Carefully prise the printed circuit from the tachometer terminals, using a similar method to that described in paragraph 5, releasing it from its retainers as necessary.
11 Remove its two Torx-head retaining screws, then unclip and withdraw the tachometer from the front of the assembly.

Fuel and temperature gauge assembly

12 Removal and refitting procedures are similar in method to those for the tachometer, but only one Torx-head screw retains the assembly.

Refitting

13 Refitting is a reversal of removal.

11 Speedometer cable - removal and refitting

Removal

1 Remove the instrument panel as described in Section 9.
2 Unscrew the speedometer cable from the pinion/speed sensor on the transmission **(see illustration)**.
3 Release the cable-ties and retaining clips in the engine compartment, and withdraw the cable grommet from the bulkhead.

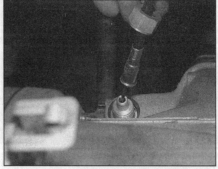

11.2 Detaching the speedometer cable at the transmission casing

4 Note the cable routing for use when refitting. Pull the speedometer cable through into the engine compartment, and remove it from the car.

Refitting

5 Refitting is the reversal of removal. Ensure that the cable is routed as noted before removal, secured with the relevant clips and cable-ties, and that the grommet is properly located in the bulkhead.

12 Cigarette lighter - removal and refitting

Removal

1 Disconnect the battery negative (earth) lead (refer to Chapter 5A, Section 1).
2 Remove the cigarette lighter element (heated section).
3 Carefully prise the element barrel out from the illuminated surround, disconnecting its multi-plug as it is withdrawn.
4 Hinge the illuminated surround out carefully, removing its bulb feed connector as it is withdrawn.

Refitting

5 Refitting is a reversal of the removal procedure.

13 Clock - removal and refitting

Removal

1 Disconnect the battery negative (earth) lead (refer to Chapter 5A, Section 1).
2 Using a thin flat-bladed screwdriver, carefully prise the clock out of the facia **(see illustration)**. Use a piece of card or similar to prevent damage to the facia. Withdraw the clock so that its multi-plug may be disconnected, then remove it from the vehicle.

Refitting

3 Refitting is a reversal of removal. Reset the clock on completion.

13.2 Carefully prise the clock out of the facia

14 Horn - removal and refitting

Removal

1 The horn is mounted forward on the left-hand side of the engine compartment, near the battery.
2 Disconnect the battery negative (earth) lead (refer to Chapter 5A, Section 1).
3 Remove the wiring loom connection from the horn(s).
4 Both single and dual horns are mounted to a bracket which is secured to the bodywork by a single bolt. Remove the bolt and withdraw the horn(s) and bracket from the vehicle. The horn(s) may be separated from the bracket, as required, by removing the retaining nut(s).

Refitting

5 Refitting is a reversal of removal.

15 Wiper arms - removal and refitting

Removal

1 With the wiper(s) "parked" (ie in the normal at-rest position), mark the positions of the blade(s) on the screen, using a wax crayon or strips of masking tape.
2 Lift up the plastic cap from the bottom of the wiper arm, and loosen the nut one or two turns.
3 Lift the wiper arm, and release it from the taper on the spindle by moving it from side to side.
4 Completely remove the nut and washer, then withdraw the wiper arm from the spindle.

Refitting

5 Refitting is a reversal of the removal procedure. Make sure that the arm is fitted in the previously-noted position.

16.6a Remove all retaining screws from the right-hand half of the bulkhead panel (upper centre screw shown) . . .

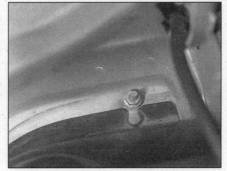

16.6b . . . then disengage the right-hand half of the panel from under its single retaining nut (left-hand shown)

16.7 Unscrew the nut from the wiper motor driving shaft

16 Windscreen wiper motor and linkage - removal and refitting

Removal

Wiper motor

1 Operate the wiper motor, then switch it off so that it returns to its rest position.
2 Disconnect the battery negative (earth) lead (refer to Chapter 5A, Section 1).
3 Dependent on model, disconnect and remove the air cleaner components as necessary to allow access to remove the bulkhead panel.
4 Remove the cooling system expansion tank as described in Chapter 3.
5 Release the wiring loom, any connectors, cable-ties and hoses from the right-hand half of the bulkhead panel, then remove its rubber seal.
6 The right-hand half of the bulkhead panel is secured by screws and a single nut. The nut is located behind the panel at the bonnet hinge end. Release the right-hand half of the panel and, having ensured that it is free to move, remove it **(see illustrations)**.
7 Unscrew the nut from the driving shaft, and pull the crank off the driving shaft taper **(see illustration)**.
8 Undo the three wiper motor retaining bolts

and withdraw the motor assembly **(see illustrations)**. Remove the motor cover, then disconnect the multi-plug and remove the motor from the vehicle.

Linkage

9 Pull the rubber seal off the bulkhead panel.
10 Bring the windscreen wiper linkage to an accessible position, using the ignition switch as a means of stopping the wiper motor returning to the parked position.
11 Disconnect the battery negative (earth) lead (refer to Chapter 5A, Section 1).
12 Prise the linkages off their ball pivots as required, using a suitably-sized open-ended spanner. The crank has a dual (vertically stacked) ball pivot with a bellows separating the two linkages **(see illustrations)**.
13 If the running faces of the ball pivots are damaged, the pivot shaft(s) or crank must be renewed.

Refitting

Wiper motor

14 Refitting is a reversal of the removal procedure, tightening all nuts and bolts to the specified torque. Refit the expansion tank as described in Chapter 3.

Linkage

15 Prior to refitting, grease the ball pivot sockets on the linkages, then locate them on their appropriate ball pivots and press into

16.8a With the crank removed from the driving shaft taper, undo the three wiper motor retaining bolts (arrowed)

position using a suitably-sized socket. The bellows between the two linkages on the crank must also be greased using the specified lubricant. Refit the bulkhead panel rubber seal on completion.

17 Windscreen wiper pivot shaft - removal and refitting

Removal

1 Remove the windscreen wiper arms as described in Section 15.

16.8b . . . and withdraw the wiper motor assembly

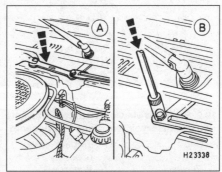

16.12a Windscreen wiper linkage

A Removal   B Refitting

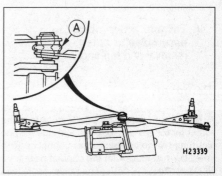

16.12b Windscreen wiper motor bracket with linkage and motor. Inset shows bellows arrangement (A)

12

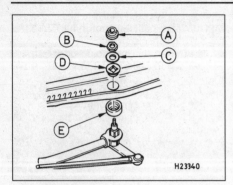

17.3 Windscreen wiper pivot shaft fixture

A Collar
B Pivot shaft securing nut
C Washer
D Outer rubber bush
E Inner rubber bush

2 Carry out the procedure detailed in Section 16, paragraphs 2 to 6.

3 Remove the collars from the pivot shafts, unscrew the pivot shaft securing nuts and remove the washers and outer rubber bushes **(see illustration)**.

4 Undo the two wiper motor bracket securing bolts and remove the bracket assembly from the vehicle, disconnecting the multi-plug from the motor as the assembly is withdrawn **(see illustration)**.

5 Remove the inner rubber bush from the pivot shaft being renewed, and disconnect its linkage as described in paragraph 12 of the previous Section.

6 Remove the circlip, washers, shims and O-ring, keeping them in order for refitting, and withdraw the pivot shaft from the wiper motor bracket assembly.

Refitting

7 Refitting is a reversal of the removal procedure, greasing the pivot shaft with the specified lubricant before inserting it to its location. Refer to paragraph 15 in the previous Section before refitting the linkage. Reference must also be made to the *Specifications* for details of tightening torques.

8 Refit the windscreen wiper arms in accordance with Section 15. Refit the expansion tank as described in Chapter 3.

18 Tailgate wiper motor assembly - removal and refitting

Removal

1 Operate the wiper, then switch it off so that it returns to its rest position. Note that the wiper motor will only operate with the tailgate shut, as the spring-tensioned connector pins must be in contact with the contact plates.

2 Disconnect the battery negative (earth) lead (refer to Chapter 5A, Section 1).

3 Remove the wiper arm with reference to Section 15.

17.4 Removing the wiper motor bracket and linkage assembly (wiper motor removed)

4 Remove the tailgate trim panel as described in Chapter 11.

5 Disconnect the wiper motor multi-plug and earth lead, then undo the three bolts securing the wiper motor bracket, and remove the assembly from the vehicle **(see illustration)**.

6 The wiper motor may be separated from its bracket by undoing the three mounting bolts securing it. Note washer/spacer and rubber insulator fitment.

Refitting

7 Refitting is a reversal of the removal procedure, ensuring that the wiper motor shaft locates through its collar on the exterior panel surface. Tighten all bolts to their specified torque.

19 Windscreen/tailgate washer system components - removal and refitting

Removal

Washer pump

1 Chock the rear wheels then jack up the

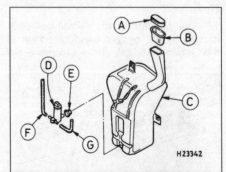

19.2 Exploded view of windscreen/tailgate washer reservoir and pump components

A Cap	F Tailgate washer
B Filter	hose
C Reservoir	G Windscreen
D Washer pump	washer hose
E Pump seal	(marked with
	adhesive tape)

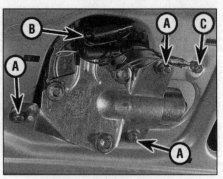

18.5 Tailgate wiper motor

A Wiper motor bracket retaining bolts
B Wiper motor and tailgate "contact fingers" multi- plugs
C Earth connection

front of the car and support it on axle stands (see *"Jacking and vehicle support"*).

2 Withdraw the washer pump from the reservoir, collecting the fluid in a suitable container as the pump is removed. Note the seal fitment **(see illustration)**.

3 Having noted hose fitment to pump connectors, remove the multi-plug and hoses, then remove the pump from the vehicle.

4 Examine the pump seal. If it is perished or otherwise damaged, it should be replaced.

Reservoir

5 Disconnect the battery negative (earth) lead (refer to Chapter 5A, Section 1).

6 Chock the rear wheels then jack up the front of the car and support it on axle stands (see *"Jacking and vehicle support"*). Remove the left-hand front roadwheel.

7 Remove the wheelarch liner as described in Chapter 11.

8 Withdraw the windscreen/tailgate washer pump from the reservoir with its hoses and multi-plug attached, collecting the fluid in a suitable container. Note the seal fitment.

9 Release the hoses and wiring from the reservoir guide and remove the three reservoir securing bolts **(see illustration)**. Remove the reservoir.

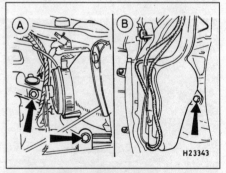

19.9 Windscreen/tailgate washer reservoir securing bolts (arrowed)

A In engine compartment
B In wheelarch (wheelarch liner removed)

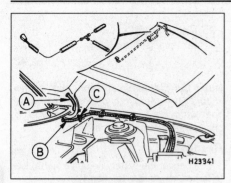

19.16 Routing of washer hoses in the engine compartment

A *Windscreen washer hose*
B *Tailgate washer hose*
C *Tailgate washer hose one-way valve*

Windscreen washer jets and hoses

10 Disconnect the battery negative (earth) lead (refer to Chapter 5A, Section 1).

11 With the bonnet raised and supported on its stay, release the fasteners securing its insulation panel (where fitted). Remove the insulation panel.

12 Carefully press in the retaining lugs on the washer jets using a flat-bladed screwdriver, then raise the washer jets from the exterior surface of the bonnet and separate them from their hoses

13 The windscreen washer jet hose may have been fitted with a one-way (non-return) valve. If this is the case, the main hose run sections can be removed from either side of the valve as required.

14 Chock the rear wheels then jack up the front of the car and support it on axle stands (see *"Jacking and vehicle support"*).

15 Disconnect the windscreen washer hose (marked with adhesive tape) from the washer pump **(see illustration 19.2)**. Withdraw the hose from the reservoir guide, and into the engine compartment.

16 Release the hose from its clips in the engine compartment, including the bonnet hinge clip, release the hose grommet from the bonnet (where fitted) and withdraw the hoses from the bonnet **(see illustration)**.

Tailgate washer jet and hose

17 Disconnect the battery negative (earth) lead (refer to Chapter 5A, Section 1).

18 On XR2i models, remove the tailgate spoiler as described in Chapter 11.

19 Remove the central blanking plug from the upper interior surface of the tailgate, to expose the washer jet base.

20 Depress the washer jet retaining lug using a flat-bladed screwdriver, then push the washer jet out through the panel. From the outside, fully withdraw the washer jet and disconnect it from its hose. Note washer jet seal fitment.

21 Remove the left-hand sun visor.

22 Remove the left-hand A-pillar trim as described in Chapter 11.

23 Release the left-hand side of the headlining by removing the retaining clips/grab handles/coat hooks, as applicable.

24 In the engine compartment, disconnect the tailgate washer hose from its valve. The forward hose run may be removed, if required, in a manner similar to that described in paragraphs 15 and 16 above, releasing it from its clips in the engine compartment.

25 Remove the tailgate washer hose grommet, then withdraw the hose through the bulkhead into the passenger compartment.

26 Release the hose from its A-pillar and roof frame locations. Release the grommet (hose protector) from its tailgate and body locations, and withdraw the hose from the vehicle.

Refitting

27 Refitting is a reversal of removal. Always renew the pump-to-reservoir seal washer, and ensure that all connections are securely made. When reconnecting the pump hoses, ensure that the hose marked with tape is connected to the correspondingly marked connection on the pump.

28 On completion, top-up the washer reservoir (*"see Weekly checks"*) and check that the operation of the washers is satisfactory. If necessary, adjust the windscreen washer jets by inserting a pin into the centre of the jet and directing the flow at the top part of the windscreen.

20 Electric window regulator motor - removal and refitting

Removal

1 Remove the window regulator from the vehicle, as described in Chapter 11.

2 To remove the motor from the regulator mechanism, undo and remove the two Torx head bolts securing it, then carefully separate by unscrewing **(see illustration)**.

Refitting

3 Carefully screw the motor shaft into the regulator mechanism.

4 Temporarily connect the multi-plug, switch

on the ignition and activate the motor, to engage and pull the motor fully into the regulator mechanism.

5 Ensure that the multi-plug connection is located on top of the motor (as if the window regulator is in position in the door), before securing the motor to the regulator mechanism with its two Torx-head bolts.

6 Switch off the ignition and disconnect the multi-plug.

7 Refit the window regulator to the vehicle, in accordance with Chapter 11.

21 Tailgate remote release motor - removal and refitting

Removal

1 Disconnect the battery negative (earth) lead (refer to Chapter 5A, Section 1).

2 Remove the tailgate inner trim panel as described in Chapter 11.

3 Remove the two motor securing screws, then twist the operating rod retaining clip and withdraw the operating rod from it.

4 Disconnect the wiring and remove the motor assembly.

5 The motor may be separated from its bracket by removing two further screws.

Refitting

6 Refitting is a reversal of the removal procedure.

22 Radio/cassette player - removal and refitting

Removal

1 Disconnect the battery negative (earth) lead (refer to Chapter 5A, Section 1).

2 Unscrew the four hexagonal head securing pins from the corners of the unit with an Allen key **(see illustration)**.

3 In order to release the radio retaining clips, two U-shaped rods must be inserted into the special holes on each side of the radio **(see**

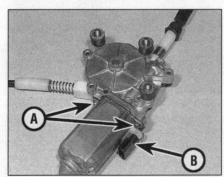

20.2 Electrically operated window motor-securing bolts (A), and multi-plug connection (B)

22.2 Unscrewing the securing pins from the radio/cassette player

12

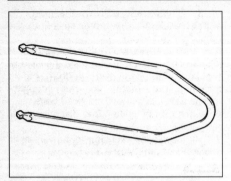

22.3 Radio/cassette player extractor tool

illustration). If possible, it is preferable to obtain purpose-made rods from an audio specialist, as these have cut-outs which snap firmly into the clips so that the radio can be pulled out. Pull the unit squarely from its aperture, or it may jam.

4 With the radio/cassette sufficiently withdrawn, disconnect the feed, earth, aerial and speaker leads.

5 Remove the tools from the unit by gently wiggling and pulling.

Refitting

6 Refitting is a reversal of removal. When the leads are reconnected to the rear of the unit, press it into position to the point where the retaining clips are felt to engage. Reactivate the unit in accordance with the code and the instructions given in the Ford Audio Operating Manual supplied with the vehicle.

23 Speakers - removal and refitting

Removal

1 Disconnect the battery negative (earth) lead (refer to Chapter 5A, Section 1).

Front speaker

2 Remove the side door inner trim panel as described in Chapter 11.

3 Remove the four screws securing the speaker assembly to the door and withdraw

23.3 Remove the screws securing the speaker assembly to the front door

the speaker from the door. Disconnect its multi-plug as it is withdrawn **(see illustration)**.

Rear speaker

4 The rear speakers are suspended beneath the parcel shelf supports and are secured in position by locating tags and screws.

5 Remove the securing screws then lower the speaker, disengaging its locating tags from the parcel shelf support **(see illustrations)**. Disconnect its multi-plug as it is withdrawn.

Refitting

6 Refitting is a reversal of the removal procedure.

24 Speaker balance control joystick - removal and refitting

Removal

1 Disconnect the battery negative (earth) lead (refer to Chapter 5A, Section 1).

2 Using a thin flat-bladed screwdriver, carefully prise the joystick assembly out of the facia. Use a piece of card or similar to prevent damage to the facia. Withdraw the assembly so that its multi-plug may be disconnected, then remove it from the vehicle **(see illustration)**.

Refitting

3 To refit, first connect its multi-plug then push home to secure.

4 Reconnect the battery negative lead.

25 Radio aerial - removal and refitting

Note: *The roof-mounted aerial mast section should be removed prior to using an automatic carwash. This is achieved by unscrewing it from the aerial base.*

Removal

1 Disconnect the battery negative (earth) lead (refer to Chapter 5A, Section 1).

2 Unscrew the aerial mast section, then remove the base section as follows. Insert a thin flat-bladed screwdriver into the slot in the interior (courtesy) light assembly and carefully lever the assembly out.

3 Through the resultant opening, the aerial base securing screw is accessible. Remove the screw and detach the aerial base from the roof of the vehicle, having noted the aerial lead fitment.

Refitting

4 Refitting is a reversal of the removal procedure, ensuring that the aerial base sits squarely on the roof. Insert the switch end of the light assembly to its aperture first, then pivot the light upwards and push home to secure.

26 "Lights-on" warning module - removal and refitting

Removal

The "lights-on" warning feature is fitted to certain models from 1993 onwards. The warning module, which resembles an ordinary relay, is located behind the facia, between the steering column and radio/cassette player. It can be removed by reaching up behind the facia and unclipping it from its mounting.

Refitting

Refitting is a reversal of removal.

23.5a Remove the rear speaker securing screws . . .

23.5b . . . then disengage the locating tags (A) from their location on the parcel shelf support (B)

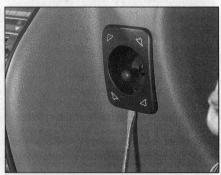

24.2 Carefully prise the speaker balance control joystick from its location

27 Anti-theft systems - general information

Anti-theft alarm system

1 This system provides an added form of vehicle security. When the system is activated, the alarm will sound if the vehicle is broken into through any one of the doors, the bonnet, or tailgate. The alarm will also be triggered if the ignition system is turned on or the radio/cassette disconnected whilst the system is activated.

2 This system is activated/de-activated whenever one of the front doors is locked/unlocked by the key. The system operates on all doors, the bonnet and tailgate whenever each door is individually locked (or, in the case of central locking, when the central locking is engaged). In addition, the ignition/starting system is also immobilised when the system is activated.

3 A further security feature included is that even though the battery may be disconnected whilst the system is activated, the alarm activation continues as soon as the battery is reconnected. Because of this feature, it is important to ensure that the system is de-activated before disconnecting the battery at any time, such as when working on the vehicle.

4 The system incorporates a diagnostic mode to enable Ford technicians to quickly identify any faults in the system. In the event of a system malfunction, any testing or component removal and refitting should be entrusted to a Ford dealer.

Passive Anti-Theft System (PATS)

5 From 1994 model year onwards, a Passive Anti-Theft System (PATS) is fitted. This system, (which works independently of the standard alarm system) is a vehicle immobiliser which prevents the engine from being started unless a specific code, programmed into the ignition key, is recognised by the PATS transceiver.

6 The PATS transceiver, fitted around the ignition switch, decodes a signal from the ignition key as the key is turned from position "O" to position "II". If the coded signal matches that stored in the memory of the PATS module, the engine will start. If the signal is not recognised, the engine will crank on the starter but will not fire.

28 Air bag (driver's side) - removal and refitting
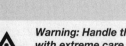

 Warning: Handle the air bag with extreme care as a precaution against personal injury, and always hold it with the cover facing away from your body. If in doubt concerning any proposed work involving the air bag or its control circuitry, consult a Ford dealer or other qualified specialist.

Removal

1 Disconnect the battery negative (earth) lead (refer to Chapter 5A, Section 1).

 Warning: Before proceeding, wait a minimum of 15 minutes, as a precaution against accidental firing of the air bag. This period ensures that any stored energy in the back-up capacitor is dissipated.

2 Undo the screws, and remove the steering column lower shroud.

3 Undo the two external screws and the two internal screws and remove the steering column upper shroud.

4 Turn the steering wheel as necessary so that one of the air bag module retaining bolts becomes accessible from the rear of the steering wheel. Undo the bolt, then turn the steering wheel again until the second bolt is accessible. Undo this bolt also.

5 Withdraw the air bag module from the steering wheel far enough to access the wiring multi-plug. Some force may be needed to free the module from the additional steering wheel spoke retainers.

6 Disconnect the multi-plug from the rear of the module, and remove the module from the vehicle.

 Warning: Position the air bag module in a safe place, with the mechanism facing downwards as a precaution against accidental operation.

 Warning: Do not attempt to open or repair the air bag unit, or apply any electrical current to it. Do not use any air bag which is visibly damaged or which has been tampered with.

Refitting

7 Refitting is a reversal of the removal procedure.

29 Air bag (passenger's side) - removal and refitting

Warning: Handle the air bag with extreme care as a precaution against personal injury, and always hold it with the cover facing away from your body. If in doubt concerning any proposed work involving the air bag or its control circuitry, consult a Ford dealer or other qualified specialist.

Removal

1 Disconnect the battery negative (earth) lead (refer to Chapter 5A, Section 1).

 Warning: Before proceeding, wait a minimum of 15 minutes, as a precaution against accidental firing of the air bag. This period ensures that any stored energy in the back-up capacitor is dissipated.

2 Remove the facia as described in Chapter 11.

3 Undo the air bag module retaining nuts and remove the unit from the facia.

 Warning: Position the air bag module in a safe place, with the mechanism facing downwards as a precaution against accidental operation.

 Warning: Do not attempt to open or repair the air bag unit, or apply any electrical current to it. Do not use any air bag which is visibly damaged or which has been tampered with.

Refitting

4 Refitting is a reversal of the removal procedure.

30 Air bag control module - removal and refitting

Removal

1 Disconnect the battery negative (earth) lead (refer to Chapter 5A, Section 1).

Warning: Before proceeding, wait a minimum of 15 minutes, as a precaution against accidental firing of the air bag unit. This period ensures that any stored energy in the back-up capacitor is dissipated.

2 Remove the module access cover from the rear of the glovebox.

3 Press the module wiring multi-plug locking tag upwards then pivot the retaining strap over and disconnect the multi-plug.

4 Remove the facia as described in Chapter 11.

5 Undo the three retaining bolts and remove the module from its location.

Refitting

6 Refitting is a reversal of the removal procedure.

31 Air bag clock spring - removal and refitting

Removal

1 Remove the steering wheel as described in Chapter 10.

2 Undo the three retaining screws, and remove the clock spring from the steering wheel. As the unit is withdrawn, note which aperture in the steering wheel the air bag

12

wiring passes through, as an aid to reassembly.

Refitting

3 Position the clock spring on the steering wheel, routing the wiring as noted on removal, and secure with the retaining screws.

4 The clock spring must now be centred as follows.

5 Depress the locking pin, and rotate the clock spring outer rotor fully anti-clockwise until it is tight **(see illustration)**.

6 Now turn the outer rotor approximately 3.75 turns clockwise, then release the locking pin. Ensure that the locking pin engages when it is released.

7 Check that the relative position of the direction indicator cancelling cam to the cable connector on the clock spring assembly is as shown **(see illustration 31.5)**.

8 Refit the steering wheel as described in Chapter 10.

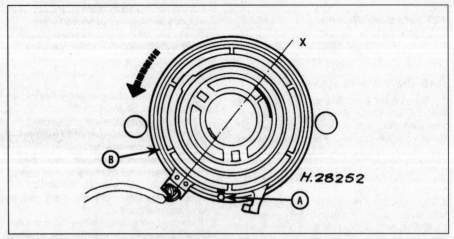

31.5 Centring the air bag clock spring. Depress locking pin (A) and rotate outer rotor (B) anti-clockwise ("X" indicates relative position of the direction indicator cancelling cam to the cable connector - see text)

NOTES:

1. All diagrams are divided into numbered circuits depending on function e.g. Diagram 2: Exterior lighting.
2. Items are arranged in relation to a plan view of the vehicle.
3. Wires may interconnect between diagrams and are located by using a grid reference e.g. 2/A1 denotes a position on diagram 2 grid location A1.
4. Complex items appear on the diagrams as blocks and are expanded on the internal connections page.
5. Brackets show how the circuit may be connected in more than one way.
6. Not all items are fitted to all models.

INTERNAL CONNECTION DETAILS

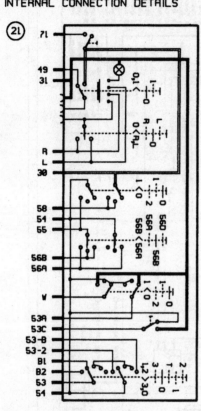

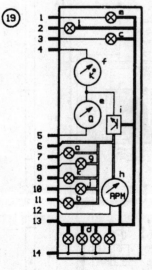

KEY TO INSTRUMENT CLUSTER

a = No Charge Warning Lamp
b = Handbrake Warning Lamp
c = Main Beam Warning Lamp
d = Instrument Illumination
e = Fuel Gauge
f = Temperature Gauge
g = Oil Pressure Lamp
h = Tachometer
i = Voltage Stabilizer
j = ABS Warning Lamp
k = Choke Warning Lamp
l = Dir. Ind. Warning Lamp LH
m = Dir. Ind. Warning Lamp RH

FUSEBOX

FUSE	RATING	CIRCUIT
1	3A	Electric Engine Control System
2	15A	Interior Lamp, Cigar Lighter, Clock And Radio Memory
3	20A	Central Locking
4	30A	Heated Rear Window
5	10A	Dim Dip Lighting
6	10A	LH Side Lamp And Rear Foglamp
7	10A	RH Side Lamp
8	10A	LH Dipped Beam
9	10A	RH Dipped Beam
10	15A	LH Main Beam And RH Spot Lamp
11	15A	RH Main Beam And LH Spot Lamp
12	20A	Heater Blower And Reversing Lamp
13	30A	Radiator Cooling Fan
14	15A	Front Foglamps (XR2i Only)
15	15A	Horn
16	20A	Wash/wipe
17	10A	Brake Lights And Instruments
18	30A	Electric Windows
19	20A	Electric Fuel Pump
20	10A	HEGO Sensor
21	10A	LH Direction Indicators
22	10A	RH Direction Indicators
23		Free
24		Free
25		Free
26	15A	Tailgate Release
27	30A	Heated Windscreen
28	30A	Heated Windscreen

FUSEBOX (CHANGES FROM 1992)

FUSE	RATING	CIRCUIT
25	15A	Tailgate Release
26	30A	Heated Windscreen
27	30A	Heated Windscreen
28	20A	Power Sunroof

KEY TO SYMBOLS

PLUG-IN CONNECTOR	—⟩
EARTH	G1004
BULB	⊗
DIODE	▷|—
SOLDERED JOINT	○ S1003
FUSE/ FUSIBLE LINK	▭

Notes, internal connection details, and key to symbols

H24500

T.H.HARKE

12

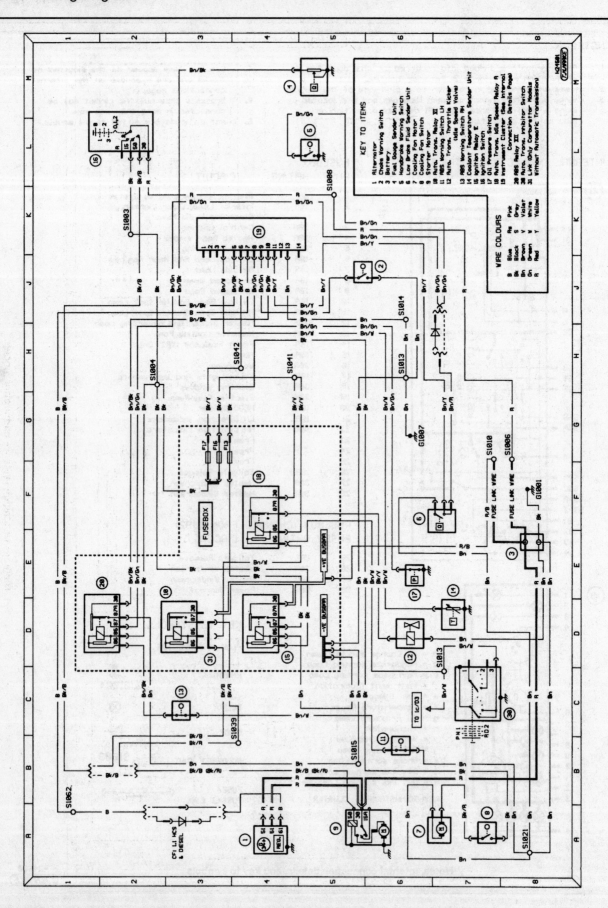

Diagram 1: Starting, charging, cooling fan, ABS, warning lamps and gauges

KEY TO ITEMS

1 Alternator
2 Choke Warning Switch
3 Battery
4 Fuel Gauge Sender Unit
5 Handbrake Warning Switch
6 Low Brake Fluid Sender Unit
7 Cooling Fan Motor
8 Cooling Fan Motor
9 Cooling Fan Switch
10 Starter Motor
11 Auto. Trans. Relay II
12 ABS Warning Switch LH
13 Auto. Trans. Throttle Kicker (Idle Speed Valve)
14 ABS Warning Switch RH
15 Coolant Temperature Sender Unit
16 Auto. Trans. Idle Speed Relay T
17 Ignition Relay T
18 Ignition Switch
19 Oil Pressure Switch
20 Auto. Trans. Idle Speed Relay R
30 Instrument Cluster (See Internal Connection Details Page)
31 ABS Relay II
38 Auto. Trans. Inhibitor Switch
39 Link (Only Carburettor Models Without Automatic Transmission)

WIRE COLOURS

B Blue
Bk Black
Bn Brown
Gn Green
R Red
Rs Pink
S Grey
V Violet
W White
Y Yellow

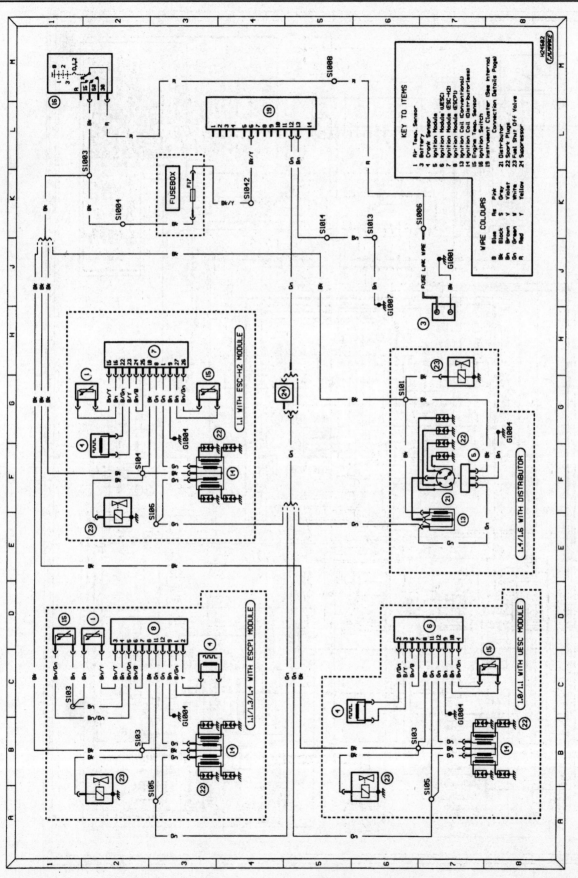

Diagram 1a: Ignition system – carburettor models

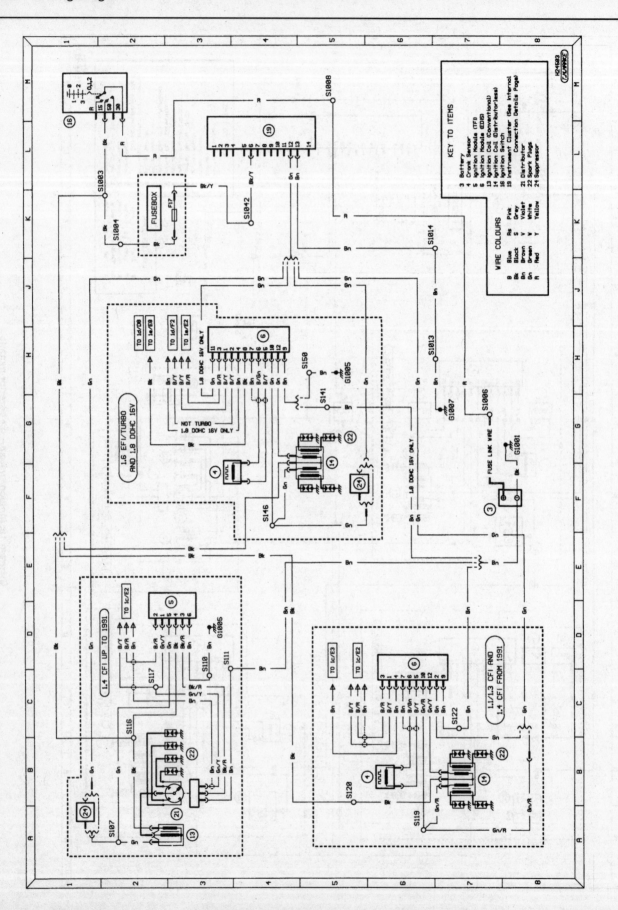

Diagram 1b: Ignition system – fuel-injected models

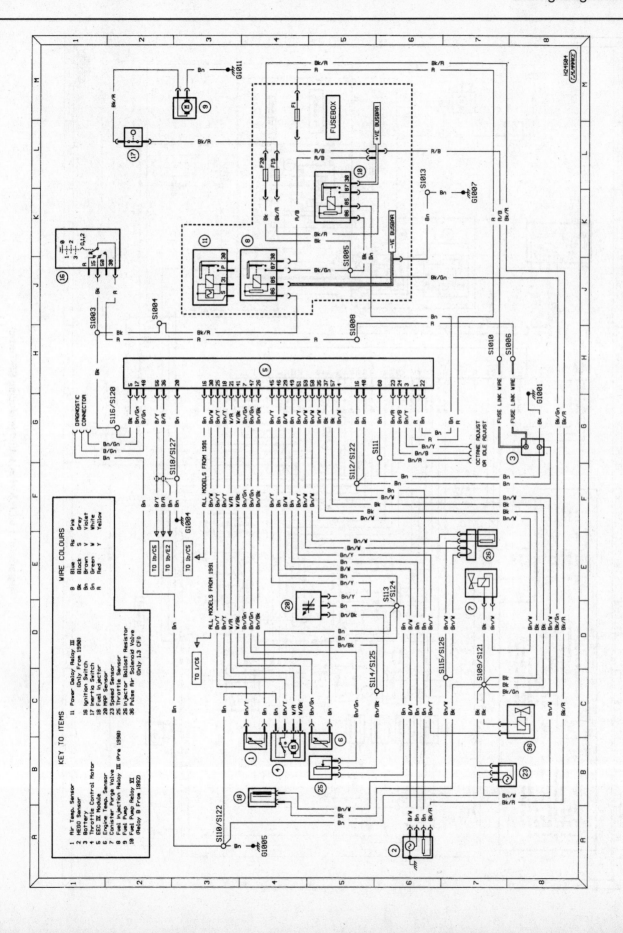

Diagram 1c: Typical 1.1/1.3/1.4 CFi fuel injection

KEY TO ITEMS

1 Air Temp. Sensor
2 HEGO Sensor
3 Battery
4 Throttle Control Motor
5 EEC IV Module
6 Engine Temp. Sensor
7 Canister Purge Valve
8 Fuel Injection Relay III (Pre 1990)
9 Fuel Pump
10 Fuel Pump Relay VI (Relay B from 1992)
11 Power Delay Relay III (Only From 1990)
16 Ignition Switch
17 Inertia Switch
18 Fuel Injector
20 MAP Sensor
23 Speed Sensor
25 Throttle Sensor
26 Injector Ballast Resistor
36 Pulse Air Solenoid Valve (Only 1.3 CFi)

WIRE COLOURS

B	Blue	Rs	Pink
Bk	Black	S	Gray
Bn	Brown	V	Violet
Gn	Green	W	White
R	Red	Y	Yellow

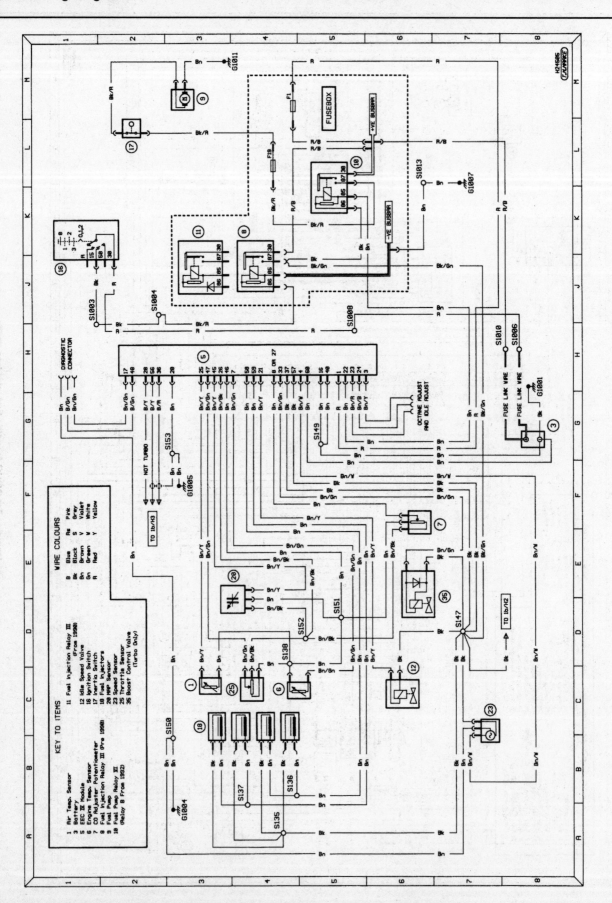

Diagram 1d: 1.6 EFi fuel injection (including RS Turbo)

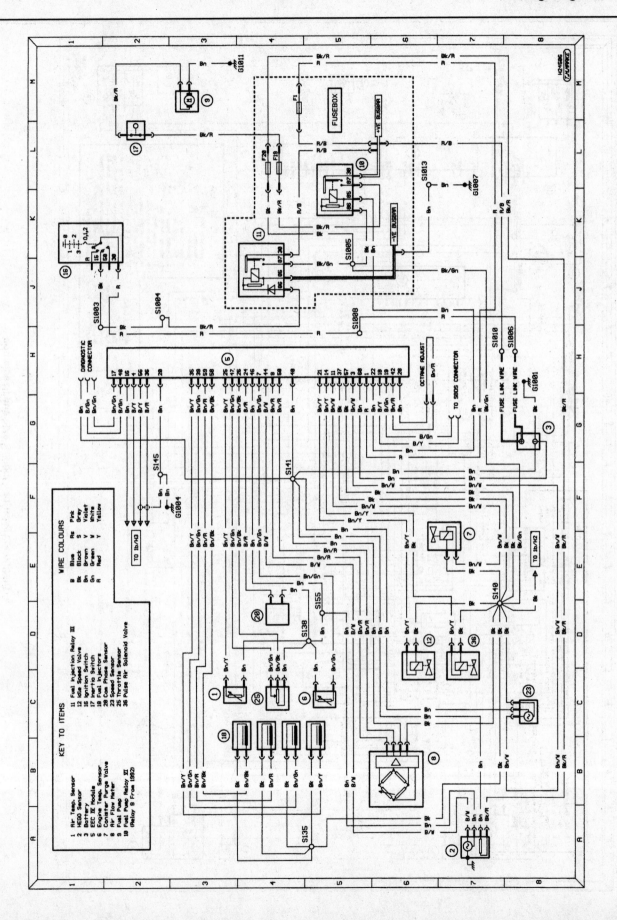

Diagram 1e: DOHC 16-valve fuel injection

KEY TO ITEMS

1 Air Temp. Sensor
2 HEGO Sensor
3 Battery
5 EEC IV Module
6 Engine Temp. Sensor
7 Canister Purge Valve
8 Air Flow Meter
9 Fuel Pump
10 Fuel Pump Relay II (Relay B from 1992)
11 Fuel Injection Relay III
12 Idle Speed Valve
16 Ignition Switch
17 Inertia Switch
18 Fuel Injectors
20 Con Phase Sensor
25 Throttle Sensor
36 Pulse Air Solenoid Valve

WIRE COLOURS

B Blue
Bk Black
Bn Brown
Gn Green
R Red
Rs Pink
S Grey
V Violet
W White
Y Yellow

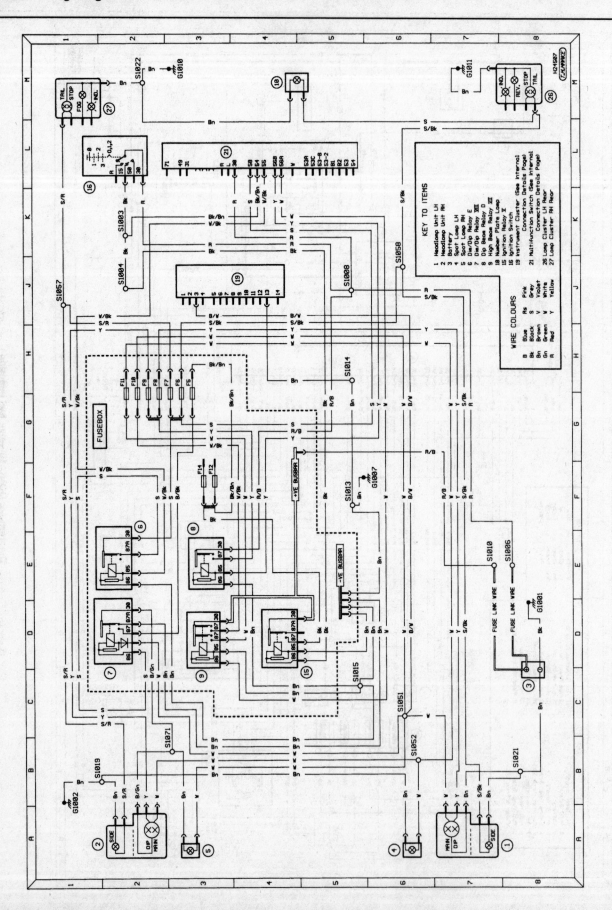

Diagram 2: Exterior lighting – side and headlamps

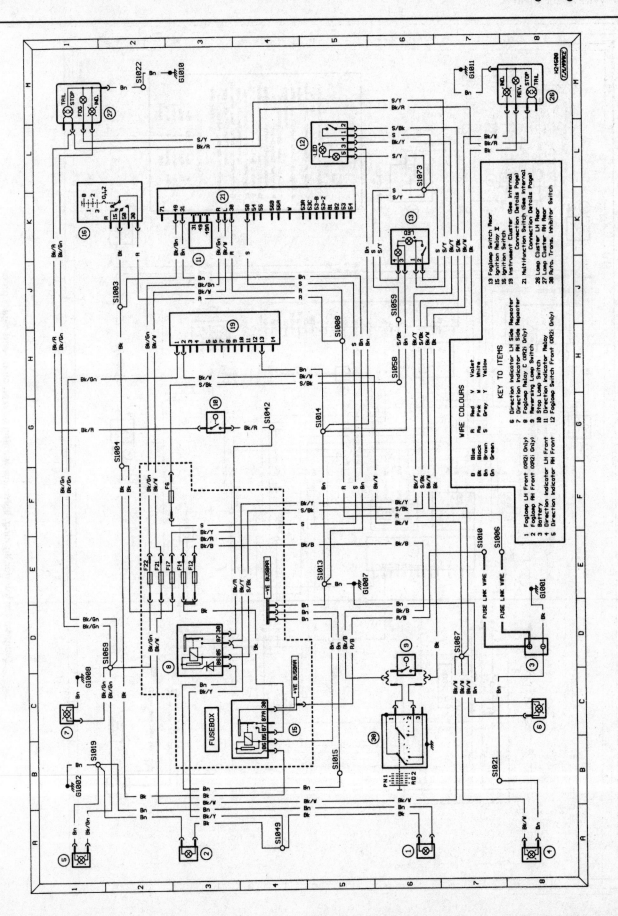

Diagram 2a: Exterior lighting – stop, reversing, fog and direction indicator lamps

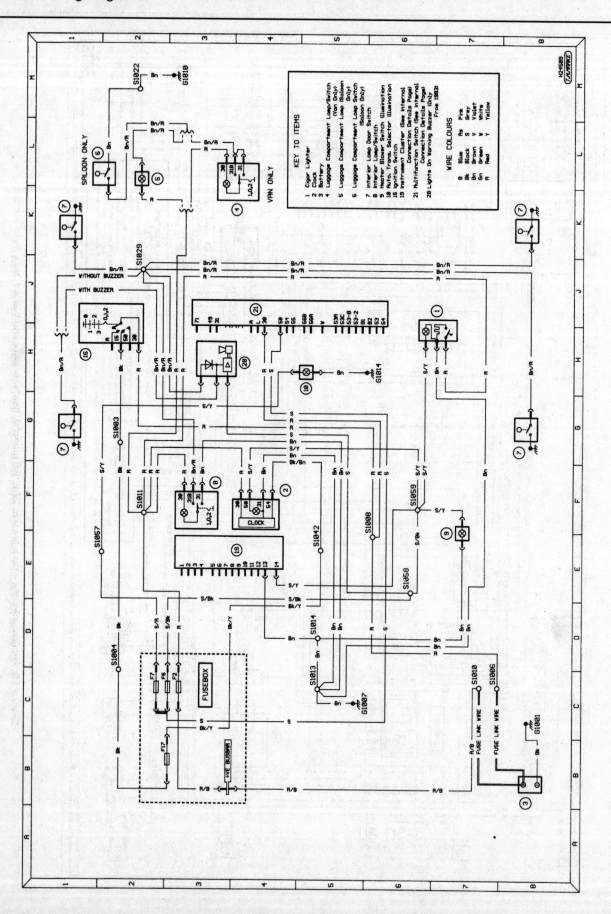

Diagram 2b: Interior lighting, lights-on warning buzzer, clock and cigar lighter

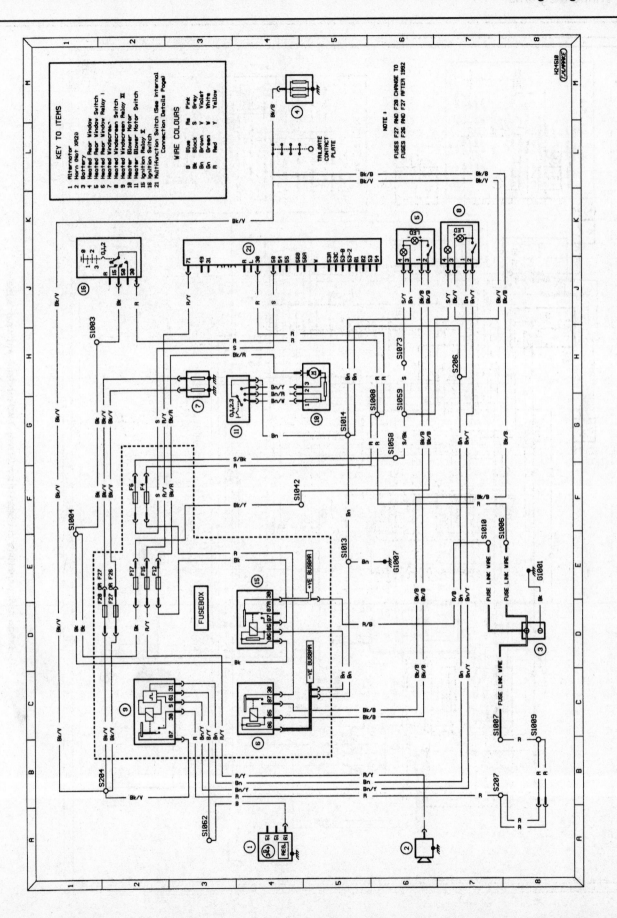

Diagram 3: Ancillary circuits – horn (except XR2i/RS models), heater blower and heated front /rear screens

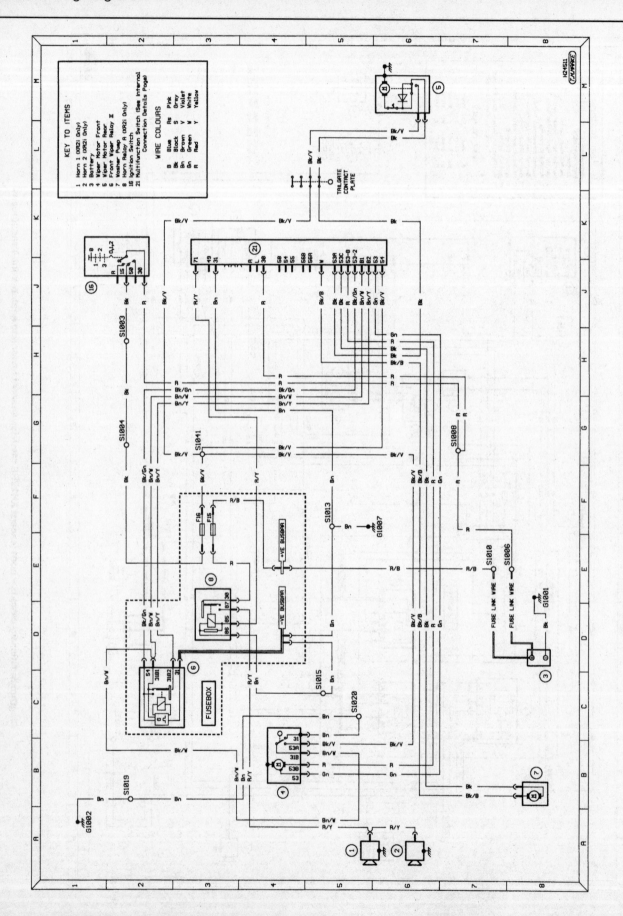

Diagram 3a: Ancillary circuits – horn (R2i and RS models) and wash/wipe

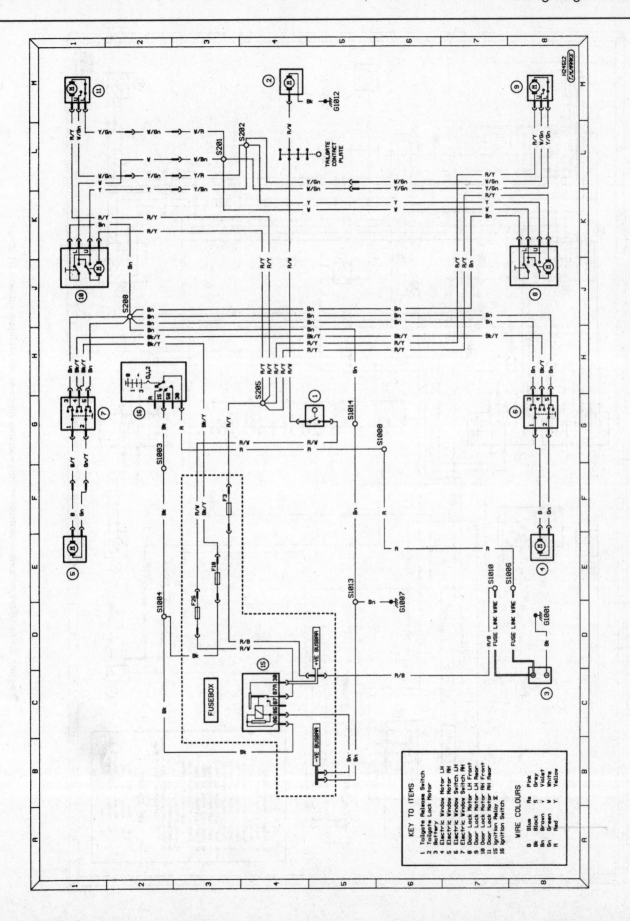

Diagram 3b: Ancillary circuits – central locking, electric windows and tailgate release (up to 1992)

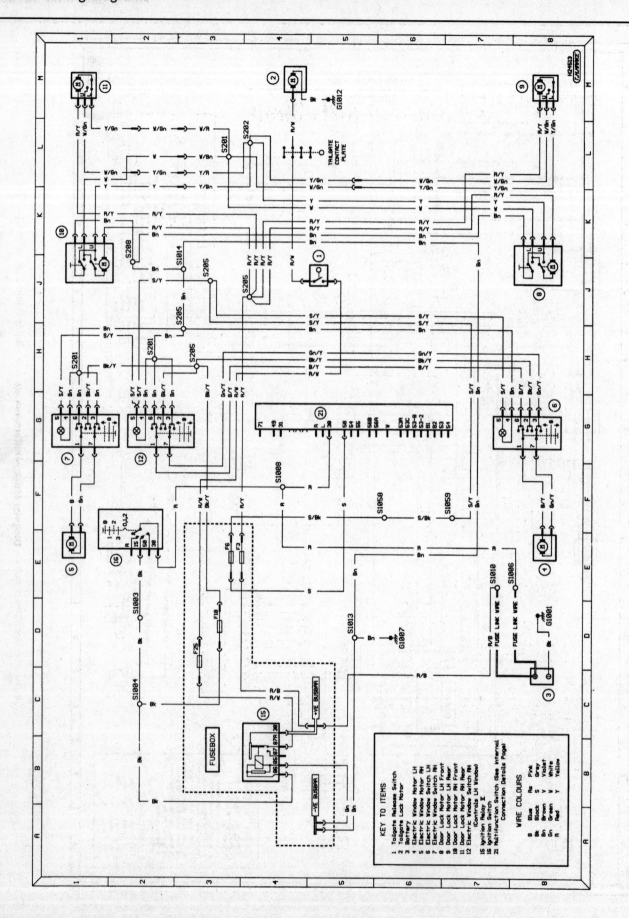

Diagram 3c: Ancillary circuits – central locking, electric windows and tailgate release (1992-on)

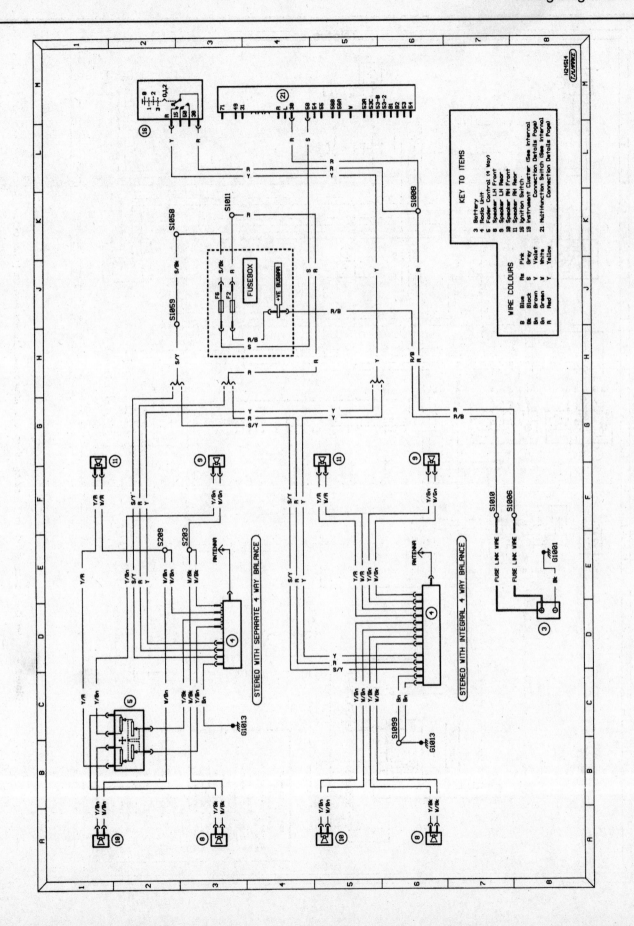

Diagram 4: In-car entertainment

Notes

Dimensions and weights	.REF•1	Conversion factors	.REF•6
Vehicle identification	.REF•3	Tools and working facilities	.REF•7
General repair procedures	.REF•4	MOT test checks	.REF•10
Jacking and vehicle support	.REF•5	Fault finding	.REF•14
Buying spare parts	.REF•5	Glossary of technical terms	.REF•22
Radio/cassette unit anti-theft system	.REF•5	Index	.REF•27

Dimensions and weights

Note: *All figures are approximate, and may vary according to model. Refer to manufacturer's data for exact figures.*

Dimensions

Overall length:
    3/5 door hatchback models .... 3743 mm
    XR2i, RS Turbo and RS 1800 models .... 3801 mm
    Courier models .... 4052 mm
Width (excluding mirrors):
    3/5 door hatchback models .... 1606 mm
    XR2i, RS Turbo and RS 1800 models .... 1630 mm
    Courier models .... 1650 mm
Overall height:
    3/5 door hatchback models .... 1376 mm
    XR2i, RS Turbo and RS 1800 models .... 1365 mm
    Courier models .... 1812 mm
Wheelbase:
    Courier models .... 2700 mm
    All other models .... 2446 mm
Front track:
    3/5 door hatchback models .... 1392 mm
    XR2i, RS Turbo and RS 1800 models .... 1406 mm
    Courier models .... 1392 mm
Rear track:
    3/5 door hatchback models .... 1384 mm
    XR2i, RS Turbo and RS 1800 models .... 1376 mm
    Courier models .... 1395 mm

Weights

Kerb weight*:

3-door hatchback:

1.0 litre models	770 to 780 kg
1.1 litre models	785 to 850 kg
1.3 litre models	825 to 870 kg
1.4 litre models	920 to 940 kg
1.6 litre models	990 to 1010 kg
XR2i (1.6 litre) models	890 to 910 kg
XR2i (1.8 litre) models	955 to 974 kg
RS Turbo models	910 to 930 kg
RS 1800 models	954 to 965 kg

5-door hatchback:

1.0 litre models	795 to 810 kg
1.1 litre models	810 to 845 kg
1.3 litre models	845 to 870 kg
1.4 litre models	840 to 870 kg
1.6 litre models	980 to 1029 kg

Vans:

1.0 litre models	775 kg
1.1 litre models	775 to 790 kg
1.3 litre models	795 kg
Courier models	920 kg

Payload:

1.0 litre Van models	310 to 335 kg
1.1 litre Van models	310 to 335 kg
1.3 litre Van models	330 kg
Courier models	515 to 525 kg
Maximum roof rack load	75 kg
Maximum towing weight	Refer to your Ford dealer for weights and legal requirements concerning anticipated gradients and altitudes.

Exact kerb weight varies depending on model - refer to VIN plate for details

Vehicle identification

Modifications are a continuing and unpublicised process in vehicle manufacture, quite apart from major model changes. Spare parts manuals and lists are compiled upon a numerical basis, the individual vehicle identification numbers being essential to correct identification of the component concerned.

When ordering spare parts, always give as much information as possible. Quote the vehicle model, year of manufacture, body and engine numbers as appropriate.

The *vehicle identification plate* is located on the top of the front crossmember in the engine compartment **(see illustration)**. In addition to many other details, it carries the Vehicle Identification Number (VIN), maximum vehicle weight information, and codes for interior trim and body colours.

The *Vehicle Identification Number (VIN)* is given on the vehicle identification plate **(see illustration)**. It is also located in a recess in the floor to the right-hand side of the driver's seat, access being gained after lifting the aperture cover. On later models, the number is also stamped on a metal tag fixed to the left-hand side of the facia, which can be read through the windscreen.

The *body number and paint code numbers* are located on the vehicle identification plate.

The *engine number* location is dependent on the engine type. On the HCS engines, it is stamped on the front left-hand side of the cylinder block towards the transmission (facing the radiator) **(see illustration)**. On the CVH and PTE engines, the location of the engine number is dependent on the equipment fitted, but is on the exhaust side of the engine, facing either towards the timing belt end or the transmission end **(see illustration)**. On the Zetec engines, the number can be found on the forward-facing side of the cylinder block, level with the starter motor, or on the cylinder head just above the thermostat housing **(see illustration)**.

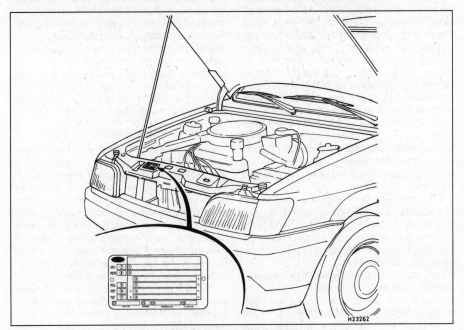

Vehicle identification plate

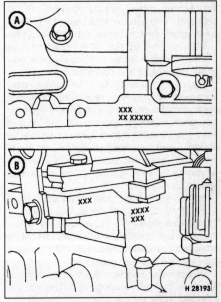

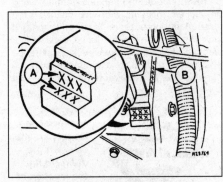

HCS engine identification numbers location

A *Engine code (side or upper face)*
B *Serial number*

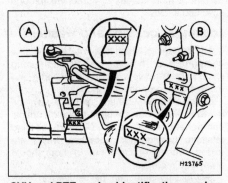

CVH and PTE engine identification number location is on (A) the right-hand side or (B) the left-hand side, according to model and equipment

Zetec engine identification number on forward-facing side of cylinder block level with the starter motor (A), or on cylinder head just above thermostat housing (B)

Whenever servicing, repair or overhaul work is carried out on the car or its components, observe the following procedures and instructions. This will assist in carrying out the operation efficiently and to a professional standard of workmanship.

Joint mating faces and gaskets

When separating components at their mating faces, never insert screwdrivers or similar implements into the joint between the faces in order to prise them apart. This can cause severe damage which results in oil leaks, coolant leaks, etc upon reassembly. Separation is usually achieved by tapping along the joint with a soft-faced hammer in order to break the seal. However, note that this method may not be suitable where dowels are used for component location.

Where a gasket is used between the mating faces of two components, a new one must be fitted on reassembly; fit it dry unless otherwise stated in the repair procedure. Make sure that the mating faces are clean and dry, with all traces of old gasket removed. When cleaning a joint face, use a tool which is unlikely to score or damage the face, and remove any burrs or nicks with an oilstone or fine file.

Make sure that tapped holes are cleaned with a pipe cleaner, and keep them free of jointing compound, if this is being used, unless specifically instructed otherwise.

Ensure that all orifices, channels or pipes are clear, and blow through them, preferably using compressed air.

Oil seals

Oil seals can be removed by levering them out with a wide flat-bladed screwdriver or similar implement. Alternatively, a number of self-tapping screws may be screwed into the seal, and these used as a purchase for pliers or some similar device in order to pull the seal free.

Whenever an oil seal is removed from its working location, either individually or as part of an assembly, it should be renewed.

The very fine sealing lip of the seal is easily damaged, and will not seal if the surface it contacts is not completely clean and free from scratches, nicks or grooves. If the original sealing surface of the component cannot be restored, and the manufacturer has not made provision for slight relocation of the seal relative to the sealing surface, the component should be renewed.

Protect the lips of the seal from any surface which may damage them in the course of fitting. Use tape or a conical sleeve where possible. Lubricate the seal lips with oil before fitting and, on dual-lipped seals, fill the space between the lips with grease.

Unless otherwise stated, oil seals must be fitted with their sealing lips toward the lubricant to be sealed.

Use a tubular drift or block of wood of the appropriate size to install the seal and, if the seal housing is shouldered, drive the seal down to the shoulder. If the seal housing is unshouldered, the seal should be fitted with its face flush with the housing top face (unless otherwise instructed).

Screw threads and fastenings

Seized nuts, bolts and screws are quite a common occurrence where corrosion has set in, and the use of penetrating oil or releasing fluid will often overcome this problem if the offending item is soaked for a while before attempting to release it. The use of an impact driver may also provide a means of releasing such stubborn fastening devices, when used in conjunction with the appropriate screwdriver bit or socket. If none of these methods works, it may be necessary to resort to the careful application of heat, or the use of a hacksaw or nut splitter device.

Studs are usually removed by locking two nuts together on the threaded part, and then using a spanner on the lower nut to unscrew the stud. Studs or bolts which have broken off below the surface of the component in which they are mounted can sometimes be removed using a stud extractor. Always ensure that a blind tapped hole is completely free from oil, grease, water or other fluid before installing the bolt or stud. Failure to do this could cause the housing to crack due to the hydraulic action of the bolt or stud as it is screwed in.

When tightening a castellated nut to accept a split pin, tighten the nut to the specified torque, where applicable, and then tighten further to the next split pin hole. Never slacken the nut to align the split pin hole, unless stated in the repair procedure.

When checking or retightening a nut or bolt to a specified torque setting, slacken the nut or bolt by a quarter of a turn, and then retighten to the specified setting. However, this should not be attempted where angular tightening has been used.

For some screw fastenings, notably cylinder head bolts or nuts, torque wrench settings are no longer specified for the latter stages of tightening, "angle-tightening" being called up instead. Typically, a fairly low torque wrench setting will be applied to the bolts/nuts in the correct sequence, followed by one or more stages of tightening through specified angles.

Locknuts, locktabs and washers

Any fastening which will rotate against a component or housing during tightening should always have a washer between it and the relevant component or housing.

Spring or split washers should always be renewed when they are used to lock a critical component such as a big-end bearing retaining bolt or nut. Locktabs which are folded over to retain a nut or bolt should always be renewed.

Self-locking nuts can be re-used in non-critical areas, providing resistance can be felt when the locking portion passes over the bolt or stud thread. However, it should be noted that self-locking stiffnuts tend to lose their effectiveness after long periods of use, and should then be renewed as a matter of course.

Split pins must always be replaced with new ones of the correct size for the hole.

When thread-locking compound is found on the threads of a fastener which is to be re-used, it should be cleaned off with a wire brush and solvent, and fresh compound applied on reassembly.

Special tools

Some repair procedures in this manual entail the use of special tools such as a press, two or three-legged pullers, spring compressors, etc. Wherever possible, suitable readily-available alternatives to the manufacturer's special tools are described, and are shown in use. In some instances, where no alternative is possible, it has been necessary to resort to the use of a manufacturer's tool, and this has been done for reasons of safety as well as the efficient completion of the repair operation. Unless you are highly-skilled and have a thorough understanding of the procedures described, never attempt to bypass the use of any special tool when the procedure described specifies its use. Not only is there a very great risk of personal injury, but expensive damage could be caused to the components involved.

Environmental considerations

When disposing of used engine oil, brake fluid, antifreeze, etc, give due consideration to any detrimental environmental effects. Do not, for instance, pour any of the above liquids down drains into the general sewage system, or onto the ground to soak away. Many local council refuse tips provide a facility for waste oil disposal, as do some garages. If none of these facilities are available, consult your local Environmental Health Department, or the National Rivers Authority, for further advice.

With the universal tightening-up of legislation regarding the emission of environmentally-harmful substances from motor vehicles, most vehicles have tamperproof devices fitted to the main adjustment points of the fuel system. These devices are primarily designed to prevent unqualified persons from adjusting the fuel/air mixture, with the chance of a consequent increase in toxic emissions. If such devices are found during servicing or overhaul, they should, wherever possible, be renewed or refitted in accordance with the manufacturer's requirements or current legislation.

Note: It is antisocial and illegal to dump oil down the drain. To find the location of your local oil recycling bank, call this number free.

OIL CARE — FOLLOW THE CODE

OIL BANK LINE
0800 66 33 66

The jack supplied with the vehicle tool kit should only be used for changing the roadwheels - see *"Wheel changing"* at the front of this manual. When jacking up the vehicle to carry out repair or maintenance tasks, a pillar or trolley type jack of suitable lifting capacity must be used, supplemented with axle stands positioned only beneath the appropriate points under the vehicle **(see illustration)**. Note that the vehicle must never be jacked up at the rear under the axle beam.

The maximum kerb weight of the vehicle must not be exceeded when jacking and supporting the vehicle. Do not under any circumstances jack up the rear of the vehicle under the rear axle. **Never** *work under, around or near a raised vehicle unless it is adequately supported in at least two places with axle stands.*

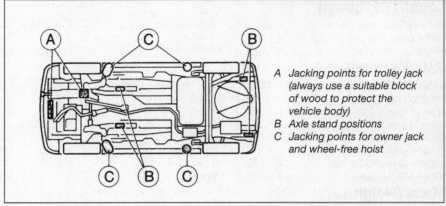

A *Jacking points for trolley jack (always use a suitable block of wood to protect the vehicle body)*
B *Axle stand positions*
C *Jacking points for owner jack and wheel-free hoist*

Underside view of the vehicle showing the jacking point locations

Buying spare parts

Buying spare parts

Spare parts are available from many sources, including maker's appointed garages, accessory shops, and motor factors. To be sure of obtaining the correct parts, it will sometimes be necessary to quote the vehicle identification number. If possible, it can also be useful to take the old parts along for positive identification. Items such as starter motors and alternators may be available under a service exchange scheme - any parts returned should always be clean.

Our advice regarding spare part sources is as follows.

Officially-appointed garages

This is the best source of parts which are peculiar to your car, and which are not otherwise generally available (eg badges, interior trim, certain body panels, etc). It is also the only place at which you should buy parts if the vehicle is still under warranty.

Accessory shops

These are very good places to buy materials and components needed for the maintenance of your car (oil, air and fuel filters, spark plugs, light bulbs, drivebelts, oils and greases, brake pads, touch-up paint, etc). Components of this nature sold by a reputable shop are of the same standard as those used by the car manufacturer.

Besides components, these shops also sell tools and general accessories, usually have convenient opening hours, charge lower prices, and can often be found not far from home. Some accessory shops have parts counters where the components needed for almost any repair job can be purchased or ordered.

Motor factors

Good factors will stock all the more important components which wear out comparatively quickly, and can sometimes supply individual components needed for the overhaul of a larger assembly (eg brake seals and hydraulic parts, bearing shells, pistons, valves, alternator brushes). They may also handle work such as cylinder block reboring, crankshaft regrinding and balancing, etc.

Tyre and exhaust specialists

These outlets may be independent, or members of a local or national chain. They frequently offer competitive prices when compared with a main dealer or local garage, but it will pay to obtain several quotes before making a decision. When researching prices, also ask what "extras" may be added - for instance, fitting a new valve and balancing the wheel are both commonly charged on top of the price of a new tyre.

Other sources

Beware of parts or materials obtained from market stalls, car boot sales or similar outlets. Such items are not invariably sub-standard, but there is little chance of compensation if they do prove unsatisfactory. In the case of safety-critical components such as brake pads, there is the risk not only of financial loss but also of an accident causing injury or death.

Second-hand components or assemblies obtained from a car breaker can be a good buy in some circumstances, but this sort of purchase is best made by the experienced DIY mechanic.

Radio/cassette unit anti-theft system - precaution

The radio/cassette unit fitted as standard or optional equipment may be equipped with a built-in security code, to deter thieves. If the power source to the unit is cut, the anti-theft system will activate. Even if the power source is immediately reconnected, the radio/cassette unit will not function until the correct security code has been entered. Therefore, if you do not know the correct security code for the radio/cassette unit **do not** disconnect either of the battery terminals, or remove the radio/cassette unit from the vehicle.

To enter the correct security code, follow the instructions provided with the radio/cassette player or vehicle handbook.

If an incorrect code is entered, the unit will become locked, and cannot be operated.

If this happens, or if the security code is lost or forgotten, seek the advice of your Ford dealer.

Conversion Factors

Length (distance)

Inches (in)	x 25.4	= Millimetres (mm)	x 0.0394	= Inches (in)
Feet (ft)	x 0.305	= Metres (m)	x 3.281	= Feet (ft)
Miles	x 1.609	= Kilometres (km)	x 0.621	= Miles

Volume (capacity)

Cubic inches (cu in; in³)	x 16.387	= Cubic centimetres (cc; cm³)	x 0.061	= Cubic inches (cu in; in³)
Imperial pints (Imp pt)	x 0.568	= Litres (l)	x 1.76	= Imperial pints (Imp pt)
Imperial quarts (Imp qt)	x 1.137	= Litres (l)	x 0.88	= Imperial quarts (Imp qt)
Imperial quarts (Imp qt)	x 1.201	= US quarts (US qt)	x 0.833	= Imperial quarts (Imp qt)
US quarts (US qt)	x 0.946	= Litres (l)	x 1.057	= US quarts (US qt)
Imperial gallons (Imp gal)	x 4.546	= Litres (l)	x 0.22	= Imperial gallons (Imp gal)
Imperial gallons (Imp gal)	x 1.201	= US gallons (US gal)	x 0.833	= Imperial gallons (Imp gal)
US gallons (US gal)	x 3.785	= Litres (l)	x 0.264	= US gallons (US gal)

Mass (weight)

Ounces (oz)	x 28.35	= Grams (g)	x 0.035	= Ounces (oz)
Pounds (lb)	x 0.454	= Kilograms (kg)	x 2.205	= Pounds (lb)

Force

Ounces-force (ozf; oz)	x 0.278	= Newtons (N)	x 3.6	= Ounces-force (ozf; oz)
Pounds-force (lbf; lb)	x 4.448	= Newtons (N)	x 0.225	= Pounds-force (lbf; lb)
Newtons (N)	x 0.1	= Kilograms-force (kgf; kg)	x 9.81	= Newtons (N)

Pressure

Pounds-force per square inch (psi; lbf/in²; lb/in²)	x 0.070	= Kilograms-force per square centimetre (kgf/cm²; kg/cm²)	x 14.223	= Pounds-force per square inch (psi; lbf/in²; lb/in²)
Pounds-force per square inch (psi; lbf/in²; lb/in²)	x 0.068	= Atmospheres (atm)	x 14.696	= Pounds-force per square inch (psi; lbf/in²; lb/in²)
Pounds-force per square inch (psi; lbf/in²; lb/in²)	x 0.069	= Bars	x 14.5	= Pounds-force per square inch (psi; lbf/in²; lb/in²)
Pounds-force per square inch (psi; lbf/in²; lb/in²)	x 6.895	= Kilopascals (kPa)	x 0.145	= Pounds-force per square inch (psi; lbf/in²; lb/in²)
Kilopascals (kPa)	x 0.01	= Kilograms-force per square centimetre (kgf/cm²; kg/cm²)	x 98.1	= Kilopascals (kPa)
Millibar (mbar)	x 100	= Pascals (Pa)	x 0.01	= Millibar (mbar)
Millibar (mbar)	x 0.0145	= Pounds-force per square inch (psi; lbf/in²; lb/in²)	x 68.947	= Millibar (mbar)
Millibar (mbar)	x 0.75	= Millimetres of mercury (mmHg)	x 1.333	= Millibar (mbar)
Millibar (mbar)	x 0.401	= Inches of water (inH$_2$O)	x 2.491	= Millibar (mbar)
Millimetres of mercury (mmHg)	x 0.535	= Inches of water (inH$_2$O)	x 1.868	= Millimetres of mercury (mmHg)
Inches of water (inH$_2$O)	x 0.036	= Pounds-force per square inch (psi; lbf/in²; lb/in²)	x 27.68	= Inches of water (inH$_2$O)

Torque (moment of force)

Pounds-force inches (lbf in; lb in)	x 1.152	= Kilograms-force centimetre (kgf cm; kg cm)	x 0.868	= Pounds-force inches (lbf in; lb in)
Pounds-force inches (lbf in; lb in)	x 0.113	= Newton metres (Nm)	x 8.85	= Pounds-force inches (lbf in; lb in)
Pounds-force inches (lbf in; lb in)	x 0.083	= Pounds-force feet (lbf ft; lb ft)	x 12	= Pounds-force inches (lbf in; lb in)
Pounds-force feet (lbf ft; lb ft)	x 0.138	= Kilograms-force metres (kgf m; kg m)	x 7.233	= Pounds-force feet (lbf ft; lb ft)
Pounds-force feet (lbf ft; lb ft)	x 1.356	= Newton metres (Nm)	x 0.738	= Pounds-force feet (lbf ft; lb ft)
Newton metres (Nm)	x 0.102	= Kilograms-force metres (kgf m; kg m)	x 9.804	= Newton metres (Nm)

Power

Horsepower (hp)	x 745.7	= Watts (W)	x 0.0013	= Horsepower (hp)

Velocity (speed)

Miles per hour (miles/hr; mph)	x 1.609	= Kilometres per hour (km/hr; kph)	x 0.621	= Miles per hour (miles/hr; mph)

Fuel consumption*

Miles per gallon (mpg)	x 0.354	= Kilometres per litre (km/l)	x 2.825	= Miles per gallon (mpg)

Temperature

Degrees Fahrenheit = (°C x 1.8) + 32

Degrees Celsius (Degrees Centigrade; °C) = (°F - 32) x 0.56

It is common practice to convert from miles per gallon (mpg) to litres/100 kilometres (l/100km), where mpg x l/100 km = 282

Introduction

A selection of good tools is a fundamental requirement for anyone contemplating the maintenance and repair of a motor vehicle. For the owner who does not possess any, their purchase will prove a considerable expense, offsetting some of the savings made by doing-it-yourself. However, provided that the tools purchased meet the relevant national safety standards and are of good quality, they will last for many years and prove an extremely worthwhile investment.

To help the average owner to decide which tools are needed to carry out the various tasks detailed in this manual, we have compiled three lists of tools under the following headings: *Maintenance and minor repair, Repair and overhaul*, and *Special*. Newcomers to practical mechanics should start off with the *Maintenance and minor repair* tool kit, and confine themselves to the simpler jobs around the vehicle. Then, as confidence and experience grow, more difficult tasks can be undertaken, with extra tools being purchased as, and when, they are needed. In this way, a *Maintenance and minor repair* tool kit can be built up into a *Repair and overhaul* tool kit over a considerable period of time, without any major cash outlays. The experienced do-it-yourselfer will have a tool kit good enough for most repair and overhaul procedures, and will add tools from the *Special* category when it is felt that the expense is justified by the amount of use to which these tools will be put.

Maintenance and minor repair tool kit

The tools given in this list should be considered as a minimum requirement if routine maintenance, servicing and minor repair operations are to be undertaken. We recommend the purchase of combination spanners (ring one end, open-ended the other); although more expensive than open-ended ones, they do give the advantages of both types of spanner.

- ☐ *Combination spanners: 8, 9, 10, 11, 12, 13, 14, 15, 16, 17, 19, 21, 22, 24 & 26 mm*
- ☐ *Adjustable spanner - 35 mm jaw (approx)*
- ☐ *Engine sump/gearbox drain plug key (where applicable)*
- ☐ *Set of feeler gauges*
- ☐ *Spark plug spanner (with rubber insert)*
- ☐ *Spark plug gap adjustment tool*
- ☐ *Brake bleed nipple spanner*
- ☐ *Screwdrivers: Flat blade and cross blade – approx 100 mm long x 6 mm dia*
- ☐ *Combination pliers*
- ☐ *Hacksaw (junior)*
- ☐ *Tyre pump*
- ☐ *Tyre pressure gauge*
- ☐ *Grease gun*
- ☐ *Oil can*
- ☐ *Oil filter removal tool*
- ☐ *Fine emery cloth*
- ☐ *Wire brush (small)*
- ☐ *Funnel (medium size)*

Repair and overhaul tool kit

These tools are virtually essential for anyone undertaking any major repairs to a motor vehicle, and are additional to those given in the *Maintenance and minor repair* list. Included in this list is a comprehensive set of sockets. Although these are expensive, they will be found invaluable as they are so versatile - particularly if various drives are included in the set. We recommend the half-inch square-drive type, as this can be used with most proprietary torque wrenches. If you cannot afford a socket set, even bought piecemeal, then inexpensive tubular box spanners are a useful alternative.

The tools in this list will occasionally need to be supplemented by tools from the *Special* list:

- ☐ *Sockets (or box spanners) to cover range in previous list (including Torx sockets)*
- ☐ *Reversible ratchet drive (for use with sockets) (see illustration)*
- ☐ *Extension piece, 250 mm (for use with sockets)*
- ☐ *Universal joint (for use with sockets)*
- ☐ *Torque wrench (for use with sockets)*
- ☐ *Self-locking grips*
- ☐ *Ball pein hammer*
- ☐ *Soft-faced mallet (plastic/aluminium or rubber)*
- ☐ *Screwdrivers:*
  Flat blade - long & sturdy, short (chubby), and narrow (electrician's) types
  Cross blade - Long & sturdy, and short (chubby) types
- ☐ *Pliers:*
  Long-nosed
  Side cutters (electrician's)
  Circlip (internal and external)
- ☐ *Cold chisel - 25 mm*
- ☐ *Scriber*
- ☐ *Scraper*
- ☐ *Centre-punch*
- ☐ *Pin punch*
- ☐ *Hacksaw*
- ☐ *Brake hose clamp*
- ☐ *Brake bleeding kit*
- ☐ *Selection of twist drills*
- ☐ *Steel rule/straight-edge*
- ☐ *Allen keys (inc. splined/Torx type) (see illustrations)*
- ☐ *Selection of files*
- ☐ *Wire brush*
- ☐ *Axle stands*
- ☐ *Jack (strong trolley or hydraulic type)*
- ☐ *Light with extension lead*

Special tools

The tools in this list are those which are not used regularly, are expensive to buy, or which need to be used in accordance with their manufacturers' instructions. Unless relatively difficult mechanical jobs are undertaken frequently, it will not be economic to buy many of these tools. Where this is the case, you could consider clubbing together with friends (or joining a motorists' club) to make a joint purchase, or borrowing the tools against a deposit from a local garage or tool hire specialist. It is worth noting that many of the larger DIY superstores now carry a large range of special tools for hire at modest rates.

The following list contains only those tools and instruments freely available to the public, and not those special tools produced by the vehicle manufacturer specifically for its dealer network. You will find occasional references to these manufacturers' special tools in the text of this manual. Generally, an alternative method of doing the job without the vehicle manufacturers' special tool is given. However, sometimes there is no alternative to using them. Where this is the case and the relevant tool cannot be bought or borrowed, you will have to entrust the work to a franchised garage.

- ☐ *Valve spring compressor (see illustration)*
- ☐ *Valve grinding tool*
- ☐ *Piston ring compressor (see illustration)*
- ☐ *Piston ring removal/installation tool (see illustration)*
- ☐ *Cylinder bore hone (see illustration)*
- ☐ *Balljoint separator*
- ☐ *Coil spring compressors (where applicable)*
- ☐ *Two/three-legged hub and bearing puller (see illustration)*

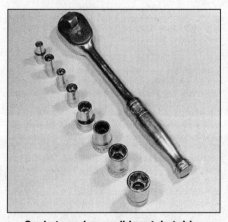

Sockets and reversible ratchet drive

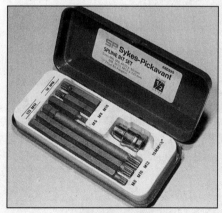

Spline bit set

Tools and working facilities

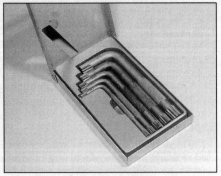

Spline key set

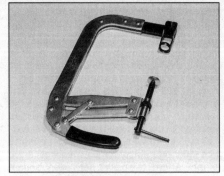

Valve spring compressor

Piston ring compressor

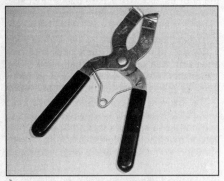

Piston ring removal/installation tool

Cylinder bore hone

Three-legged hub and bearing puller

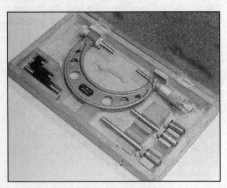

Micrometer set

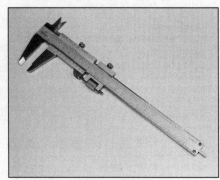

Vernier calipers

Dial test indicator and magnetic stand

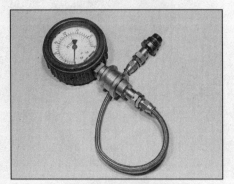

Compression testing gauge

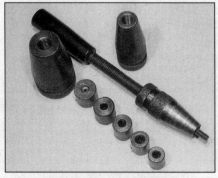

Clutch plate alignment set

Brake shoe steady spring cup removal tool

☐ Impact screwdriver
☐ Micrometer and/or vernier calipers *(see illustrations)*
☐ Dial gauge *(see illustration)*
☐ Universal electrical multi-meter
☐ Cylinder compression gauge *(see illustration)*
☐ Clutch plate alignment set *(see illustration)*
☐ Brake shoe steady spring cup removal tool *(see illustration)*
☐ Bush and bearing removal/installation set *(see illustration)*
☐ Stud extractors *(see illustration)*
☐ Tap and die set *(see illustration)*
☐ Lifting tackle
☐ Trolley jack

Buying tools

For practically all tools, a tool factor is the best source, since he will have a very comprehensive range compared with the average garage or accessory shop. Having said that, accessory shops often offer excellent quality tools at discount prices, so it pays to shop around.

Remember, you don't have to buy the most expensive items on the shelf, but it is always advisable to steer clear of the very cheap tools. There are plenty of good tools around at reasonable prices, but always aim to purchase items which meet the relevant national safety standards. If in doubt, ask the proprietor or manager of the shop for advice before making a purchase.

Care and maintenance of tools

Having purchased a reasonable tool kit, it is necessary to keep the tools in a clean and serviceable condition. After use, always wipe off any dirt, grease and metal particles using a clean, dry cloth, before putting the tools away. Never leave them lying around after they have been used. A simple tool rack on the garage or workshop wall for items such as screwdrivers and pliers is a good idea. Store all normal spanners and sockets in a metal box. Any measuring instruments, gauges, meters, etc, must be carefully stored where they cannot be damaged or become rusty.

Take a little care when tools are used. Hammer heads inevitably become marked, and screwdrivers lose the keen edge on their blades from time to time. A little timely attention with emery cloth or a file will soon restore items like this to a good serviceable finish.

Working facilities

Not to be forgotten when discussing tools is the workshop itself. If anything more than routine maintenance is to be carried out, some form of suitable working area becomes essential.

It is appreciated that many an owner-mechanic is forced by circumstances to remove an engine or similar item without the benefit of a garage or workshop. Having done this, any repairs should always be done under the cover of a roof.

Wherever possible, any dismantling should be done on a clean, flat workbench or table at a suitable working height.

Any workbench needs a vice; one with a jaw opening of 100 mm is suitable for most jobs. As mentioned previously, some clean dry storage space is also required for tools, as well as for any lubricants, cleaning fluids, touch-up paints and so on, which become necessary.

Another item which may be required, and which has a much more general usage, is an electric drill with a chuck capacity of at least 8 mm. This, together with a good range of twist drills, is virtually essential for fitting accessories.

Last, but not least, always keep a supply of old newspapers and clean, lint-free rags available, and try to keep any working area as clean as possible.

Bush and bearing removal/installation set

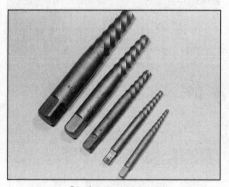

Stud extractor set

Tap and die set

This is a guide to getting your vehicle through the MOT test. Obviously it will not be possible to examine the vehicle to the same standard as the professional MOT tester. However, working through the following checks will enable you to identify any problem areas before submitting the vehicle for the test.

Where a testable component is in borderline condition, the tester has discretion in deciding whether to pass or fail it. The basis of such discretion is whether the tester would be happy for a close relative or friend to use the vehicle with the component in that condition. If the vehicle presented is clean and evidently well cared for, the tester may be more inclined to pass a borderline component than if the vehicle is scruffy and apparently neglected.

It has only been possible to summarise the test requirements here, based on the regulations in force at the time of printing. Test standards are becoming increasingly stringent, although there are some exemptions for older vehicles. For full details obtain a copy of the Haynes publication Pass the MOT! (available from stockists of Haynes manuals).

An assistant will be needed to help carry out some of these checks.

The checks have been sub-divided into four categories, as follows:

1 Checks carried out **FROM THE DRIVER'S SEAT**

2 Checks carried out **WITH THE VEHICLE ON THE GROUND**

3 Checks carried out **WITH THE VEHICLE RAISED AND THE WHEELS FREE TO TURN**

4 Checks carried out on **YOUR VEHICLE'S EXHAUST EMISSION SYSTEM**

1 Checks carried out **FROM THE DRIVER'S SEAT**

Handbrake

☐ Test the operation of the handbrake. Excessive travel (too many clicks) indicates incorrect brake or cable adjustment.

☐ Check that the handbrake cannot be released by tapping the lever sideways. Check the security of the lever mountings.

Footbrake

☐ Depress the brake pedal and check that it does not creep down to the floor, indicating a master cylinder fault. Release the pedal, wait a few seconds, then depress it again. If the pedal travels nearly to the floor before firm resistance is felt, brake adjustment or repair is necessary. If the pedal feels spongy, there is air in the hydraulic system which must be removed by bleeding.

☐ Check that the brake pedal is secure and in good condition. Check also for signs of fluid leaks on the pedal, floor or carpets, which would indicate failed seals in the brake master cylinder.

☐ Check the servo unit (when applicable) by operating the brake pedal several times, then keeping the pedal depressed and starting the engine. As the engine starts, the pedal will move down slightly. If not, the vacuum hose or the servo itself may be faulty.

Steering wheel and column

☐ Examine the steering wheel for fractures or looseness of the hub, spokes or rim.

☐ Move the steering wheel from side to side and then up and down. Check that the steering wheel is not loose on the column, indicating wear or a loose retaining nut. Continue moving the steering wheel as before, but also turn it slightly from left to right.

☐ Check that the steering wheel is not loose on the column, and that there is no abnormal

movement of the steering wheel, indicating wear in the column support bearings or couplings.

Windscreen and mirrors

☐ The windscreen must be free of cracks or other significant damage within the driver's field of view. (Small stone chips are acceptable.) Rear view mirrors must be secure, intact, and capable of being adjusted.

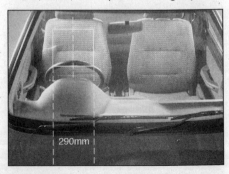

290mm

Seat belts and seats

Note: *The following checks are applicable to all seat belts, front and rear.*

☐ Examine the webbing of all the belts (including rear belts if fitted) for cuts, serious fraying or deterioration. Fasten and unfasten each belt to check the buckles. If applicable, check the retracting mechanism. Check the security of all seat belt mountings accessible from inside the vehicle.

☐ The front seats themselves must be securely attached and the backrests must lock in the upright position.

Doors

☐ Both front doors must be able to be opened and closed from outside and inside, and must latch securely when closed.

2 Checks carried out WITH THE VEHICLE ON THE GROUND

Vehicle identification

☐ Number plates must be in good condition, secure and legible, with letters and numbers correctly spaced – spacing at (A) should be twice that at (B).

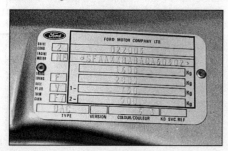

☐ The VIN plate and/or homologation plate must be legible.

Electrical equipment

☐ Switch on the ignition and check the operation of the horn.

☐ Check the windscreen washers and wipers, examining the wiper blades; renew damaged or perished blades. Also check the operation of the stop-lights.

☐ Check the operation of the sidelights and number plate lights. The lenses and reflectors must be secure, clean and undamaged.

☐ Check the operation and alignment of the headlights. The headlight reflectors must not be tarnished and the lenses must be undamaged.

☐ Switch on the ignition and check the operation of the direction indicators (including the instrument panel tell-tale) and the hazard warning lights. Operation of the sidelights and stop-lights must not affect the indicators - if it does, the cause is usually a bad earth at the rear light cluster.

☐ Check the operation of the rear foglight(s), including the warning light on the instrument panel or in the switch.

Footbrake

☐ Examine the master cylinder, brake pipes and servo unit for leaks, loose mountings, corrosion or other damage.

☐ The fluid reservoir must be secure and the fluid level must be between the upper (**A**) and lower (**B**) markings.

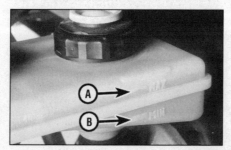

☐ Inspect both front brake flexible hoses for cracks or deterioration of the rubber. Turn the steering from lock to lock, and ensure that the hoses do not contact the wheel, tyre, or any part of the steering or suspension mechanism. With the brake pedal firmly depressed, check the hoses for bulges or leaks under pressure.

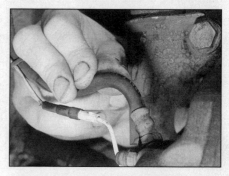

Steering and suspension

☐ Have your assistant turn the steering wheel from side to side slightly, up to the point where the steering gear just begins to transmit this movement to the roadwheels. Check for excessive free play between the steering wheel and the steering gear, indicating wear or insecurity of the steering column joints, the column-to-steering gear coupling, or the steering gear itself.

☐ Have your assistant turn the steering wheel more vigorously in each direction, so that the roadwheels just begin to turn. As this is done, examine all the steering joints, linkages, fittings and attachments. Renew any component that shows signs of wear or damage. On vehicles with power steering, check the security and condition of the steering pump, drivebelt and hoses.

☐ Check that the vehicle is standing level, and at approximately the correct ride height.

Shock absorbers

☐ Depress each corner of the vehicle in turn, then release it. The vehicle should rise and then settle in its normal position. If the vehicle continues to rise and fall, the shock absorber is defective. A shock absorber which has seized will also cause the vehicle to fail.

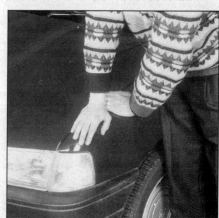

Exhaust system

☐ Start the engine. With your assistant holding a rag over the tailpipe, check the entire system for leaks. Repair or renew leaking sections.

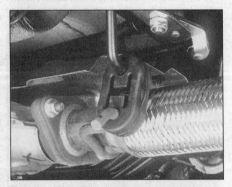

3 Checks carried out **WITH THE VEHICLE RAISED AND THE WHEELS FREE TO TURN**

Jack up the front and rear of the vehicle, and securely support it on axle stands. Position the stands clear of the suspension assemblies. Ensure that the wheels are clear of the ground and that the steering can be turned from lock to lock.

Steering mechanism

☐ Have your assistant turn the steering from lock to lock. Check that the steering turns smoothly, and that no part of the steering mechanism, including a wheel or tyre, fouls any brake hose or pipe or any part of the body structure.

☐ Examine the steering rack rubber gaiters for damage or insecurity of the retaining clips. If power steering is fitted, check for signs of damage or leakage of the fluid hoses, pipes or connections. Also check for excessive stiffness or binding of the steering, a missing split pin or locking device, or severe corrosion of the body structure within 30 cm of any steering component attachment point.

Front and rear suspension and wheel bearings

☐ Starting at the front right-hand side, grasp the roadwheel at the 3 o'clock and 9 o'clock positions and shake it vigorously. Check for free play or insecurity at the wheel bearings, suspension balljoints, or suspension mountings, pivots and attachments.

☐ Now grasp the wheel at the 12 o'clock and 6 o'clock positions and repeat the previous inspection. Spin the wheel, and check for roughness or tightness of the front wheel bearing.

☐ If excess free play is suspected at a component pivot point, this can be confirmed by using a large screwdriver or similar tool and levering between the mounting and the component attachment. This will confirm whether the wear is in the pivot bush, its retaining bolt, or in the mounting itself (the bolt holes can often become elongated).

☐ Carry out all the above checks at the other front wheel, and then at both rear wheels.

Springs and shock absorbers

☐ Examine the suspension struts (when applicable) for serious fluid leakage, corrosion, or damage to the casing. Also check the security of the mounting points.

☐ If coil springs are fitted, check that the spring ends locate in their seats, and that the spring is not corroded, cracked or broken.

☐ If leaf springs are fitted, check that all leaves are intact, that the axle is securely attached to each spring, and that there is no deterioration of the spring eye mountings, bushes, and shackles.

☐ The same general checks apply to vehicles fitted with other suspension types, such as torsion bars, hydraulic displacer units, etc. Ensure that all mountings and attachments are secure, that there are no signs of excessive wear, corrosion or damage, and (on hydraulic types) that there are no fluid leaks or damaged pipes.

☐ Inspect the shock absorbers for signs of serious fluid leakage. Check for wear of the mounting bushes or attachments, or damage to the body of the unit.

Driveshafts (fwd vehicles only)

☐ Rotate each front wheel in turn and inspect the constant velocity joint gaiters for splits or damage. Also check that each driveshaft is straight and undamaged.

Braking system

☐ If possible without dismantling, check brake pad wear and disc condition. Ensure that the friction lining material has not worn excessively, (A) and that the discs are not fractured, pitted, scored or badly worn (B).

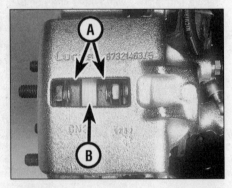

☐ Examine all the rigid brake pipes underneath the vehicle, and the flexible hose(s) at the rear. Look for corrosion, chafing or insecurity of the pipes, and for signs of bulging under pressure, chafing, splits or deterioration of the flexible hoses.

☐ Look for signs of fluid leaks at the brake calipers or on the brake backplates. Repair or renew leaking components.

☐ Slowly spin each wheel, while your assistant depresses and releases the footbrake. Ensure that each brake is operating and does not bind when the pedal is released.

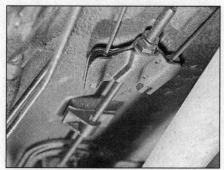

□ Examine the handbrake mechanism, checking for frayed or broken cables, excessive corrosion, or wear or insecurity of the linkage. Check that the mechanism works on each relevant wheel, and releases fully, without binding.

□ It is not possible to test brake efficiency without special equipment, but a road test can be carried out later to check that the vehicle pulls up in a straight line.

Fuel and exhaust systems

□ Inspect the fuel tank (including the filler cap), fuel pipes, hoses and unions. All components must be secure and free from leaks.

□ Examine the exhaust system over its entire length, checking for any damaged, broken or missing mountings, security of the retaining clamps and rust or corrosion.

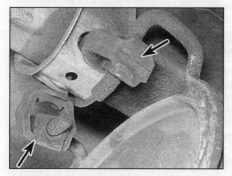

Wheels and tyres

□ Examine the sidewalls and tread area of each tyre in turn. Check for cuts, tears, lumps, bulges, separation of the tread, and exposure of the ply or cord due to wear or damage. Check that the tyre bead is correctly seated on the wheel rim, that the valve is sound and

properly seated, and that the wheel is not distorted or damaged.

□ Check that the tyres are of the correct size for the vehicle, that they are of the same size and type on each axle, and that the pressures are correct.

□ Check the tyre tread depth. The legal minimum at the time of writing is 1.6 mm over at least three-quarters of the tread width. Abnormal tread wear may indicate incorrect front wheel alignment.

Body corrosion

□ Check the condition of the entire vehicle structure for signs of corrosion in load-bearing areas. (These include chassis box sections, side sills, cross-members, pillars, and all suspension, steering, braking system and seat belt mountings and anchorages.) Any corrosion which has seriously reduced the thickness of a load-bearing area is likely to cause the vehicle to fail. In this case professional repairs are likely to be needed.

□ Damage or corrosion which causes sharp or otherwise dangerous edges to be exposed will also cause the vehicle to fail.

4 Checks carried out on YOUR VEHICLE'S EXHAUST EMISSION SYSTEM

Petrol models

□ Have the engine at normal operating temperature, and make sure that it is in good tune (ignition system in good order, air filter element clean, etc).

□ Before any measurements are carried out, raise the engine speed to around 2500 rpm, and hold it at this speed for 20 seconds. Allow

the engine speed to return to idle, and watch for smoke emissions from the exhaust tailpipe. If the idle speed is obviously much too high, or if dense blue or clearly-visible black smoke comes from the tailpipe for more than 5 seconds, the vehicle will fail. As a rule of thumb, blue smoke signifies oil being burnt (engine wear) while black smoke signifies unburnt fuel (dirty air cleaner element, or other carburettor or fuel system fault).

□ An exhaust gas analyser capable of measuring carbon monoxide (CO) and hydrocarbons (HC) is now needed. If such an instrument cannot be hired or borrowed, a local garage may agree to perform the check for a small fee.

CO emissions (mixture)

□ At the time of writing, the maximum CO level at idle is 3.5% for vehicles first used after August 1986 and 4.5% for older vehicles. From January 1996 a much tighter limit (around 0.5%) applies to catalyst-equipped vehicles first used from August 1992. If the CO level cannot be reduced far enough to pass the test (and the fuel and ignition systems are otherwise in good condition) then the carburettor is badly worn, or there is some problem in the fuel injection system or catalytic converter (as applicable).

HC emissions

□ With the CO emissions within limits, HC emissions must be no more than 1200 ppm (parts per million). If the vehicle fails this test at idle, it can be re-tested at around 2000 rpm; if the HC level is then 1200 ppm or less, this counts as a pass.

□ Excessive HC emissions can be caused by oil being burnt, but they are more likely to be due to unburnt fuel.

Diesel models

□ The only emission test applicable to Diesel engines is the measuring of exhaust smoke density. The test involves accelerating the engine several times to its maximum unloaded speed.

Note: *It is of the utmost importance that the engine timing belt is in good condition before the test is carried out.*

□ Excessive smoke can be caused by a dirty air cleaner element. Otherwise, professional advice may be needed to find the cause.

Engine

- ☐ Engine backfires
- ☐ Engine difficult to start when cold
- ☐ Engine difficult to start when hot
- ☐ Engine fails to rotate when attempting to start
- ☐ Engine hesitates on acceleration
- ☐ Engine idles erratically
- ☐ Engine lacks power
- ☐ Engine misfires at idle speed
- ☐ Engine misfires throughout the driving speed range
- ☐ Engine noises
- ☐ Engine rotates, but will not start
- ☐ Engine runs-on after switching off
- ☐ Engine stalls
- ☐ Engine starts, but stops immediately
- ☐ Oil pressure warning light illuminated with engine running
- ☐ Starter motor noisy or excessively-rough in engagement

Cooling system

- ☐ Corrosion
- ☐ External coolant leakage
- ☐ Internal coolant leakage
- ☐ Overcooling
- ☐ Overheating

Fuel and exhaust systems

- ☐ Excessive fuel consumption
- ☐ Excessive noise or fumes from exhaust system
- ☐ Fuel leakage and/or fuel odour

Clutch

- ☐ Clutch fails to disengage (unable to select gears)
- ☐ Clutch slips (engine speed increases, with no increase in vehicle speed)
- ☐ Judder as clutch is engaged
- ☐ Noise when depressing or releasing clutch pedal
- ☐ Pedal travels to floor - no pressure or very little resistance

Manual transmission

- ☐ Jumps out of gear
- ☐ Lubricant leaks
- ☐ Noisy in neutral with engine running
- ☐ Noisy in one particular gear
- ☐ Vibration

Automatic transmission

- ☐ Engine will not start in any gear, or starts in gears other than Park or Neutral
- ☐ Fluid leakage
- ☐ General gear selection problems
- ☐ Transmission fluid brown, or has burned smell
- ☐ Transmission slips, shifts roughly, is noisy, or has no drive in forward or reverse gears
- ☐ Transmission will not downshift (kickdown) with accelerator fully depressed

Driveshafts

- ☐ Clicking or knocking noise on turns (at slow speed on full-lock)
- ☐ Vibration when accelerating or decelerating

Braking system

- ☐ Brake pedal feels spongy when depressed
- ☐ Brakes binding
- ☐ Excessive brake pedal effort required to stop vehicle
- ☐ Excessive brake pedal travel
- ☐ Judder felt through brake pedal or steering wheel when braking
- ☐ Noise (grinding or high-pitched squeal) when brakes applied
- ☐ Rear wheels locking under normal braking
- ☐ Vehicle pulls to one side under braking

Suspension and steering systems

- ☐ Excessive pitching and/or rolling around corners, or during braking
- ☐ Excessive play in steering
- ☐ Excessively-stiff steering
- ☐ Lack of power assistance
- ☐ Tyre wear excessive
- ☐ Vehicle pulls to one side
- ☐ Wandering or general instability
- ☐ Wheel wobble and vibration

Electrical system

- ☐ Battery will not hold a charge for more than a few days
- ☐ Electric windows inoperative, or unsatisfactory in operation
- ☐ Horn inoperative, or unsatisfactory in operation
- ☐ Ignition warning light fails to come on
- ☐ Ignition warning light remains illuminated with engine running
- ☐ Instrument readings inaccurate or erratic
- ☐ Lights inoperative
- ☐ Windscreen/tailgate washers inoperative, or unsatisfactory in operation
- ☐ Windscreen/tailgate wipers inoperative, or unsatisfactory in operation

Introduction

The vehicle owner who does his or her own maintenance according to the recommended service schedules should not have to use this section of the manual very often. Modern component reliability is such that, provided those items subject to wear or deterioration are inspected or renewed at the specified intervals, sudden failure is comparatively rare. Faults do not usually just happen as a result of sudden failure, but develop over a period of time. Major mechanical failures in particular are usually preceded by characteristic symptoms over hundreds or even thousands of miles. Those components which do occasionally fail without warning are often small and easily carried in the vehicle.

With any fault-finding, the first step is to decide where to begin investigations. Sometimes this is obvious, but on other occasions, a little detective work will be necessary. The owner who makes half a dozen haphazard adjustments or replacements may be successful in curing a fault (or its symptoms), but will be none the wiser if the fault recurs, and ultimately may have spent more time and money than was necessary. A calm and logical approach will be found to be more satisfactory in the long run. Always take into account any warning signs or abnormalities that may have been noticed in the period preceding the fault - power loss, high or low gauge readings, unusual smells, etc - and remember that failure of components such as fuses or spark plugs may only be pointers to some underlying fault.

The pages which follow provide an easy reference guide to the more common problems which may occur during the operation of the vehicle. These problems and their possible causes are grouped under headings denoting various components or systems, such as Engine, Cooling system, etc. The Chapter and/or Section which deals with the problem is also shown in brackets. Whatever the fault, certain basic principles apply. These are as follows:

Verify the fault. This is simply a matter of being sure that you know what the symptoms are before starting work. This is particularly important if you are investigating a fault for someone else, who may not have described it very accurately.

Don't overlook the obvious. For example, if the vehicle won't start, is there petrol in the tank? (Don't take anyone else's word on this particular point, and don't trust the fuel gauge either!) If an electrical fault is indicated, look for loose or broken wires before digging out the test gear.

Cure the disease, not the symptom. Substituting a flat battery with a fully-charged one will get you off the hard shoulder, but if the underlying cause is not attended to, the new battery will go the same way. Similarly, changing oil-fouled spark plugs for a new set will get you moving again, but remember that the reason for the fouling (if it wasn't simply an incorrect grade of plug) will have to be established and corrected.

Don't take anything for granted. Particularly, don't forget that a "new" component may itself be defective (especially if it's been rattling around in the boot for months), and don't leave components out of a fault diagnosis sequence just because they are new or recently fitted. When you do finally diagnose a difficult fault, you'll probably realise that all the evidence was there from the start.

Engine

Engine fails to rotate when attempting to start

- ☐ Battery terminal connections loose or corroded (Chapter 5A).
- ☐ Battery discharged or faulty (Chapter 5A).
- ☐ Broken, loose or disconnected wiring in the starting circuit (Chapter 5A).
- ☐ Defective starter solenoid or switch (Chapter 5A).
- ☐ Defective starter motor (Chapter 5A).
- ☐ Flywheel ring gear or starter pinion teeth loose or broken (Chapters 2A, 2B, 2C or 5A).
- ☐ Engine earth strap broken or disconnected (Chapter 5A).
- ☐ Automatic transmission not in Park/Neutral position, or starter inhibitor switch faulty (Chapter 7B).

Engine rotates, but will not start

- ☐ Fuel tank empty.
- ☐ Battery discharged (engine rotates slowly) (Chapter 5A).
- ☐ Battery terminal connections loose or corroded (Chapter 5A).
- ☐ Ignition components damp or damaged (Chapters 1 and 5B).
- ☐ Broken, loose or disconnected wiring in the ignition circuit (Chapters 1 and 5B).
- ☐ Worn, faulty or incorrectly-gapped spark plugs (Chapter 1).
- ☐ Major mechanical failure (eg camshaft drive) (Chapters 2A, 2B or 2C).

Engine difficult to start when cold

- ☐ Battery discharged (Chapter 5A).
- ☐ Battery terminal connections loose or corroded (Chapter 5A).
- ☐ Worn, faulty or incorrectly-gapped spark plugs (Chapter 1).
- ☐ Other ignition system fault (Chapters 1 and 5B).
- ☐ Engine management system fault (Chapters 1, 4A, 4B, 4C, 4D, 4E or 5B).
- ☐ Low cylinder compressions (Chapters 2A, 2B or 2C).

Engine difficult to start when hot

- ☐ Air filter element dirty or clogged (Chapter 1).
- ☐ Engine management system fault (Chapters 1, 4A, 4B, 4C, 4D, 4E or 5B).
- ☐ Low cylinder compressions (Chapters 2A, 2B or 2C).
- ☐ Faulty hydraulic tappet(s) (Chapters 2B or 2C).

Starter motor noisy or excessively-rough in engagement

- ☐ Flywheel ring gear or starter pinion teeth loose or broken (Chapters 2A, 2B, 2C or 5A).
- ☐ Starter motor mounting bolts loose or missing (Chapter 5A).
- ☐ Starter motor internal components worn or damaged (Chapter 5A).

Engine starts but stops immediately

- ☐ Loose or faulty electrical connections in the ignition circuit (Chapters 1 and 5B).
- ☐ Engine management system fault (Chapters 1, 4A, 4B, 4C, 4D, 4E or 5B).
- ☐ Vacuum leak at the inlet manifold (Chapters 1, 4A, 4B, 4C, 4D or 4E).

Engine idles erratically

- ☐ Engine management system fault (Chapters 1, 4A, 4B, 4C, 4D, 4E or 5B).
- ☐ Air filter element clogged (Chapter 1).
- ☐ Vacuum leak at the inlet manifold or associated hoses (Chapters 1, 4A, 4B, 4C, 4D or 4E).
- ☐ Worn, faulty or incorrectly-gapped spark plugs (Chapter 1).
- ☐ Incorrect valve clearances (Chapter 2A).
- ☐ Faulty hydraulic tappet(s) (Chapters 2B or 2C).
- ☐ Uneven or low cylinder compressions (Chapters 2A, 2B or 2C).
- ☐ Camshaft lobes worn (Chapters 2A, 2B or 2C).
- ☐ Timing chain and sprockets worn (Chapter 2A).
- ☐ Timing belt incorrectly-tensioned (Chapters 2B or 2C).

Engine misfires at idle speed

- ☐ Worn, faulty or incorrectly-gapped spark plugs (Chapter 1).
- ☐ Faulty spark plug HT leads (Chapter 1).
- ☐ Engine management system fault (Chapters 1, 4A, 4B, 4C, 4D, 4E or 5B).
- ☐ Vacuum leak at the inlet manifold or associated hoses (Chapters 1, 4A, 4B, 4C, 4D or 4E).
- ☐ Incorrect valve clearances (Chapter 2A).
- ☐ Faulty hydraulic tappet(s) (Chapters 2B or 2C).
- ☐ Uneven or low cylinder compressions (Chapters 2A, 2B and 2C).
- ☐ Disconnected, leaking or perished crankcase ventilation hoses (Chapters 1 and 4E).

Engine misfires throughout the driving speed range

- ☐ Fuel filter choked (Chapter 1).
- ☐ Fuel pump faulty or delivery pressure low (Chapters 4A, 4B, 4C or 4D).
- ☐ Fuel tank vent blocked or fuel pipes restricted (Chapters 4A, 4B, 4C, 4D or 4E).
- ☐ Vacuum leak at the inlet manifold or associated hoses (Chapters 1, 4A, 4B, 4C, 4D or 4E).
- ☐ Worn, faulty or incorrectly-gapped spark plugs (Chapter 1).
- ☐ Faulty spark plug HT leads (Chapter 1).
- ☐ Faulty ignition coil (Chapter 5B).
- ☐ Engine management system fault (Chapters 1, 4A, 4B, 4C, 4D, 4E or 5B).
- ☐ Uneven or low cylinder compressions (Chapters 2A, 2B or 2C).

Engine (continued)

Engine hesitates on acceleration

- ☐ Worn, faulty or incorrectly-gapped spark plugs (Chapter 1).
- ☐ Engine management system fault (Chapters 1, 4A, 4B, 4C, 4D, 4E or 5B).
- ☐ Vacuum leak at the inlet manifold or associated hoses (Chapters 1, 4A, 4B, 4C, 4D, 4E or 5B).

Engine stalls

- ☐ Engine management system fault (Chapters 1, 4A, 4B, 4C, 4D, 4E, or 5B).
- ☐ Vacuum leak at the inlet manifold or associated hoses (Chapters 1, 4A, 4B, 4C, 4D or 4E).
- ☐ Fuel filter choked (Chapter 1).
- ☐ Fuel pump faulty or delivery pressure low (Chapters 4A, 4B, 4C or 4D).
- ☐ Fuel tank vent blocked or fuel pipes restricted (Chapters 4A, 4B, 4C. 4D or 4E).

Engine lacks power

- ☐ Engine management system fault (Chapters 1, 4A, 4B, 4C, 4D, 4E or 5B).
- ☐ Timing chain or belt incorrectly fitted or incorrectly tensioned (Chapters 2A, 2B or 2C).
- ☐ Fuel filter choked (Chapter 1).
- ☐ Fuel pump faulty or delivery pressure low (Chapters 4A, 4B, 4C or 4D).
- ☐ Uneven or low cylinder compressions (Chapters 2A, 2B or 2C).
- ☐ Worn, faulty or incorrectly-gapped spark plugs (Chapter 1).
- ☐ Vacuum leak at the inlet manifold or associated hoses (Chapters 1, 4A, 4B, 4C, 4D or 4E).
- ☐ Brakes binding (Chapters 1 and 9).
- ☐ Clutch slipping (Chapter 6).
- ☐ Automatic transmission fluid level incorrect (Chapter 1).

Oil pressure warning light illuminated with engine running

- ☐ Low oil level or incorrect oil grade (Chapter 1).
- ☐ Faulty oil pressure warning light switch (Chapters 2A, 2B or 2C).
- ☐ Worn engine bearings and/or oil pump (Chapters 2A, 2B, 2C or 2D).
- ☐ High engine operating temperature (Chapter 3).
- ☐ Oil pressure relief valve defective (Chapters 2A, 2B or 2C).
- ☐ Oil pick-up strainer clogged (Chapters 2A, 2B or 2C).

Engine backfires

- ☐ Engine management system fault (Chapters 1, 4A, 4B, 4C, 4D, 4E or 5B).
- ☐ Timing chain or belt incorrectly fitted or incorrectly tensioned (Chapters 2A, 2B or 2C).
- ☐ Vacuum leak at the inlet manifold or associated hoses (Chapters 1, 4A, 4B, 4C, 4D or 4E).

Engine runs-on after switching off

- ☐ Idle speed excessively high (Chapters 4A, 4B, 4C or 4D).
- ☐ Engine management system fault (Chapters 1, 4A, 4B, 4C, 4D, 4E or 5B).
- ☐ Excessive carbon build-up in engine (Chapters 2A, 2B or 2C).
- ☐ High engine operating temperature (Chapter 3).

Engine noises

Pre-ignition (pinking) or knocking during acceleration or under load

- ☐ Incorrect grade of fuel (Chapters 4A, 4B, 4C or 4D).
- ☐ Vacuum leak at the inlet manifold or associated hoses (Chapters 1, 4A, 4B, 4C, 4D or 4E).
- ☐ Excessive carbon build-up in engine (Chapters 2A, 2B or 2C).

Whistling or wheezing noises

- ☐ Leaking inlet manifold gasket (Chapters 4A, 4B, 4C, 4D).
- ☐ Leaking exhaust manifold gasket or downpipe-to-manifold joint (Chapter 4E).
- ☐ Leaking vacuum hose (Chapters 1, 4A, 4B, 4C, 4D, 4E or 9).
- ☐ Blowing cylinder head gasket (Chapters 2A, 2B or 2C).

Tapping or rattling noises

- ☐ Incorrect valve clearance adjustment (Chapter 2A).
- ☐ Faulty hydraulic tappet(s) (Chapters 2B or 2C).
- ☐ Worn valve gear or camshaft (Chapters 2A, 2B, 2C or 2D).
- ☐ Worn timing chain, belt or tensioner (Chapters 2A, 2B or 2C).
- ☐ Ancillary component fault (water pump, alternator, etc) (Chapters 3 and 5A).

Knocking or thumping noises

- ☐ Worn big-end bearings (regular heavy knocking, perhaps less under load) Chapter 2D.
- ☐ Worn main bearings (rumbling and knocking, perhaps worsening under load) Chapter 2D.
- ☐ Piston slap (most noticeable when cold) (Chapter 2D).
- ☐ Ancillary component fault (water pump, alternator, etc) (Chapters 3 and 5A).

Cooling system

Overheating

- ☐ Insufficient coolant in system (Chapter 1).
- ☐ Thermostat faulty (Chapter 3).
- ☐ Radiator core blocked or grille restricted (Chapter 3).
- ☐ Radiator electric cooling fan(s) or coolant temperature sensor faulty Chapter 3).
- ☐ Engine management system fault (Chapters 1, 4A, 4B, 4C, 4D, 4E or 5B).
- ☐ Pressure cap faulty (Chapter 3).
- ☐ Auxiliary drivebelt worn or slipping (Chapter 1).
- ☐ Inaccurate coolant temperature gauge sender (Chapter 3).
- ☐ Airlock in cooling system (Chapter 1).

Overcooling

- ☐ Thermostat faulty (Chapter 3).
- ☐ Inaccurate coolant temperature gauge sender (Chapter 3).

External coolant leakage

- ☐ Deteriorated or damaged hoses or hose clips (Chapter 1).
- ☐ Radiator core or heater matrix leaking (Chapter 3).
- ☐ Pressure cap faulty (Chapter 3).
- ☐ Water pump seal leaking (Chapter 3).
- ☐ Boiling due to overheating (Chapter 3).
- ☐ Core plug leaking (Chapter 2D).

Internal coolant leakage

- ☐ Leaking cylinder head gasket (Chapters 2A, 2B or 2C).
- ☐ Cracked cylinder head or cylinder bore (Chapter 2D).

Corrosion

- ☐ Infrequent draining and flushing (Chapter 1).
- ☐ Incorrect antifreeze mixture, or inappropriate antifreeze type (Chapters 1 and 3).

Fuel and exhaust systems

Excessive fuel consumption

☐ Unsympathetic driving style, or adverse conditions.
☐ Air filter element dirty or clogged (Chapter 1).
☐ Engine management system fault (Chapters 1, 4A, 4B, 4C, 4D, 4E or 5B).
☐ Tyres under-inflated (*"Weekly Checks"*).

Fuel leakage and/or fuel odour

☐ Damaged or corroded fuel tank, pipes or connections (Chapter 1).
☐ Charcoal canister and/or connecting pipes leaking (Chapters 1 and 4E).

Excessive noise or fumes from exhaust system

☐ Leaking exhaust system or manifold joints (Chapters 1 or 4E).
☐ Leaking, corroded or damaged silencers or pipe (Chapters 1 or 4E).
☐ Broken mountings, causing body or suspension contact (Chapters 1 or 4E).

Clutch

Pedal travels to floor - no pressure or very little resistance

☐ Broken clutch cable (Chapter 6).
☐ Faulty clutch automatic adjuster (Chapter 6).
☐ Broken clutch release bearing or fork (Chapter 6).
☐ Broken diaphragm spring in clutch pressure plate (Chapter 6).

Clutch fails to disengage (unable to select gears)

☐ Faulty clutch automatic adjuster (Chapter 6).
☐ Clutch disc sticking on transmission input shaft splines (Chapter 6).
☐ Clutch disc sticking to flywheel or pressure plate (Chapter 6).
☐ Faulty pressure plate assembly (Chapter 6).
☐ Clutch release mechanism worn or incorrectly assembled (Chapter 6).

Clutch slips (engine speed increases, with no increase in vehicle speed)

☐ Faulty clutch automatic adjuster (Chapter 6).
☐ Clutch disc linings excessively worn (Chapter 6).
☐ Clutch disc linings contaminated with oil or grease (Chapter 6).
☐ Faulty pressure plate or weak diaphragm spring (Chapter 6).

Judder as clutch is engaged

☐ Clutch disc linings contaminated with oil or grease (Chapter 6).
☐ Clutch disc linings excessively worn (Chapter 6).
☐ Clutch cable sticking or frayed (Chapter 6).
☐ Faulty or distorted pressure plate or diaphragm spring (Chapter 6).
☐ Worn or loose engine/transmission mountings (Chapters 2A, 2B or 2C).
☐ Clutch disc hub or transmission input shaft splines worn (Chapter 6).

Noise when depressing or releasing clutch pedal

☐ Worn clutch release bearing (Chapter 6).
☐ Worn or dry clutch pedal bushes (Chapter 6).
☐ Faulty pressure plate assembly (Chapter 6).
☐ Pressure plate diaphragm spring broken (Chapter 6).
☐ Broken clutch disc cushioning springs (Chapter 6).

Manual transmission

Noisy in neutral with engine running

☐ Input shaft bearings worn (noise apparent with clutch pedal released, but not when depressed) (Chapter 7A).*
☐ Clutch release bearing worn (noise apparent with clutch pedal depressed, possibly less when released) (Chapter 6).

Noisy in one particular gear

☐ Worn, damaged or chipped gear teeth (Chapter 7A).*

Difficulty engaging gears

☐ Clutch fault (Chapter 6).
☐ Worn or damaged gear linkage (Chapter 7A).
☐ Incorrectly-adjusted gear linkage (Chapter 7A).
☐ Worn synchroniser assemblies (Chapter 7A).*

Vibration

☐ Lack of oil (Chapter 1).
☐ Worn bearings (Chapter 7A).*

Jumps out of gear

☐ Worn or damaged gear linkage (Chapter 7A).
☐ Incorrectly-adjusted gear linkage (Chapter 7A).
☐ Worn synchroniser assemblies (Chapter 7A).*
☐ Worn selector forks (Chapter 7A).*

Lubricant leaks

☐ Leaking differential side gear oil seal (Chapter 7A).
☐ Leaking housing joint (Chapter 7A).*
☐ Leaking input shaft oil seal (Chapter 7A).*
☐ Leaking selector shaft oil seal (Chapter 7A).
☐ Leaking speedometer drive pinion O-ring (Chapter 7A).

Although the corrective action necessary to remedy the symptoms described is beyond the scope of the home mechanic, the above information should be helpful in isolating the cause of the condition, so that the owner can communicate clearly with a professional mechanic.

Automatic transmission

Note: *Due to the complexity of the automatic transmission, it is difficult for the home mechanic to properly diagnose and service this unit. For problems other than the following, the vehicle should be taken to a dealer service department or automatic transmission specialist.*

Fluid leakage

☐ Automatic transmission fluid is usually deep red in colour. Fluid leaks should not be confused with engine oil, which can easily be blown onto the transmission by airflow.

☐ To determine the source of a leak, first remove all built-up dirt and grime from the transmission housing and surrounding areas, using a degreasing agent, or by steam-cleaning. Drive the vehicle at low speed, so airflow will not blow the leak far from its source. Raise and support the vehicle, and determine where the leak is coming from. The following are common areas of leakage:
  a) *Transmission fluid sump (Chapters 1 and 7B).*
  b) *Dipstick tube (Chapters 1 and 7B).*
  c) *Transmission-to-fluid cooler pipes/unions (Chapter 7B).*
  d) *Speedometer drive pinion O-ring.*
  e) *Differential output fluid seals (Chapter 7B).*

Transmission fluid brown, or has burned smell

☐ Transmission fluid level low, or fluid in need of renewal (Chapter 1).

Engine will not start in any gear, or starts in gears other than Park or Neutral

☐ Starter inhibitor switch faulty (Chapter 7B).
☐ Incorrect selector cable adjustment (Chapter 7B).

General gear selection problems

☐ Chapter 7B deals with checking and adjusting the selector cable on automatic transmissions. The following are common problems which may be caused by a poorly-adjusted cable:
  a) *Engine starting in gears other than Park or Neutral.*
  b) *Indicator on gear selector lever pointing to a gear other than the one actually being used.*
  c) *Vehicle moves when in Park or Neutral.*
  d) *Poor gear shift quality or erratic gear changes.*
Refer to Chapter 7B for the selector cable adjustment procedure.

Transmission will not downshift (kickdown) with accelerator pedal fully depressed

☐ Low transmission fluid level (Chapter 1).
☐ Incorrect selector cable adjustment (Chapter 7B).
☐ Engine management system fault (Chapters 1, 4A, 4B, 4C, 4D, 4E or 5B).

Transmission slips, is noisy, or has no drive in forward or reverse gears

☐ There are many probable causes for the above problems, but the home mechanic should be concerned with only one possibility - fluid level. Before taking the vehicle to a dealer or transmission specialist, check the fluid level and condition of the fluid as described in Chapter 1. Correct the fluid level as necessary, or change the fluid if needed. If the problem persists, professional help will be necessary.

Braking system

Note: *Before assuming that a brake problem exists, make sure that the tyres are in good condition and correctly inflated, that the front wheel alignment is correct, and that the vehicle is not loaded with weight in an unequal manner. Apart from checking the condition of all pipe and hose connections, any faults occurring on the Anti-lock Braking System (ABS) should be referred to a Ford dealer for diagnosis.*

Vehicle pulls to one side under braking

☐ Worn, defective, damaged or contaminated front or rear brake pads/shoes on one side (Chapter 1).
☐ Seized or partially-seized front or rear brake caliper/wheel cylinder piston (Chapter 9).
☐ A mixture of brake pad/shoe lining materials fitted between sides Chapter 1).
☐ Brake caliper mounting bolts loose (Chapter 9).
☐ Rear brake backplate mounting bolts loose (Chapter 9).
☐ Worn or damaged steering or suspension components (Chapter 10).

Noise (grinding or high-pitched squeal) when brakes applied

☐ Brake pad or shoe friction lining material worn down to metal backing Chapter 1).
☐ Excessive corrosion of brake disc or drum (may be apparent after the vehicle has been standing for some time) (Chapter 1).

Excessive brake pedal travel

☐ Inoperative rear brake self-adjust mechanism (Chapter 9).
☐ Faulty master cylinder (Chapter 9).
☐ Air in hydraulic system (Chapter 9).

Rear wheels locking under normal braking

☐ Rear brake shoe linings contaminated (Chapter 1).
☐ Faulty brake pressure regulator (Chapter 9).

Brake pedal feels spongy when depressed

☐ Air in hydraulic system (Chapter 9).
☐ Deteriorated flexible rubber brake hoses (Chapter 9).
☐ Master cylinder mounting nuts loose (Chapter 9).
☐ Faulty master cylinder (Chapter 9).

Excessive brake pedal effort required to stop vehicle

☐ Faulty vacuum servo unit (Chapter 9).
☐ Disconnected, damaged or insecure brake servo vacuum hose (Chapter 9).
☐ Primary or secondary hydraulic circuit failure (Chapter 9).
☐ Seized brake caliper or wheel cylinder piston(s) (Chapter 9).
☐ Brake pads or brake shoes incorrectly fitted (Chapter 9).
☐ Incorrect grade of brake pads or brake shoes fitted (Chapter 1).
☐ Brake pads or brake shoe linings contaminated (Chapter 1).

Judder felt through brake pedal or steering wheel when braking

☐ Excessive run-out or distortion of front discs or rear drums (Chapter 9).
☐ Brake pad or brake shoe linings worn (Chapter 1).
☐ Brake caliper or rear brake backplate mounting bolts loose (Chapter 9).
☐ Wear in suspension or steering components or mountings (Chapter 10).

Brakes binding

☐ Seized brake caliper or wheel cylinder piston(s) (Chapter 9).
☐ Faulty handbrake mechanism (Chapter 9).
☐ Faulty master cylinder (Chapter 9).

Driveshafts

Clicking or knocking noise on turns (at slow speed on full-lock)

- [ ] Lack of constant velocity joint lubricant (Chapter 8).
- [ ] Worn outer constant velocity joint (Chapter 8).

Vibration when accelerating or decelerating

- [ ] Worn inner constant velocity joint (Chapter 8).
- [ ] Bent or distorted driveshaft (Chapter 8).

Suspension and steering systems

Note: *Before diagnosing suspension or steering faults, be sure that the trouble is not due to incorrect tyre pressures, mixtures of tyre types, or binding brakes.*

Vehicle pulls to one side

- [ ] Faulty or damaged tyre (*"Weekly Checks"*).
- [ ] Excessive wear in suspension or steering components (Chapter 10).
- [ ] Incorrect front wheel alignment (Chapter 10).
- [ ] Accident damage to steering or suspension components (Chapter 10).

Wheel wobble and vibration

- [ ] Front roadwheels out of balance (vibration felt mainly through the steering wheel) (Chapter 1).
- [ ] Rear roadwheels out of balance (vibration felt throughout the vehicle) Chapter 1).
- [ ] Roadwheels damaged or distorted (Chapter 1).
- [ ] Faulty or damaged tyre (*"Weekly Checks"*).
- [ ] Worn steering or suspension joints, bushes or components (Chapter 10).
- [ ] Roadwheel nuts loose (Chapter 1).
- [ ] Wear in driveshaft joint, or loose driveshaft nut (vibration worst when under load) (Chapter 8).

Excessive pitching and/or rolling around corners, or during braking

- [ ] Defective shock absorbers (Chapter 10).
- [ ] Broken or weak coil spring and/or suspension component (Chapter 10).
- [ ] Worn or damaged anti-roll bar or mountings (Chapter 10).

Wandering or general instability

- [ ] Incorrect front wheel alignment (Chapter 10).
- [ ] Worn steering or suspension joints, bushes or components (Chapter 10).
- [ ] Tyres out of balance (*"Weekly Checks"*).
- [ ] Faulty or damaged tyre (*"Weekly Checks"*).
- [ ] Roadwheel nuts loose (Chapter 1).
- [ ] Defective shock absorbers (Chapter 10).

Excessively-stiff steering

- [ ] Lack of steering gear lubricant (Chapter 10).
- [ ] Seized track-rod end balljoint or suspension balljoint (Chapter 10).
- [ ] Broken or slipping auxiliary drivebelt (Chapter 1).
- [ ] Incorrect front wheel alignment (Chapter 10).
- [ ] Steering rack or column bent or damaged (Chapter 10).

Excessive play in steering

- [ ] Worn steering column universal joint(s) or flexible coupling (Chapter 10).
- [ ] Worn steering track-rod end balljoints (Chapter 10).
- [ ] Worn rack-and-pinion steering gear (Chapter 10).
- [ ] Worn steering or suspension joints, bushes or components (Chapter 10).

Lack of power assistance

- [ ] Broken or slipping auxiliary drivebelt (Chapter 1).
- [ ] Incorrect power steering fluid level (Chapter 1).
- [ ] Restriction in power steering fluid hoses (Chapter 10).
- [ ] Faulty power steering pump (Chapter 10).
- [ ] Faulty rack-and-pinion steering gear (Chapter 10).

Tyre wear excessive

Tyres worn on inside or outside edges

- [ ] Tyres under-inflated (wear on both edges) (*"Weekly Checks"*).
- [ ] Incorrect camber or castor angles (wear on one edge only) (Chapter 10).
- [ ] Worn steering or suspension joints, bushes or components (Chapter 10).
- [ ] Excessively-hard cornering.
- [ ] Accident damage.

Tyre treads exhibit feathered edges

- [ ] Incorrect toe setting (Chapter 10).

Tyres worn in centre of tread

- [ ] Tyres over-inflated (*"Weekly Checks"*).

Tyres worn on inside and outside edges

- [ ] Tyres under-inflated (*"Weekly Checks"*).

Tyres worn unevenly

- [ ] Tyres out of balance (*"Weekly Checks"*).
- [ ] Excessive wheel or tyre run-out (Chapter 1).
- [ ] Worn shock absorbers (Chapter 10).
- [ ] Faulty tyre (*"Weekly Checks"*).

Electrical system

Note: *For problems associated with the starting system, refer to the faults listed under "Engine" earlier in this Section.*

Battery will not hold a charge for more than a few days

- ☐ Battery defective internally (Chapter 5A).
- ☐ Battery terminal connections loose or corroded (Chapter 5A).
- ☐ Auxiliary drivebelt worn or incorrectly-adjusted (Chapter 1).
- ☐ Alternator not charging at correct output (Chapter 5A).
- ☐ Alternator or voltage regulator faulty (Chapter 5A).
- ☐ Short-circuit causing continual battery drain (Chapters 5A and 12).

Ignition (no-charge) warning light remains illuminated with engine running

- ☐ Auxiliary drivebelt broken, worn, or incorrectly-adjusted (Chapter 1).
- ☐ Alternator brushes worn, sticking, or dirty (Chapter 5A).
- ☐ Alternator brush springs weak or broken (Chapter 5A).
- ☐ Internal fault in alternator or voltage regulator (Chapter 5A).
- ☐ Broken, disconnected, or loose wiring in charging circuit (Chapter 5A).

Ignition (no-charge) warning light fails to come on

- ☐ Warning light bulb blown (Chapter 12).
- ☐ Broken, disconnected, or loose wiring in warning light circuit (Chapters 5A and 12).
- ☐ Alternator faulty (Chapter 5A).

Lights inoperative

- ☐ Bulb blown (Chapter 12).
- ☐ Corrosion of bulb or bulbholder contacts (Chapter 12).
- ☐ Blown fuse (Chapter 12).
- ☐ Faulty relay (Chapter 12).
- ☐ Broken, loose, or disconnected wiring (Chapter 12).
- ☐ Faulty switch (Chapter 12).

Instrument readings inaccurate or erratic

Instrument readings increase with engine speed

- ☐ Faulty voltage regulator (Chapter 12).

Fuel or temperature gauges give no reading

- ☐ Faulty gauge sender unit (Chapters 3 or 4A, 4B, 4C, or 4D).
- ☐ Wiring open-circuit (Chapter 12).
- ☐ Faulty gauge (Chapter 12).

Fuel or temperature gauges give continuous maximum reading

- ☐ Faulty gauge sender unit (Chapters 3 or 4A, 4B, 4C, or 4D).
- ☐ Wiring short-circuit (Chapter 12).
- ☐ Faulty gauge (Chapter 12).

Horn inoperative, or unsatisfactory in operation

Horn fails to operate

- ☐ Blown fuse (Chapter 12).
- ☐ Cable or cable connections loose, broken or disconnected (Chapter 12).
- ☐ Faulty horn (Chapter 12).

Horn emits intermittent or unsatisfactory sound

- ☐ Cable connections loose (Chapter 12).
- ☐ Horn mountings loose (Chapter 12).
- ☐ Faulty horn (Chapter 12).

Horn operates all the time

- ☐ Horn push either earthed or stuck down (Chapter 12).
- ☐ Horn cable to horn push earthed (Chapter 12).

Windscreen/tailgate wipers inoperative or unsatisfactory in operation

Wipers fail to operate, or operate very slowly

- ☐ Wiper blades stuck to screen, or linkage seized or binding (Chapter 12).
- ☐ Blown fuse (Chapter 12).
- ☐ Cable or cable connections loose, broken or disconnected (Chapter 12).
- ☐ Faulty relay (Chapter 12).
- ☐ Faulty wiper motor (Chapter 12).

Wiper blades sweep over too large or too small an area of the glass

- ☐ Wiper arms incorrectly-positioned on spindles (Chapter 1).
- ☐ Excessive wear of wiper linkage (Chapter 1).
- ☐ Wiper motor or linkage mountings loose or insecure (Chapter 12).

Wiper blades fail to clean the glass effectively

- ☐ Wiper blade rubbers worn or perished (*"Weekly Checks"*).
- ☐ Wiper arm tension springs broken, or arm pivots seized (Chapter 1).
- ☐ Insufficient windscreen washer additive to adequately remove road film (*"Weekly Checks"*).

Windscreen/tailgate washers inoperative, or unsatisfactory in operation

One or more washer jets inoperative

- ☐ Blocked washer jet (*"Weekly Checks"* or Chapter 1).
- ☐ Disconnected, kinked or restricted fluid hose (Chapter 1).
- ☐ Insufficient fluid in washer reservoir (*"Weekly Checks"*).

Washer pump fails to operate

- ☐ Broken or disconnected wiring or connections (Chapter 12).
- ☐ Blown fuse (Chapter 12).
- ☐ Faulty washer switch (Chapter 12).
- ☐ Faulty washer pump (Chapter 12).

Washer pump runs for some time before fluid is emitted from jets

- ☐ Faulty one-way valve in fluid supply hose (Chapter 12).

Electric windows inoperative, or unsatisfactory in operation

Window glass will only move in one direction

- ☐ Faulty switch (Chapter 12).

Window glass slow to move

- ☐ Incorrectly-adjusted door glass guide channels (Chapter 11).
- ☐ Regulator seized or damaged, or in need of lubrication (Chapter 11).
- ☐ Door internal components or trim fouling regulator (Chapter 11).
- ☐ Faulty motor (Chapter 12).

Window glass fails to move

- ☐ Incorrectly-adjusted door glass guide channels (Chapter 11).
- ☐ Blown fuse (Chapter 12).
- ☐ Faulty relay (Chapter 12).
- ☐ Broken or disconnected wiring or connections (Chapter 12).
- ☐ Faulty motor (Chapter 12).

Notes

A

ABS (Anti-lock brake system) A system, usually electronically controlled, that senses incipient wheel lockup during braking and relieves hydraulic pressure at wheels that are about to skid.

Air bag An inflatable bag hidden in the steering wheel (driver's side) or the dash or glovebox (passenger side). In a head-on collision, the bags inflate, preventing the driver and front passenger from being thrown forward into the steering wheel or windscreen.

Air cleaner A metal or plastic housing, containing a filter element, which removes dust and dirt from the air being drawn into the engine.

Air filter element The actual filter in an air cleaner system, usually manufactured from pleated paper and requiring renewal at regular intervals.

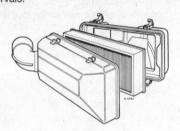

Air filter

Allen key A hexagonal wrench which fits into a recessed hexagonal hole.

Alligator clip A long-nosed spring-loaded metal clip with meshing teeth. Used to make temporary electrical connections.

Alternator A component in the electrical system which converts mechanical energy from a drivebelt into electrical energy to charge the battery and to operate the starting system, ignition system and electrical accessories.

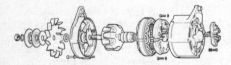

Alternator (exploded view)

Ampere (amp) A unit of measurement for the flow of electric current. One amp is the amount of current produced by one volt acting through a resistance of one ohm.

Anaerobic sealer A substance used to prevent bolts and screws from loosening. Anaerobic means that it does not require oxygen for activation. The Loctite brand is widely used.

Antifreeze A substance (usually ethylene glycol) mixed with water, and added to a vehicle's cooling system, to prevent freezing of the coolant in winter. Antifreeze also contains chemicals to inhibit corrosion and the formation of rust and other deposits that would tend to clog the radiator and coolant passages and reduce cooling efficiency.

Anti-seize compound A coating that reduces the risk of seizing on fasteners that are subjected to high temperatures, such as exhaust manifold bolts and nuts.

Anti-seize compound

Asbestos A natural fibrous mineral with great heat resistance, commonly used in the composition of brake friction materials. Asbestos is a health hazard and the dust created by brake systems should never be inhaled or ingested.

Axle A shaft on which a wheel revolves, or which revolves with a wheel. Also, a solid beam that connects the two wheels at one end of the vehicle. An axle which also transmits power to the wheels is known as a live axle.

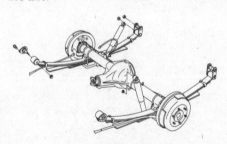

Axle assembly

Axleshaft A single rotating shaft, on either side of the differential, which delivers power from the final drive assembly to the drive wheels. Also called a driveshaft or a halfshaft.

B

Ball bearing An anti-friction bearing consisting of a hardened inner and outer race with hardened steel balls between two races.

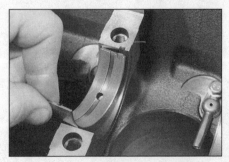

Bearing

Bearing The curved surface on a shaft or in a bore, or the part assembled into either, that permits relative motion between them with minimum wear and friction.

Big-end bearing The bearing in the end of the connecting rod that's attached to the crankshaft.

Bleed nipple A valve on a brake wheel cylinder, caliper or other hydraulic component that is opened to purge the hydraulic system of air. Also called a bleed screw.

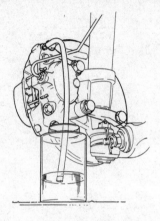

Brake bleeding

Brake bleeding Procedure for removing air from lines of a hydraulic brake system.

Brake disc The component of a disc brake that rotates with the wheels.

Brake drum The component of a drum brake that rotates with the wheels.

Brake linings The friction material which contacts the brake disc or drum to retard the vehicle's speed. The linings are bonded or riveted to the brake pads or shoes.

Brake pads The replaceable friction pads that pinch the brake disc when the brakes are applied. Brake pads consist of a friction material bonded or riveted to a rigid backing plate.

Brake shoe The crescent-shaped carrier to which the brake linings are mounted and which forces the lining against the rotating drum during braking.

Braking systems For more information on braking systems, consult the *Haynes Automotive Brake Manual*.

Breaker bar A long socket wrench handle providing greater leverage.

Bulkhead The insulated partition between the engine and the passenger compartment.

C

Caliper The non-rotating part of a disc-brake assembly that straddles the disc and carries the brake pads. The caliper also contains the hydraulic components that cause the pads to pinch the disc when the brakes are applied. A caliper is also a measuring tool that can be set to measure inside or outside dimensions of an object.

Camshaft A rotating shaft on which a series of cam lobes operate the valve mechanisms. The camshaft may be driven by gears, by sprockets and chain or by sprockets and a belt.

Canister A container in an evaporative emission control system; contains activated charcoal granules to trap vapours from the fuel system.

Canister

Carburettor A device which mixes fuel with air in the proper proportions to provide a desired power output from a spark ignition internal combustion engine.

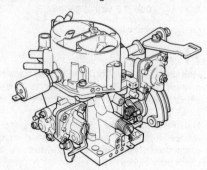

Carburettor

Castellated Resembling the parapets along the top of a castle wall. For example, a castellated balljoint stud nut.

Castellated nut

Castor In wheel alignment, the backward or forward tilt of the steering axis. Castor is positive when the steering axis is inclined rearward at the top.

Catalytic converter A silencer-like device in the exhaust system which converts certain pollutants in the exhaust gases into less harmful substances.

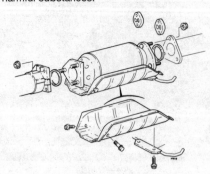

Catalytic converter

Circlip A ring-shaped clip used to prevent endwise movement of cylindrical parts and shafts. An internal circlip is installed in a groove in a housing; an external circlip fits into a groove on the outside of a cylindrical piece such as a shaft.

Clearance The amount of space between two parts. For example, between a piston and a cylinder, between a bearing and a journal, etc.

Coil spring A spiral of elastic steel found in various sizes throughout a vehicle, for example as a springing medium in the suspension and in the valve train.

Compression Reduction in volume, and increase in pressure and temperature, of a gas, caused by squeezing it into a smaller space.

Compression ratio The relationship between cylinder volume when the piston is at top dead centre and cylinder volume when the piston is at bottom dead centre.

Constant velocity (CV) joint A type of universal joint that cancels out vibrations caused by driving power being transmitted through an angle.

Core plug A disc or cup-shaped metal device inserted in a hole in a casting through which core was removed when the casting was formed. Also known as a freeze plug or expansion plug.

Crankcase The lower part of the engine block in which the crankshaft rotates.

Crankshaft The main rotating member, or shaft, running the length of the crankcase, with offset "throws" to which the connecting rods are attached.

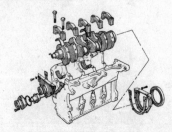

Crankshaft assembly

Crocodile clip See Alligator clip

D

Diagnostic code Code numbers obtained by accessing the diagnostic mode of an engine management computer. This code can be used to determine the area in the system where a malfunction may be located.

Disc brake A brake design incorporating a rotating disc onto which brake pads are squeezed. The resulting friction converts the energy of a moving vehicle into heat.

Double-overhead cam (DOHC) An engine that uses two overhead camshafts, usually one for the intake valves and one for the exhaust valves.

Drivebelt(s) The belt(s) used to drive accessories such as the alternator, water pump, power steering pump, air conditioning compressor, etc. off the crankshaft pulley.

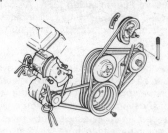

Accessory drivebelts

Driveshaft Any shaft used to transmit motion. Commonly used when referring to the axleshafts on a front wheel drive vehicle.

Driveshaft

Drum brake A type of brake using a drum-shaped metal cylinder attached to the inner surface of the wheel. When the brake pedal is pressed, curved brake shoes with friction linings press against the inside of the drum to slow or stop the vehicle.

Drum brake assembly

E

EGR valve A valve used to introduce exhaust gases into the intake air stream.

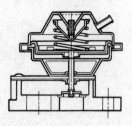

EGR valve

Electronic control unit (ECU) A computer which controls (for instance) ignition and fuel injection systems, or an anti-lock braking system. For more information refer to the *Haynes Automotive Electrical and Electronic Systems Manual.*

Electronic Fuel Injection (EFI) A computer controlled fuel system that distributes fuel through an injector located in each intake port of the engine.

Emergency brake A braking system, independent of the main hydraulic system, that can be used to slow or stop the vehicle if the primary brakes fail, or to hold the vehicle stationary even though the brake pedal isn't depressed. It usually consists of a hand lever that actuates either front or rear brakes mechanically through a series of cables and linkages. Also known as a handbrake or parking brake.

Endfloat The amount of lengthwise movement between two parts. As applied to a crankshaft, the distance that the crankshaft can move forward and back in the cylinder block.

Engine management system (EMS) A computer controlled system which manages the fuel injection and the ignition systems in an integrated fashion.

Exhaust manifold A part with several passages through which exhaust gases leave the engine combustion chambers and enter the exhaust pipe.

Exhaust manifold

F

Fan clutch A viscous (fluid) drive coupling device which permits variable engine fan speeds in relation to engine speeds.

Feeler blade A thin strip or blade of hardened steel, ground to an exact thickness, used to check or measure clearances between parts.

Feeler blade

Firing order The order in which the engine cylinders fire, or deliver their power strokes, beginning with the number one cylinder.

Flywheel A heavy spinning wheel in which energy is absorbed and stored by means of momentum. On cars, the flywheel is attached to the crankshaft to smooth out firing impulses.

Free play The amount of travel before any action takes place. The "looseness" in a linkage, or an assembly of parts, between the initial application of force and actual movement. For example, the distance the brake pedal moves before the pistons in the master cylinder are actuated.

Fuse An electrical device which protects a circuit against accidental overload. The typical fuse contains a soft piece of metal which is calibrated to melt at a predetermined current flow (expressed as amps) and break the circuit.

Fusible link A circuit protection device consisting of a conductor surrounded by heat-resistant insulation. The conductor is smaller than the wire it protects, so it acts as the weakest link in the circuit. Unlike a blown fuse, a failed fusible link must frequently be cut from the wire for replacement.

G

Gap The distance the spark must travel in jumping from the centre electrode to the side

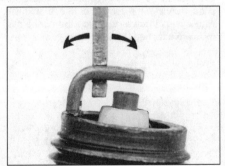

Adjusting spark plug gap

electrode in a spark plug. Also refers to the spacing between the points in a contact breaker assembly in a conventional points-type ignition, or to the distance between the reluctor or rotor and the pickup coil in an electronic ignition.

Gasket Any thin, soft material - usually cork, cardboard, asbestos or soft metal - installed between two metal surfaces to ensure a good seal. For instance, the cylinder head gasket seals the joint between the block and the cylinder head.

Gasket

Gauge An instrument panel display used to monitor engine conditions. A gauge with a movable pointer on a dial or a fixed scale is an analogue gauge. A gauge with a numerical readout is called a digital gauge.

H

Halfshaft A rotating shaft that transmits power from the final drive unit to a drive wheel, usually when referring to a live rear axle.

Harmonic balancer A device designed to reduce torsion or twisting vibration in the crankshaft. May be incorporated in the crankshaft pulley. Also known as a vibration damper.

Hone An abrasive tool for correcting small irregularities or differences in diameter in an engine cylinder, brake cylinder, etc.

Hydraulic tappet A tappet that utilises hydraulic pressure from the engine's lubrication system to maintain zero clearance (constant contact with both camshaft and valve stem). Automatically adjusts to variation in valve stem length. Hydraulic tappets also reduce valve noise.

I

Ignition timing The moment at which the spark plug fires, usually expressed in the number of crankshaft degrees before the piston reaches the top of its stroke.

Inlet manifold A tube or housing with passages through which flows the air-fuel mixture (carburettor vehicles and vehicles with throttle body injection) or air only (port fuel-injected vehicles) to the port openings in the cylinder head.

J

Jump start Starting the engine of a vehicle with a discharged or weak battery by attaching jump leads from the weak battery to a charged or helper battery.

L

Load Sensing Proportioning Valve (LSPV) A brake hydraulic system control valve that works like a proportioning valve, but also takes into consideration the amount of weight carried by the rear axle.

Locknut A nut used to lock an adjustment nut, or other threaded component, in place. For example, a locknut is employed to keep the adjusting nut on the rocker arm in position.

Lockwasher A form of washer designed to prevent an attaching nut from working loose.

M

MacPherson strut A type of front suspension system devised by Earle MacPherson at Ford of England. In its original form, a simple lateral link with the anti-roll bar creates the lower control arm. A long strut - an integral coil spring and shock absorber - is mounted between the body and the steering knuckle. Many modern so-called MacPherson strut systems use a conventional lower A-arm and don't rely on the anti-roll bar for location.

Multimeter An electrical test instrument with the capability to measure voltage, current and resistance.

N

NOx Oxides of Nitrogen. A common toxic pollutant emitted by petrol and diesel engines at higher temperatures.

O

Ohm The unit of electrical resistance. One volt applied to a resistance of one ohm will produce a current of one amp.

Ohmmeter An instrument for measuring electrical resistance.

O-ring A type of sealing ring made of a special rubber-like material; in use, the O-ring is compressed into a groove to provide the sealing action.

O-ring

Overhead cam (ohc) engine An engine with the camshaft(s) located on top of the cylinder head(s).

Overhead valve (ohv) engine An engine with the valves located in the cylinder head, but with the camshaft located in the engine block.

Oxygen sensor A device installed in the engine exhaust manifold, which senses the oxygen content in the exhaust and converts this information into an electric current. Also called a Lambda sensor.

P

Phillips screw A type of screw head having a cross instead of a slot for a corresponding type of screwdriver.

Plastigage A thin strip of plastic thread, available in different sizes, used for measuring clearances. For example, a strip of Plastigage is laid across a bearing journal. The parts are assembled and dismantled; the width of the crushed strip indicates the clearance between journal and bearing.

Plastigage

Propeller shaft The long hollow tube with universal joints at both ends that carries power from the transmission to the differential on front-engined rear wheel drive vehicles.

Proportioning valve A hydraulic control valve which limits the amount of pressure to the rear brakes during panic stops to prevent wheel lock-up.

R

Rack-and-pinion steering A steering system with a pinion gear on the end of the steering shaft that mates with a rack (think of a geared wheel opened up and laid flat). When the steering wheel is turned, the pinion turns, moving the rack to the left or right. This movement is transmitted through the track rods to the steering arms at the wheels.

Radiator A liquid-to-air heat transfer device designed to reduce the temperature of the coolant in an internal combustion engine cooling system.

Refrigerant Any substance used as a heat transfer agent in an air-conditioning system. R-12 has been the principle refrigerant for many years; recently, however, manufacturers have begun using R-134a, a non-CFC substance that is considered less harmful to

the ozone in the upper atmosphere.

Rocker arm A lever arm that rocks on a shaft or pivots on a stud. In an overhead valve engine, the rocker arm converts the upward movement of the pushrod into a downward movement to open a valve.

Rotor In a distributor, the rotating device inside the cap that connects the centre electrode and the outer terminals as it turns, distributing the high voltage from the coil secondary winding to the proper spark plug. Also, that part of an alternator which rotates inside the stator. Also, the rotating assembly of a turbocharger, including the compressor wheel, shaft and turbine wheel.

Runout The amount of wobble (in-and-out movement) of a gear or wheel as it's rotated. The amount a shaft rotates "out-of-true." The out-of-round condition of a rotating part.

S

Sealant A liquid or paste used to prevent leakage at a joint. Sometimes used in conjunction with a gasket.

Sealed beam lamp An older headlight design which integrates the reflector, lens and filaments into a hermetically-sealed one-piece unit. When a filament burns out or the lens cracks, the entire unit is simply replaced.

Serpentine drivebelt A single, long, wide accessory drivebelt that's used on some newer vehicles to drive all the accessories, instead of a series of smaller, shorter belts. Serpentine drivebelts are usually tensioned by an automatic tensioner.

Serpentine drivebelt

Shim Thin spacer, commonly used to adjust the clearance or relative positions between two parts. For example, shims inserted into or under bucket tappets control valve clearances. Clearance is adjusted by changing the thickness of the shim.

Slide hammer A special puller that screws into or hooks onto a component such as a shaft or bearing; a heavy sliding handle on the shaft bottoms against the end of the shaft to knock the component free.

Sprocket A tooth or projection on the periphery of a wheel, shaped to engage with a chain or drivebelt. Commonly used to refer to the sprocket wheel itself.

Starter inhibitor switch On vehicles with an

automatic transmission, a switch that prevents starting if the vehicle is not in Neutral or Park.

Strut See MacPherson strut.

T

Tappet A cylindrical component which transmits motion from the cam to the valve stem, either directly or via a pushrod and rocker arm. Also called a cam follower.

Thermostat A heat-controlled valve that regulates the flow of coolant between the cylinder block and the radiator, so maintaining optimum engine operating temperature. A thermostat is also used in some air cleaners in which the temperature is regulated.

Thrust bearing The bearing in the clutch assembly that is moved in to the release levers by clutch pedal action to disengage the clutch. Also referred to as a release bearing.

Timing belt A toothed belt which drives the camshaft. Serious engine damage may result if it breaks in service.

Timing chain A chain which drives the camshaft.

Toe-in The amount the front wheels are closer together at the front than at the rear. On rear wheel drive vehicles, a slight amount of toe-in is usually specified to keep the front wheels running parallel on the road by offsetting other forces that tend to spread the wheels apart.

Toe-out The amount the front wheels are closer together at the rear than at the front. On front wheel drive vehicles, a slight amount of toe-out is usually specified.

Tools For full information on choosing and using tools, refer to the *Haynes Automotive Tools Manual*.

Tracer A stripe of a second colour applied to a wire insulator to distinguish that wire from another one with the same colour insulator.

Tune-up A process of accurate and careful adjustments and parts replacement to obtain the best possible engine performance.

Turbocharger A centrifugal device, driven by exhaust gases, that pressurises the intake air. Normally used to increase the power output from a given engine displacement, but can also be used primarily to reduce exhaust emissions (as on VW's "Umwelt" Diesel engine).

U

Universal joint or U-joint A double-pivoted connection for transmitting power from a driving to a driven shaft through an angle. A U-joint consists of two Y-shaped yokes and a cross-shaped member called the spider.

V

Valve A device through which the flow of liquid, gas, vacuum, or loose material in bulk may be started, stopped, or regulated by a movable part that opens, shuts, or partially obstructs one or more ports or passageways. A valve is also the movable part of such a device.

Valve clearance The clearance between the valve tip (the end of the valve stem) and the rocker arm or tappet. The valve clearance is measured when the valve is closed.

Vernier caliper A precision measuring instrument that measures inside and outside dimensions. Not quite as accurate as a micrometer, but more convenient.

Viscosity The thickness of a liquid or its resistance to flow.

Volt A unit for expressing electrical "pressure" in a circuit. One volt that will produce a current of one ampere through a resistance of one ohm.

W

Welding Various processes used to join metal items by heating the areas to be joined to a molten state and fusing them together. For more information refer to the *Haynes Automotive Welding Manual*.

Wiring diagram A drawing portraying the components and wires in a vehicle's electrical system, using standardised symbols. For more information refer to the *Haynes Automotive Electrical and Electronic Systems Manual*.

Note: *References throughout this index relate to Chapter•page number*

A

Accelerator cable - 4A•4, 4B•4, 4C•4, 4D•3
Accelerator pedal - 4A•4, 4B•4, 4C•4, 4D•3
Accelerator pump - 4A•8
Acknowledgements - 0•4
Aerial - 12•16
Air bags - 0•5, 12•17
Air cleaner - 1•22, 1•23, 4A•3, 4B•4, 4C•3, 4D•3, 4E•5
Air temperature control system - 1•23, 4B•8, 4C•7, 4D•6
Alarm system - 12•17, REF•5
Alternator - 5A•4
Anti-lock braking system (ABS) - 9•11, 9•14, 9•16
Anti-roll bar - 10•7, 10•11
Anti-theft alarm system - 12•17, REF•5
Antifreeze - 0•12, 0•17, 1•21, 1•22, 3•2
Asbestos - 0•5
ATF - 0•17, 1•18, 1•24
Automatic choke - 4A•16, 4A•17
Automatic transmission - 2A•10, 2B•13, 2C•15, 2D•6, 2D•8, 2D•10, 7B•1 *et seq*, 12•6, 12•8
Automatic transmission fault finding - REF•18
Automatic transmission fluid - 0•17, 1•18, 1•24
Auxiliary lights - 12•7, 12•10
Axle - 10•10

B

Backfire - REF•16
Backrest - 11•17
Ballast resistor - 4B•9
Balljoint - 10•17
Battery - 0•5, 0•14, 5A•2, 5A•3
Battery fault - REF•20
Big-end bearings - 2D•21, 2D•24
Bleeding braking system - 9•10, 9•11
Bleeding power steering - 10•17
Body electrical systems - 1•18, 12•1 *et seq*, REF•11
Body electrical system fault finding - 5A•2, 12•3, REF•20
Bodywork and fittings - 1•18, 11•1 *et seq*, REF•13
Bonnet - 1•18, 11•4, 11•5
Boot - 1•16
Boots - 8•3, 8•4, 10•15
Brake fluid - 0•13, 0•17, 1•26, 12•6
Braking system - 1•17, 9•1 *et seq*, 12•6, REF•10, REF•11, REF•12
Braking system fault finding - REF•18

Bulbs - 0•16, 12•7, 12•8
Bumpers - 11•7, 11•8
Burning - 0•5
Buying spare parts - REF•5

C

Cables - 4A•4, 4B•4, 4C•4, 4D•3, 6•1, 7B•2, 9•12, 9•13, 12•12
Calipers - 9•3
Camshaft - 2B•6, 2B•7, 2C•7, 2C•8, 2D•16
Camshaft position sensor - 4D•6
Carburettor - 4A•7, 4A•8, 4A•9, 4A•11, 4A•13, 4A•14, 4A•15, 4A•17, 4A•18
Carpets - 11•2
Cassette player - 12•15, REF•5
Catalytic converter - 4E•2, 4E•5
Centre console - 11•20, 12•5
Charcoal canister - 4E•6
Charging system - 5A•3
Choke - 4A•4, 4A•16, 4A•17
Cigarette lighter - 12•9, 12•12
Clock - 12•8, 12•12
Clutch - 1•18, 6•1 *et seq*
Clutch fault finding - REF•17
Coil - 5B•4
Compression test - 2A•3, 2B•3, 2C•3
Connecting rods - 2D•17, 2D•24, 2D•25
Console - 11•20, 12•5
Contents - 0•2
Conversion factors - REF•6
Coolant - 0•12, 0•17, 1•21, 1•22, 3•2
Coolant pump - 3•7
Coolant temperature sensor - 4B•8, 4C•7, 4D•6
Cooling, heating and ventilation systems - 3•1 *et seq*
Cooling system fault finding - REF•16
Courtesy light - 12•6, 12•9
Crankcase - 2D•19
Crankcase ventilation system - 1•24
Crankshaft - 2A•6, 2A•9, 2B•4, 2B•6, 2B•12, 2C•4, 2C•7, 2C•14, 2D•18, 2D•22, 2D•24
Crankshaft position sensor - 4B•8, 4C•7, 4D•6, 5B•5
Crossmember - 10•7
Crushing - 0•5
Cushion - 11•17
CV joint - 1•16, 8•3, 8•4
CVH and PTE engine in-car repair procedures - 2B•1 *et seq*
Cylinder block - 2D•19
Cylinder head - 2A•4, 2A•5, 2B•4, 2B•9, 2C•3, 2C•10, 2D•12, 2D•14, 2D•15

D

Dents in bodywork - 11•2
Depressurising fuel system - 4B•3, 4C•3, 4D•2
Differential - 7A•3, 7B•3
Dimensions - REF•1
Direction indicators - 12•7, 12•9, 12•10
Discs - 9•4
Distributor - 1•20, 5B•5, 5B•6, 5B•7
Doors - 1•18, 11•6, 11•9, 11•10,,11•11, 11•13, 11•14, 11•15, REF•11
Drip rail moulding - 11•5
Drivebelt - 1•11
Driveplate - 2B•14, 2C•16
Driveshafts - 1•16, 8•1 *et seq*, REF•12
Driveshafts fault finding - REF•19
Drivetrain - 1•18
Drums - 9•4

E

Earth fault - 12•4
EEC IV engine management module - 4C•6
Electric shock - 0•5
Electric windows - 11•14, 12•7, 12•15, REF•20
Emblems - 11•5
Emission control system - 1•24, 4E•1
Engine fault finding - REF•15, REF•16, REF•18
Engine oil - 0•12, 0•17, 1•9
Engine removal and overhaul procedures - 2D•1 *et seq*
Environmental considerations - REF•4
Evaporative emission control systems - 1•24, 4E•2, 4E•5
Exhaust and emission control systems - 4E•1 *et seq*
Exhaust emission checks - REF•13
Exhaust manifold - 4E•3
Exhaust system - 1•16, 4E•1, 4E•2, REF•5, REF•12
Exhaust system fault - REF•17
Expansion tank - 3•6

F

Facia - 11•20, 12•5
Fan - 3•4
Fast-idle speed adjustment - 4A•13, 4A•15, 4A•9, 4A•7
Fault finding - REF•14 *et seq*
Fault finding - automatic transmission - REF•18
Fault finding - braking system - REF•18

Fault finding - clutch - REF•17
Fault finding - cooling system - REF•16
Fault finding - driveshafts - REF•19
Fault finding - electrical system - 5A•2, 12•3, REF•20
Fault finding - engine - REF•15, REF•16, REF•18
Fault finding - fuel and exhaust systems - REF•17
Fault finding - manual transmission - REF•17
Fault finding - suspension and steering systems - REF•19
Filling - 11•3
Filter, air - 1•22, 1•23, 4A•3, 4B•4, 4C•3, 4D•3, 4E•5
Filter, oil - 1•9
Filter, fuel - 1•25
Fire - 0•5
Float - 4A•7, 4A•9, 4A•16
Fluid seals - 7B•3
Fluids - 0•17
Flywheel - 2A•11, 2B•14, 2C•16
Fuel consumption high - REF•17
Fuel cut-off switch - 4B•5, 4C•5, 4D•4
Fuel filler pipe - 4A•6, 4B•5, 4C•5, 4D•4
Fuel filter - 1•25
Fuel gauge - 4A•6, 4B•4, 4C•5, 4D•4, 12•12
Fuel gauge fault - REF•20
Fuel hoses - 1•13
Fuel injectors - 4B•5, 4C•5, 4D•5
Fuel lines - 1•17, 4B•3, 4C•3, 4D•2
Fuel pressure check - 4C•4
Fuel pressure regulator - 4B•6, 4C•6, 4D•5
Fuel pump - 4A•5, 4B•4, 4C•4, 4C•5, 4D•4
Fuel rail - 4C•5, 4D•5
Fuel system - carburettor engines - 4A•1 et seq
Fuel system - central fuel injection engines - 4B•1 et seq
Fuel system - electronic fuel injection engines - 4C•1 et seq
Fuel system - sequential electronic fuel injection engines - 4D•1 et seq
Fuel and exhaust systems - REF•13
Fuel and exhaust systems fault finding - REF•17
Fuel tank - 4A•5, 4A•6, 4B•4, 4B•5, 4C•5, 4D•4
Fuel trap - 4B•7
Fume or gas intoxication - 0•5
Fuses - 0•16, 12•4

G

Gaiters - 1•16, 8•3, 8•4, 10•15
Gashes in bodywork - 11•3
Gaskets - REF•4
Gear lever - 7A•2
Gear selection problems - REF•18
Gear selector - 7B•2
Gearbox oil - 0•17, 1•14
Gearbox - See *Manual gearbox*
Gearchange linkage - 7A•2
Gearchange selector - 7A•3
Glossary of technical terms - REF•22 et seq
Grab handle - 11•20

H

Handbrake - 1•25, 9•12, 9•13, 12•6, REF•10
Handles - 11•11, 11•13, 11•20
Hazard warning switch - 12•8
HC emissions - REF•13
HCS engine in-car repair procedures - 2A•1 et seq
Headlight - 12•7, 12•9, 12•10
Heater - 3•2, 3•8, 12•6, 12•9
Horn - 12•12
Horn fault - REF•20
HT lead - 1•20
Hub bearings - 10•5, 10•8, REF•12
Hydraulic pipes and hoses - 9•9
Hydraulic tappets - 2C•8
Hydrofluoric acid - 0•5

I

Idle speed - 1•14, 1•15, 1•20, 4C•6
Idle speed control valve - 4D•6
Idling fault - REF•15
Ignition amplifier - 5B•5
Ignition switch - 12•5
Ignition system - 5B•1 et seq
Ignition fault - REF•20
Ignition timing - 5B•7
Indicators - 12•7, 12•9, 12•10
Injector ballast resistor - 4B•9
Injectors - 4C•5, 4D•5
Inlet manifold - 4A•18, 4B•9, 4C•8, 4D•7
Instruments - 1•18, 12•8, 12•11
Instrument fault - REF•20
Intercooler - 4C•8
Interior light - 12•6, 12•9

J

Jacking and vehicle support - REF•5
Joint mating faces - REF•4
Joystick - 12•16
Jump starting - 0•7

L

Leaks - 0•9, 1•12, REF•16, REF•17, REF•18, REF•20
Light-laden valve - 9•13, 9•14
Lighter - 12•9, 12•12
Lights-on warning module - 12•16
Load compartment - 11•20
Load-apportioning valve - 9•16
Locknuts, locktabs and washers - REF•4
Locks - 11•11, 11•12, 11•13, 12•5
Loudspeaker housing - 11•20
Lower arm - 10•8
Lubricants - 0•17
Luggage area - 12•6, 12•9

M

Main bearings - 2D•21, 2D•22
Manifold absolute pressure sensor - 4B•8, 4C•7

Manifolds - 4A•18, 4B•9, 4C•8, 4D•7, 4E•3
Manual gearbox
Manual transmission - 2A•10, 2B•13, 2C•15, 2D•6, 2D•8, 2D•10, 7A•1 et seq
Manual transmission fault finding - REF•17
Manual transmission oil - 0•17, 1•14
Mass air flow sensor - 4D•6
Master cylinder - 9•7
Minor scratches in bodywork - 11•2
Mirrors - 11•8, 11•9, REF•10
Misfire - REF•15
Mixture - 1•14, 1•15, 4C•7, REF•13
Modulator - 9•16
MOT test checks - REF•10 et seq
Mountings - 2A•10, 2B•13, 2C•15

N

Needle valve - 4A•7, 4A•9, 4A•16
Number plate light - 12•8, 12•10

O

Oil filter - 1•9
Oil pressure fault - REF•16
Oil pump - 2A•8, 2A•9, 2B•11, 2B•12, 2C•13
Oil seals - 2A•9, 2B•7, 2B•12, 2C•8, 2C•14, 7A•3, 7B•3, REF•4
Oil separator - 4E•5
Oil, engine - 0•12, 0•17, 1•9
Oil, manual transmission - 0•17, 1•14
Open-circuit - 12•4
Overcooling - REF•16
Overheating - REF•16
Oxygen sensor - 4B•8, 4C•7, 4D•7

P

Pads - 9•2
Paint - 1•18
Parcel shelf - 11•20
Parking light - 12•7
Passive Anti-Theft System (PATS) - 12•17
Pedals - 4A•4, 4B•4, 4C•4, 4D•3, 6•2, 9•8, 9•9
Pinking - REF•16
Piston rings - 2D•22
Pistons - 2D•17, 2D•24, 2D•25
Plastic components - 11•4
Poisonous or irritant substances - 0•5
Positive crankcase ventilation system - 4E•1, 4E•5
Power steering - 10•14, 10•15, 10•16, 10•17
Power steering fluid - 0•13, 0•17
Power steering pressure switch - 4B•8, 4C•7, 4D•7
Pre-ignition - REF•16
Printed circuit - 12•11
Pulse-air system - 4E•2, 4E•6, 4E•7

Q

Quarter mouldings - 11•8

Haynes Manuals – The Complete List

Title	Book No.
ALFA ROMEO	
Alfa Romeo Alfasud/Sprint (74 - 88)	0292
Alfa Romeo Alfetta (73 - 87)	0531
AUDI	
Audi 80 (72 - Feb 79)	0207
Audi 80, 90 (79 - Oct 86) & Coupe (81 - Nov 88)	0605
Audi 80, 90 (Oct 86 - 90) & Coupe (Nov 88 - 90)	1491
Audi 100 (Oct 76 - Oct 82)	0428
Audi 100 (Oct 82 - 90) & 200 (Feb 84 - Oct 89)	0907
AUSTIN	
Austin Ambassador (82 - 84)	0871
Austin/MG Maestro 1.3 & 1.6 (83 - 95)	0922
Austin Maxi (69 - 81)	0052
Austin/MG Metro (80 - May 90)	0718
Austin Montego 1.3 & 1.6 (84 - 94)	1066
Austin/MG Montego 2.0 (84 - 95)	1067
Mini (59 - 69)	0527
Mini (69 - Oct 96)	0646
Austin/Rover 2.0 litre Diesel Engine (86 - 93)	1857
BEDFORD	
Bedford CF (69 - 87)	0163
Bedford Rascal (86 - 93)	3015
BL	
BL Princess & BLMC 18-22 (75 - 82)	0286
BMW	
BMW 316, 320 & 320i (4-cyl) (75 - Feb 83)	0276
BMW 320, 320i, 323i & 325i (6-cyl) (Oct 77 - Sept 87)	0815
BMW 3-Series (Apr 91 - 96)	3210
BMW 3-Series (sohc) (83 - 91)	1948
BMW 520i & 525e (Oct 81 - June 88)	1560
BMW 525, 528 & 528i (73 - Sept 81)	0632
BMW 5-Series (sohc) (81 - 93)	1948
BMW 1500, 1502, 1600, 1602, 2000 & 2002 (59 - 77)	0240
CITROEN	
Citroen 2CV, Ami & Dyane (67 - 90)	0196
Citroen AX Petrol & Diesel (87 - 94)	3014
Citroen BX (83 - 94)	0908
Citroen CX (75 - 88)	0528
Citroen Visa (79 - 88)	0620
Citroen Xantia Petrol & Diesel (93 - Oct 95)	3082
Citroen ZX Diesel (91 - 93)	1922
Citroen ZX Petrol (91 - 94)	1881
Citroen 1.7 & 1.9 litre Diesel Engine (84 - 96)	1379
COLT	
Colt 1200, 1250 & 1400 (79 - May 84)	0600
DAIMLER	
Daimler Sovereign (68 - Oct 86)	0242
Daimler Double Six (72 - 88)	0478
DATSUN *(see also Nissan)*	
Datsun 120Y (73 - Aug 78)	0228
Datsun 1300, 1400 & 1600 (69 - Aug 72)	0123
Datsun Cherry (71 - 76)	0195
Datsun Pick-up (75 - 78)	0277
Datsun Sunny (Aug 78 - May 82)	0525
Datsun Violet (78 - 82)	0430

Title	Book No.
FIAT	
Fiat 126 (73 - 87)	0305
Fiat 127 (71 - 83)	0193
Fiat 500 (57 - 73)	0090
Fiat 850 (64 - 81)	0038
Fiat Panda (81 - 95)	0793
Fiat Punto (94 - 96)	3251
Fiat Regata (84 - 88)	1167
Fiat Strada (79 - 88)	0479
Fiat Tipo (88 - 91)	1625
Fiat Uno (83 - 95)	0923
Fiat X1/9 (74 - 89)	0273
FORD	
Ford Capri II (& III) 1.6 & 2.0 (74 - 87)	0283
Ford Capri II (& III) 2.8 & 3.0 (74 - 87)	1309
Ford Cortina Mk IV (& V) 1.6 & 2.0 (76 - 83)	0343
Ford Cortina Mk IV (& V) 2.3 V6 (77 - 83)	0426
Ford Escort (75 - Aug 80)	0280
Ford Escort (Sept 80 - Sept 90)	0686
Ford Escort (Sept 90 - 97)	1737
Ford Escort Mk II Mexico, RS 1600 & RS 2000 (75 - 80)	0735
Ford Fiesta (inc. XR2) (76 - Aug 83)	0334
Ford Fiesta (inc. XR2) (Aug 83 - Feb 89)	1030
Ford Fiesta (Feb 89 - Oct 95)	1595
Ford Granada (Sept 77 - Feb 85)	0481
Ford Granada (Mar 85 - 94)	1245
Ford Mondeo 4-cyl (93 - 96)	1923
Ford Orion (83 - Sept 90)	1009
Ford Orion (Sept 90 - 93)	1737
Ford Sierra 1.3, 1.6, 1.8 & 2.0 (82 - 93)	0903
Ford Sierra 2.3, 2.8 & 2.9 (82 - 91)	0904
Ford Scorpio (Mar 85 - 94)	1245
Ford Transit Petrol (Mk 1) (65 - Feb 78)	0377
Ford Transit Petrol (Mk 2) (78 - Jan 86)	0719
Ford Transit Petrol (Mk 3) (Feb 86 - 89)	1468
Ford Transit Diesel (Feb 86 - 95)	3019
Ford 1.6 & 1.8 litre Diesel Engine (84 - 96)	1172
Ford 2.1, 2.3 & 2.5 litre Diesel Engine (77 - 90)	1606
FREIGHT ROVER	
Freight Rover Sherpa (74 - 87)	0463
HILLMAN	
Hillman Avenger (70 - 82)	0037
Hillman Minx & Husky (56 - 66)	0009
HONDA	
Honda Accord (76 - Feb 84)	0351
Honda Accord (Feb 84 - Oct 85)	1177
Honda Civic 1300 (80 - 81)	0633
Honda Civic (Feb 84 - Oct 87)	1226
Honda Civic (Nov 91 - 96)	3199
HYUNDAI	
Hyundai Pony (85 - 94)	3398
JAGUAR	
Jaguar E Type (61 - 72)	0140
Jaguar MkI & II, 240 & 340 (55 - 69)	0098
Jaguar XJ6, XJ & Sovereign (68 - Oct 86)	0242
Jaguar XJ6 & Sovereign (Oct 86 - Sept 94)	3261
Jaguar XJ12, XJS & Sovereign (72 - 88)	0478

Title	Book No.
JEEP	
Jeep Cherokee Petrol (93 - 96)	1943
LADA	
Lada 1200, 1300, 1500 & 1600 (74 - 91)	0413
Lada Samara (87 - 91)	1610
LAND ROVER	
Land Rover 90, 110 & Defender Diesel (83 - 95)	3017
Land Rover Discovery Diesel (89 - 95)	3016
Land Rover Series IIA & III Diesel (58 - 85)	0529
Land Rover Series II, IIA & III Petrol (58 - 85)	0314
MAZDA	
Mazda 323 fwd (Mar 81 - Oct 89)	1608
Mazda 626 fwd (May 83 - Sept 87)	0929
Mazda B-1600, B-1800 & B-2000 Pick-up (72 - 88)	0267
MERCEDES-BENZ	
Mercedes-Benz 190 & 190E (83 - 87)	0928
Mercedes-Benz 200, 240, 300 Diesel (Oct 76 - 85)	1114
Mercedes-Benz 250 & 280 (68 - 72)	0346
Mercedes-Benz 250 & 280 (123 Series) (Oct 76 - 84)	0677
Mercedes-Benz 124 Series (85 - Aug 93)	3253
MG	
MGB (62 - 80)	0111
MG Maestro 1.3 & 1.6 (83 - 95)	0922
MG Metro (80 - May 90)	0718
MG Midget & AH Sprite (58 - 80)	0265
MG Montego 2.0 (84 - 95)	1067
MITSUBISHI	
Mitsubishi 1200, 1250 & 1400 (79 - May 84)	0600
Mitsubishi Shogun & L200 Pick-Ups (83 - 94)	1944
MORRIS	
Morris Ital 1.3 (80 - 84)	0705
Morris Marina 1700 (78 - 80)	0526
Morris Marina 1.8 (71 - 78)	0074
Morris Minor 1000 (56 - 71)	0024
NISSAN *(See also Datsun)*	
Nissan Bluebird 160B & 180B rwd (May 80 - May 84)	0957
Nissan Bluebird fwd (May 84 - Mar 86)	1223
Nissan Bluebird (T12 & T72) (Mar 86 - 90)	1473
Nissan Cherry (N12) (Sept 82 - 86)	1031
Nissan Micra (K10) (83 - Jan 93)	0931
Nissan Micra (93 - 96)	3254
Nissan Primera (90 - Oct 96)	1851
Nissan Stanza (82 - 86)	0824
Nissan Sunny (B11) (May 82 - Oct 86)	0895
Nissan Sunny (Oct 86 - Mar 91)	1378
Nissan Sunny (Apr 91 - 95)	3219
OPEL	
Opel Ascona & Manta (B Series) (Sept 75 - 88)	0316
Opel Ascona (81 - 88)	3215
Opel Astra (Oct 91 - 96)	3156
Opel Corsa (83 - Mar 93)	3160
Opel Corsa (Mar 93 - 94)	3159
Opel Kadett (Nov 79 - Oct 84)	0634
Opel Kadett (Oct 84 - Oct 91)	3196
Opel Omega & Senator (86 - 94)	3157

R

Radiator - 3•6
Radiator fan - 3•4
Radiator grille - 11•7
Radio - 12•15, REF•5
Rear axle - 10•10
Rear light cluster - 12•7, 12•8, 12•10
Regulator (window) - 11•14
Relays - 12•4
Release bearing - 6•4
Repair procedures - REF•4
Respraying - 11•3
Reversing light - 7A•4, 12•6
Ride height - 10•12
Road test - 1•18
Roadside repairs - 0•6 *et seq*
Roadwheels - 1•15, 1•16, 1•17
Rocker arms - 2B•7
Rocker cover - 2B•4
Rocker gear - 2A•4
Roof drip rail moulding - 11•5
Rotor arm - 1•20, 5B•5
Routine maintenance and servicing - 1•1
    et seq
Routine maintenance - bodywork and
    underframe - 11•2
Routine maintenance - upholstery and
    carpets - 11•2
Rubber boots - 1•16, 8•3, 8•4, 10•15
Rust holes in bodywork - 11•3

S

Safety first - 0•5
Scalding - 0•5
Screw threads and fastenings - REF•4
Seat belts - 1•18, 11•17, REF•11
Seats - 11•17, REF•11
Selector - 7B•2, 12•8
Servo - 9•9, 9•11, 9•12
Shock absorbers - 10•11, REF•11, REF•12
Shoes - 9•5
Short-circuit - 12•4
Sidelight - 12•7
Sill moulding - 11•6
Sill scuff plate - 11•19
Spark plug - 1•19
Speakers - 12•16

Speedometer - 7A•3, 7B•3, 12•11, 12•12
Spoiler - 11•12
Springs - REF•12
Starter inhibitor switch - 7B•4, 12•6
Starter motor - 5A•7
Starter motor fault - REF•15
Starting and charging systems - 5A•1 *et
    seq*
Steering - See *Suspension and steering*
Stop-light switch - 12•6
Struts - 10•6, 10•9
Sump - 2A•7, 2B•10, 2C•12
Sunroof - 11•16
Suspension and steering - 1•15, 1•18, 10•1
    et seq, 12•5, REF•10, REF•11, REF•12
Suspension and steering fault finding -
    REF•19
Switches - 3•5, 4B•5, 4B•8, 4C•5, 4C•7,
    4D•4, 4D•7, 7A•4, 7B•4, 9•16, 12•5

T

Tachometer - 12•12
Tailgate - 1•18, 11•12, 11•16, 12•15, 2B•7,
    2C•8, 2D•16
Temperature gauge - 3•5, 12•12
Temperature gauge fault - REF•20
Thermostat - 3•3
Throttle housing - 4C•6, 4D•4
Throttle kicker unit - 4A•10, 4A•11,
    4A•13
Throttle plate control motor - 4B•7
Throttle position sensor - 4B•8, 4C•7,
    4D•6
Timing - 5B•7
Timing belt - 1•25, 2B•5, 2B•6, 2C•5, 2C•7
Timing chain - 2A•6, 2A•7
Tools - REF•4, REF•7, REF•9
Top Dead Centre (TDC) for No 1 piston -
    2A•3, 2B•3, 2C•3
Towing - 0•9
Track rod end - 10•17
Trim - 1•18
Trim panels - 11•5, 11•6, 11•8, 11•10,
    11•12, 11•13, 11•19, 11•20
Turbocharger - 4C•8, 4C•9
Tyres - 0•15, REF•5, REF•13
Tyre fault - REF•19
Tyre pressures - 0•18

U

Underbody - 1•17
Underframe - 11•2
Upholstery - 11•2

V

Vacuum hoses - 1•13
Vacuum servo - 9•9, 9•11, 9•12
Valve clearance - 1•14, 2A•4, 2B•4, 2C•4
Valves - 2D•14, 2D•15
Vehicle identification - REF•3, REF•11
Vehicle speed sensor - 4B•8, 4C•7, 4D•7
Vehicle support - REF•5
Ventilation components - 3•2, 3•8
Voltage regulator - 5A•4

W

Warning lights - 12•8, 12•11
Washer system - 0•14, 12•14, 12•15
Washers fault - REF•20
Water pump - 3•7
Weatherseal - 11•6, 11•16
Weekly checks - 0•10 *et seq*
Weights - REF•2
Wheel alignment - 1•25, 10•17
Wheel bearings - 10•5, 10•8, REF•12
Wheel changing - 0•8
Wheel cylinders - 9•6
Wheelarch liners - 11•6
Wheels - REF•13
Wheels locking - REF•18
Wind deflector - 11•7
Windows - 11•14, 11•15, 12•7, 12•15,
    REF•20
Windscreen - 11•16, REF•10
Wipers - 0•16, 12•12, 12•13, 12•14
Wipers fault - REF•20
Wiring check - 1•13
Wiring diagrams - 12•19 *et seq*
Working facilities - REF•9

Z

Zetec engine in-car repair procedures -
    2C•1 *et seq*

Title	Book No.
Opel Rekord (Feb 78 - Oct 86)	0543
Opel Vectra (88 - Oct 95)	3158
PEUGEOT	
Peugeot 106 Petrol & Diesel (91 - June 96)	1882
Peugeot 205 (83 - 95)	0932
Peugeot 305 (78 - 89)	0538
Peugeot 306 Petrol & Diesel (93 - 95)	3073
Peugeot 309 (86 - 93)	1266
Peugeot 405 Petrol (88 - 96)	1559
Peugeot 405 Diesel (88 - 96)	3198
Peugeot 406 Petrol & Diesel (96 - 97)	3394
Peugeot 505 (79 - 89)	0762
Peugeot 1.7 & 1.9 litre Diesel Engines (82 - 96)	0950
Peugeot 2.0, 2.1, 2.3 & 2.5 litre Diesel Engines (74 - 90)	1607
PORSCHE	
Porsche 911 (65 - 85)	0264
Porsche 924 & 924 Turbo (76 - 85)	0397
PROTON	
Proton (89 - 97)	3255
RANGE ROVER	
Range Rover V8 (70 - Oct 92)	0606
RELIANT	
Reliant Robin & Kitten (73 - 83)	0436
RENAULT	
Renault 5 (72 - Feb 85)	0141
Renault 5 (Feb 85 - 96)	1219
Renault 9 & 11 (82 - 89)	0822
Renault 12 (70 - 80)	0097
Renault 15 & 17 (72 - 79)	0763
Renault 18 (79 - 86)	0598
Renault 19 Petrol (89 - 94)	1646
Renault 19 Diesel (89 - 95)	1946
Renault 21 (86 - 94)	1397
Renault 25 (84 - 86)	1228
Renault Clio Petrol (91 - 93)	1853
Renault Clio Diesel (91 - June 96)	3031
Renault Espace (85 - 96)	3197
Renault Fuego (80 - 86)	0764
Renault Laguna (94 - 96)	3252
ROVER	
Rover 111 & 114 (95 - 96)	1711
Rover 213 & 216 (84 - 89)	1116
Rover 214 & 414 (Oct 89 - 92)	1689
Rover 216 & 416 (Oct 89 - 92)	1830
Rover 618, 620 & 623 (93 - 97)	3257
Rover 820, 825 & 827 (86 - 95)	1380
Rover 2000, 2300 & 2600 (77 - 87)	0468
Rover 3500 (76 - 87)	0365
Rover Metro (May 90 - 94)	1711
SAAB	
Saab 90, 99 & 900 (79 - Oct 93)	0765
Saab 9000 (4-cyl) (85 - 95)	1686
SEAT	
Seat Ibiza & Malaga (85 - 92)	1609
SIMCA	
Simca 1100 & 1204 (67 - 79)	0088
Simca 1301 & 1501 (63 - 76)	0199

Title	Book No.
SKODA	
Skoda Estelle 105, 120, 130 & 136 (77 - 89)	0604
Skoda Favorit (89 - 92)	1801
SUBARU	
Subaru 1600 (77 - Oct 79)	0237
Subaru 1600 & 1800 (Nov 79 - 90)	0995
SUZUKI	
Suzuki SJ Series, Samurai & Vitara (82 - 97)	1942
Suzuki Supercarry (86 - Oct 94)	3015
TALBOT	
Talbot Alpine, Solara, Minx & Rapier (75 - 86)	0337
Talbot Horizon (78 - 86)	0473
Talbot Samba (82 - 86)	0823
TOYOTA	
Toyota Carina E (May 92 - 97)	3256
Toyota Celica (Feb 82 - Sept 85)	1135
Toyota Corolla (fwd) (Sept 83 - Sept 87)	1024
Toyota Corolla (rwd) (80 - 85)	0683
Toyota Corolla (Sept 87 - 92)	1683
Toyota Corolla (Aug 92 - 97)	3259
Toyota Hi-Ace & Hi-Lux (69 - Oct 83)	0304
Toyota Starlet (78 - Jan 85)	0462
TRIUMPH	
Triumph Acclaim (81 - 84)	0792
Triumph Herald (59 - 71)	0010
Triumph Spitfire (62 - 81)	0113
Triumph Stag (70 - 78)	0441
Triumph TR7 (75 - 82)	0322
VAUXHALL	
Vauxhall Astra (80 - Oct 84)	0635
Vauxhall Astra & Belmont (Oct 84 - Oct 91)	1136
Vauxhall Astra (Oct 91 - 96)	1832
Vauxhall Carlton (Oct 78 - Oct 86)	0480
Vauxhall Carlton (Nov 86 - 94)	1469
Vauxhall Cavalier 1300 (77 - July 81)	0461
Vauxhall Cavalier 1600, 1900 & 2000 (75 - July 81)	0315
Vauxhall Cavalier (81 - Oct 88)	0812
Vauxhall Cavalier (Oct 88 - Oct 95)	1570
Vauxhall Chevette (75 - 84)	0285
Vauxhall Corsa (Mar 93 - 94)	1985
Vauxhall Nova (83 - 93)	0909
Vauxhall Rascal (86 - 93)	3015
Vauxhall Senator (Sept 87 - 94)	1469
Vauxhall Viva HB Series (ohv) (66 - 70)	0026
Vauxhall Viva & Firenza (ohc) (68 - 73)	0093
Vauxhall/Opel 1.5, 1.6 & 1.7 litre Diesel Engines (82 - 96)	1222
VOLKSWAGEN	
VW Beetle 1200 (54 - 77)	0036
VW Beetle 1300 & 1500 (65 - 75)	0039
VW Beetle 1302 & 1302S (70 - 72)	0110
VW Beetle 1303, 1303S & GT (72 - 75)	0159
VW Golf Mk 1 1.1 & 1.3 (74 - Feb 84)	0716
VW Golf Mk 1 1.5, 1.6 & 1.8 (74 - 85)	0726
VW Golf Mk 1 Diesel (78 - Feb 84)	0451
VW Golf Mk 2 (Mar 84 - Feb 92)	1081
VW Golf Mk 3 Petrol & Diesel (Feb 92 - 96)	3097

Title	Book No.
VW Jetta Mk 1 1.1 & 1.3 (80 - June 84)	0716
VW Jetta Mk 1 1.5, 1.6 & 1.8 (80 - June 84)	0726
VW Jetta Mk 1 Diesel (81 - June 84)	0451
VW Jetta Mk 2 (July 84 - 92)	1081
VW LT vans & light trucks (76 - 87)	0637
VW Passat (Sept 81 - May 88)	0814
VW Passat (May 88 - 91)	1647
VW Polo & Derby (76 - Jan 82)	0335
VW Polo (82 - Oct 90)	0813
VW Polo (Nov 90 - Aug 94)	3245
VW Santana (Sept 82 - 85)	0814
VW Scirocco Mk 1 1.5, 1.6 & 1.8 (74 - 82)	0726
VW Scirocco (82 - 90)	1224
VW Transporter 1600 (68 - 79)	0082
VW Transporter 1700, 1800 & 2000 (72 - 79)	0226
VW Transporter with air-cooled engine (79 - 82)	0638
VW Type 3 (63 - 73)	0084
VW Vento Petrol & Diesel (Feb 92 - 96)	3097
VOLVO	
Volvo 66 & 343, Daf 55 & 66 (68 - 79)	0293
Volvo 142, 144 & 145 (66 - 74)	0129
Volvo 240 Series (74 - 93)	0270
Volvo 262, 264 & 260/265 (75 - 85)	0400
Volvo 340, 343, 345 & 360 (76 - 91)	0715
Volvo 440, 460 & 480 (87 - 92)	1691
Volvo 740 & 760 (82 - 91)	1258
Volvo 850 (92 - 96)	3260
Volvo 940 (90 - 96)	3249
YUGO/ZASTAVA	
Yugo/Zastava (81 - 90)	1453

TECH BOOKS	
Automotive Brake Manual	3050
Carburettor Manual	3288
Diesel Engine Service Guide	3286
Automotive Electrical & Electronic Systems	3049
Automotive Engine Management and Fuel Injection Manual	3344
In-Car Entertainment Manual	3363
Automotive Tools Manual	3052
Automotive Welding Manual	3053

CAR BOOKS	
Automotive Fuel Injection Systems	9755
Car Bodywork Repair Manual	9864
Caravan Manual (2nd Edition)	9894
Haynes Technical Data Book (88 - 97)	1997
How to Keep Your Car Alive	9868
Japanese Vehicle Carburettors	1786
Small Engine Repair Manual	1755
SU Carburettors	0299
Weber Carburettors (to 79)	0393

C6684.CL04.04/97

All the products featured on this page are available through most motor accessory shops, cycle shops and book stores. Our policy of continuous updating and development means that titles are being constantly added to the range. For up-to-date information on our complete list of titles, please telephone: (UK) 01963 442030 • (USA) (805) 498-6703 • (France) (1) 47 03 61 80 • (Sweden) 018 124016

Preserving Our Motoring Heritage

< The Model J Duesenberg Derham Tourster. Only eight of these magnificent cars were ever built – this is the only example to be found outside the United States of America

Almost every car you've ever loved, loathed or desired is gathered under one roof at the Haynes Motor Museum. Over 300 immaculately presented cars and motorbikes represent every aspect of our motoring heritage, from elegant reminders of bygone days, such as the superb Model J Duesenberg to curiosities like the bug-eyed BMW Isetta. There are also many old friends and flames. Perhaps you remember the 1959 Ford Popular that you did your courting in? The magnificent 'Red Collection' is a spectacle of classic sports cars including AC, Alfa Romeo, Austin Healey, Ferrari, Lamborghini, Maserati, MG, Riley, Porsche and Triumph.

A Perfect Day Out

Each and every vehicle at the Haynes Motor Museum has played its part in the history and culture of Motoring. Today, they make a wonderful spectacle and a great day out for all the family. Bring the kids, bring Mum and Dad, but above all bring your camera to capture those golden memories for ever. You will also find an impressive array of motoring memorabilia, a comfortable 70 seat video cinema and one of the most extensive transport book shops in Britain. The Pit Stop Cafe serves everything from a cup of tea to wholesome, home-made meals or, if you prefer, you can enjoy the large picnic area nestled in the beautiful rural surroundings of Somerset.

John Haynes O.B.E., Founder and Chairman of the museum at the wheel of a Haynes Light 12.

< Graham Hill's Lola Cosworth Formula 1 car next to a 1934 Riley Sports.

The Museum is situated on the A359 Yeovil to Frome road at Sparkford, just off the A303 in Somerset. It is about 40 miles south of Bristol, and 25 minutes drive from the M5 intersection at Taunton.
Open 9.30am - 5.30pm (10.00am - 4.00pm Winter) 7 days a week, *except Christmas Day, Boxing Day and New Years Day*
Special rates available for schools, coach parties and outings Charitable Trust No. 292048